Addison-Wesley
Mathematics

Robert E. Eicholz
Phares G. O'Daffer
Charles R. Fleenor

Randall I. Charles
Sharon Young
Carne S. Barnett

Addison-Wesley Publishing Company

Menlo Park, California • Reading, Massachusetts • Don Mills, Ontario • Wokingham, England
Amsterdam • Sydney • Singapore • Tokyo • Madrid • Bogotá • Santiago • San Juan

Illustration Acknowledgments

R.R. Donnelley Cartographic Services: 125, 312
Lisa French: 396
Linda Harris-Sweezy: 32, 116, 126, 132, 168, 215, 373
Jane McCreary: 182, 195, 282
Masami Miyamoto: 31, 35, 59, 70, 83, 87, 92, 142, 155, 160, 250, 254, 255, 261, 303, 309, 404, 405
Debby Morse: 164
Sandra Popovich: 246, 272, 300
Valerie Randall: 94
"Renaissance Intarsia: The Art of Geometry" by Alan Tormey and Judith Tormey. Copyright © 1982 by Scientific American, Inc. All rights reserved.: 215
Linda Stinchfield: 256, 327, 345
Cynthia Swann-Brodie: 257, 265, 429, 430

Photograph Acknowledgments

Cover Photograph: NASA/Rainbow

© 1979 Russell Abraham/Stock, Boston: 82
Greg Adams/Atoz Images: 349 bottom
B. and C. Alexander/Black Star: 109 top left
American Red Cross: 269 bottom
© A.N. Anderson/Focus on Sports: 177 top right
Erik Anderson/Stock, Boston: 144–145
© 1979 Jim Anderson/Woodfin Camp & Associates: 148–149
© William W. Bacon III/Alaska Photo: 77 top right
Jim Ballard*: 121, 171, 194, 198, 320, 341 bottom, 368
© 1983 Harry Benson: 376
The Bettmann Archive, Inc.: 188 (a, c, f)
© Ken Biggs/After-Image: 60
S.C. Bisserot/Bruce Coleman Inc.: 31 top
Richard A. Blake/Atoz Images: 339
© 1979 John Blaustein/Woodfin Camp & Associates: 250, 251
Elihu Blotnick*: 101
Donald Brewster/Bruce Coleman Inc.: 36
Daniel Brody/Stock, Boston: 90
David Brownell: 395 top
© 1959 California Institute of Technology: 71
© 1985 Cameramann International Ltd./Marilyn Gartman Agency: 196
© Robert P. Carr/Bruce Coleman Inc.: 191
Ron Church/Tom Stack & Associates: 67
John Colwell/Grant Heilman Photography: 18
Eric Crichton/Bruce Coleman Inc. 131 center right
Culver Pictures: 188 (b, d, e)
© Bill Curtsinger: 241 bottom left
© Ron Dahlquist/After-Image: 395 bottom
E.R. Degginger: 200, 413 (both)
E.R. Degginger/Bruce Coleman Inc.: 336 top
© 1980 Doris DeWitt/Atoz Images: 278

Glen Donahue/Atoz Images: 45
© Jessica Ehlers/Bruce Coleman Inc.: 131 bottom
© Pat Lanza Field/Bruce Coleman Inc.: 132, 325 center
Stephen Frisch*: 245
© 1981 Peter Fronk/Atoz Images: 53 top, 53 bottom
George B. Fry III*: 114, 122, 178, 306, 382
© Paul Fusco/Magnum Photos: 192–193
© 1979 Bill Gillette/After-Image: 325 top, 360
© Burt Glinn/Magnum Photos: 20, 270
© Albert J. Gordon/After-Image: 131 bottom center
© George Hall/Woodfin Camp & Associates: 15
© 1982 George Hall/Woodfin Camp & Associates: 12–13
Dirck Halstead/Liaison: 417
© Erich Hartmann/Magnum Photos: 156, 242
Grant Heilman: 256 top right
© 1980 Michal Heron/Woodfin Camp & Associates: 10
© 1982 Michal Heron/Woodfin Camp & Associates: 103
© Ethan Hoffman/Archive Pictures: 1 bottom right
Interstate Electronics Corporation: 209
© Robert A. Isaacs: 299 (all)
JPL/NASA: 294
Peter Jordan/Liaison: 241 top left, 241 center left
Manfred Kage/Peter Arnold, Inc.: 269 center
© Breck P. Kent/Animals Animals: 118 top, 263
Ira Kirschenbaum/Stock, Boston: 140
Wayland Lee*/Addison-Wesley Publishing Company: 28–29, 43, 56, 86, 94, 138–139, 147, 155 top left, 159, 246, 248, 272, 280, 287, 300, 307 (all), 330, 332 (all), 333 (all), 334 (all), 335 (all), 336 bottom (both), 337 (all), 338 bottom (all), 340 (all), 341 (1–6), 345 (all), 346 (all), 352, 354, 385, 390, 403, 414–415, 420 (both), 421 (all)
© John Lei/Stock, Boston: 325 bottom
© 1979 Andy Levin/Black Star: 177 center right
© 1982 Andy Levin/Black Star: 62
Library of Congress: 350 bottom, 351 (all)

Continued on page 473

ISBN 0-201-26800-0

FGHIJK-VH-89

Contents

CHAPTER 4

Addition and Subtraction of Fractions, 77

CHAPTER 5

Multiplication and Division of Fractions, 109

CHAPTER 6

Equations, 131

CHAPTER 7

Measurement: Metric Units, 155

CHAPTER 8

Integers and Rational Numbers, 177

CHAPTER 9

Geometry, 215

CHAPTER 10

Ratio and Proportion, 241

CHAPTER 11

Percent, 269

CHAPTER 12

Perimeter, Area, and Volume, 299

CHAPTER 13

Probability, 325

CHAPTER 14

Statistics and Graphs, 349

CHAPTER 15

Square Roots and Right Triangles, 373

CHAPTER 16

Measurement: Customary Units, 395

TECHNOLOGY RESOURCE BANK

APPENDIX

Whole Number Operations

Road jockeys (truck drivers) work everywhere, driving every type of rig (truck) from cackle crates (poultry trucks) to rolling refineries (oil or gas trucks). There were only 700 trucks in America in 1904. By 1980 the number of trucks had grown to 32,238,223.

Truck driving offers independent work schedules, travel, and good pay. There are no formal training requirements, but there are hardships. The average haul in 1980 was 533 kilometers. Long-distance drivers could be working away from home for a week or more. The drivers must also work with vibration, noise, and nervous tension. Local drivers have to fight heavy city traffic.

Conditions have improved, however. Long-distance drivers can drive no more than 60 hours in a 7-day period and no more than 10 hours without an 8-hour break. Seats are more comfortable and ventilation is better. Some rigs even have fancy sound systems.

So, truckers keep on truckin'. They drove over 618,905,000 kilometers in 1980.

Whole Number Place Value

In 1962 computers could store about 40,000 bits of information. By 1980 some computers could store as many as 77,768,000,000 bits of information and could do 12,000,000,000 calculations per second.

The **place-value chart** will help you to read and write **whole numbers**.

Place-value names	hundred trillions	ten trillions	trillions	hundred billions	ten billions	billions	hundred millions	ten millions	millions	hundred thousands	ten thousands	thousands	hundreds	tens	ones
Numeral				7	7	7	6	8	0	0	0	0	0	0	0
Period names	Trillions			Billions			Millions			Thousands			Units		

Standard numeral: **77,768,000,000**

Read: "seventy-seven billion, seven hundred sixty-eight million"
or "77 billion, 768 million"

Other Examples

12,000,000: twelve million   or   12 million

639,500: six hundred thirty-nine thousand, five hundred   or   639 thousand, 5 hundred
The 9 in the thousands place means 9 thousand or 9,000.

Sometimes numbers may be read another way.

2,400 = 24 hundred   **15,000,000 = 15,000 thousand**   **2,000,000,000 = 2,000 million**

(hundreds)   (thousands)   (millions)

Warm Up

Read each numeral aloud. Tell what each underlined digit means.

1. 16,729

2. 450,800

3. 2,750,000

4. 32,046,000,000

5. 101,022

6. 8,000,000,000

7. 399,936

8. 100,100,100

9. 6,546,250,000

10. 205,010,053

11. 1,077

12. 63,000,000,000,000

Practice Write each standard numeral in words.

1. 6,500

2. 23,700

3. 15,000,000

4. 419,100

5. 56,800,000,000

6. 88,000,000,000,000

Write the numeral.

7. five hundred thirty-seven thousand

8. four million, three hundred two thousand

9. two hundred six trillion

10. three trillion, ninety-six billion, forty-six million

11. three billion, seven hundred thousand

12. twenty-two million, sixty-five

13. sixty-eight thousand, thirty-four

14. ninety-seven billion, thirty-two million

15. 87 billion, 295 million

16. 6 trillion, 800 billion

17. 209 billion, 466 million, 819 thousand, 557

18. 404 trillion, 819 billion, 500 million

Write the standard numerals for each amount given in the tables.

U.S. Book Sales

	Year	Books sold (millions)
19.	1977	1,514
20.	1978	1,593
21.	1979	1,644
22.	1980	1,693
23.	1981	1,900

Cable TV Subscribers

	Year	Subscribers (thousands)
24.	1960	650
25.	1965	1,275
26.	1970	4,500
27.	1975	9,800
28.	1980	15,500

29. It is estimated that the human brain can store about 10,000 million bits of information. Write the standard numeral for this number.

30. A calculator can display a maximum of eight digits at a time. Write the largest number it can show as a standard numeral.

Comparing, Ordering, and Rounding Whole Numbers

Which candidate for president in 1960 got the greater number of votes?

To compare two numbers, we compare the digits in the same places of the two numbers.

Presidential Election 1960

Candidate	Number of Votes
John Kennedy	34,226,731
Richard Nixon	34,108,157

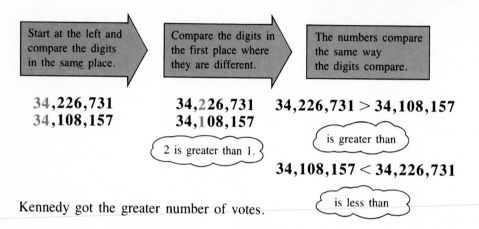

Start at the left and compare the digits in the same place.	Compare the digits in the first place where they are different.	The numbers compare the same way the digits compare.

34,226,731
34,108,157

34,226,731
34,108,157

2 is greater than 1.

34,226,731 > 34,108,157

is greater than

34,108,157 < 34,226,731

is less than

Kennedy got the greater number of votes.

Arrange the number of votes by region in **order** from greatest to least.

Northeast	20,053,000	Order: 22,979,000
South	14,389,000	20,053,000
North Central	22,979,000	14,389,000
West	11,417,000	11,417,000

Round the number of votes for Kennedy to the nearest thousand.

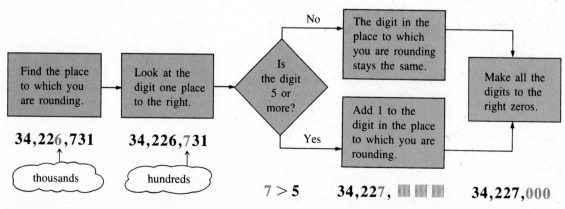

| Find the place to which you are rounding. | Look at the digit one place to the right. | Is the digit 5 or more? | No → The digit in the place to which you are rounding stays the same. | Make all the digits to the right zeros. |
| | | | Yes → Add 1 to the digit in the place to which you are rounding. | |

34,226,731

thousands

34,226,731

hundreds

7 > 5   34,227,▓▓▓ ▓▓▓ ▓▓▓   34,227,000

To the nearest thousand, Kennedy got 34,227,000 votes.

4

Practice Write $<$ or $>$ for each ⬤.

1. 2,873 ⬤ 2,894
2. 64,688 ⬤ 63,937
3. 435,742 ⬤ 335,742
4. 18,400 ⬤ 1,840
5. 3,754,000 ⬤ 3,574,000
6. 601,500 ⬤ 599,473
7. 8,943 ⬤ 8,945
8. 139,568 ⬤ 138,568
9. 1,000,000 ⬤ 10,000,000

Order the numbers from greatest to least.

10. 54,291,733
    59,066,927
    59,066,907
11. 13,992,249
    13,920,929
    13,992,248
12. 1,101,000,000
    1,010,000,000
    1,111,000,000

Round to the nearest thousand.

13. 2,780
14. 8,500
15. 28,309
16. 66,078
17. 125,822
18. 299,718
19. 3,455,725
20. 29,809,457

Round to the nearest ten thousand.

21. 66,814
22. 19,257
23. 514,712
24. 937,003
25. 809,466
26. 1,408,043
27. 5,992,640
28. 267,208,106

Round to the nearest million.

29. 3,784,126
30. 15,912,199
31. 83,050,000
32. 107,495,614
33. 99,912,000
34. 1,875,398,000
35. 3,784,468,925
36. 10,120,807,744

37. How many votes, rounded to the nearest ten thousand, did Nixon get in the 1960 election?

38. Rounded to the nearest hundred thousand, about how many more votes did Kennedy get than Nixon?

SKILLKEEPER

1. $6 + 3$
2. $9 + 7$
3. $11 - 6$
4. $17 - 8$
5. $9 + 7$
6. 8×7
7. 7×4
8. $27 \div 3$
9. $42 \div 6$
10. 0×8
11. $9 + 9$
12. $10 - 7$
13. $6 + 6$
14. $12 - 8$
15. $18 - 9$
16. 6×8
17. $36 \div 9$
18. $0 \div 7$
19. 7×7
20. $63 \div 9$

More Practice, page 433, Set A

Basic Properties for Addition and Multiplication

These are the basic properties for adding and multiplying whole numbers.

The Zero and One Properties

For any number **a**,

a + 0 = a

a × 1 = a

Examples:

23 + 0 = 23

16 × 1 = 16

The Commutative Property

For any numbers **a** and **b**,

a + b = b + a

a × b = b × a

Examples:

15 + 9 = 9 + 15

6 × 27 = 27 × 6

The Associative Property

For any numbers **a**, **b**, and **c**,

a + (b + c) = (a + b) + c

a × (b × c) = (a × b) × c

Examples:

9 + (6 + 4) = (9 + 6) + 4

6 × (5 × 2) = (6 × 5) × 2

The Distributive Property

For any numbers **a**, **b**, and **c**,

a × (b + c) = (a × b) + (a × c)

Example:

3 × (6 + 4) = 3 × 10 = 30

(3 × 6) + (3 × 4) = 18 + 12 = 30

Use the basic properties to find each missing number. Name the property used.

1. $28 + 0 = $ ▥

2. $219 \times 1 = $ ▥

3. $6,188 + $ ▥ $ = 6,188$

4. $63 \times 29 = 1,827$
$29 \times 63 = $ ▥

5. $32 + (19 + 49) = 100$
$(32 + 19) + 49 = $ ▥

6. $(16 \times 15) \times 8 = 1,920$
$16 \times (15 \times 8) = $ ▥

7. $7 \times (6 + 4) = 70$
$7 \times 6 + 7 \times 4 = $ ▥

8. $(15 \times 21) + (15 \times 35) = 840$
$15 \times (21 + 35) = $ ▥

9. $654 + 277 = 931$
$277 + 654 = $ ▥

10. $32 \times $ ▥ $ = 32$

11. $103 \times 46 = 46 \times $ ▥

12. $(9 + 72) + $ ▥ $ = 9 + (72 + 8)$

Name each property.

13. The way in which addends or factors are *grouped* does not change the result.

14. Changing the *order* of addends or factors does not change the sum or the product.

15. The sum of any given number and 0 is the given number.

16. The product of any given number and 1 is the given number.

6

Order of Operations

Sue Kim gave this instruction to her home computer.

PRINT 2 * (12 - 3) + 32/8

> The computer uses * for × and / for ÷.

What number should the computer print?

The computer performs the operations in the order given by the rules below.

- Perform the operations inside the parentheses first. $2 \times (12 - 3) + 32 \div 8$

- Then do the multiplication and division from left to right. $2 \times 9 + 32 \div 8$

- Then do the addition and subtraction from left to right. $18 + 4$

  The computer should print 22. 22

We perform operations in the same order as the computer.

$2 \times 7 + 3$	$2 \times (7 + 3)$	$(19 - 14) \div (7 - 2)$	$19 - (14 \div 7) - 2$
$14 + 3$	2×10	$5 \div 5$	$19 - 2 - 2$
17	20	1	15

Practice Perform the operations.

1. $16 - 9 + 2$
2. $16 - (9 + 2)$
3. $20 - 12 \div 2$
4. $3 \times 8 - 7$
5. $3 \times (8 - 7)$
6. $(20 - 12) \div 2$
7. $2 \times 6 + 2 \times 4$
8. $2 \times (6 + 4)$
9. $9 \times 3 - 10 \div 5$
10. $30 - 5 \times 4$
11. $8 \times 2 - (6 \times 2 + 1)$
12. $6 \times 8 - 6 \times 7$
13. $6 \times (8 - 7)$
14. $24 \div 3 \div 2$
15. $16 \div 8 \times 8$
16. $20 \times 2 \div 2$
17. $(27 + 5) \div (4 + 4)$
18. $4 \times 4 \times 4 \div 4 + 1$
19. $25 - 5 - 5 \div 5$
20. $25 - (5 - 5) \div 5$
21. $(18 \div 6) + (3 \times 9) - 20$

Use operation signs and parentheses to write each statement. Then perform the operations.

22. Multiply 3 and 7 and subtract the product from 25.

23. Subtract 9 from 12, then multiply the difference by 7.

7

Estimating Sums and Differences

Oceans and seas cover over two-thirds of the earth's surface. Estimate the combined area of the Atlantic and Pacific oceans.

Oceans

	Area (km²)	Greatest depth (m)
Pacific	165,760,000	11,516
Atlantic	82,527,000	9,219
Indian	65,440,000	7,455
Arctic	14,090,000	5,025

To estimate the total area you can **round** each number to the same place, then add.

$$165,760,000 \rightarrow 170,000,000$$
$$+\ 82,527,000 \rightarrow +\ 80,000,000$$
$$\text{Estimate} \rightarrow 250,000,000$$

The combined area of the Atlantic and Pacific oceans is about 250,000,000 square kilometers (km²).

You can also use **front-end** numbers to estimate sums or differences.

Add the front-end digits.	Look at the rest.	Improve the estimate.
9,333	333	
1,157	157	About
+ 3,628	+628	1,000 → 14,000
13,000		

Subtract the front-end digits.	Look at the rest.	Improve the estimate.
11,516	516	About
− 9,329 (11 − 9 = 2)	−329	200 → 2,200
2,000		

Warm Up

Estimate each sum or difference by rounding to the nearest thousand.

1. 6,827 + 3,374   **2.** 12,838 − 6,704   **3.** 24,402 − 15,211   **4.** $4,019 + $2,845

Estimate each sum or difference by using front-end estimation.

5. 624
     198
   + 593

6. 6,724
    − 2,349

7. 9,843
     3,761
   + 4,508

8. 47,069
    − 44,518

Practice Estimate each sum or difference by rounding.

1. 822 +476	**2.** 906 −474	**3.** 1,216 +3,577	**4.** 1,319 − 778	**5.** $81,426 − 45,947
6. 455 629 +433	**7.** $1,325 2,774 + 5,109	**8.** 629 331 +807	**9.** $277 440 + 198	**10.** 276 384 +433
11. 9,011 −4,644	**12.** $67,819 − 29,429	**13.** 15,619 − 7,195	**14.** 947 −618	**15.** $5,055 − 1,875

Estimate each sum or difference. Use front-end estimation.

16. 56,337 − 42,406	**17.** 6,413 − 2,439	**18.** 24,559 − 18,628	**19.** 94,500 − 1,519	**20.** $8,026 − 1,519
21. 317 268 542 + 197	**22.** 8,292 3,448 + 5,048	**23.** 389 646 263 + 518	**24.** 73 27 48 + 53	**25.** 2,816 3,727 + 3,544
26. 6,827 − 1,909	**27.** 35,188 22,664 + 14,137	**28.** 3,384 + 4,724	**29.** $591 − 204	**30.** 662 375 +589

Mixed Applications

Solve. Use the table on page 8.

31. Estimate the difference in the greatest depths of the Pacific and Atlantic oceans.

32. Estimate the combined area of the Indian and Arctic oceans. Is the combined area as large as the Atlantic Ocean?

33. Use information about the Pacific and Arctic oceans to write your own problem. Then solve the problem.

34. DATA HUNT Find the area of the five largest seas in the world. Estimate the total area of the seas.

■ **THINK MATH** ■

Logical Reasoning

How many whole numbers, when rounded to the nearest thousand, would be reported as 5,000?

How many whole numbers, when rounded to the nearest million, would be reported as 5,000,000?

More Practice, page 433, Set B

Adding and Subtracting Whole Numbers

The Whitcomb family kept a record of their living expenses for a year. What is the total of the expenses for transportation, utilities, and housing? How much less is their food expense than this total?

To find the total for the three items, we need to **add** their amounts. To find the difference between the sum of the three items and the food expense, we can **subtract**.

Family Expenses	
Food	$5,239
Transportation	1,046
Utilities	1,358
Housing	6,724
Clothing	780
Child care	1,472
Medical	898
Vacations	1,250
Entertainment	260
Other	940

Add the digits in each column, starting with the ones. Regroup if necessary.

Subtract the digits, starting with the ones. Regroup if necessary.

$$
\begin{array}{r}
1\ \ 1 \\
\$\,1,0\,4\,6 \\
1,3\,5\,8 \\
+\,6,7\,2\,4 \\
\hline
\$\,9,1\,2\,8
\end{array}
$$

Check by adding in the opposite direction.

1 ten and 8 ones

$$
\begin{array}{r}
8\ \ 10\ \ 11\ \ 18 \\
\$\,9,\!1\,2\,8 \\
-\,5,2\,3\,9 \\
\hline
\$\,3,8\,8\,9
\end{array}
$$

Check: same

$$
\begin{array}{r}
1\ \ 1\ \ 1 \\
\$\,3,8\,8\,9 \\
+\,5,2\,3\,9 \\
\hline
\$\,9,1\,2\,8
\end{array}
$$

The total expense for transportation, utilities, and housing is $9,128.
The food expense is $3,899 less than this total.

Other Examples

$$
\begin{array}{r}
1\ \ \ \ 1\ \ 1 \\
7\,2,4\,1\,4 \\
6,1\,7\,6 \\
+\,2\,7\,7,2\,8\,9 \\
\hline
3\,5\,5,8\,7\,9
\end{array}
\qquad
\begin{array}{r}
5\ \ 11\ \ 9\ \ 11 \\
6\,2,0\,1\,7 \\
-\,2\,7,4\,2\,6 \\
\hline
3\,4,5\,9\,1
\end{array}
\qquad
\begin{array}{r}
1\ \ 9\ \ 9\ \ 9\ \ 10 \\
\$\,1\,2\,0,0\,0\,0 \\
-\ \ \ \ 9\,7,3\,4\,5 \\
\hline
\$\,2\,2,6\,5\,5
\end{array}
$$

Warm Up

Give the sums or differences. Check your answers.

1.
$$
\begin{array}{r}
3,578 \\
10,269 \\
8,406 \\
+\,9,440 \\
\hline
\end{array}
$$

2.
$$
\begin{array}{r}
345,639 \\
129,813 \\
+\,447,096 \\
\hline
\end{array}
$$

3.
$$
\begin{array}{r}
73,454,187 \\
-\,57,508,216 \\
\hline
\end{array}
$$

4.
$$
\begin{array}{r}
\$84,575 \\
51,967 \\
+\,33,385 \\
\hline
\end{array}
$$

5.
$$
\begin{array}{r}
\$10,000 \\
-\,3,333 \\
\hline
\end{array}
$$

10

Practice Estimate each sum or difference. Then add or subtract.
Find the difference between the estimate and the answer.

1. 5,436
9,274
+ 3,865

2. 63,857
21,296
+ 47,847

3. 386,547
127,226
93,795
+ 212,619

4. 7,500,000
8,698,000
5,087,000
+ 5,196,000

5. 8,742
− 3,129

6. 53,109
− 23,256

7. 184,717
− 96,562

8. 7,500,000
− 1,929,663

Add or subtract.

9. $918
288
+ 594

10. $8,314
7,977
+ 10,848

11. $22,575
18,296
21,747
+ 30,908

12. $6,488
5,109
8,305
+ 1,119

13. 9,384
− 5,768

14. 20,910
− 14,566

15. $5,000
− 2,516

16. $73,040,000
− 46,185,000

17. 1,215 + 4,719 + 8,078

18. 60,507 − 33,815

19. 22,462 + 8,975 + 166,409

20. 8,404,177 − 5,608,250

Find the missing number in each exercise.

21.   8, 2 1 9
6, 4 8 1
▓▓, ▓▓▓▓▓▓
+ 3, 5 9 4
2 0, 6 1 5

22. 7 1, 4 2 9
− ▓▓, ▓▓▓▓▓▓
2 9, 8 4 3

23. 1 3 8, 4 2 9
▓▓▓▓, ▓▓▓▓▓
3 7 0, 5 6 6
+ 2 4 2, 9 1 6
8 5 2, 4 5 6

24. ▓▓▓▓, ▓▓▓▓▓
− 3 7 9, 2 8 4
5 2 0, 7 1 6

Mixed Applications Use the family expense table on page 10.

25. How much more is the Whitcomb family's expense for housing than their expense for food?

26. What is the total of the four items of greatest expense for the Whitcomb family?

27. The Whitcombs have $24,000 in their budget for yearly expenses. How much less than their yearly expense is their total expense?

28. Write a question that could be answered by adding and subtracting these numbers:

$780 + $1,250 − $1,472

Answer your question.

PROBLEM SOLVING: The 5-Point Checklist

| QUESTION |
| DATA |
| PLAN |
| ANSWER |
| CHECK |

To Solve a Problem

1. Understand the QUESTION
2. Find the needed DATA
3. PLAN what to do
4. Find the ANSWER
5. CHECK back

The 5-Point Checklist can help you organize your attack on a problem.

One year Fresno County grew 34,880 acres (a.) of tomatoes, San Joaquin County grew 27,460 a., and Yolo County grew 51,950 a. How many less acres of tomatoes did Yolo County grow than the combined acreage of Fresno and San Joaquin counties?

1. Understand the QUESTION
You must find how much less the acreage in Yolo County is than the total acreage for Fresno and San Joaquin counties.

2. Find the needed DATA

Fresno	34,880 a.
San Joaquin	27,460 a.
Yolo	51,950 a.

3. PLAN what to do
To find the combined acreage of Fresno and San Joaquin counties, you must add. Then subtract the Yolo County acres.

4. Find the ANSWER

$$
\begin{array}{r} 34{,}880 \\ + 27{,}460 \\ \hline 62{,}340 \end{array}
\qquad
\begin{array}{r} 62{,}340 \\ - 51{,}950 \\ \hline 10{,}390 \end{array}
$$

Yolo County grew 10,390 a. less than Fresno and San Joaquin counties combined.

5. CHECK back
You can use estimation to see if the answer is reasonable.

$$
\begin{array}{r} 30{,}000 \\ + 30{,}000 \\ \hline 60{,}000 \end{array}
\qquad
\begin{array}{r} 60{,}000 \\ - 50{,}000 \\ \hline 10{,}000 \text{ Estimate} \end{array}
$$

The estimate is close to the computed answer. The answer seems reasonable.

Solve. Use the 5-Point Checklist.

1. One year California farms produced 31,484 tons (T) of fresh asparagus and 7,484 T of asparagus to be processed. What was the total amount of asparagus produced?

2. The total value of strawberries grown in California in 1980 was $203,812,000. This was $33,120,000 more than the value of the strawberry crop in 1979. What was the value of the 1979 strawberry crop?

12

Solve.

1. One year 5,000 a. were planted for spring sweet corn, 7,200 a. for summer sweet corn, and 950 a. for fall sweet corn. What was the total acreage of sweet corn?

2. Alameda County grew 30,500 a. of summer lettuce. The total for all counties was 41,000 a. How many acres of summer lettuce did all other counties grow?

3. The total value of garlic grown in California in a year was $33,816,000. The total value of spinach for that year was $11,382,000. How much greater was the value of the garlic?

4. There were 1,000 a. planted in spring spinach. Monterey County had 310 a., Santa Barbara County had 150 a., and Ventura County had 450 a. How many acres did all other counties have planted in spring spinach?

5. Fresh chili peppers had a value of $12,260,000 and dried chili peppers had a value of $12,610,000. What was the total value for chili peppers?

6. Brussels sprouts had a total value of $15,928,000 one year. The following year the total value was $15,706,000. How much less was the total value the second year?

7. One year 113,161 T of honeydew melons were grown. Of these, 89,560 T were summer melons and the remainder were fall melons. How many tons of fall melons were grown?

8. How many more acres were for cantaloupes than for all other melons?

Melon	Acreage
Cantaloupe	51,900
Watermelon	4,000
Honeydew	11,900
Crenshaw	1,000
Casaba	200
Persian	200

9. The 30,254 a. of winter cabbage in 1979 had a total value of $7,737,000. The 24,176 a. of cabbage had a total value of $2,846,000 in 1980. How many acres less cabbage were there in 1980?

10. The total value of the vegetable and melon crop in California in 1972 was $1,014,498,000. If this number is added to itself, the sum is $224,379,000 less than the value of the vegetable and melon crop in 1980. What was the value of the two crops in 1980?

13

Special Products and Quotients: Mental Math

The patterns below show multiplication and division of numbers
by 10, 100, and 1,000.

$7 \times 10 = 70$ $70 \div 10 = 7$ $245 \times 10 = 2,450$
$7 \times 100 = 700$ $700 \div 100 = 7$ $245 \times 100 = 24,500$
$7 \times 1,000 = 7,000$ $7,000 \div 1,000 = 7$ $245 \times 1,000 = 245,000$

Special products and special quotients can be found without
using paper and a pencil. Study the patterns below.

$6 \times 40 = 240$ $240 \div 40 = 6$ $90 \times 8 = 720$ $720 \div 8 = 90$
$60 \times 40 = 2,400$ $2,400 \div 40 = 60$ $90 \times 80 = 7,200$ $7,200 \div 80 = 90$
$600 \times 40 = 24,000$ $24,000 \div 40 = 600$ $90 \times 800 = 72,000$ $72,000 \div 800 = 90$

Practice Write the products only.

1. 6×10 **2.** 8×100 **3.** $5 \times 1,000$ **4.** 15×10 **5.** 23×10

6. 4×20 **7.** 9×30 **8.** 10×60 **9.** 8×200 **10.** $9 \times 5,000$

11. 30×500 **12.** 70×40 **13.** 800×500 **14.** 90×90 **15.** $60 \times 9,000$

16. $20 \times 20 \times 10$ **17.** $6 \times 700 \times 100$ **18.** $50 \times 50 \times 20$ **19.** $80 \times 30 \times 2$ **20.** $200 \times 20 \times 10$

Write the quotients only.

21. $200 \div 20$ **22.** $180 \div 6$ **23.** $350 \div 70$ **24.** $600 \div 100$ **25.** $4,000 \div 2$

26. $2,800 \div 70$ **27.** $3,700 \div 100$ **28.** $540 \div 90$ **29.** $8,100 \div 90$ **30.** $1,000 \div 100$

31. $2,700 \div 90$ **32.** $3,600 \div 400$ **33.** $1,400 \div 7$ **34.** $350 \div 70$ **35.** $16,000 \div 8,000$

36. $900 \div 30$ **37.** $320 \div 80$ **38.** $72,000 \div 900$ **39.** $20,000 \div 500$ **40.** $63,000 \div 9,000$

Find each product and quotient mentally.

41. $(3 \times 10) \times 4$ **42.** $20 \times (5 \times 6)$ **43.** $8 \times (2 \times 30)$

44. $(20 \times 30) \div 300$ **45.** $(320 \div 40) \times 9$ **46.** $(30 \times 40) \div 20$

14

Estimating Products and Quotients

A fully-loaded B-747 airplane could carry 369 people. Estimate the total number of people the plane could carry in 22 trips.

To estimate the product, we can round each factor.

22×369

$\downarrow \qquad \downarrow$

$20 \times 400 = 8,000$ Estimate

The plane could carry about 8,000 passengers.

When estimating quotients, it often helps to replace a number with a more **compatible number** so you can use basic facts and mental math.

$2,578 \div 83$	$3,209 \div 52$	$1,564 \div 8$
$2,400 \div 80 = 30$	$3,000 \div 50 = 60$	$1,600 \div 8 = 200$
Compatible numbers	Compatible numbers	Compatible numbers

Practice Estimate the products.

1. 49×68
2. 23×77
3. 8×493
4. $7 \times 6,078$
5. 92×92

6. 66×102
7. 37×608
8. 599×8
9. $2,119 \times 5$
10. 207×185

11. 297×67
12. 419×787
13. $23,807 \times 9$
14. $41,226 \times 8$
15. $2,774 \times 205$

Estimate the quotients.

16. $237 \div 8$
17. $319 \div 39$
18. $6,249 \div 9$
19. $169 \div 37$ 4
20. $2,376 \div 78$

21. $1,855 \div 28$
22. $297 \div 51$
23. $5,875 \div 30$
24. $14,000 \div 73$
25. $819 \div 22$

26. $16,200 \div 84$
27. $2,365 \div 43$
28. $4,380 \div 74$
29. $53,225 \div 58$
30. $3,433 \div 72$

31. $88\overline{)2,682}$
32. $43\overline{)3,701}$
33. $77\overline{)5,626}$
34. $89\overline{)18,123}$
35. $617\overline{)2,950}$

Mixed Applications

36. A Super DC-8 can carry a maximum of 195 people. The plane made 63 fully-loaded flights. What is an estimate of the total number of people carried?

37. A B-747 can carry 369 passengers. Estimate the number of trips a B-747 would make to carry 12,000 passengers.

More Practice, page 433, Set D

Multiplying Whole Numbers

Vernon Marshall uses a motorcycle to drive to work. The total distance driven each day is 48 miles (mi). The motorcycle is used 247 days in a year. What is the total distance driven for the year?

Since the same distance is driven each day, we can multiply.

Multiply by the ones.	Multiply by the tens.	Add the products.

```
    2 4 7          2 4 7          2 4 7
  ×  4 8         ×  4 8         ×  4 8
  -------        -------        -------
  1 9 7 6        1 9 7 6        1 9 7 6
                 9 8 8 0        9 8 8 0
                                -------
                              1 1,8 5 6
```

The total distance for the year is 11,856 mi.

Other Examples

```
      3 4 6              9 4 2          1,0 7 7         $ 2,7 5 1
    × 7 9 8            × 1 0 8          ×  5 0 0        ×    3 6
    -------            -------          --------        ---------
    2 7 6 8            7 5 3 6          5 3 8,5 0 0     1 6 5 0 6
  3 1 1 4 0            9 4 2 0 0                        8 2 5 3
2 4 2 2 0 0            ---------                        ---------
  ---------          1 0 1,7 3 6                        $ 9 9,0 3 6
2 7 6,1 0 8
```

We can omit these zeros.

Warm Up

Multiply.

1. 233 × 7		**2.** 4,809 × 6		**3.** 95 × 78		**4.** 804 × 63	
5. 206 × 215		**6.** 816 × 70		**7.** $875 × 24		**8.** $5,999 × 72	

16

Practice Estimate the products. Then find the products.

1. $\begin{array}{r} 59 \\ \times\ 8 \\ \hline \end{array}$
2. $\begin{array}{r} 317 \\ \times\ 7 \\ \hline \end{array}$
3. $\begin{array}{r} 1,884 \\ \times\quad 5 \\ \hline \end{array}$
4. $\begin{array}{r} 23,706 \\ \times\qquad 9 \\ \hline \end{array}$
5. $\begin{array}{r} 93 \\ \times 74 \\ \hline \end{array}$

6. $\begin{array}{r} 59 \\ \times 75 \\ \hline \end{array}$
7. $\begin{array}{r} 49 \\ \times 68 \\ \hline \end{array}$
8. $\begin{array}{r} 98 \\ \times 87 \\ \hline \end{array}$
9. $\begin{array}{r} 408 \\ \times\ 25 \\ \hline \end{array}$
10. $\begin{array}{r} 872 \\ \times\ 39 \\ \hline \end{array}$

11. 947×70
12. 882×66
13. 981×267
14. 683×207
15. 652×427

16. 740×950
17. $\$3,115 \times 18$
18. $\$1,375 \times 50$
19. $\$6,266 \times 900$
20. $\$6,035 \times 108$

21. 175×23
22. 46×224
23. 921×70
24. 77×274
25. $283 \times 5,803$

26. $784 \times 3,967$
27. $58 \times 43 \times 100$
28. $64 \times 64 \times 64$
29. $101 \times 97 \times 3$
30. $83 \times 205 \times 7$

31. What is 947 multiplied by 608?

32. What is the product of 5,743 and 827?

Mixed Applications

33. The total cost of operating a carpool van for a year is shared equally by 6 riders. Each person pays $427. Estimate, then find the total cost of operating the van.

34. Betty Brill's expenses to operate her motorcycle for 49 weeks are $407. She estimates that it would have cost her $25 a week to drive a car. Estimate, then find how much money she saves by using her motorcycle for the 49 weeks.

35. This problem has missing data. Make up the data and then solve the problem. Ron paid insurance by the month to operate his motorcycle. How much was his insurance for a year?

36. An auto club estimated that it costs about 49 cents a mile to operate an automobile. Estimate, then find the cost of driving 612 miles in a week.

THINK MATH

Reversed Number Products

$$12 \times 84 = 1,008$$
$$21 \times 48 = 1,008$$

Why are the pairs of products the same? Find more pairs like these.

Find each pair of products.

1. $36 \times 42 =$
   $63 \times 24 =$
2. $62 \times 39 =$
   $26 \times 93 =$
3. $96 \times 46 =$
   $69 \times 64 =$
4. $39 \times 31 =$
   $93 \times 13 =$

Dividing Whole Numbers

A dairy farmer is filling a tank with 27,000 liters (L) of milk. The milk enters the tank at a rate of 360 L each minute (min). How many minutes will it take to fill the tank?

Since the same number of liters go into the tank each minute, we can divide.

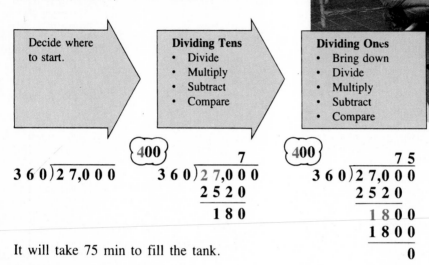

Decide where to start.

Dividing Tens
• Divide
• Multiply
• Subtract
• Compare

Dividing Ones
• Bring down
• Divide
• Multiply
• Subtract
• Compare

$$360\overline{)27{,}000}$$

400
$$\begin{array}{r} 7 \\ 360\overline{)27{,}000} \\ 2520 \\ \hline 180 \end{array}$$

400
$$\begin{array}{r} 75 \\ 360\overline{)27{,}000} \\ 2520 \\ \hline 1800 \\ 1800 \\ \hline 0 \end{array}$$

It will take 75 min to fill the tank.

Other Examples

$48{,}102 \div 79$

$$\begin{array}{r} 608 \text{ R } 70 \\ 79\overline{)48{,}102} \\ 474 \\ \hline 70 \\ 0 \\ \hline 702 \\ 632 \\ \hline 70 \end{array}$$

Check: $\begin{array}{r} 608 \leftarrow \text{quotient} \\ \times \quad 79 \leftarrow \text{divisor} \\ \hline 5472 \\ 42560 \\ \hline 48032 \\ + \quad 70 \leftarrow \text{remainder} \\ \hline 48{,}102 \leftarrow \text{dividend} \end{array}$

$\begin{array}{r} 3{,}787 \\ 18 \end{array}$

$$\begin{array}{r} 210 \text{ R } 7 \\ 18\overline{)3{,}787} \\ 36 \\ \hline 18 \\ 18 \\ \hline 07 \\ 0 \\ \hline 7 \end{array}$$

$\$10{,}944 \div 38$

$$\begin{array}{r} \$288 \\ 38\overline{)\$10{,}944} \\ 76 \\ \hline 334 \\ 304 \\ \hline 304 \\ 304 \\ \hline 0 \end{array}$$

Warm Up

Give the quotients and remainders. Check your answers.

1. $73\overline{)25{,}604}$ **2.** $24\overline{)\$168}$ **3.** $819\overline{)54{,}873}$ **4.** $600\overline{)40{,}806}$

5. $204 \div 51$ **6.** $168 \div 21$ **7.** $7{,}466 \div 129$ **8.** $\$7{,}268 \div 92$

18

Practice Find the quotients and remainders.

1. $52\overline{)726}$ 2. $77\overline{)1,862}$ 3. $49\overline{)5,200}$ 4. $86\overline{)7,842}$

5. $8\overline{)2,344}$ 6. $5\overline{)825,000}$ 7. $19\overline{)3,920}$ 8. $81\overline{)5,186}$

9. $48\overline{)4,331}$ 10. $6\overline{)2,284}$ 11. $75\overline{)7,956}$ 12. $97\overline{)48,513}$

13. $112\overline{)6,657}$ 14. $427\overline{)15,833}$ 15. $825\overline{)100,000}$ 16. $717\overline{)9,884,626}$

17. $30\overline{)\$120}$ 18. $54\overline{)\$216}$ 19. $59\overline{)\$177}$ 20. $128\overline{)\$768}$

21. $\dfrac{1,957}{64}$ 22. $\dfrac{9,384}{23}$ 23. $\dfrac{414}{65}$ 24. $\dfrac{20,000}{160}$

25. $38,062 \div 408$ 26. $38,906 \div 575$ 27. $95,589 \div 457$ 28. $26,842 \div 827$

Estimate each quotient. Then find the quotient.

29. $563\overline{)346,245}$ 30. $87\overline{)13,311}$ 31. $4,284\overline{)98,532}$ 32. $7,995\overline{)471,705}$

33. What is the quotient and remainder when 62,100 is divided by 88?

34. When 2,784 is divided by a number, the quotient is 92 and the remainder is 24. What is the divisor?

Mixed Applications

35. A tank holding 20,250 L of liquid is being emptied at a rate of 250 L each minute. How many minutes will it take to empty the tank?

36. Make up a *word problem* that could be solved by dividing these numbers. $435 \div 25$

SKILLKEEPER

Estimate the sum or difference.

1. $\$835 + \$274$ 2. $\$913 - \$564$ 3. $\$557 - \$310$ 4. $\$618 + \$449$ 5. $\$391 + \$58$

6. $\begin{array}{r} 1,342 \\ -\ \ 605 \end{array}$ 7. $\begin{array}{r} 8,567 \\ +\ \ 636 \end{array}$ 8. $\begin{array}{r} 3,702 \\ -\ \ 592 \end{array}$ 9. $\begin{array}{r} 5,498 \\ -\ \ 332 \end{array}$ 10. $\begin{array}{r} 6,901 \\ +\ \ 783 \end{array}$

11. $\begin{array}{r} 8,942 \\ +2,365 \end{array}$ 12. $\begin{array}{r} 5,762 \\ -1,983 \end{array}$ 13. $\begin{array}{r} 4,189 \\ +5,582 \end{array}$ 14. $\begin{array}{r} 7,716 \\ -3,829 \end{array}$ 15. $\begin{array}{r} 6,499 \\ +9,391 \end{array}$

PROBLEM SOLVING: Understanding the Question

QUESTION
DATA
PLAN
ANSWER
CHECK

To solve a problem, you must know what the problem asks you to find. You need to read the problem carefully to understand the meaning of the question.

Tell which of the three questions can be answered from the data that is given. Then solve the problem.

1. A concert hall has 1,600 seats. The seats cost $3, $5, and $8. The paid attendance at a concert was 1,365 people.
   A What was the total amount of money paid for the seats?
   B How many seats were not used?
   C How many more $5-tickets were sold than $8-tickets?

2. Two families shared the cost equally of leasing a ski cabin for the months of December, January, and February. The total cost was $2,058.
   A What is the cost of renting the cabin for the months of June, July, and August?
   B How many days will each family use the cabin?
   C What is the cost of the cabin per month for each family?

3. Apples are shipped in boxes with about 75 apples per box. Each apple weighs about 250 grams (g).
   A What is the weight of a box of apples?
   B What is the value of a box of apples?
   C What is the cost of shipping 380 boxes of apples?

4. Leonard bought a shirt, a jacket, and a pair of socks for a total of $75. The socks cost $6.
   A What was the cost of the shirt?
   B How much money would he get back if he paid with four $20 bills?
   C How much less did the socks cost than the shirt?

5. Light bulbs are on sale at 4 for $3. The regular price of the bulbs is 2 for $2.
   A What is the cost of four 25-watt light bulbs?
   B How many hours will a light bulb last?
   C How much would be saved by buying four light bulbs at the sale price?

★ 6. The planets rotate around the sun in approximately circular orbits. Earth is about 147,000,000 kilometers (km) from the sun. Mars is about 207,000,000 km distant. Mercury is about 46,000,000 km from the sun.
   A How far is it from Earth to Mercury?
   B How far is it from Earth to Mars?
   C How much closer to the sun is Mercury than Earth?

PROBLEM SOLVING: Estimating Reasonable Answers

QUESTION
DATA
PLAN
ANSWER
CHECK

An estimate can help you decide if the answer to a problem is reasonable.

Is the total attendance of 178 reasonable?

Period	Attendance
1	35
2	29
3	24
4	33
5	31
6	26
Total	178

Each of the attendance numbers is close to 30. We say the numbers **cluster** around 30. An estimate of the total is 6 × 30 or 180.

The total of 178 seems reasonable.

Estimate the answer to each problem. Write **yes** if the answer given is reasonable. If it is not reasonable, give the correct answer.

1. Mr. Sanchez had 26 students in the first period, 31 in period 2, 34 in period 3, 29 in period 4, and 28 in period 5. What was the total number of students?
Answer: 128 students

2. Out of 672 students, 398 of them ride a bus to school. How many students do not ride a bus to school?
Answer: 274 students

3. There were 4 buses to take on a field trip. There were 53 students on the first bus, 48 on the second, 55 on the third, and 42 students on the last bus. How many students were on the four buses?
Anwer: 198 students

4. There were 672 students enrolled at Monroe Junior High School. The principal puts the students into 21 homerooms. If each homeroom has the same number of students, how many students are there in each homeroom?
Answer: 26 students per room

5. Concert tickets were sold to the school at a special rate. A block of tickets for 272 students cost $1,360. How much was each ticket?
Answer: $4.00

6. The cafeteria has 8 chairs at each table. There are 48 tables with chairs. How many chairs are there?
Answer: 384 chairs

7. Ms. Freeley has a science budget of $500. She has ordered materials costing $189, $116, and $97. How much less than her budget amount is the total for ordered materials?
Answer: $198

8. The Monroe basketball team has score 354 points in its first 6 games. It has 3 more games to play. If the team scores at the same rate as the first 6 games, what would be their total number of points for the 9 games?
Answer: 591 points

Mixed Practice: Whole Numbers

Add, subtract, multiply, or divide.

1. $\begin{array}{r} 15,288 \\ 19,407 \\ + 22,556 \\ \hline \end{array}$

2. $\begin{array}{r} 67,209 \\ - 38,435 \\ \hline \end{array}$

3. $\begin{array}{r} \$22 \\ 67 \\ 59 \\ + 33 \\ \hline \end{array}$

4. $\begin{array}{r} 408 \\ \times 37 \\ \hline \end{array}$

5. $37\overline{)63,409}$

6. $\begin{array}{r} 870,000 \\ - 129,757 \\ \hline \end{array}$

7. $\begin{array}{r} 2,758 \\ \times 9 \\ \hline \end{array}$

8. $52\overline{)1,834}$

9. $\begin{array}{r} 384,500 \\ 517,800 \\ 770,900 \\ + 662,100 \\ \hline \end{array}$

10. $\begin{array}{r} \$3,250 \\ \times 8 \\ \hline \end{array}$

11. $\begin{array}{r} 253,182 \\ - 79,546 \\ \hline \end{array}$

12. $90\overline{)7,070}$

13. $\begin{array}{r} 568 \\ \times 219 \\ \hline \end{array}$

14. $\begin{array}{r} \$100 \\ - 56 \\ \hline \end{array}$

15. $\begin{array}{r} 8,744,612 \\ + 9,188,605 \\ \hline \end{array}$

16. $8\overline{)23,640}$

17. $\begin{array}{r} 664 \\ 827 \\ 522 \\ 903 \\ + 777 \\ \hline \end{array}$

18. $\begin{array}{r} 9,108,633 \\ - 5,411,784 \\ \hline \end{array}$

19. $\begin{array}{r} 574 \\ \times 126 \\ \hline \end{array}$

20. $92\overline{)125,438}$

21. $\begin{array}{r} 1,089 \\ \times 6 \\ \hline \end{array}$

22. $311\overline{)96,721}$

23. $\begin{array}{r} \$129 \\ 278 \\ + 164 \\ \hline \end{array}$

24. $\begin{array}{r} 28,261 \\ - 27,938 \\ \hline \end{array}$

25. $\begin{array}{r} 3,334 \\ 6,729 \\ 846 \\ + 12,419 \\ \hline \end{array}$

26. $\begin{array}{r} 9,006 \\ \times 537 \\ \hline \end{array}$

27. $\begin{array}{r} 730,125 \\ - 259,938 \\ \hline \end{array}$

28. $\begin{array}{r} 467,132 \\ 9,008 \\ 9,267,130 \\ + 27,894 \\ \hline \end{array}$

29. $\begin{array}{r} \$600 \\ - 599 \\ \hline \end{array}$

30. $63\overline{)30,568}$

31. $\begin{array}{r} \$5,265 \\ \times 2,340 \\ \hline \end{array}$

32. $82\overline{)48,406}$

PROBLEM SOLVING: Using a Data Bank

QUESTION
DATA
PLAN
ANSWER
CHECK

A **data bank** is a source of information or data.

Modern computers and microcomputers are useful for storing and retrieving data. Large amounts of data can be stored on magnetic discs. The computer can be used to quickly **retrieve** the data and a printer can be used to print out the data.

Computers are connected by telephone, and data from one computer can be passed to another computer. Data can be stored in a central library or **data bank** and the data can be obtained quickly and used by people all over the world.

There is a data bank for you to use in the Appendix of this book. Throughout the book you will find data bank problems which will require the data from the data bank in order to solve the problems.

Use the Data Bank on page 429 to help you solve these problems.

1. What is the area, in square kilometers, of the largest natural lake?

2. How much larger is the Great Salt Lake in Utah than Lake Okeechobee in Florida?

3. What is the total area of the four lakes in Alaska?

4. Which lake is nearest in size to Lake Becharof in Alaska?

5. Lake Michigan is about how many times as large as Lake Tahoe?

6. Is Lake Superior more than 3 times as large as Lake Erie? Is it more than 4 times as large?

7. The Great Lakes are Superior, Michigan, Huron, Ontario, and Erie. What is the total area of the Great Lakes?

PROBLEM-SOLVING STRATEGY: Guess and Check

QUESTION
DATA
PLAN
ANSWER
CHECK

Try This

Hilary scored 8 more points in a basketball game than Emily. If Emily doubled the number of points she scored and then subtracted 3, the result would equal Hilary's points. How many points did Hilary score? How many points did Emily score?

To solve a problem like the one above, you may need to use the **strategy** called **Guess and Check**. Here is the way it works.

Make a first guess of Hilary's points:	Find Emily's points.	Check Emily's points.
20 points $\rightarrow$	**20 − 8 = 12** $\rightarrow$	Is 2 × 12 − 3 equal to Hilary's points? **24 − 3 = 21 21 ≠ 20**

Make a second guess of Hilary's points:	Find Emily's points.	Check Emily's points.
18 points $\rightarrow$	**18 − 8 = 10** $\rightarrow$	Is 2 × 10 − 3 equal to 18? **20 − 3 = 17 17 ≠ 18**

Make a third guess:	Find Emily's points.	Check Emily's points.
19 points $\rightarrow$	**19 − 8 = 11** $\rightarrow$	Is 2 × 11 − 3 equal to 19? **22 − 3 = 19 19 = 19** It checks.

Hilary scored 19 points.
Emily scored 11 points.

Solve.

1. The Pirates beat the Jets by 10 points. If the Jets had scored twice as many points as they did, they would have beaten the Pirates by 10 points. How many points did the Pirates score? How many points did the Jets score?

2. Stefan scored 17 more points than Adrian in a basketball game. If Adrian had scored 3 times as many points as he did, he would have scored 1 point less than Stefan. How many points did each person score?

24

Write < or > for each ⬤.

1. 7,736 ⬤ 7,751 **2.** 26,414 ⬤ 29,106 **3.** 364,187 ⬤ 360,278

Round to the nearest million.

4. 2,919,744 **5.** 85,409,647 **6.** 419,874,000 **7.** 32,448,850

Perform the operations.

8. $2 + 6 \times 4$ **9.** $(9 + 6) \div (12 - 7)$ **10.** $9 \times (6 - 4) + 3$

Estimate each sum or difference.

11. $2,371 + 1,997 + 4,751$ **12.** $8,139 - 3,884$ **13.** $\$758 + \$4,170 + \$880$

Find the sums or differences.

14. 8,282
      7,665
    + 3,934

15. 68,182
     − 39,558

16. $1,875
       2,642
     + 5,377

17. $10,000
      − 6,479

Estimate each product or quotient.

18. 91×73 **19.** $4,200 \div 61$ **20.** $15,026 \div 521$ **21.** 23×900

Multiply or divide.

22. 629
     $\times$ 84

23. 577
     $\times$ 108

24. $88\overline{)50,529}$

25. $177\overline{)12,070}$

26. Jim Tanaka had $1,018 in his checking account. He wrote a check for $375 and a check for $118. How much was left in his checking account?

27. A B-727 airplane carried 131 passengers. The cost for each passenger was $187. What was the total paid by all the passengers?

$8,519 < 8,539$

$1 < 3$

$8,539 > 8,519$

8,519 rounded to the nearest:

10	100	1,000
8,520	8,500	9,000

Write < or > for each ⬤.

1. 23,407 ⬤ 23,392 **2.** 485,667 ⬤ 487,567

3. 6,474 ⬤ 64,474 **4.** 18,279 ⬤ 18,296

Round to the nearest thousand.

5. 72,672 **6.** 247,500 **7.** 9,784

8. 267,817 **9.** 1,519,609 **10.** 65,475,108

Work inside parentheses first.
Then multiply or divide.
Then add or subtract.

Perform the operations.

11. $(6 \times 4) + 5$ **12.** $10 + (32 \div 4)$

13. $(9 + 7) \div (10 - 2)$ **14.** $36 \div (6 + 3) \times 7$

$127 \to 100$
$+ 318 \to + 300$

$400 \leftarrow$ estimate

Estimate each sum or difference by rounding to the nearest hundred. Then add or subtract.

15. $627 + 877$ **16.** $1,821 - 1,657$

17. $\$817 - \$395$ **18.** $239 + 186 + 579$

```
 2  10 9 15 13              1 1  1 1
 3 1,0 6 3   Check.    12,588
-1 8,4 7 5            + 18,475
 1 2,5 8 8              31,063
```

Add or subtract.

19. 3,147 **20.** 48,716 **21.** 40,272
        4,778   53,096   − 28,613
      + 1,842   + 38,445

```
      3 0 R6              2
2 1 9)6,5 7 6  Check.    219
      6 5 7            ×  30
      0 6             6,570
      0               +    6
      6               6,576
```

Find the products.

22. 40×60 **23.** 817 **24.** 328
                             $\times$ 25 $\times$ 279

Find the quotients.

25. $2,800 \div 7$ **26.** $54,000 \div 900$

27. $83\overline{)12,444}$ **28.** $279\overline{)58,081}$

Mental Math

Study the multiplication patterns.

10 is the middle number in each pair of factors.

9 and 11 are 1 unit from 10.
8 and 12 are 2 units from 10.
7 and 13 are 3 units from 10.

Can you find 6 × 14 by this method?

$$
\begin{array}{l}
\overbrace{9}^{10-1} \quad \overbrace{11}^{10+1} \\
9 \quad \times \quad 11 \; = \; (10 \times 10) - (1 \times 1) \\
\qquad\qquad\qquad = \; 100 \quad - \quad 1 \; = 99 \\
\overbrace{8}^{10-2} \quad \overbrace{12}^{10+2} \\
8 \quad \times \quad 12 \; = \; (10 \times 10) - (2 \times 2) \\
\qquad\qquad\qquad = \; 100 \quad - \quad 4 \; = 96 \\
\overbrace{7}^{10-3} \quad \overbrace{13}^{10+3} \\
7 \quad \times \quad 13 \; = \; (10 \times 10) - (3 \times 3) \\
\qquad\qquad\qquad = \; 100 \quad - \quad 9 \; = 91
\end{array}
$$

You can use mental math to find other products like these.

Find 19 × 21 mentally.

> Think
> The middle number is 20.
> 20 − 1 = 19
> 20 + 1 = 21

> Think
> (20 × 20) − (1 × 1)
> 400 − 1

→ 19 × 21 = 399

Find 43 × 37 mentally.

> Think
> The middle number is 40.
> 40 − 3 = 37
> 40 + 3 = 43

> Think
> (40 × 40) − (3 × 3)
> 1,600 − 9

→ 43 × 37 = 1,591

Find each product mentally.

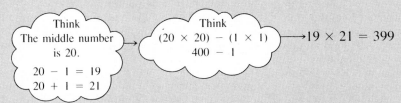

1. 18 × 22
(20 × 20) − (2 × 2)

2. 17 × 23
(20 × 20) − (3 × 3)

3. 39 × 41
(40 × 40) − (1 × 1)

4. 28 × 32
(30 × 30) − (2 × 2)

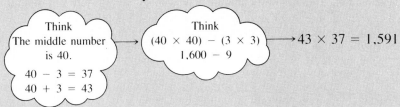

5. 49 × 51
middle number is 50

6. 33 × 27
middle number is 30

7. 58 × 62
middle number is 60

8. 42 × 38
middle number is 40

9. 69 × 71

10. 34 × 26

11. 25 × 35

12. 45 × 55

13. 52 × 48

14. 83 × 77

15. 89 × 91

16. 98 × 102

Using a Calculator

Most simple calculators have special function keys that can be used in certain kinds of problems.

You must decide which operations to use and the order in which to use them.

Use the standard order of operations.

- Perform the operations in parentheses.
- Multiply or divide from left to right.
- Add or subtract from left to right.

M+	Stores or adds a number in the memory.
M−	Subtracts a number from the memory.
MR	Recalls and displays a number in the memory.
MC	Clears the memory.
CE	Clears the entry number.

Find $(829 + 642) \times 94 - 829 \times 17$.

Enter	Press	Display	Comments
829	+	829.	829 is entered.
642	=	1471.	$829 + 642 = 1,471$
	×	1471.	Multiply 1,471 by
94	=	138274.	$1,471 \times 94 = 138,274$
	M+	M 138274.	138,274 is stored in the memory.
829	×	M 829.	829 is entered. Memory is in use.
17	=	M 14093.	$829 \times 17 = 14,093$
	M−	M 14093.	14,093 is subtracted from 138,274.
	MR	M 124181.	Memory number is recalled. $138,274 - 14,093 = 124,181$
	MC	124181.	Memory is cleared.

The answer is 124,181.

2. Subtract consecutive odd numbers from 64, beginning with 1. How many odd numbers must you subtract to get to 0?

3. Subtract consecutive odd numbers from 100. Guess how many odd numbers you must subtract to get to 0. Then check your guess.

4. If you multiply the whole numbers consecutively starting with 1, what is the largest number you can use and not go over 1,000,000? Make a guess, then check your guess.

5. Suppose your parents put 1¢ in a savings account on your first birthday, 2¢ on your second birthday, 4¢ on your third birthday and so on, doubling the previous year's amount on each succeeding birthday. How much money would there be in the account on your 13th birthday? How much would there be on your 21st birthday?

Use a calculator to solve these problems.

1. Which problem has an answer different from the others?

A $126 \times 45 \div 72$ **B** $45 \div 72 \times 126$
C $45 \div 126 \times 72$ **D** $126 \div 72 \times 45$

The sum of 3,728 and its reverse, 8,273, is exactly divisible by 11.

$$\begin{array}{r} 3,728 \\ + 8,273 \\ \hline 12,001 \end{array}$$ $12,001 \div 11 = 1,091$

Find the sums. Are the sums always exactly divisible by 11? no

6.   6,442
       + 2,446

7.   47
       + 74

8.   273,695
       + 596,372

9.   591
       + 195

10.   9,876
       + 6,789

11.   61,098
       + 89,016

12.   72,281,891
       + 19,818,227

13.   64,783
       + 38,746

1. Round 84,547 to the nearest thousand.

A 80,000   **B** 84,000
C 85,000   **D** not given

2. Which is correct?

A 23,500 > 25,300
B 67,173 > 67,098
C 8,909 = 8,099
D not given

3. Which is not correct?

A $8 \times (12 \times 7) = (7 \times 8) \times 12$
B $9 \times 7 + 9 \times 3 = 9 \times (7 + 3)$
C $15 + (9 + 6) = (15 + 9) + 6$
D not given

4. Estimate the sum.

$3,841 + 2,359 + 4,778$

A 11,000   **B** 10,000
C 9,000   **D** not given

5. Add.

23,785   **A** 235,070
54,761   **B** 230,570
69,895   **C** 230,560
+ 82,129   **D** not given

6. Subtract.

8,084,625   **A** 4,707,788
− 3,376,837   **B** 5,707,788
                 C 4,707,888
                 D not given

Find the products.

7. 50×700

A 3,500   **B** 35,000
C 350,000   **D** not given

8.   364   **A** 31,204   **B** 31,304
      × 86   **C** 5,096   **D** not given

9.   837   **A** 39,339   **B** 340,659
      × 407   **C** 3,353,859   **D** not given

Divide.

10. $63,000 \div 900$

A 7   **B** 70
C 700   **D** not given

11. $87\overline{)36,548}$

A 420 R8
B 42 R8
C 402 R8
D not given

12. $63\overline{)19,348}$

A 37 R7
B 307 R7
C 370 R7
D not given

13. A B-747 jet airplane will seat 370 people. A computer showed that 284 seats were taken. How many seats were not taken?

A 86   **B** 377
C 96   **D** not given

14. A tank with a capacity of 64,000 L is to be filled at a rate of 256 L each minute. How long will it take to fill the tank?

A between 2 and 3 hours
B between 3 and 4 hours
C a little more than 4 hours
D not given

Addition and Subtraction of Decimals

A bat flying in the dark sends out pulses of high-pitched sound through its mouth or nostrils. The sound bounces off objects, such as insects, and is reflected back to the bat's ears. From the echo alone, the bat can tell the direction, distance, and speed of an insect. Some species of bats are able to detect objects as small as 0.08 millimeter in diameter. Bats can detect and capture an insect in only 0.25 second.

This method of direction-finding is called *echo-location*. Using echoes, or "sound pictures," bats can be very accurate hunters. A brown bat that weighed 8.2 grams before hunting weighed 9.5 grams after 70 minutes of hunting. The insects that the bat ate had an average weight of 0.002 grams each.

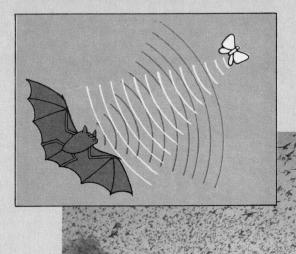

Decimal Place Value

An atom of helium is made up of 2 protons, 2 neutrons, and 2 electrons. Atomic scientists use **decimals** to record the weights of protons and neutrons.

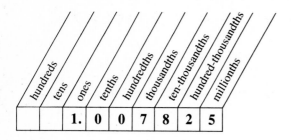

		1.	0	0	7	8	2	5

Decimal numeral: 1.007825

Read: "one **and** seven thousand, eight hundred twenty-five millionths" or

"one **point** zero zero seven eight two five"

A Helium Atom

	Atomic weight
Proton	1.007825 units
Neutron	1.008665 units

The 8 in the ten-thousandths place means 8 ten-thousandths or 0.0008.

The 5 in the millionths place means 5 millionths or 0.000005.

Other Examples

0.3125	three thousand, one hundred twenty-five **ten-thousandths**
19.04	nineteen **and** four **hundredths**

3.1416	three **point** one four one six
0.00007	7 **hundred-thousandths**
0.000025	25 **millionths**

Warm Up

Read both ways. Tell what each underlined digit means.

1. 0.8<u>1</u>2 **2.** 6.4<u>8</u> **3.** 63.<u>5</u> **4.** 0.0<u>7</u> **5.** 1.12<u>3</u>

6. <u>3</u>24.84 **7.** 0.000<u>5</u> **8.** 80.8<u>0</u> **9.** 0.3075<u>3</u> **10.** 4.09166<u>4</u>

11. 0.0000<u>1</u> **12.** 200.0<u>2</u> **13.** 0.01<u>6</u>4 **14.** 26.<u>5</u> **15.** 89.0612<u>5</u>

Practice Write the decimal.

1. seven and sixteen hundredths

2. eight and twelve thousandths

3. fifty-four hundred-thousandths

4. seven hundred fifty-six thousandths

5. nine millionths

6. eleven and eleven ten-thousandths

7. sixteen and zero tenths

8. eight point eight

9. zero point four four zero six

10. two thousand and two thousandths

Give the place value of each underlined digit.

11. 6.13<u>5</u>9

12. 0.0538<u>6</u>

13. 29.<u>4</u>14

14. 0.00428<u>4</u>

15. 3,<u>8</u>29.45

16. 25.0075<u>6</u>

17. 0.708<u>9</u>2

18. 128.1<u>2</u>9

19. 0.298<u>2</u>

20. 6.88<u>2</u>5

21. 0.12345<u>6</u>

22. 187.0781<u>0</u>4

Write each decimal numeral described in exercises 23–26.

23. 6 in the tenths place,
8 in the ones place, and
7 in the hundredths place

24. 9 in the thousandths place,
0 in the hundredths place, and
6 in the tenths place

25. 9 in the millionths place,
5 in the ten-thousandths place,
and zero in all other places

26. 4 in the hundreds place,
7 in the hundredths place,
and zero in all other places

Write each number.

27. 17 million
17 millionths

28. 100 thousand
100 thousandths

29. 1 millionth
1 million

30. 3 ten-thousandths
3 ten-thousands

31. 23 hundred
23 hundredths

32. one hundred and one hundredth
one hundred one and one hundredth

33. A neutron particle has 1.008665 units of atomic weight. Write the word name of this decimal.

34. The weight of an electron is about five thousand, four hundred eighty-nine ten-millionths of an atomic unit. Write the decimal for this number.

Comparing and Ordering Decimals

Bob Namara is a skilled machinist. He must grind a steel rod to a diameter of 5.7648 centimeters (cm). He measured a rod with a micrometer and found that it was 5.7651 cm. Is the measurement greater than or less than 5.7648 cm?

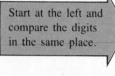

We need to compare 5.7648 and 5.7651.

Start at the left and compare the digits in the same place.	Compare the digits in the first place where they are different.	The numbers compare the same way the digits compare.

5.7648
5.7651

5.7648
5.7651

5 > 4

5.7651 > 5.7648

The measurement is greater than 5.7648 cm.

Other Examples

0.07 < 0.7

0.0539 < 0.054

0.0040 = 0.004

12 = 12.0 = 12.00

1.60 > 1.06

742.148 > 724.148

Warm Up

Write >, <, or = for each ▦

1. 6.324 ▦ 6.240   **2.** 0.309 ▦ 0.306   **3.** 0.006 ▦ 0.06   **4.** 1.008200 ▦ 1.0082

5. 12.86 ▦ 12.80   **6.** 0.921 ▦ 0.912   **7.** 4.00006 ▦ 4   **8.** 0.0071 ▦ 0.00071

Practice Write $<$, $>$, or $=$ for 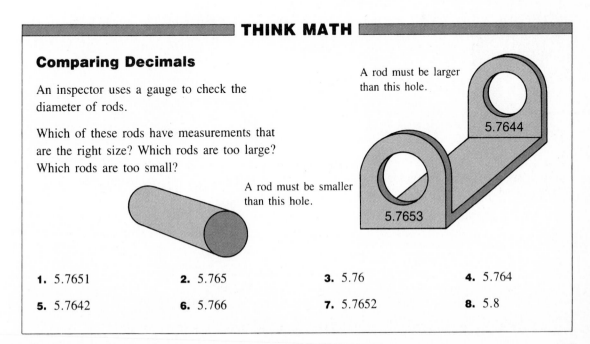.

1. 0.25 ___ 0.21
2. 2.73 ___ 2.83
3. 0.428 ___ 0.433
4. 5 ___ 4.9
5. 0.734 ___ 7.24
6. 16.9 ___ 16.89
7. 0.046 ___ 0.45
8. 3.14 ___ 3.142
9. 0.85 ___ 0.850
10. 0.1877 ___ 0.1868
11. 0.0627 ___ 0.6270
12. 4,006.6 ___ 4,060.6
13. 0.1000 ___ 0.1
14. 0.3333 ___ 0.33333
15. 0.500 ___ 0.50
16. 0.6267 ___ 0.6267
17. 239.90 ___ 239.09
18. 14 ___ 14.000

Order the numbers from least to greatest.

19. 0.613
    0.642
    0.6
    0.599

20. 2.0704
    2.1066
    2.0045
    2.16

21. 4.7
    4.6991
    4.967
    4.98

Mixed Applications

22. Bob measured a rod and found that it had a diameter of 5.7561 cm. Is this greater than or less than 5.7651?

23. An inspector measured a rod and found that the diameter was 1.2499 cm. The rod was one ten-thousandth centimeter smaller than it should have been. What should the measurement have been?

THINK MATH

Comparing Decimals

An inspector uses a gauge to check the diameter of rods.

Which of these rods have measurements that are the right size? Which rods are too large? Which rods are too small?

A rod must be larger than this hole.

5.7644

A rod must be smaller than this hole.

5.7653

1. 5.7651
2. 5.765
3. 5.76
4. 5.764
5. 5.7642
6. 5.766
7. 5.7652
8. 5.8

More Practice, page 434, Set C

Rounding Decimals

Bars of pure gold must be weighed carefully to determine their value. One bar of gold weighs 391.168 troy ounces. What is the weight rounded to the nearest hundredth of an ounce?

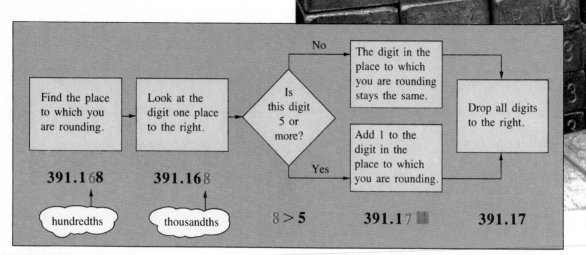

391.168 rounded to the nearest hundredth is 391.17.

Other Examples

Decimal	Nearest tenth	Nearest hundredth	Nearest thousandth	Nearest whole number
12.8154	12.8	12.82	12.815	13
0.92667	0.9	0.93	0.927	1
0.06495	0.1	0.06	0.065	0
$9.5288	$9.5 or $9.50	$9.53	$9.529	$10 or $10.00

Sometimes numbers are rounded to **1-digit accuracy**. Starting at the left, round to the first place that is not zero.

Number	1-Digit Accuracy
72.67	70
0.9368	0.9
0.06621	0.07

Warm Up

Round to the nearest thousandth.

1. 1.72814   **2.** 30.0676   **3.** 0.0625

Round to 1-digit accuracy.

4. $6.928   **5.** 0.7703   **6.** 0.045

Practice Round to the nearest whole number.

1. 85.75
2. 606.5
3. 1.492
4. $2.875
5. 129.09
6. 0.333
7. $39.87
8. 0.6668348

Round to the nearest tenth.

9. 8.44
10. 25.672
11. $0.88
12. 3.1966001
13. 70.07
14. 0.0881
15. $19.45
16. 0.1159876

Round to the nearest hundredth.

17. 0.125
18. 6.0386
19. 54.441
20. 0.9295392
21. 8.007
22. 0.1964
23. 0.0048
24. 0.0483333

Round to the nearest thousandth.

25. 0.5656
26. 1.7824
27. 0.0084
28. 12.9288
29. 6.0635
30. 0.00069
31. 2.9995
32. 0.3372799

Round to 1-digit accuracy.

33. 0.8662
34. $23.75
35. 1.884
36. $0.085
37. 0.1236
38. 125.9
39. 0.6064
40. 0.0029371

Estimate the sum or difference. Example:

$$83.28 \rightarrow 80$$
$$-32.57 \rightarrow -30$$
$$\overline{ \rightarrow 50} \leftarrow \text{Estimate}$$

41.
   12.093
   + 8.128

42.
   29.44
   − 18.5

43.
   $8.19
   3.77
   + 5.29

44.
   281.33
   119.47
   +308.722

45.
   609.47
   − 193.66

46.
   $81.75
   39.22
   +50.48

47.
   1.326
   0.984
   +1.828

48.
   $8,744.25
   − 2,819.69

Mixed Applications

49. Gold can be pounded into leaves that are about 0.0000069 cm thick. Round this number to 1-digit accuracy.

50. **DATA HUNT** One metric ton (t) of sea water contains about 1 grain of gold. What part of 1 gram is 1 grain? Round the decimal to the nearest hundredth.

More Practice, page 434, Set D

Adding Decimals

Four runners for a relay team had individual times in seconds (s) of 50.82, 52.44, 51.39, and 50.47. What was the total time in seconds for the team in the relay race?

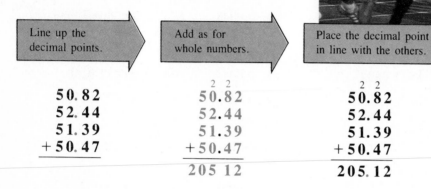

Since we want to find the total time, we add.

Line up the decimal points.	Add as for whole numbers.	Place the decimal point in line with the others.

50.82	$\overset{2\ 2}{50.82}$	$\overset{2\ 2}{50.82}$
52.44	52.44	52.44
51.39	51.39	51.39
+ 50.47	+ 50.47	+ 50.47
	205 12	205.12

The total time for the team was 205.12 s.

Other Examples

1.8 + 3.77 + 4

1.8 0	
3.7 7	
+ 4.0 0	Annex zeros to line up decimal places.
9.5 7	

$25.44
16.95
+ 9.37
$51.76

0.256
0.399
+ 0.056
0.711

Warm Up

Add.

1.	**2.**	**3.**	**4.**	**5.**
1.636	0.166	23.4	$0.77	$239.48
10.755	0.083	2.95	0.89	177.59
+ 6.072	1.277	+ 2.886	1.06	+ 4,007.85
	+ 0.518		+ 0.61	

6. 0.7 + 0.39 + 0.682

7. $83.75 + $95.64

8. $0.73 + $0.99 + $0.84

38

Practice Add.

1.	2.	3.	4.	5.
56.73 + 87.46	0.928 + 0.736	92.7 + 86.8	576.34 + 821.98	0.7635 + 0.0438

6.	7.	8.	9.	10.
67.2 88.7 + 54.3	9.26 0.83 + 5.91	0.834 6.275 + 0.098	9.842 7.665 + 0.560	28.6925 4.8361 + 37.9624

11.	12.	13.	14.	15.
$67.23 56.78 70.35 + 8.95	$52.20 76.35 4.38 + 92.47	$75.62 0.65 8.92 + 56.34	$215.92 83.67 0.83 + 1.56	$15.76 28.93 7.98 + 6.77

Estimate the sum. Check with a calculator.

16. $7.26 + 5.1 + 4.26$

17. $119.4 + 88.69 + 9.059 + 58.2$

18. $212.14 + $368.63

19. $7.2 + 3.8 + 7.5 + 6.5$

20. $2,756.75 + $1,809.25

21. $985.66 + $1,538.49 + $77.27

22. $0.231 + 4.023 + 1$

23. $12 + 15.5 + 10.75$

Mixed Applications

24. Four times for a relay team were 1.030 min, 1.042 min, 1.048 min, and 1.061 min. What is the total time in minutes for the team?

25. Blair ran the first 2 laps of a race in 118 s and the second 2 laps in 135 s. How much faster was Blair's time for the first half of the race than for the second half?

⬛ THINK MATH ⬛

Shape Perception

Which of these figures can be traced without lifting your pencil from the paper and without retracing any part of the figure?

A
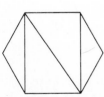

B
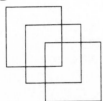

C

D

Subtracting Decimals

Halley races her horse in a barrel race competition. Her best time for the race is 31.04 s. Last year's champion had a time of 28.77 s. How much more is Halley's best time?

Since we want to find how much more one number is than another, we subtract.

Write the problem with the decimal points in line.	Subtract as with whole numbers.	Place the decimal point in line with the others.

$$\begin{array}{r} 31.04 \\ -28.77 \\ \hline \end{array}$$

$$\begin{array}{r} {\scriptstyle 2\;10\;9\;14} \\ \cancel{31.04} \\ -28.77 \\ \hline 2\;27 \end{array}$$

$$\begin{array}{r} {\scriptstyle 2\;10\;9\;14} \\ \cancel{31.04} \\ -28.77 \\ \hline 2.27 \end{array}$$

Halley's best time is 2.27 s more than the champion's time.

Other Examples

22 − 15.184

$$\begin{array}{r} 22.000 \\ -15.184 \\ \hline 6.816 \end{array}$$

Annex zeros to line up the decimal places.

78.8573 − 3.9

$$\begin{array}{r} 78.8573 \\ -\ 3.9000 \\ \hline 74.9573 \end{array}$$

$2,700 − $948.75

$$\begin{array}{r} \$2,700.00 \\ -\ \ \ 948.75 \\ \hline \$1,751.25 \end{array}$$

Warm Up

Subtract.

1. $\begin{array}{r} 42.78 \\ -19.92 \\ \hline \end{array}$ **2.** $\begin{array}{r} 0.6255 \\ -0.4776 \\ \hline \end{array}$ **3.** $\begin{array}{r} 231.2 \\ -186.9 \\ \hline \end{array}$ **4.** $\begin{array}{r} 9.0462 \\ -3.7759 \\ \hline \end{array}$ **5.** $\begin{array}{r} \$703.00 \\ -499.78 \\ \hline \end{array}$

6. 41.2 − 28.41   **7.** $20 − $13.65   **8.** $234.16 − $159.86

9. 5 − 4.85   **10.** 0.4 − 0.0684   **11.** 17.4 − 0.09

Practice Subtract.

1. 87.2
-29.5

2. 76.04
-25.59

3. 0.834
-0.289

4. 8.149
-5.227

5. 60.00
-35.78

6. 900.5
-168.3

7. 37.86
-31.49

8. 0.0628
-0.0468

9. 50.77
-23.99

10. 0.00623
-0.00147

11. $\$78.03$
-14.67

12. $\$38.00$
$-\ 9.85$

13. $\$659.81$
-570.50

14. $\$152.00$
$-\ 79.98$

15. $\$2,041.39$
$-1,859.75$

Estimate the difference. Check with a calculator. 🖩

16. $7.04 - 3.594$

17. $5.395 - 0.47$

18. $20 - 12.32$

19. $43.25 - 27.6$

20. $151 - 82.8$

21. $100.3 - 75.97$

22. $\$505.00 - \$326.44$

23. $\$6,255.11 - \$2,777.76$

24. $\$60,000 - \$48,250.50$

Solve.

25. $26.55 - (8.48 + 9.35)$

26. $(1.094 - 0.775) + 2.527$

27. $585.3 - (743.8 - 476.2)$

28. $(16.44 + 38.77) - (25.71 + 29.50)$

29. $(\$100 - \$59.38) + \$3.29$

30. $\$250.00 - (\$119.35 - \$84.63)$

Mixed Applications

31. Pam's time in the first barrel race was 26.35 s. Her time in the second barrel race was 30.05 s. What was her total time for the two barrel races?

32. The time for a barrel race was 26.44 s. Because a barrel was knocked over, 5 s were added to the time. How much more than 28.77 s was the total?

SKILLKEEPER

1. 37.54
$+46.01$

2. 46.76
$+\ 9.8$

3. 0.873
$+0.529$

4. 631.92
$+701.49$

5. 0.8335
$+0.0976$

6. $\$91.63$
$+47.14$

7. $\$8.63$
$+12.99$

8. $\$32.01$
$+56.92$

9. $\$94.33$
$+\ 6.72$

10. $\$55.75$
$+123.82$

11. $0.004 + 0.053 + 0.009$

12. $\$314.97 + \$1.69 + \$33.03$

13. $1.387 + 0.048 + 10.02$

More Practice, page 435, Set B

Estimating Sums and Differences with Decimals

Jon Stein needed some supplies for his home computer system. He made this list of prices from a catalog. Then he made an estimate of the total cost. What is his estimate of the total?

Floppy disc	$ 3.15
Printer ribbon	6.95
Print wheel	9.67
Printer paper	8.09

To estimate the total we can **round** the numbers or we can use **front-end** estimation.

Rounding

$3.15 ⟶ $3.00
6.95 ⟶ 7.00
9.67 ⟶ 10.00
+ 8.09 ⟶ + 8.00

Estimate ⟶ $28.00

His estimate is $28.00.

Front-end

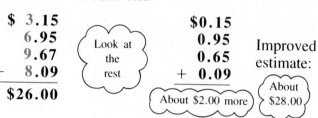

$ 3.15
6.95
9.67
+ 8.09

$26.00

Look at the rest

$0.15
0.95
0.65
+ 0.09

Improved estimate:

About $2.00 more

About $28.00

Other Examples

0.0813 ⟶ 0.08
−0.0324 ⟶ −0.03

Estimate ⟶ 0.05

0.718 ⟶ 0.7
0.893 ⟶ 0.9
+0.415 ⟶ +0.4

Estimate ⟶ 2.0

Practice Estimate the sum or difference by rounding.

1. 0.937
    − 0.329

2. 61.37
    38.44
    + 23.81

3. 0.52
    0.277
    + 0.3954

4. $87.19
    − 28.75

5. $0.59
    0.79
    0.42
    + 0.39

6. 31.87 + 18.75 + 22.05

7. 0.23 + 0.40 + 0.883

8. $20.66 − $14.95

Estimate. Use the front-end method.

9. 0.613
    0.184
    + 0.511

10. 0.892
    − 0.257

11. $2.69
    3.57
    + 5.98

12. 0.072
    0.0309
    + 0.05941

13. 29.804
    − 14.766

14. 838.06 − 337.45

15. $82.46 + $75.98 + $19.95

16. 0.0848 − 0.0559

Mixed Applications

17. Estimate how much more the printer paper costs than the floppy disc.

18. Estimate the total cost of 6 printer ribbons.

42

More Practice, page 435, Set C

PROBLEM SOLVING: Using Estimation

QUESTION
DATA
PLAN
ANSWER
CHECK

Estimate the answers to the problems. Then use a calculator to find the exact answers.

1. One complete home computer system is priced at $2,399.99. A second system costs $1,998.00. How much less expensive is the second system?

2. A home computer costs $649.99. The disc drive costs $275.50 and the printer costs $319.25. What is the total cost of the three pieces of equipment?

3. A box of ten floppy discs regularly costs $47.50. The box of discs is on sale for $29.95. How much less is the reduced price?

4. A word-processing program for a computer costs $319.85. A bookkeeping program costs $237.99. A home filing program sells for $99.95. What is the total cost of the three programs?

5. Daisy print wheels for a printer cost $8.95 each. About how much is the cost of a box of three wheels?

6. Koyo bought a surge protector for his computer. He saved $9.85 by buying it on sale for $29.95. What was the regular price of the surge protector?

7. Lela bought a special data stand for her computer that cost $179.98. She also bought an office chair for $133.50. She had $633.14 in her checking account. How much would be left after paying for the data stand and the office chair?

8. A floppy disc storage and filing unit holds 50 discs and costs $41.35. Each of the discs costs $3.89. What is the total cost of the storage unit and 50 floppy discs?

9. A roll of 2,200 sheets of computer printout paper costs $169.95. A business used 39 rolls of computer paper per year. What was the cost of the paper per year?

10. Strategy Practice The total cost for parts and labor to repair a home computer was $192. The labor cost 5 times as much as the parts. What was the cost for the parts? What was the cost for the labor? Hint: Guess and check.

Practice: Adding and Subtracting Decimals

Find the sums.

1.	6.1 + 8.3	**2.**	14.31 + 3.67	**3.**	3.008 + 9.779	**4.**	173.5 + 5.28	**5.**	54.93 + 27.555

1. 6.1
     $+ 8.3$

2. 14.31
     $+ \ 3.67$

3. 3.008
     $+ 9.779$

4. 173.5
     $+ \ \ \ 5.28$

5. 54.93
     $+ 27.555$

6. 92.34
     66.81
     $+ 37.98$

7. 129.1
     88.36
     $+ \ 60.5$

8. 0.0095
     0.0484
     $+ 0.0778$

9. 136.12
     275.09
     $+ 481.25$

10. 62.717
      39.447
      $+ 86.225$

11. 1.83
      0.76
      0.39
      $+ 2.75$

12. 48.9
      80.4
      88.6
      $+ 59.7$

13. 15.993
      29.207
      58.992
      $+ 43.065$

14. 2.5
      3.808
      15.0
      $+ \ 0.9283$

15. 7,442.6
      3,982.9
      6,033.5
      $+ 1,768.0$

Find the differences.

16. 28.9
      $- 19.7$

17. 47.84
      $- \ 9.39$

18. 0.838
      $- 0.445$

19. 208.4
      $- 127.9$

20. 0.1884
      $- 0.0937$

21. 12.4
      $- \ 9.55$

22. 200
      $- 175.58$

23. 0.2
      $- 0.145$

24. 7.333
      $- 5.9$

25. 308.00
      $- 177.25$

26. 14.53
      $- \ 9.65$

27. 0.85
      $- 0.836$

28. 4.102
      $- 0.003$

29. 100.01
      $- \ 84.56$

30. 2,701.84
      $- \ \ 967.35$

Find the amounts.

31. $75.42
      83.44
      $+ 15.98$

32. $10.00
      $- \ 9.47$

33. $250.00
      184.50
      $+ 327.85$

34. $199.35
      $- 198.64$

35. $3.50
      $- 0.99$

36. $6,114.25
      $- 3,207.50$

37. $30,000.00
      $- 25,780.89$

38. $0.60
      $+ 0.38$

39. $809.95
      670.40
      322.66
      $+ 379.87$

40. $0.77
      0.85
      0.96
      $+ 0.82$

Add or subtract.

41. $4.5 + 10.06 + 1.385$

42. $22.117 - 16.5$

43. $0.2775 - 0.1994$

44. $0.07234 - 0.03955$

45. $5.14 + 0.9 + 3$

46. $2.006 + 0.48 + 1.76$

PROBLEM SOLVING: Choosing a Calculation Method

QUESTION
DATA
PLAN
ANSWER
CHECK

Your choice!
- **Pencil-Paper**
- **Mental Math**
- **Estimation**
- **Calculator**

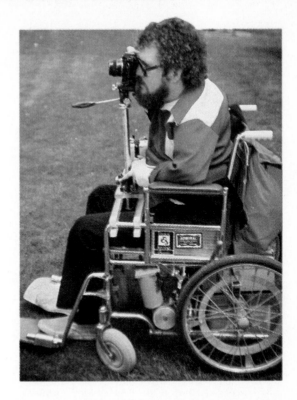

You may use any of these methods to solve the problems, but use each method at least once.

1. Joyce bought an instant camera for $179.95. Film for the camera costs $17.95 a pack. What is the cost of the camera and two packs of film?

2. Glenn looked at a camera that cost $179.99. Later he was able to buy the same camera on sale for $149.99. How much less was the sale price?

3. Jutta saw a camera for $297.97, a zoom lens for $149.82, and a camera case for $23.94. Is the total cost of the three items more or less than $500.00?

4. Warren bought a camera tripod for $39.95 and an electronic flash for $59.95 plus $2.89 for batteries. The total cost, including sales tax, was $109.47. How much was the sales tax?

5. A camera has a regular price of $55.95. Carmen found the same camera on sale for $10.95 less than the regular price. What is the sale price?

6. A projector was listed at a regular price of $394.50. Leah found a store that had it on sale for $314.80. How much less than the regular price was this?

7. A sound movie camera costs $379.95. The sales tax is $22.79. Is the total more than $400.00?

8. Ashley bought 3 rolls of film for $3.19 a roll. How much change should she get back if she paid for it with a $10 bill?

9. **DATA BANK** (Use the Data Bank on page 429.) What would be the cost of a disc camera and 3 disc packs of film?

10. **Strategy Practice** A camera and a zoom lens had a total cost of $360. The lens cost $100 less than the camera. What was the cost of the lens? What was the cost of the camera?

PROBLEM SOLVING: Using Data from a Table

QUESTION
DATA
PLAN
ANSWER
CHECK

A tax on the price of an item sold is called a **sales tax**. Sales people must use a sales tax table to find the amount of tax and then add it to the price of the item.

Sales Tax Table $(6\frac{1}{2}\%)$

Transaction	Tax	Transaction	Tax	Transaction	Tax	Transaction	Tax	Transaction	Tax
.01– .10	.00	5.31– 5.46	.35	10.70–10.84	.70	16.08–16.23	1.05	21.47–21.61	1.40
.11– .20	.01	5.47– 5.61	.36	10.85–10.99	.71	16.24–16.38	1.06	21.62–21.76	1.41
.21– .35	.02	5.62– 5.76	.37	11.00–11.15	.72	16.39–16.53	1.07	21.77–21.92	1.42
.36– .51	.03	5.77– 5.92	.38	11.16–11.30	.73	16.54–16.69	1.08	21.93–22.07	1.43
.52– .67	.04	5.93– 6.07	.39	11.31–11.46	.74	16.70–16.84	1.09	22.08–22.23	1.44
.68– .83	.05	6.08– 6.23	.40	11.47–11.61	.75	16.85–16.99	1.10	22.24–22.38	1.45
.84– .99	.06	6.24– 6.38	.41	11.62–11.76	.76	17.00–17.15	1.11	22.39–22.53	1.46
1.00– 1.15	.07	6.39– 6.53	.42	11.77–11.92	.77	17.16–17.30	1.12	22.54–22.69	1.47
1.16– 1.30	.08	6.54– 6.69	.43	11.93–12.07	.78	17.31–17.46	1.13	22.70–22.84	1.48
1.31– 1.46	.09	6.70– 6.84	.44	12.08–12.23	.79	17.47–17.61	1.14	22.85–22.99	1.49
1.47– 1.61	.10	6.85– 6.99	.45	12.24–12.38	.80	17.62–17.76	1.15	23.00–23.15	1.50
1.62– 1.76	.11	7.00– 7.15	.46	12.39–12.53	.81	17.77–17.92	1.16	23.16–23.30	1.51
1.77– 1.92	.12	7.16– 7.30	.47	12.54–12.69	.82	17.93–18.07	1.17	23.31–23.46	1.52
1.93– 2.07	.13	7.31– 7.46	.48	12.70–12.84	.83	18.08–18.23	1.18	23.47–23.61	1.53
2.08– 2.23	.14	7.47– 7.61	.49	12.85–12.99	.84	18.24–18.38	1.19	23.62–23.76	1.54
2.24– 2.38	.15	7.62– 7.76	.50	13.00–13.15	.85	18.39–18.53	1.20	23.77–23.92	1.55
2.39– 2.53	.16	7.77– 7.92	.51	13.16–13.30	.86	18.54–18.69	1.21	23.93–24.07	1.56
2.54– 2.69	.17	7.93– 8.07	.52	13.31–13.46	.87	18.70–18.84	1.22	24.08–24.23	1.57
2.70– 2.84	.18	8.08– 8.23	.53	13.47–13.61	.88	18.85–18.99	1.23	24.24–24.38	1.58
2.85– 2.99	.19	8.24– 8.38	.54	13.62–13.76	.89	19.00–19.15	1.24	24.39–24.53	1.59
3.00– 3.15	.20	8.39– 8.53	.55	13.77–13.92	.90	19.16–19.30	1.25	24.54–24.69	1.60
3.16– 3.30	.21	8.54– 8.69	.56	13.93–14.07	.91	19.31–19.46	1.26	24.70–24.84	1.61
3.31– 3.46	.22	8.70– 8.84	.57	14.08–14.23	.92	19.47–19.61	1.27	24.85–24.99	1.62
3.47– 3.61	.23	8.85– 8.99	.58	14.24–14.38	.93	19.62–19.76	1.28	25.00–25.15	1.63
3.62– 3.76	.24	9.00– 9.15	.59	14.39–14.53	.94	19.77–19.92	1.29	25.16–25.30	1.64
3.77– 3.92	.25	9.16– 9.30	.60	14.54–14.69	.95	19.93–20.07	1.30	25.31–25.46	1.65
3.93– 4.07	.26	9.31– 9.46	.61	14.70–14.84	.96	20.08–20.23	1.31	25.47–25.61	1.66
4.08– 4.23	.27	9.47– 9.61	.62	14.85–14.99	.97	20.24–20.38	1.32	25.62–25.76	1.67
4.24– 4.38	.28	9.62– 9.76	.63	15.00–15.15	.98	20.39–20.53	1.33	25.77–25.92	1.68
4.39– 4.53	.29	9.77– 9.92	.64	15.16–15.30	.99	20.54–20.69	1.34	25.93–26.07	1.69
4.54– 4.69	.30	9.93–10.07	.65	15.31–15.46	1.00	20.70–20.84	1.35	26.08–26.23	1.70
4.70– 4.84	.31	10.08–10.23	.66	15.47–15.61	1.01	20.85–20.99	1.36	26.24–26.38	1.71
4.85– 4.99	.32	10.24–10.38	.67	15.62–15.76	1.02	21.00–21.15	1.37	26.39–26.53	1.72
5.00– 5.15	.33	10.39–10.53	.68	15.77–15.92	1.03	21.16–21.30	1.38	26.54–26.69	1.73
5.16– 5.30	.34	10.54–10.69	.69	15.93–16.07	1.04	21.31–21.46	1.39	26.70–26.84	1.74

What is the sales tax on items that cost $6.49, $10.50, and $3.89? What is the total cost?

$$
\begin{array}{rl}
\$ 6.49 & \\
10.50 & \\
+\ 3.89 & \\
\hline
\$20.88 & \text{Subtotal} \\
+\ 1.36 & \text{Sales tax from table} \\
\hline
\$22.24 & \text{Total cost}
\end{array}
$$

Find the total cost, with tax, for each purchase.

1. $5.00

2. $14.49

3. $10.95

4. $16.88

5. $11.29

6. $17.34

Solve. Use the table on page 46 to find the tax.

7. Martin bought a sweater for $19.75. How much sales tax must be added to the price? What is the total cost?

8. Marlena bought articles that cost 89¢, 66¢, 79¢, and 59¢. What is the subtotal? How much is the sales tax? What is the total cost?

9. Leroy bought some slacks for a total cost, including sales tax, of $24.03. The sales tax was $1.53. What was the price of the slacks without sales tax?

10. Tennis shoes were on sale for $16.99. How much is the sales tax? Tad has $20.00. If he buys the shoes, how much money will he have left?

11. A $25.00 blouse was reduced to $13.99. How much less is the sales tax now?

12. Randy bought art supplies. The sales tax was $1.71. What was the least he could have paid for the supplies? What was the most he could have paid?

13. Lara cashed a check for $60.00. She bought articles that cost $9.65, $11.50, and $5.49. How much money will she have left after paying for the articles, including sales tax?

★ **14.** A coat cost $80.00. How can the sales tax table be used to find the sales tax on this amount? What is the sales tax? What is the cost of the coat, including sales tax?

★ **15.** Marie has $50.00. She wants a sweat suit that costs $48.95. How much more is the total cost of the sweat suit, including sales tax, than the amount Marie has?

16. DATA HUNT What would be the sales tax on an item that costs $49.95 in a store near you? Use the sales tax rate for your community to find out.

17. Strategy Practice A shirt cost $9.00 more than a tie. The total cost, without sales tax, was $24.50. What was the cost of the shirt? What was the cost of the tie?

47

PROBLEM-SOLVING STRATEGY: Choose the Operations

QUESTION
DATA
PLAN
ANSWER
CHECK

Try This

Calvin Duke's telephone bill had a long distance call to Detroit that cost $8.03. The call cost $4.35 for the first 3 min and $0.46 for each additional minute. How many minutes long was the call?

When you solve a problem, it is important to **Choose the Operations** to use and to know the order in which they must be used. Use this strategy to solve the problem above.

What must be found	Operation	Computation
First: The cost for the additional minutes	Subtraction	$8.0 3 ← Total − 4.3 5 ← First 3 min $3.6 8 ← Cost for additional minutes
Second: The number of additional minutes	Division	Cost per minute → 46)368 ← Total cost — 8 ← Additional minutes
Third: The total number of minutes	Addition	3 min ← First 3 min + 8 min ← Additional minutes 11 min

The telephone call was 11 min long.

Solve.

1. Heidi Lanski had to pay income tax on $32,789. According to the tax table, she had to pay $5,034 in taxes plus 1 dollar out of every 3 dollars for all income over $29,900. How much income tax did Heidi have to pay?

2. An auditorium has a center section of 23 rows with 20 seats to a row. The first 6 "orchestra" rows cost $8 a seat. The other "reserved" rows cost $5 a seat. There are 3 "press" seats in the reserved rows that cannot be sold. How much money could be received for the sale of seats in the center section?

Write the decimal.

1. twenty-seven thousandths

2. one hundred and eighteen hundredths

3. 17 millionths

4. zero point four seven two five

Write >, <, or = for each ⬤.

5. 2.176 ⬤ 2.725

6. 0.0910 ⬤ 0.091

7. 10.10 ⬤ 10.01

Round each number to the underlined place.

8. 0.7_1_47

9. 12.5_5_2

10. 1.9_5_0

11. 0.0059_3_7

Round to 1-digit accuracy.

12. 0.78

13. 0.0818

14. 27.646

15. 0.00767

Find the sums.

16.
```
  1.35
  3.86
+ 2.77
```

17.
```
  62.83
  39.17
+ 29.08
```

18.
```
  $189.50
+ 137.50
```

19.
```
  $0.67
   1.39
   0.88
+ 2.58
```

20. 3.75 + 12.6 + 18.62

21. 544.09 + 168.8 + 96.22

Find the differences.

22.
```
  38.2
− 26.6
```

23.
```
  205.03
− 163.85
```

24.
```
  $2,140.00
− 1,585.16
```

25.
```
  $850.00
− 666.66
```

26. 3.5 − 1.956

27. 60.35 − 29.733

28. $178.20 − $92.08

Estimate each sum or difference.

29. 32.44 + 17.68

30. $31.95 − $27.17

31. 217.48 − 96.77

32. 7.89 + 8.33

33. Kelly's times for 4 swimming laps were 48.5 s, 47.4 s, 47.3 s, and 49.1 s. What was the total time?

34. Jack paid a total of $53.12 for a jacket. This included $3.24 for sales tax. What was the cost of the jacket without the sales tax?

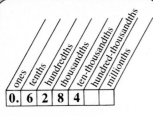

0.6284: Six thousand, two hundred eighty-four ten-thousandths

Rounded to the nearest hundredth: **0.63**

Write the decimal.

1. fifteen hundredths

2. one point four two nine

3. 38 ten-thousandths

4. twenty and four tenths

5. zero point zero five

6. 275 millionths

Round each number to the underlined place.

7. 7.4<u>8</u>51

8. 0.06<u>4</u>28

9. 18.<u>6</u>993

10. 12<u>7</u>.75

11. 0.24<u>5</u>73

12. 0.000<u>5</u>5

$0.9 + 0.12 + 0.023$

```
   1
  0.9 0 0     Annex zeros to
  0.1 2 0     line up decimal
+ 0.0 2 3     places.
  ───────
  1.0 4 3
```

Find the sums.

13.
```
   2.19
   3.76
 + 9.09
 ──────
```

14.
```
  0.449
  0.6
  0.739
 + 0.1
 ──────
```

15.
```
  36.4
  55.118
  47.6
 + 70.003
 ────────
```

16.
```
  $12.50
   33.75
 + 29.88
 ───────
```

17.
```
  $5,628.33
 + 8,755.49
 ──────────
```

18.
```
  $0.79
   0.25
   0.37
 + 1.17
 ──────
```

$20 - 12.87$

```
    1 9 9 10
   2 0.0 0 0     Annex zeros
 - 1 2.8 7
 ──────────
    7.1 3
```

Find the differences.

19.
```
   0.723
 - 0.558
 ───────
```

20.
```
   8.5
 - 3.771
 ───────
```

21. $0.024 - 0.0085$

22.
```
  $50.00
 - 29.67
 ───────
```

23.
```
  $209.14
 -  89.55
 ────────
```

24.
```
  $64,000.00
 - 39,999.95
 ───────────
```

```
  0.2 3 6 8 →   0.2
  0.3 9 9 5 →   0.4
+ 0.4 8 0 9 → + 0.5
              ──────
      estimate  1.1
```

Estimate each sum or difference by rounding.

25.
```
  $3.77
   5.15
   1.83
 + 2.23
```

26.
```
   0.08376
 - 0.02918
```

27.
```
   0.6514
   0.8277
   0.3729
 + 0.5404
```

Reconciling A Bank Statement

People who have bank checking accounts receive a **statement** of their
balance each month. The statement should be checked with the **check
register balance** to see if they agree. This is called **reconciling the
statement**.

Bank statement balance	Deposits not shown	Total of checks not shown	Bank service charges	Check register balance
$847.63	$186.40	$275.86	$1.75	$759.92

Follow the steps below to reconcile the bank statement.

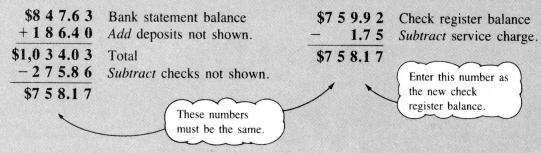

$8 4 7.6 3	Bank statement balance
+ 1 8 6.4 0	*Add* deposits not shown.
$1,0 3 4.0 3	Total
− 2 7 5.8 6	*Subtract* checks not shown.
$7 5 8.1 7	

$7 5 9.9 2	Check register balance
− 1.7 5	*Subtract* service charge.
$7 5 8.1 7	

Enter this number as the new check register balance.

These numbers must be the same.

The statement has been reconciled. If the two numbers do not match,
there must be an error either in the bank statement or the check register.

Reconcile each bank statement balance. Which balances cannot be reconciled?

	Bank statement balance	Deposits not shown	Total of checks not shown	Bank service charges	Check register balance
1.	$400.00	$200.00	$150.00	$1.00	$451.00
2.	$187.60	$549.50	$277.80	$3.25	$462.55
3.	$1,416.53	$359.75	$866.92	$10.75	$965.11
4.	$66.18	$53.42	$25.88	$0.65	$94.37
5.	$666.48	$250.00	$188.83	$4.10	$731.75
6.	$698.41	$411.83	$719.85	$2.90	$393.29

1. Which is correct?

  A $10,099 > 10,009$ **B** $89,742 > 89,945$
  C $6,959 > 6,979$ **D** not given

2. Estimate the difference.

  $76,952 - 49,200$

  A 27,000   **B** 30,000
  C 20,000   **D** not given

3. Perform the operations.

  $5 \times (7 - 4)$

  A 31   **B** 7
  C 15   **D** not given

Estimate the sums.

4. $109,267 + 29,245$

  A 140,000   **B** 120,000
  C 130,000   **D** not given

5. $7.95 + $2.25 + 10.09

  A $20   **B** $19
  C $21   **D** not given

6. Multiply.

  $\begin{array}{r} 947 \\ \times\, 203 \\ \hline \end{array}$ **A** 193,244
              B 193,188
              C 194,244
              D not given

7. Divide.

  $3,425 \div 27$

  A 126 R13   **B** 127
  C 126 R23   **D** not given

8. Which is correct?

  A $0.315 > 0.517$ **B** $0.017 > 0.009$
  C $1.2978 < 1.2878$ **D** not given

9. Round 25.1416 to the nearest hundredth.

  A 25.14   **B** 26.09
  C 25.15   **D** not given

10. Add. $1.52 + 23.3 + 12$

  A 35.452   **B** 36.4
  C 36.82   **D** not given

11. Subtract. $19 - 2.659$

  A 16.451   **B** 16.341
  C 17.659   **D** not given

12. Estimate the difference.

  $7,199.75 - 2,952.9$

  A 3,500   **B** 3,000
  C 5,000   **D** not given

13. Butch bought a backpack for $17.95. The sales tax was $1.17. How much change did he receive from a $20 bill?

  A $0.88   **B** $0.94
  C $2.05   **D** not given

14. A tank holding 13,260 L of water empties at a rate of 195 L each minute. How many minutes will it take to empty the tank?

  A 72 min   **B** 66.9 min
  C 68 min   **D** not given

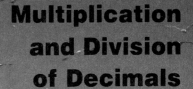

Multiplication and Division of Decimals

Our environment is continually threatened by the increasing amount of rubbish we produce. In a recent year in the United States it was estimated that for each person about 4.5 pounds of rubbish was produced every day. This amount of rubbish would completely fill the New Orleans Superdome at least twice a day.

It takes about 17 trees to make 1 ton of paper. Yet 0.6 of the paper we use ends up as rubbish. We import about 0.9 of our aluminum, but most of it gets tossed out. Many communities bury rubbish in landfills. Some landfills are even landscaped and used as parks or wildlife preserves.

Part of the solution to the rubbish problem lies in the recycling of materials. Recycling centers accept paper, metal, glass, and used motor oil. The materials are sorted and sold to industry for reuse. This reuse of materials often results in large savings in energy and helps reduce air pollution. For example, by recycling aluminum we can save 0.96 of the energy needed to make aluminum from ore.

Multiplying Decimals

Kalani put 8.3 gallons (gal) of gasoline in his car. The gasoline cost $1.129 per gallon. What was the total cost of the gasoline?

Multiply as with whole numbers.

Write the product so it has the same number of decimal places as the sum of the decimal places in the factors.

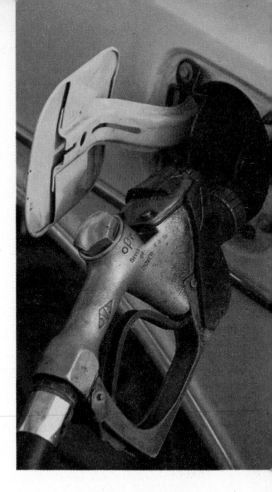

$$\begin{array}{r} \$1.129 \\ \times\ 8.3 \\ \hline 3387 \\ 9032 \\ \hline 93707 \end{array}$$

$$\begin{array}{r} \$1.129 \leftarrow 3 \text{ decimal places} \\ \times\ 8.3 \leftarrow 1 \text{ decimal place} \\ \hline 3387 \\ 9032 \\ \hline 9.3707 \leftarrow 4 \text{ decimal places} \end{array}$$

The gasoline costs $9.3707.
Rounded to the nearest cent, the cost is $9.37.

Other Examples

$$\begin{array}{r} 2.8 \leftarrow 1 \text{ decimal place} \\ \times 26 \leftarrow 0 \text{ decimal places} \\ \hline 168 \\ 56 \\ \hline 72.8 \leftarrow 1 \text{ decimal place} \end{array}$$

$$\begin{array}{r} 0.27 \leftarrow 2 \text{ decimal places} \\ \times\ 0.3 \leftarrow 1 \text{ decimal place} \\ \hline 0.081 \leftarrow 3 \text{ decimal places} \end{array}$$

Annex zero to make 3 decimal places.

$$\begin{array}{r} \$12.42 \leftarrow 2 \text{ decimal places} \\ \times\ 0.06 \leftarrow 2 \text{ decimal places} \\ \hline \$0.7452 \leftarrow 4 \text{ decimal places} \end{array}$$

Rounded to the nearest cent, the product is $0.75.

Warm Up

Find the products.

1. 3.8 ×0.7	**2.** 38.7 × 9	**3.** $7.09 × 0.4	**4.** 0.046 × 0.8	**5.** 375 × 0.8
6. $8.35 × 3.7	**7.** 40.5 ×0.76	**8.** 0.949 ×0.067	**9.** 2,148 × 0.25	**10.** $62.70 ×0.0084

Practice Multiply. Round amounts of money to the nearest cent.

1. $\begin{array}{r} 6.7 \\ \times\, 0.8 \\ \hline \end{array}$

2. $\begin{array}{r} 0.483 \\ \times\quad 6 \\ \hline \end{array}$

3. $\begin{array}{r} 25.7 \\ \times\, 0.09 \\ \hline \end{array}$

4. $\begin{array}{r} \$418 \\ \times\, 0.008 \\ \hline \end{array}$

5. $\begin{array}{r} 9.44 \\ \times\, 0.0007 \\ \hline \end{array}$

6. $\begin{array}{r} 3.2 \\ \times\, 0.83 \\ \hline \end{array}$

7. $\begin{array}{r} \$0.47 \\ \times\, 0.74 \\ \hline \end{array}$

8. $\begin{array}{r} 320 \\ \times\, 0.55 \\ \hline \end{array}$

9. $\begin{array}{r} \$600 \\ \times\, 3.8 \\ \hline \end{array}$

10. $\begin{array}{r} 3.142 \\ \times\quad 800 \\ \hline \end{array}$

11. $\begin{array}{r} 0.86 \\ \times\, 3.2 \\ \hline \end{array}$

12. $\begin{array}{r} 517 \\ \times\, 0.48 \\ \hline \end{array}$

13. $\begin{array}{r} 8.33 \\ \times\, 5.7 \\ \hline \end{array}$

14. $\begin{array}{r} \$0.64 \\ \times\quad 75 \\ \hline \end{array}$

15. $\begin{array}{r} 3.8 \\ \times\, 0.28 \\ \hline \end{array}$

16. $\begin{array}{r} \$2.66 \\ \times\, 1.32 \\ \hline \end{array}$

17. $\begin{array}{r} \$1.73 \\ \times\, 30.4 \\ \hline \end{array}$

18. $\begin{array}{r} 0.624 \\ \times\, 6.21 \\ \hline \end{array}$

19. $\begin{array}{r} \$7.65 \\ \times\, 0.314 \\ \hline \end{array}$

20. $\begin{array}{r} \$8.54 \\ \times\, 70.2 \\ \hline \end{array}$

21. 5.23×4.1

22. 46.3×0.28

23. 6.82×0.057

24. 7.506×0.96

25. $1.0155 \times 8,000$

26. 0.75×0.75

27. 10.08×0.5

28. 764×6.19

29. $2,104.8 \times 3.5$

Find the products.

30. $(0.2 \times 0.3) \times 0.2$

31. $(8 \times 5) \times 0.1$

32. $10 \times (5 \times 0.2)$

33. $(0.1 \times 0.1) \times 100$

34. $0.2 \times (5 \times 4)$

35. $(4 \times 25) \times 0.01$

36. $(0.3 \times 0.1) \times 1,000$

37. $0.9 \times (0.9 \times 0.9)$

38. $(100 \times 10) \times 0.01$

Mixed Applications

39. Shelley put 16.5 gal of gasoline in her car. The cost of gasoline was $1.329 per gallon. What was the cost of the gasoline, rounded to the nearest cent?

40. Lisa used the "Self-Serve" pump to buy 16.8 gal of gasoline at $1.339 per gallon. The cost at the "Full-Serve" pump would have been $1.459 per gallon. How much money did Lisa save by using the "Self-Serve" pump?

★ 41. "Self-Serve" gasoline costs $1.359 per gallon using a credit card. It costs 4¢ per gallon less using cash. Gasoline costs 13¢ more per gallon using a credit card at the "Full-Serve" pump. What would be the greatest cost of 18.3 gal of gasoline? What would be the least cost?

42. **DATA HUNT** What would be the cost of 13.2 gal of unleaded gasoline at a service station in your area?

Multiplying Decimals: Mental Math

Ben saw a pattern when he used a calculator to multiply 26.39 by 10, 100, 1,000, and 10,000.

We can find the products mentally when one of the factors is 10, 100, 1,000, or 10,000.

Multiplication	Decimal shifts
$26.39 \times 10 = 263.9$	1 place right
$26.39 \times 100 = 2,639$	2 places right
$26.39 \times 1,000 = 26,390$	3 places right
$26.39 \times 10,000 = 263,900$	4 places right

We can also multiply a decimal by 0.1, 0.01, and 0.001 mentally.

$671.8 \times 0.1 = 67.18$

Shift 1 place left

$671.8 \times 0.01 = 6.718$

Shift 2 places left

$671.8 \times 0.001 = 0.6718$

Shift 3 places left

Other Examples

$0.42 \times 10 = 4.2$ **$3.887 \times 0.01 = 0.03887$**   **$0.0286 \times 0.001 = 0.0000286$**

$\$0.065 \times 1,000 = \$65$ **$39¢ \times 10 = 390¢ = \$3.90$**   **$\$2.29 \times 10 = \$22.9 = \$22.90$**

Practice Find the products mentally.

1. 3.45×10
2. 16.67×0.1
3. $1.428 \times 1,000$

4. 0.0278×100
5. 4.5×0.01
6. $1.9094 \times 10,000$

7. 0.0028×10
8. 14.278×100
9. $0.7 \times 1,000$

10. 0.1×92.36
11. 0.001×8.9
12. $3.67 \times 10,000$

13. 100×4.75
14. $1,000 \times 0.0112$
15. $1,000 \times 7.1265$

16. $1,000 \times 0.001$
17. $10,000 \times 6.88$
18. 10×0.00049

19. 5.25×0.01
20. 456.23×0.001
21. 100×0.00875

Find the amounts mentally.

22. $\$1.39 \times 10$
23. $\$0.05 \times 100$
24. $\$16.33 \times 10$

25. $15¢ \times 100$
26. $8¢ \times 1,000$
27. $79¢ \times 100$

28. $\$12.50 \times 100$
29. $\$1.429 \times 10$
30. $\$0.065 \times 1,000$

Estimating Products with Decimals

Estimates of products with decimals can be made by rounding the factors or by using the **front-end** digits of the factors.

Rounding	Front-end
Problem: 0.28×425	Problem: 6×8.29 Estimate the rest $0.29 \approx 0.30$
Estimate: $0.3 \times 400 = 120.0$	$6 \times 8 = 48$
	$6 \times 0.30 = 1.80$
	Improve the estimate. $\longrightarrow 48 + 1.80 = 49.80$

Other Examples

0.629×0.504

$0.6 \times 0.5 = 0.30$

2 decimal places in the product

$7 \times \$3.48$

$7 \times \$3 = \$21$

$7 \times \$0.50 = \$3.50$

Estimate $\rightarrow \$21 + \$3.50 = \$24.50$

Practice Estimate each product by rounding.

1. 5.9×3.1

2. 0.72×11.4

3. 0.228×0.893

4. 31.75×8.114

5. 0.903×8.38

6. 0.073×389

7. $9.1 \times \$3.97$

8. $3.8 \times \$5.15$

9. $\$89.95 \times 0.33$

10. $48 \times 7.25¢$

11. $8.8 \times 79¢$

12. $19 \times 28¢$

Estimate using front-end estimation.

13. $9 \times \$3.61$

14. 7×0.7219

15. $8 \times \$4.57$

16. $3 \times \$9.88$

17. 6×0.0682

18. 12×2.537

19. 9×10.68

20. 8×1.215

21. 5×20.8

22. $\$8.14 \times 4$

23. $\$207.69 \times 6$

24. $20 \times \$1.29$

Mixed Applications

25. There were 119 students at the museum. About 0.08 of the students had been before. Estimate the number of students who had been to the museum before.

26. Postcards showing exhibits at the science museum cost $0.49 for 3 cards. Estimate the cost of 24 postcards.

More Practice, page 436, Set A

PROBLEM SOLVING: Missing Data in Problems

QUESTION
DATA
PLAN
ANSWER
CHECK

Some problems may contain data that is not needed to solve the problem. Sometimes data may be **missing** and the problem cannot be solved.

Solve. If a problem cannot be solved, identify the missing data.

1. It is estimated that by 1990, 80 out of every 100 homes in the United States will have a home computer. What is the total number of homes that will have home computers in 1990?

2. A **bit** is one of the digits 0 or 1. A **byte** is a computer symbol made up of 8 bits. How many bytes are there in 16,384 bits?

3. Floppy discs cost $4.55 each. For 20 or more, the cost is $4.10 each. What is the cost of one dozen floppy discs?

4. Carolyn bought a microcomputer with a 16K memory. The letter K stands for 1,024 bytes. How many bytes does the memory have?

5. A computer terminal screen can show 1,944 characters arranged in lines. How many characters per line can be shown?

6. The cost for 3 daisy-print wheels is $24. What is the cost for 1 wheel?

7. A daisy-wheel printer prints 150 lines per minute. A laser printer prints 140 times as many lines per minute. What is the printing rate of a laser printer?

8. It takes a small computer 1 millisecond (0.001 s) to carry out an instruction. A large computer may take only 1 **nanosecond** (0.000000001 s). How many times faster is the large computer?

9. A carton of computer printout paper weighs 19.5 kg and costs 2.2¢ per sheet. What is the cost of 2,400 sheets of paper?

10. In 1953 a space of about 12 cubic meters (m^3) was needed to store 1 million characters of data in a computer. By 1983 a space only the size of a deck of playing cards was needed. By how many times had the storage space been reduced?

11. **Strategy Practice** One computer printer can print 640 pages of data per hour. A slower printer can print 0.25 as many pages of data per hour. How many pages could the two printers produce in all if they printed continuously for 3 hours? Hint: Choose the operations.

PROBLEM SOLVING: Choosing a Calculation Method

QUESTION
DATA
PLAN
ANSWER
CHECK

Your choice!
• **Pencil-Paper**
• **Mental Math**
• **Estimation**
• **Calculator**

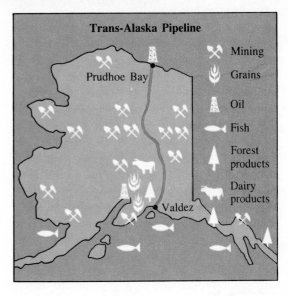

Trans-Alaska Pipeline

Prudhoe Bay

Valdez

Mining

Grains

Oil

Fish

Forest products

Dairy products

You may use any of these methods to solve the problems, but use each method at least once.

1. The Trans-Alaska Pipeline is 1,286 km long. About 555 km of the pipeline is buried in a trench. The rest is above ground. How many kilometers of pipeline are above the ground?

2. An estimated 1.2 million barrels of oil a day can flow down the pipeline. Is this more or less than 365 million barrels a year?

3. Alaska was purchased from Russia in 1867. The pipeline was started 107 years later and completed in 3 years. In what year was the pipeline completed?

4. Alaska was purchased for $7,200,000. The cost of building the pipeline was $7,700,000,000. Was the cost of the pipeline about 10, 100, or 1000 times the cost of the purchase of Alaska?

5. A pipeline worker earned about $37,000 one year. About how much per week is this?

6. A pipeline worker earned $13.10 an hour (h) for the first 40 h of work. The worker earned 1.5 times the hourly rate for every hour over 40 h. How much was earned for 40 h, plus 12 h "overtime?"

7. Some pipeline workers worked 84 h a week with 1.5 times their hourly rate for time over 40 h a week. How much was earned in 84 h if the basic hourly rate was $12.80?

★ 8. The pipeline is 1,286 km long and cost $7,700,000,000 to build. What was the cost per kilometer to build the pipeline? Round your answer to the nearest million dollars.

9. **Strategy Practice** A worker was paid $12 an hour and 1.5 times that for time over 40 h a week. The worker was paid for 84 h of work, but $418 was deducted for taxes. How much was the worker paid?

Dividing a Decimal by a Whole Number

A telephone splicer needs to cut a piece of wire 22.8 meters (m) long into 6 pieces of equal length. How long should each piece be?

Since each piece is to be the same length, we can divide.

Divide the whole number part.	Place the decimal point. Divide the tenths.

$$\begin{array}{r} 3 \\ 6\overline{)2\,2.8} \\ 1\,8 \\ \hline 4 \end{array}$$

$$\begin{array}{r} 3.8 \\ 6\overline{)2\,2.8} \\ 1\,8 \\ \hline 4\,8 \\ 4\,8 \\ \hline 0 \end{array}$$

Check:
$$\begin{array}{r} 3.8 \\ \times\;\;6 \\ \hline 22.8 \end{array}$$

Each piece should be 3.8 m long.

Other Examples

Find $14.24 ÷ 16.

$$\begin{array}{r} \$\,0.8\,9 \\ 1\,6\overline{)\$\,1\,4.2\,4} \\ 1\,2\,8 \\ \hline 1\,4\,4 \\ 1\,4\,4 \\ \hline 0 \end{array}$$

Find 18.3 ÷ 72 to the nearest tenth.

$$\begin{array}{r} 0.2\,5 \to 0.3 \\ 7\,2\overline{)1\,8.3\,0} \\ 1\,4\,4 \\ \hline 3\,9\,0 \\ 3\,6\,0 \\ \hline 3\,0 \end{array}$$

Find 3.7 ÷ 9 to the nearest hundredth.

$$\begin{array}{r} 0.4\,1\,1 \to 0.4\,1 \\ 9\overline{)3.7\,0\,0} \\ 3\,6 \\ \hline 1\,0 \\ 9 \\ \hline 1\,0 \end{array}$$

Warm Up

Find the quotients. Divide until the remainder is zero.

1. $57\overline{)364.8}$ **2.** $8\overline{)237.84}$ **3.** $19\overline{)8.303}$

Find the quotients to the nearest hundredth.

4. $7\overline{)45.256}$ **5.** $89\overline{)128}$ **6.** $64\overline{)16.277}$

Practice Find the quotients. Divide until the remainder is zero.

1. $6\overline{)15.12}$ 　　　 2. $4\overline{)7.28}$ 　　　 3. $9\overline{)2.511}$ 　　　 4. $7\overline{)43.96}$

5. $4.2 \div 15$ 　　 6. $0.46 \div 50$ 　　 7. $\$10.01 \div 7$ 　　 8. $\$52.36 \div 17$

Find the quotients to the nearest hundredth.

9. $37\overline{)25.2}$ 　　 10. $8\overline{)46.95}$ 　　 11. $38\overline{)51.4}$ 　　 12. $96\overline{)890}$

13. $66\overline{)2,500}$ 　　 14. $371\overline{)72.5}$ 　　 15. $85\overline{)268}$ 　　 16. $400\overline{)1,233}$

Find the quotients to the nearest thousandth.

17. $6\overline{)25.4}$ 　　 18. $18\overline{)3.75}$ 　　 19. $72\overline{)284.1}$ 　　 20. $93\overline{)566.72}$

21. $3\overline{)6.16}$ 　　 22. $8\overline{)70.5}$ 　　 23. $59\overline{)800}$ 　　 24. $35\overline{)6.041}$

Use a calculator to find the quotients. Round the quotients to the nearest thousandth. 🖩

25. $966.44 \div 57$ 　　 26. $137 \div 518$ 　　 27. $26.25 \div 88$ 　　 28. $2,000 \div 747$

29. $\dfrac{68.014}{37}$ 　　 30. $\dfrac{904.66}{195}$ 　　 31. $\dfrac{6,333.18}{250}$ 　　 32. $\dfrac{23,600}{842}$

Mixed Applications

33. The climbing pins on a telephone pole are in a 10.6 m space. There are 12 equal spaces between the pins. What is the distance between the pins , rounded to the nearest hundredth of a meter?

34. A piece of telephone wire 60.4 m long is cut into pieces 8 m long. What would be the length of the remaining piece?

SKILLKEEPER

1. $\begin{array}{r} 53.12 \\ -49.54 \\ \hline \end{array}$	2. $\begin{array}{r} 0.6321 \\ -0.5986 \\ \hline \end{array}$	3. $\begin{array}{r} 391.02 \\ -299.98 \\ \hline \end{array}$	4. $\begin{array}{r} 6.0053 \\ -5.6766 \\ \hline \end{array}$	5. $\begin{array}{r} 0.0093 \\ -0.0085 \\ \hline \end{array}$
6. $\begin{array}{r} \$93.84 \\ -57.75 \\ \hline \end{array}$	7. $\begin{array}{r} \$347.62 \\ -98.33 \\ \hline \end{array}$	8. $\begin{array}{r} \$481.01 \\ -9.04 \\ \hline \end{array}$	9. $\begin{array}{r} \$1,364.12 \\ -983.62 \\ \hline \end{array}$	10. $\begin{array}{r} \$5,833.61 \\ -4,566.08 \\ \hline \end{array}$
11. $\begin{array}{r} 0.00871 \\ -0.00732 \\ \hline \end{array}$	12. $\begin{array}{r} 1.9832 \\ -0.0654 \\ \hline \end{array}$	13. $\begin{array}{r} 62.314 \\ -9.803 \\ \hline \end{array}$	14. $\begin{array}{r} 983.29 \\ -1.40 \\ \hline \end{array}$	15. $\begin{array}{r} 36.9004 \\ -35.9995 \\ \hline \end{array}$

Dividing by a Decimal

An architect found the weight of steel beams used in a building. One beam weighed 321.84 kilograms (kg) and was 3.6 m long. What is the weight for each meter of length of the beam?

Since each meter of the beam weighs the same, we can divide the weight by the length.

| Multiply the divisor by a power of 10 to make it a whole number. | Multiply the dividend by the same power of ten. | Divide. |

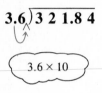

3.6×10

321.84×10

$$
\begin{array}{r}
8\,9.4 \\
3.6\,\overline{)3\,2\,1.8\,4} \\
2\,8\,8 \\
\hline
3\,3\,8 \\
3\,2\,4 \\
\hline
1\,4\,4 \\
1\,4\,4 \\
\hline
0
\end{array}
$$

Check:
$$
\begin{array}{r}
8\,9.4 \\
\times\ \ 3.6 \\
\hline
5\,3\,6\,4 \\
2\,6\,8\,2 \\
\hline
3\,2\,1.8\,4
\end{array}
$$

The beam weighs 89.4 kg per meter.

Other Examples

Find the quotient to the nearest tenth.

$$
\begin{array}{r}
3\,0.7\,6 \to 3\,0.8 \\
0.1\,3\,\overline{)4.0\,0\,0\,0} \\
3\,9 \\
\hline
1\,0\,0 \\
9\,1 \\
\hline
9\,0 \\
7\,8 \\
\hline
1\,2
\end{array}
$$

Find the quotient to the nearest hundredth.

$$
\begin{array}{r}
0.6\,2\,2 \to 0.6\,2 \\
0.0\,9\,\overline{)0.0\,5\,6\,0\,0} \\
5\,4 \\
\hline
2\,0 \\
1\,8 \\
\hline
2\,0 \\
1\,8 \\
\hline
2
\end{array}
$$

Warm Up

Find the quotients to the nearest tenth.

1. $0.7\overline{)5.82}$

2. $0.15\overline{)28.5}$

Find the quotients to the nearest hundredth.

3. $0.006\overline{)0.034}$

4. $9.2\overline{)50.4}$

Practice Find the quotients to the nearest tenth.

1. $5.8\overline{)30.8}$ 2. $0.24\overline{)3.6}$ 3. $3.14\overline{)87.16}$ 4. $3.25\overline{)8}$

5. $4.8\overline{)6.75}$ 6. $0.72\overline{)0.915}$ 7. $0.0035\overline{)0.00175}$ 8. $16.4\overline{)9.22}$

9. $7.21 \div 0.3$ 10. $81.46 \div 2.8$ 11. $209.15 \div 9.8$ 12. $4.5 \div 1.25$

Find the quotients to the nearest hundredth.

13. $0.48\overline{)1.33}$ 14. $3.8\overline{)64}$ 15. $9.4\overline{)5}$ 16. $0.075\overline{)1.82}$

17. $2.8\overline{)5.4}$ 18. $3.5\overline{)162}$ 19. $0.15\overline{)5.55}$ 20. $0.85\overline{)0.64}$

21. $12.4 \div 0.9$ 22. $7.33 \div 0.25$ 23. $1,000 \div 6.6$ 24. $0.113 \div 0.049$

Find the quotients to the nearest thousandth.

25. $827.4 \div 4.25$ 26. $7,000 \div 16.67$ 27. $2.949 \div 10.95$ 28. $500 \div 3.1416$

29. $\dfrac{257.626}{78.44}$ 30. $\dfrac{8.123}{0.276}$ 31. $\dfrac{50.69}{38.17}$ 32. $\dfrac{1,000,000}{99.9}$

Mixed Applications

33. A steel beam weighs 237.6 kg and is 2.5 m long. What is the weight of each meter of length of the beam?

34. A steel beam weighs 96.4 kg for each meter of length. The beam weighs a total of 627.5 kg. How long, to the nearest tenth of a meter, is the beam?

35. This problem contains unneeded data. Find the needed data and solve the problem. Five steel beams that are 8 m long and 0.65 m wide are used in a building. Each beam weighs 712.8 kg. What is the total weight of the beams for the building?

36. **DATA BANK** A large steel I-beam has a height (h) of 38.1 cm, a width (w) of 15.4 cm, and a web thickness (t) of 1.7 cm. How long can the beam be if it is not to weigh more than 500 kg? (See page 431.)

THINK MATH

Estimation

Estimate how high a stack of quarters would have to be to have a value of $1,000.

Check your estimate. One quarter is about 0.23 cm thick.

Dividing Decimals: Mental Math

Kathy used a calculator to divide 43.56 by 10, 100, 1,000, and 10,000. She saw a pattern in the quotients.

Division		Decimal shifts
43.56 ÷ 10	= 4.356	1 place left
43.56 ÷ 100	= 0.4356	2 places left
43.56 ÷ 1,000	= 0.04356	3 places left
43.56 ÷ 10,000	= 0.004356	4 places left

We can find quotients mentally when dividing by 10, 100, 1,000, or 10,000.

Other Examples

6.8 ÷ 10 = 0.68   **209.5 ÷ 100 = 2.095**   **86 ÷ 1,000 = 0.086**

$27.00 ÷ 10 = $2.70   **$5.00 ÷ 100 = $0.05 = 5¢**   **10 ÷ 1,000 = 0.01**

Find the quotients mentally.

1. 26.7 ÷ 10   **2.** 814 ÷ 100   **3.** 2,786 ÷ 1,000

4. 0.9 ÷ 10   **5.** 5,600 ÷ 10,000   **6.** 409.4 ÷ 100

7. 1.75 ÷ 100   **8.** 9.3 ÷ 1,000   **9.** 0.5 ÷ 10

10. 1.8 ÷ 10   **11.** 7.5 ÷ 100   **12.** 0.26 ÷ 1,000

13. 0.047 ÷ 100   **14.** 3 ÷ 1,000   **15.** 814 ÷ 10,000

16. 0.1 ÷ 10   **17.** 0.05 ÷ 100   **18.** 95.8 ÷ 1,000

19. 0.557 ÷ 10   **20.** 100 ÷ 1,000   **21.** 28.7 ÷ 10,000

Find the amounts mentally.

22. $600 ÷ 10   **23.** $84 ÷ 100   **24.** $1,200 ÷ 1,000

25. $5.50 ÷ 10   **26.** $10 ÷ 1,000   **27.** $12.70 ÷ 10

28. $3,000 ÷ 100   **29.** $6,700 ÷ 1,000   **30.** 90¢ ÷ 10

Estimating Quotients: Compatible Numbers and Rounding

A special electric town car can travel 62.5 miles on 1 gallon of gasoline. Estimate the number of gallons the car would use on a trip of 371 miles.

Since the car uses 1 gallon every 62.5 miles, we can divide.

To estimate the quotient we can choose compatible numbers so that mental math can be used.

Problem   Estimate

$$62.5\overline{)371} \qquad 60\overline{)360} \;=\; 6$$

The car will use about 6 gallons of gasoline.

Some estimates can be made by rounding the numbers.

Problem   Estimate   Problem   Estimate

$$0.7\,8\overline{)3.9\,4} \rightarrow 0.8\overline{)4.0} = 5 \qquad\qquad 0.3\,1\,4\overline{)0.0\,6\,2\,3} \rightarrow 0.3\overline{)0.0\,6} = 0.2$$

Practice Estimate the quotients. Use compatible numbers or rounding.

1. $8.4\overline{)32.9}$
2. $7.25\overline{)28.77}$
3. $7.85\overline{)41.27}$

4. $0.61\overline{)3.91}$
5. $309\overline{)62.7}$
6. $0.077\overline{)3.93}$

7. $0.575\overline{)29.33}$
8. $0.0049\overline{)1.987}$
9. $1.91\overline{)7.883}$

10. $38.9 \div 9.8$
11. $9.104 \div 0.285$
12. $1.01 \div 0.005$

13. $\$32.25 \div 4.9$
14. $\$378.20 \div 18.5$
15. $\$6.11 \div 1.9$

Mixed Applications

16. It costs Georgia about $0.19 for each mile she drives her car. Estimate the distance she can drive for a cost of $100.

17. Make up a problem in which you would estimate the quotient for $8.13 \div 3.77$.

More Practice, page 436, Set D

Practice: Multiplying and Dividing Decimals

Multiply.

1. 1.27
$\times$ 0.9

2. 38
$\times$ 3.6

3. 0.48
$\times$ 0.7

4. 29.4
$\times$ 5.8

5. 11.3
$\times$ 0.6

6. 8.73
$\times$ 0.4

7. 85
$\times$ 2.4

8. 16.7
$\times$ 4.5

9. 0.772×100

10. 6.054×10

11. $0.0456 \times 1,000$

12. 14.2×0.1

13. 0.0712
$\times$ 400

14. 3.95
$\times 0.15$

15. 0.025
$\times 0.066$

16. 72.75
$\times 0.848$

Divide.

17. $8\overline{)2.96}$

18. $40\overline{)29.60}$

19. $11\overline{)5.83}$

20. $0.3\overline{)0.0255}$

21. $2.6 \div 10$

22. $0.5 \div 100$

23. $345 \div 100$

24. $9,254.8 \div 1,000$

25. $63.75 \div 10$

26. $3.8 \div 1,000$

27. $872.3 \div 100$

28. $0.93 \div 10$

29. $5.1\overline{)42.84}$

30. $29\overline{)10.73}$

31. $0.71\overline{)1.704}$

32. $0.004\overline{)0.208}$

Find the quotients to the nearest tenth.

33. $0.6\overline{)7.4}$

34. $9\overline{)12.33}$

35. $0.03\overline{)0.161}$

36. $80\overline{)224.16}$

Find the quotients to the nearest hundredth.

37. $23\overline{)75.4}$

38. $8.7\overline{)250}$

39. $0.77\overline{)3.848}$

40. $0.029\overline{)0.1115}$

Find the quotients to the nearest thousandth.

41. $7\overline{)5}$

42. $0.6\overline{)23.45}$

43. $9.5\overline{)12.466}$

44. $0.044\overline{)1.08}$

66

PROBLEM SOLVING: Using Data from a Table

QUESTION
DATA
PLAN
ANSWER
CHECK

A young gray whale named Gigi was kept for a year at a marine park. An aquarist recorded data on Gigi's length and weight.

Gigi's Growth

Days	Length (m)	Weight (kg)
1	5.54	1,882
60	6.05	2,506
240	7.62	3,447
365	8.14	6,350

Use the data from the table, if necessary, to solve the problems below.

1. How much did Gigi's weight increase in the first 60 days? How many kilograms per day was the increase?

2. How much did Gigi's length increase in the first 60 days?

3. How much did Gigi's weight increase between the 60th day and the 240th day?

4. How much did Gigi's length increase between the 60th day and the 240th day?

5. How much did Gigi's weight increase during one year? How many kilograms per day was the increase? Round the answer to the nearest kilogram.

6. If Gigi's weight continued to increase at the same rate as in the first year, how many more years would it be until she reached an adult weight of 36,200 kg?

7. An adult gray whale has a length of about 15 m. How much less than this length was Gigi at the end of 1 year?

8. Gigi was released when she was 8.14 m long. If she continued to grow 2.6 m in length each year, about how many more years would it take her to reach the adult length of 15 m? Round your answer to the nearest tenth.

9. Each day an adult gray whale eats about 3,600 kg of a kind of plankton called krill. A krill weighs only 0.0001 kg. About how many krill does an adult gray whale eat per day?

10. **Strategy Practice** A fin whale is twice as long as a beaked whale. A blue whale is 6 m longer than the fin whale. If the total length of all three whales is 66 m, how long is each whale?

Exponential Notation

Exponents are used to show how many times the same factor is repeated. The repeated factor is called the **base**. Exponents show **powers** of the base.

$$10 \times 10 \times 10 \times 10 = 10^4 \leftarrow \text{Exponent}$$

$$\uparrow$$
$$\text{Base}$$
$$\text{(repeated factor)}$$

$2^5 = 2 \times 2 \times 2 \times 2 \times 2 = 32$ Read 2^5 as "2 to the **fifth power**."

$8^2 = 8 \times 8 = 64$ Read 8^2 as "8 **squared**."

$(0.1)^3 = 0.1 \times 0.1 \times 0.1 = 0.001$ Read $(0.1)^3$ as "1 tenth **cubed**."

To multiply two powers with the same base, we *add* the exponents.

To divide two powers with the same base, we *subtract* the exponents. The exponents 0 and 1 have special meanings.

$$3^2 \cdot 3^4 = (3 \cdot 3) \cdot (3 \cdot 3 \cdot 3 \cdot 3) = 3^{2+4} = 3^6$$

multiplication

$$10^3 \cdot 10^1 = (10 \cdot 10 \cdot 10) \cdot 10 = 10^{3+1} = 10^4$$

$$5^4 \div 5^3 = \frac{5 \cdot 5 \cdot 5 \cdot 5}{5 \cdot 5 \cdot 5} = 5^{4-3} = 5^1 = 5$$

$$2^5 \div 2^5 = \frac{2 \cdot 2 \cdot 2 \cdot 2 \cdot 2}{2 \cdot 2 \cdot 2 \cdot 2 \cdot 2} = 2^{5-5} = 2^0 = 1$$

Warm Up

State which number is the **base** and which number is the **exponent**.

1. 3^5 **2.** 10^4 **3.** $(1.5)^3$ **4.** 9^{19} **5.** 4^2

Give the standard numeral.

6. 3^2 **7.** 2^5 **8.** 3^4 **9.** 10^4 **10.** 1^8

11. 8^1 **12.** 6^0 **13.** 7^2 **14.** 4^3 **15.** 5^3

Give in exponential notation.

16. $7 \cdot 7 \cdot 7 \cdot 7 \cdot 7$ **17.** $12 \cdot 12$ **18.** 1.3×1.3 **19.** $6 \cdot 6 \cdot 6 \cdot 6$ **20.** $5 \cdot 5 \cdot 5 \cdot 5 \cdot 5$

Practice Write in exponential notation.

1. $8 \cdot 8 \cdot 8 \cdot 8$ **2.** $3 \cdot 3 \cdot 3$ **3.** $9 \cdot 9 \cdot 9 \cdot 9 \cdot 9$

4. $10 \cdot 10 \cdot 10 \cdot 10 \cdot 10 \cdot 10$ **5.** $2 \cdot 2 \cdot 2 \cdot 2 \cdot 2 \cdot 2 \cdot 2 \cdot 2$ **6.** $(3.4) \cdot (3.4) \cdot (3.4)$

Write the standard numeral.

7. 6^2 **8.** 2^6 **9.** $(0.4)^2$ **10.** 7^3 **11.** 20^2

12. 9^3 **13.** 3^5 **14.** 15^2 **15.** 11^3 **16.** 4^5

17. $(0.01)^2$ **18.** 12^3 **19.** 8^4 **20.** 17^0 **21.** 67^1

Write the exponent for each ▦.

22. $2^3 \cdot 2^4 = 2^{▦}$ **23.** $5^6 \cdot 5^4 = 5^{▦}$ **24.** $8^1 \cdot 8^2 = 8^{▦}$

25. $10^5 \cdot 10^2 = 10^{▦}$ **26.** $(0.3)^2 \cdot (0.3)^2 = (0.3)^{▦}$ **27.** $7^6 \cdot 7^0 = 7^{▦}$

28. $4^5 \div 4^2 = 4^{▦}$ **29.** $10^7 \div 10^6 = 10^{▦}$ **30.** $2^{10} \div 2^{10} = 2^{▦}$

31. $9^2 \div 9^1 = 9^{▦}$ **32.** $(1.5)^6 \div (1.5)^4 = (1.5)^{▦}$ **33.** $100^{100} \div 100^{98} = 100^{▦}$

Use a calculator to find each missing base or exponent. 🖩

34. $13^{▦} = 4,826,809$ **35.** $(0.9)^{▦} = 0.4304672$

★ **36.** $▦^8 = 16,777,216$ ★ **37.** $▦^9 = 1,953,125$

SKILLKEEPER

1.
$$\begin{array}{r} 8.31 \\ \times\ 0.4 \\ \hline \end{array}$$

2.
$$\begin{array}{r} 0.397 \\ \times\ 6.8 \\ \hline \end{array}$$

3.
$$\begin{array}{r} 36.92 \\ \times 0.055 \\ \hline \end{array}$$

4.
$$\begin{array}{r} \$0.75 \\ \times\ 63 \\ \hline \end{array}$$

5.
$$\begin{array}{r} \$73.41 \\ \times\ 198 \\ \hline \end{array}$$

6.
$$\begin{array}{r} 0.062 \\ \times 0.391 \\ \hline \end{array}$$

7.
$$\begin{array}{r} 984.3 \\ \times 0.146 \\ \hline \end{array}$$

8.
$$\begin{array}{r} 56.03 \\ \times 1.874 \\ \hline \end{array}$$

9.
$$\begin{array}{r} 4.132 \\ \times\ 900 \\ \hline \end{array}$$

10.
$$\begin{array}{r} 1,034.9 \\ \times\ 0.45 \\ \hline \end{array}$$

11. $38 \overline{)3,157.8}$ **12.** $12 \overline{)10.591}$ **13.** $4.8 \overline{)\$462.72}$ **14.** $33.3 \overline{)\$5,694.30}$

15. $74.5 \overline{)\$4.47}$ **16.** $1.1 \overline{)1.1121}$ **17.** $0.035 \overline{)0.0637}$ **18.** $9.13 \overline{)0.02739}$

Scientific Notation

The distance from our galaxy, the Milky Way, to the galaxy Andromeda is about 1.9×10^{19} km.

This distance is expressed in **scientific notation**.

$$1.9 \quad \times \quad 10^{19} \quad = 19,000,000,000,000,000,000$$

A number from   A power of 10   Shift decimal 19 places
  1 to 10

Other Examples

$8.24 \times 10^5 = 824,000$
       5 places

$37,000 = 3.7 \times 10^4$
       4 places

$3.0 \times 10^6 = 3,000,000$
       6 places

$500,000,000 = 5.0 \times 10^8$
       8 places

Warm Up

Give the missing exponent.

1. $4,700 = 4.7 \times 10^{\text{▦}}$

2. $3,800,000 = 3.8 \times 10^{\text{▦}}$

3. $685,000,000,000 = 6.85 \times 10^{\text{▦}}$

4. $90,000 = 9.0 \times 10^{\text{▦}}$

Give the missing factor.

5. $2,800 = \text{▦} \times 10^3$

6. $550,000,000,000,000 = \text{▦} \times 10^{14}$

7. $10,000,000,000,000,000 = \text{▦} \times 10^{16}$

8. $145 = \text{▦} \times 10^2$

70

Practice Write the standard numeral.

1. 4.5×10^4 45000

2. 7.92×10^3

3. 1.5×10^9

4. 5.07×10^{12}

5. 2×10^6

6. 3.19×10^5

7. 2.77×10^8

8. 3.8×10^2

9. 4.27×10^{15}

10. 8.33×10^{10}

11. 6.01×10^7

12. 7×10^{11}

Write in scientific notation.

13. 62,000,000

14. 185,000,000,000

15. 2,000

16. 860

17. 590,000,000,000

18. 7,500,000,000,000,000

19. 5,000,000

20. 30,000,000,000

21. 94,600,000,000,000

22. 860,000

23. 1,000,000,000

24. 50

Find the products. Then write the products in scientific notation. 🖩

25. 625×500

26. 875×400

27. $3.4 \times 9,000$

28. $25,000 \times 70$

29. $1,250 \times 8,000$

30. $64,000 \times 550$

Mixed Applications

31. It takes light from the galaxy Andromeda about 2.0×10^6 years to reach the earth. Write the number of years as a standard numeral.

32. Light travels about 300,000 km in 1 second. Write this speed in scientific notation.

33. A **light year** is the distance light can travel in 1 year. It is about 9.46×10^{12} km. Write this distance as a standard numeral.

34. **DATA HUNT** What is the average distance from the earth to the sun in kilometers? Write the distance in scientific notation.

Photograph of Andromeda galaxy

More Practice, page 437, Set B

PROBLEM-SOLVING STRATEGY: Make an Organized List

| QUESTION |
| DATA |
| PLAN |
| ANSWER |
| CHECK |

Try This

A restaurant, a book store, a pet store, and a dry cleaner would like to rent spaces side-by-side in a shopping mall. All the spaces are the same, but local zoning laws will not allow the pet store to be located next to the restaurant. How many different ways can the four stores be arranged?

The problem above asks that you count the number of ways the stores can be located. In order to do this you can use the strategy called **Make an Organized List**.

To make the list easy to write, use these symbols.

R = Restaurant   B = Book store
P = Pet store   C = Dry Cleaner

R First	B First	P First	C First
RBCP	BRCP	PRBC	CPBR
RBPC	BRPC	PRCB	CPRB
RPBC	BCPR	PBRC	CBRP
RPCB	BCRP	PBCR	CBPR
RCBP	BPCR	PCBR	CRBP
RCPB	BPRC	PCRB	CRPB

List all the possible arrangements of the four stores in a row. Cross out any arrangements with RP or PR together. Do this in a systematic way so that you do not miss an arrangement.

The list will show 12 different ways the stores can be arranged.

R First	B First	P First	C First
RBCP	BRCP	~~PRBC~~	CPBR

Solve.

1. Four students—Anne, Seth, Eric, and Carol—are to sit in four seats, one behind the other. Seth and Eric are not to sit in front of or behind each other. How many different ways can the four students be seated?

2. A restaurant serves beef, chicken, or fish dinners. With each meal there is a choice of one vegetable—peas, beans, or zucchini. With the beef dinner, the dessert is fruit. With the chicken dinner, the dessert is either fruit or carrot cake. With the fish dinner, the dessert is fruit, carrot cake, or pie. How many different dinner combinations are possible?

Find the products.

1.   7.8
     × 0.5

2.   0.254
     ×   9

3.   30.8
     × 0.7

4.   8.48
     ×   6

5.   75
     × 0.24

6.   0.0635
     ×   86

7. $28.50
     × 0.07

8. $187.50
     ×   4.7

Multiply.

9. 1.65 × 10

10. 0.442 × 100

11. 0.0715 × 1,000

12. 5.97 × 100

Estimate the products.

13. 6.93 × 2.44

14. 22.6 × 3.04

15. 0.7849 × 104.7

16. 617.56 × 0.9

Find the quotients.

17. 0.8)2.4

18. 2.5)8.00

19. 0.58)1.972

20. 0.071)1.7821

Find the quotients to the nearest hundredth.

21. 62)346.5

22. 37)8.49

23. 0.8)0.164

24. 0.0071)0.0166

Find the quotients.

25. 72.3 ÷ 10

26. 0.64 ÷ 100

27. 2,477 ÷ 1,000

28. 35 ÷ 100

Estimate each quotient.

29. 19.7 ÷ 3.9

30. 8.15 ÷ 4.04

31. 2.57 ÷ 9.66

32. 94.6 ÷ 33.5

33. Write using exponents.
6·6·6·6·6

34. Write as a standard numeral.
10^4

35. Write in scientific notation.
43,000,000

36. Write as a standard numeral.
$7.5 × 10^6$

37. Find the cost of 12.8 gal of gasoline if each gallon costs $1.368 per gallon. Round the answer to the nearest cent.

38. An electrician worked 2.5 h on a repair job and charged $46.25 for labor. What is the cost of each hour worked?

0.1 2 ← 2 places
× 0.0 4 ← 2 places
0.0 0 4 8 ← 4 places

Add zeros to make
4 decimal places.

Find the products.

1. 3.8
   × 0.4

2. 0.065
   × 0.9

3. 7.08
   × 3.6

4. 427.3
   × 0.75

5. 21.05
   × 0.013

6. 7.058
   × 0.137

To estimate, round and
multiply.

0.36 × 17.9
  ↓   ↓
0.4 × 20 = 8.0

Estimate each product.

7. 8.38 × 21.6

8. 53.04 × 29.8

9. 0.54 × 0.98

10. 3.84 × 0.067

Make the divisor a whole
number.

    1 4.8
0.0 9)1.3 3 2

× 100   × 100

Divide.

11. 0.5)0.21

12. 6.2)3.41

13. 0.4)0.058

Find the quotients to the nearest hundredth.

14. 27)86.48

15. 0.077)0.0828

16. 6.5)25.25

17. 0.95)1.483

18. 0.4)1.355

19. 0.02)4.559

To estimate, round and
divide.

15.08 ÷ 0.49

    3 0.   estimate
0.5)1 5.0

Estimate each quotient.

20. 49.92 ÷ 9.75

21. 0.093 ÷ 0.31

22. 14.08 ÷ 0.67

23. 9.81 ÷ 20

Computer Literacy

Computers may seem intelligent, but they really only understand **On** and **Off** commands. The digit 1 can be represented as On and the digit 0 can be represented as Off. These two digits are called **bits**. You can think of a light bulb showing On and Off for each bit.

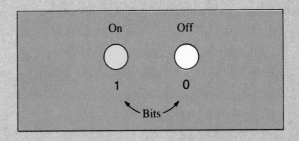

Some computers use a series of 8 bits called a **byte** to represent a single digit, a letter of the alphabet, or other characters such as those found on a typewriter keyboard.

The table below gives a **computer byte code** for the nine digits, the alphabet, and some special characters.

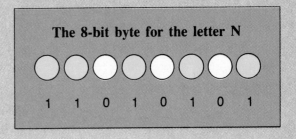

0	11110000	**A**	11000001	**K**	11010010	**U**	11100100	**$**	01011011
1	11110001	**B**	11000010	**L**	11010011	**V**	11100101	**.**	01011100
2	11110010	**C**	11000011	**M**	11010100	**W**	11100110	**?**	01101111
3	11110011	**D**	11000100	**N**	11010101	**X**	11100111	**:**	01111010
4	11110100	**E**	11000101	**O**	11010110	**Y**	11101000	**#**	01111011
5	11110101	**F**	11000110	**P**	11010111	**Z**	11101001	**@**	01111100
6	11110110	**G**	11000111	**Q**	11011000			**,**	01111101
7	11110111	**H**	11001000	**R**	11011001			Space	01000000
8	11111000	**I**	11001001	**S**	11100010				
9	11111001	**J**	11010001	**T**	11100011				

What does a computer expert call 11110011?
Use the table above to decode the answer.

11100011 11001000 11000101 01000000 11000110 11001001 11011001
11100010 11100011 01000000 11000010 11101000 11100011 11000101
01000000 11010110 11000110 01000000 11010111 11001001

1. Write your name using the computer byte code.

2. Write your own secret message using the code.

1. What is the place value of the underlined digit?

   0.01<u>9</u>3

   A 9   **B** 900
   C 0.009   **D** not given

2. Which is correct?

   A 0.5 < 0.12   **B** 0.075 < 0.174
   C 9.09 > 9.67   **D** not given

3. Which is not correct?

   A 17.15 > 17.015   **B** 4.92 < 4.12
   C 0.700 = 0.7   **D** not given

4. Round 0.0182 to the nearest thousandth.

   A 0.02   **B** 0.10
   C 0.19   **D** not given

Add.

5. $17.95 + $2.50 + $105.27

   A $125.72   **B** $124.62
   C $125.62   **D** not given

6.   0.956
      1.25
   + 0.007
   ‾‾‾‾‾‾‾

   A 2.203
   B 1.213
   C 2.213
   D not given

Subtract.

7.   92,957.63
   − 28,295.85
   ‾‾‾‾‾‾‾‾‾

   A 64,661.78
   B 64,662.68
   C 72,562.88
   D not given

8. $119.75 − $27.29

   A $52.56   **B** $92.46
   C $92.56   **D** not given

Estimate the sums.

9. 21.92 + 19.75 + 17.07

   A 50   **B** 65
   C 60   **D** not given

10. $9.95
      17.52
    + 0.67
    ‾‾‾‾‾

    A $30
    B $26
    C $29
    D not given

Estimate the differences.

11. 2,695.79 − 728.17

    A 2,000   **B** 1,900
    C 1,800   **D** not given

12.   217.578
    − 83.989
    ‾‾‾‾‾‾

    A 135
    B 140
    C 130
    D not given

13. Rick bought two packs of film for $2.59 each and a flash battery for $1.65. What is the total cost of the items?

    A $4.24   **B** $6.83
    C $5.65   **D** not given

14. A floppy disc storage unit for a computer costs $79.95. It is on sale for $19.95 off the original price. What is an estimate of the sale price?

    A $60   **B** $100
    C $50   **D** not given

Addition and Subtraction of Fractions

As the kayaker negotiates the $1\frac{9}{10}$-mile downriver course, she encounters boulders, medium rapids, fallen trees, and other obstacles. To steer the craft and brace herself, she uses her $6\frac{2}{3}$-foot paddle with a blade on each end. Although she doesn't think about it as she maneuvers through the churning water, she owes a debt to the past.

In North America, three types of boats were developed by Native Americans. Of the dugout canoes, birchbark canoes, and arctic skin boats, the best known is the skin boat, or kayak. It was originally used as a hunting boat in the icy, wild arctic waters. The sleek, closed-deck Eskimo kayak was about 18 feet long and 18 inches wide. Today's slalom kayak is about $4\frac{7}{8}$ inches shorter and $5\frac{3}{5}$ inches wider.

Even though the designs of the original Native American kayaks have changed, one maneuver remains the same. If the kayak turns over, the kayaker still performs an "Eskimo roll" to flip the craft upright.

Prime and Composite Numbers

Some numbers have many **factors**. The factors of 12 are 1, 2, 3, 4, 6, and 12.

$$\begin{array}{ccccc} \text{Factor} & & \text{Factor} & & \text{Product} \\ \downarrow & & \downarrow & & \downarrow \\ 1 & \times & 12 & = & 12 \\ 2 & \times & 6 & = & 12 \\ 3 & \times & 4 & = & 12 \end{array}$$

The number 7 has only two factors: 1 and 7. $1 \times 7 = 7$

Whole numbers with exactly two factors are **prime numbers**.

7 is a prime number.

Whole numbers other than 0 that have more than two factors are **composite numbers**.

12 is a composite number.

The numbers 0 and 1 are neither prime nor composite.

1 has only **1** factor.
Every number is a factor of **0**.

Each composite number can be written as a product of prime numbers. This is called the **prime factorization** of the composite number.

$$\begin{array}{lll} 12 = 2 \cdot 2 \cdot 3 & = 2^2 \cdot 3 \\ 27 = 3 \cdot 3 \cdot 3 & = 3^3 \\ 100 = 2 \cdot 2 \cdot 5 \cdot 5 = 2^2 \cdot 5^2 \end{array}$$

Practice Copy and complete the table.

	Number	Factors	Prime or Composite	Prime Factorization
1.	18		?	?
2.	11		?	?
3.	21		?	?
4.	28		?	?
5.	32		?	?
6.	41		?	?
7.	45		?	?
8.	51		?	?
9.	63		?	?
10.	81		?	?

The Greek mathematician Euclid (c. 300 B.C.) proved that there is no largest prime number.

Computers can be programmed to find prime numbers or to decide if a large number is prime or composite.

One large prime number is

$2^{21,701} + 1$

This number has 6,533 digits.

The First 100 Prime Numbers

2	3	5	7	11	13	17	19	23	29
31	37	41	43	47	53	59	61	67	71
73	79	83	89	97	101	103	107	109	113
127	131	137	139	149	151	157	163	167	173
179	181	191	193	197	199	211	223	227	229
233	239	241	251	257	263	269	271	277	281
283	293	307	311	313	317	331	337	347	349
353	359	367	373	379	383	389	397	401	409
419	421	431	433	439	443	449	457	461	463
467	479	487	491	499	503	509	521	523	541

Practice Use the table of prime numbers above for these exercises.

1. What is the smallest prime number?

2. How many even prime numbers are there? Even numbers have 2 as a factor.

3. How many prime numbers are less than 100?

4. Which numbers are prime?

   A 101   B 201
   C 301   D 401

5. Which sum is not a prime number?

   A $2 + 3$
   B $2 + 3 + 5 + 7$
   C $2 + 3 + 5 + 7 + 11 + 13$
   D $2 + 3 + 5 + 7 + 11 + 13 + 17 + 19$

6. Here is one way to express 39 as the sum of three primes:

   $39 = 7 + 13 + 19$

   How many other ways can it be done? Write the sums.

7. Find the sum of the nine smallest prime numbers. Give the prime factorization of the sum.

8. Which are prime numbers?

   A $2 \times 3 - 1$ B $2 \times 3 + 1$
   C $2 \times 3 \times 5 - 1$ D $2 \times 3 \times 5 + 1$
   E $2 \times 3 \times 5 \times 7 - 1$ F $2 \times 3 \times 5 \times 7 + 1$

Use a calculator for exercises 9–12.

9. The prime factorization of a number is $37^2 \cdot 97$. What is the number?

10. Find the prime factorization of 441. Hint: Divide 441 by some prime numbers.

11. $1,001 = 7 \cdot 11 \cdot 13$. The factors are three **consecutive primes**. 409,457 is also the product of three consecutive primes. What are they?

12. Find the smallest number that has eight different primes in its prime factorization.

Greatest Common Factor (GCF)

The largest number that is a factor of two numbers is called the **greatest common factor (GCF)** of the numbers.

What is the greatest common factor of 16 and 24?

Study the two different ways to find the greatest common factor.

List the Factors Method	**Prime Factorization Method**

Number   Factors
 16   **1,2,4,8,16**
 24   **1,2,4,6,8,12,24**
            1,2,4,8
          Common factors
 	
 The **greatest common factor** **(GCF)** of 16 and 24 is 8.
	Find the prime factors of 16 and 24
	 $16 = 2 \cdot 2 \cdot 2 \cdot 2$
	 $24 = 2 \cdot 2 \cdot 2 \cdot 3$
	 The product $2 \cdot 2 \cdot 2$ is common to both prime factorizations.
	
	 The **greatest common factor** of 16 and 24 is $2 \cdot 2 \cdot 2 = 8$.

Other Examples

The GCF of 6 and 35 is 1. Two numbers are **relatively prime** if their GCF is 1.

Factors of 6:   **1, 2, 3, 6**
Factors of 35: **1, 5, 7, 35**

Use the prime factorizations of 42 and 72 to find the GCF.

$42 = 2 \cdot 3 \cdot 7$
$72 = 2 \cdot 2 \cdot 2 \cdot 3 \cdot 3$

The product $2 \cdot 3$ is common to both factorizations. The GCF is $2 \cdot 3 = 6$.

Warm Up

List the common factors of each number. Then give the GCF.

1. 8, 10   **2.** 12, 15   **3.** 20, 30   **4.** 18, 45

Use the prime factorizations of each pair of numbers to find the GCF.

5. $20 = 2 \cdot 2 \cdot 5$
    $24 = 2 \cdot 2 \cdot 2 \cdot 3$

6. $40 = 2 \cdot 2 \cdot 2 \cdot 5$
    $30 = 2 \cdot 3 \cdot 5$

7. $56 = 2 \cdot 2 \cdot 2 \cdot 7$
    $30 = 2 \cdot 3 \cdot 5$

Practice Find the GCF of each pair of numbers.

1. 6, 9   **2.** 8, 12   **3.** 10, 15   **4.** 8, 16

5. 5, 6   **6.** 20, 24   **7.** 40, 50   **8.** 18, 24

9. 28, 35   **10.** 12, 30   **11.** 9, 16   **12.** 16, 44

13. 18, 27   **14.** 36, 48   **15.** 14, 21   **16.** 60, 80

17. 9, 14   **18.** 15, 18   **19.** 75, 100   **20.** 16, 64

Use prime factorizations to find the GCF of each pair of numbers.

21. $20 = 2 \cdot 2 \cdot 5$
$70 = 2 \cdot 5 \cdot 7$

22. $24 = 2 \cdot 2 \cdot 2 \cdot 3$
$30 = 2 \cdot 3 \cdot 5$

23. $14 = 2 \cdot 7$
$49 = 7 \cdot 7$

24. $9 = 3 \cdot 3$
$36 = 3 \cdot 3 \cdot 2 \cdot 2$

25. $45 = 3 \cdot 3 \cdot 5$
$63 = 3 \cdot 3 \cdot 7$

26. $24 = 2 \cdot 2 \cdot 2 \cdot 3$
$60 = 2 \cdot 2 \cdot 3 \cdot 5$

Find the GCF of each pair of numbers.

27. 12, 15   **28.** 24, 18   **29.** 40, 100

30. 36, 63   **31.** 25, 60   **32.** 80, 200

33. 30, 36   **34.** 54, 60   **35.** 14, 30

★ **36.** 2,210, 494   ★ **37.** 1,449, 3,255   ★ **38.** 3,030, 3,090

SKILLKEEPER

1. $\begin{array}{r} 0.1934 \\ \times\ \ 0.05 \\ \hline \end{array}$ **2.** $\begin{array}{r} 8.34 \\ \times\ 6.2 \\ \hline \end{array}$ **3.** $\begin{array}{r} 53.21 \\ \times\ 0.64 \\ \hline \end{array}$ **4.** $\begin{array}{r} 93.2 \\ \times 1.15 \\ \hline \end{array}$ **5.** $\begin{array}{r} 0.0081 \\ \times\ \ 2.92 \\ \hline \end{array}$

6. 9.461×0.011 **7.** 0.736×30.4 **8.** 500×4.01 **9.** 8.6×0.052

10. $0.02\overline{)0.00162}$ **11.** $4.01\overline{)2.0451}$ **12.** $0.75\overline{)4.575}$ **13.** $6.9\overline{)3.657}$

14. $0.00372 \div 0.031$ **15.** $216.474 \div 33.1$ **16.** $0.04002 \div 0.02$ **17.** $537.24 \div 6.6$

18. $23.618 \div 24.1$ **19.** 0.55×4.51 **20.** $0.31284 \div 0.033$ **21.** 0.091×46.2

Equivalent Fractions

Russell bought $\frac{3}{4}$ lb of sliced turkey and 12 oz, or $\frac{12}{16}$ lb, of cheese at Delio's Deli.

The turkey and cheese have equal weights.

$\frac{3}{4}$ and $\frac{12}{16}$ are **equivalent fractions**.

$\frac{3}{4} = \frac{12}{16}$ ← Numerator
  ← Denominator

Equivalent fractions can be found by multiplying the numerator and the denominator by the same nonzero number.

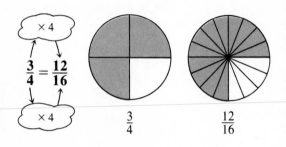

We can use **cross products** to decide if two fractions are equivalent.

$5 \times 9 = 45$
$3 \times 15 = 45$

$\frac{3}{5} = \frac{9}{15}$ ← Equivalent fractions

$8 \times 9 = 72$
$5 \times 15 = 75$

$\frac{5}{8} \neq \frac{9}{15}$ ← Not equivalent fractions

Warm Up

Give the next three fractions in each set of equivalent fractions.

1. $\frac{1}{2}, \frac{2}{4}, \frac{3}{6}, \frac{\text{▥}}{\text{▥}}, \frac{\text{▥}}{\text{▥}}, \frac{\text{▥}}{\text{▥}}$

2. $\frac{3}{8}, \frac{6}{16}, \frac{9}{24}, \frac{\text{▥}}{\text{▥}}, \frac{\text{▥}}{\text{▥}}, \frac{\text{▥}}{\text{▥}}$

3. $\frac{9}{10}, \frac{18}{20}, \frac{27}{30}, \frac{\text{▥}}{\text{▥}}, \frac{\text{▥}}{\text{▥}}, \frac{\text{▥}}{\text{▥}}$

Write = or ≠ for each ▥. Use cross products to decide.

4. $\frac{3}{5}$ ▥ $\frac{12}{20}$

5. $\frac{1}{3}$ ▥ $\frac{3}{10}$

6. $\frac{15}{24}$ ▥ $\frac{5}{8}$

Practice Write the missing fraction.

1. $\dfrac{3}{8} = \dfrac{3 \times 4}{8 \times 4} = \dfrac{\text{||||}}{\text{||||}}$

2. $\dfrac{1}{7} = \dfrac{1 \times 5}{7 \times 5} = \dfrac{\text{||||}}{\text{||||}}$

3. $\dfrac{5}{3} = \dfrac{5 \times 10}{3 \times 10} = \dfrac{\text{||||}}{\text{||||}}$

4. $\dfrac{5}{6} = \dfrac{5 \times 3}{6 \times 3} = \dfrac{\text{||||}}{\text{||||}}$

5. $\dfrac{9}{16} = \dfrac{9 \times 4}{16 \times 4} = \dfrac{\text{||||}}{\text{||||}}$

6. $\dfrac{11}{4} = \dfrac{11 \times 9}{4 \times 9} = \dfrac{\text{||||}}{\text{||||}}$

Write the missing numerator or denominator.

7. $\dfrac{1}{2} = \dfrac{\text{||||}}{20}$

8. $\dfrac{2}{9} = \dfrac{\text{||||}}{45}$

9. $\dfrac{9}{10} = \dfrac{\text{||||}}{100}$

10. $\dfrac{15}{16} = \dfrac{45}{\text{||||}}$

11. $\dfrac{3}{2} = \dfrac{\text{||||}}{8}$

12. $\dfrac{7}{8} = \dfrac{28}{\text{||||}}$

13. $\dfrac{7}{12} = \dfrac{\text{||||}}{60}$

14. $\dfrac{6}{15} = \dfrac{36}{\text{||||}}$

15. $\dfrac{4}{3} = \dfrac{\text{||||}}{60}$

16. $\dfrac{3}{5} = \dfrac{600}{\text{||||}}$

Write $=$ or $\neq$ for each ||||. Use cross products to decide.

17. $\dfrac{4}{32}$ |||| $\dfrac{5}{40}$

18. $\dfrac{10}{15}$ |||| $\dfrac{25}{40}$

19. $\dfrac{10}{15}$ |||| $\dfrac{12}{18}$

20. $\dfrac{12}{15}$ |||| $\dfrac{16}{20}$

21. $\dfrac{12}{18}$ |||| $\dfrac{14}{20}$

22. $\dfrac{4}{25}$ |||| $\dfrac{6}{36}$

23. $\dfrac{25}{45}$ |||| $\dfrac{30}{54}$

24. $\dfrac{9}{15}$ |||| $\dfrac{18}{30}$

25. $\dfrac{12}{44}$ |||| $\dfrac{16}{55}$

26. $\dfrac{15}{18}$ |||| $\dfrac{25}{30}$

Find an equivalent fraction with a denominator of 32.

27. $\dfrac{1}{2}$

28. $\dfrac{3}{4}$

29. $\dfrac{5}{8}$

30. $\dfrac{11}{16}$

31. $\dfrac{7}{4}$

Find an equivalent fraction with a denominator of 60.

32. $\dfrac{1}{4}$

33. $\dfrac{3}{5}$

34. $\dfrac{11}{12}$

35. $\dfrac{13}{20}$

36. $\dfrac{7}{6}$

Mixed Applications

37. Arabella bought $\frac{1}{2}$ lb of Swiss cheese and $\frac{8}{16}$ lb of Monterey Jack cheese. Did she buy the same weight of each kind of cheese?

38. Adam bought $\frac{3}{4}$ lb of potato salad and 10 oz of gelatin salad. Did he buy the same weight of each kind of salad?

THINK MATH

Logical Reasoning

Each vegetable in this division problem represents one of the digits 0 to 9.

Find the digit for each vegetable.

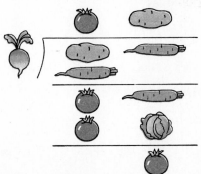

More Practice, page 438, Set A

Lowest-Terms Fractions

There are 88 keys on a piano keyboard. 36 out of 88 keys, or $\frac{36}{88}$ of the keys, are black keys. What is the **lowest-terms fraction** for $\frac{36}{88}$?

A fraction is in lowest terms if the greatest common factor (GCF) of the numerator and denominator is 1.

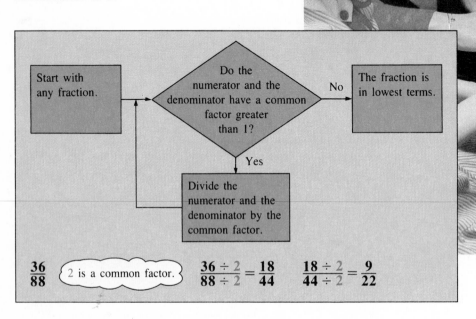

$$\frac{36}{88} \quad \text{2 is a common factor.} \quad \frac{36 \div 2}{88 \div 2} = \frac{18}{44} \quad \frac{18 \div 2}{44 \div 2} = \frac{9}{22}$$

The lowest-terms fraction for $\frac{36}{88}$ is $\frac{9}{22}$.

Dividing by the GCF can save steps. $\quad \dfrac{36 \div 4}{88 \div 4} = \dfrac{9}{22}$

Other Examples

$$\frac{30}{45} = \frac{30 \div 15}{45 \div 15} = \frac{2}{3} \qquad \frac{18}{24} = \frac{18 \div 6}{24 \div 6} = \frac{3}{4} \qquad \frac{7}{10} \quad \text{GCF} = 1$$

Warm Up

Give each fraction in lowest terms.

1. $\frac{8}{10}$ 2. $\frac{9}{12}$ 3. $\frac{35}{40}$ 4. $\frac{90}{100}$ 5. $\frac{16}{32}$

6. $\frac{11}{33}$ 7. $\frac{4}{6}$ 8. $\frac{12}{30}$ 9. $\frac{9}{27}$ 10. $\frac{15}{60}$

Practice   Write each fraction in lowest terms.

1. $\frac{14}{21}$ 2. $\frac{15}{20}$ 3. $\frac{9}{54}$ 4. $\frac{7}{35}$

5. $\frac{40}{60}$ 6. $\frac{32}{40}$ 7. $\frac{12}{18}$ 8. $\frac{14}{16}$

9. $\frac{24}{30}$ 10. $\frac{6}{9}$ 11. $\frac{63}{72}$ 12. $\frac{84}{100}$

13. $\frac{40}{48}$ 14. $\frac{25}{10}$ 15. $\frac{30}{36}$ 16. $\frac{55}{75}$

17. $\frac{10}{40}$ 18. $\frac{12}{15}$ 19. $\frac{75}{90}$ 20. $\frac{24}{33}$

21. $\frac{18}{48}$ 22. $\frac{48}{120}$ 23. $\frac{76}{100}$ 24. $\frac{13}{91}$

Find the lowest-terms fractions. Write = or ≠ for each ▓. Then compare the fractions.

25. $\frac{9}{12}$ ▓ $\frac{15}{20}$ 26. $\frac{4}{12}$ ▓ $\frac{8}{24}$ 27. $\frac{8}{12}$ ▓ $\frac{12}{16}$ 28. $\frac{9}{24}$ ▓ $\frac{6}{16}$

29. $\frac{30}{36}$ ▓ $\frac{50}{60}$ 30. $\frac{21}{35}$ ▓ $\frac{12}{20}$ 31. $\frac{10}{16}$ ▓ $\frac{16}{24}$ 32. $\frac{15}{48}$ ▓ $\frac{25}{80}$

One fraction in each group is *not* in lowest terms. Write this fraction in lowest terms.

33. $\frac{8}{15}, \frac{10}{27}, \frac{15}{33}$ 34. $\frac{13}{16}, \frac{13}{39}, \frac{13}{27}$

35. $\frac{13}{44}, \frac{14}{42}, \frac{15}{46}$ 36. $\frac{42}{51}, \frac{21}{32}, \frac{10}{33}$

Mixed Applications

37. On a piano keyboard, 52 out of 88 keys are white. What is the lowest-terms fraction for $\frac{52}{88}$?

38. **DATA HUNT** What fraction of the keys on an accordian are white? Write the fraction in lowest terms.

THINK MATH

Logical Reasoning

An escalator has 36 visible steps and it takes 36 seconds to ride from the bottom to the top. Juanita ran up the escalator steps, one at a time. She took 27 steps. How many seconds did it take Juanita to get to the top?

Improper Fractions and Mixed Numbers

The "Z"-gauge electric train engine is $2\frac{1}{2}$ inches (in.) long. It is also $\frac{5}{2}$ in. long.

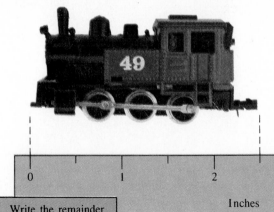

Improper fraction $\dfrac{5}{2}$ ← Numerator is greater than or equal to the denominator.

Mixed number $2\dfrac{1}{2}$ ← Fraction ↑ Whole number

Find a mixed number for $\frac{23}{8}$.

Divide the numerator by the denominator.	Write the quotient as the whole number part.	Write the remainder over the divisor as the fraction part.

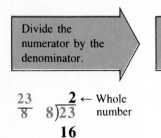 $2\frac{7}{8}$

$\dfrac{23}{8}$ $8\overline{)23}$ ← Whole number

$\underline{16}$

7 ← Number of eighths

Find an improper fraction for $4\frac{2}{5}$.

Multiply the whole number by the denominator.	Add the numerator to the product.	Write the sum over the denominator.

$4\dfrac{2}{5}$ $(4 \times 5 = 20)$ $20 + 2 = 22$ $\dfrac{22}{5}$

Other Examples $\dfrac{21}{7} = 3$ $\dfrac{26}{4} = 6\dfrac{2}{4} = 6\dfrac{1}{2}$ $3\dfrac{1}{3} = \dfrac{10}{3}$ $12\dfrac{1}{2} = \dfrac{25}{2}$

Warm Up

Write each mixed number as an improper fraction.

1. $2\frac{3}{4}$ **2.** $7\frac{2}{3}$ **3.** $1\frac{7}{8}$ **4.** $3\frac{4}{5}$ **5.** $33\frac{1}{3}$

Write each improper fraction as a mixed number.

6. $\frac{8}{5}$ **7.** $\frac{42}{5}$ **8.** $\frac{11}{3}$ **9.** $\frac{75}{2}$ **10.** $\frac{31}{8}$

Practice Write each mixed number as an improper fraction.

1. $2\frac{2}{3}$ 2. $7\frac{1}{8}$ 3. $1\frac{3}{4}$ 4. $3\frac{2}{3}$ 5. $3\frac{1}{7}$

6. $4\frac{2}{5}$ 7. $3\frac{5}{6}$ 8. $10\frac{1}{2}$ 9. $1\frac{5}{6}$ 10. $3\frac{3}{10}$

11. $16\frac{2}{3}$ 12. $4\frac{3}{8}$ 13. $5\frac{9}{10}$ 14. $3\frac{3}{4}$ 15. $2\frac{7}{10}$

16. $1\frac{1}{8}$ 17. $5\frac{7}{8}$ 18. $17\frac{1}{2}$ 19. $56\frac{1}{4}$ 20. $66\frac{2}{3}$

Write each improper fraction as a mixed number or a whole number.

21. $\frac{8}{3}$ 22. $\frac{19}{6}$ 23. $\frac{23}{10}$ 24. $\frac{9}{8}$ 25. $\frac{25}{3}$

26. $\frac{15}{5}$ 27. $\frac{15}{6}$ 28. $\frac{23}{6}$ 29. $\frac{35}{10}$ 30. $\frac{51}{4}$

31. $\frac{46}{8}$ 32. $\frac{16}{4}$ 33. $\frac{22}{7}$ 34. $\frac{99}{10}$ 35. $\frac{47}{12}$

36. $\frac{60}{9}$ 37. $\frac{223}{100}$ 38. $\frac{65}{8}$ 39. $\frac{18}{2}$ 40. $\frac{72}{16}$

Mixed Applications

41. An electric train engine is $\frac{19}{8}$ in. long. What is the length as a mixed number?

42. An "N"-gauge passenger car is $4\frac{1}{2}$ in. long. How many fourths of an inch long is the car?

43. There are $\frac{365}{7}$ weeks in a nonleap year. Write this number of weeks as a mixed number.

44. **DATA HUNT** What is your height in inches, measured to the nearest $\frac{1}{4}$ in.? Write your height in inches as a mixed number and as an improper fraction.

THINK MATH

Shape Perception: A Möbius Strip

1. Use a strip of paper.

2. Give it a half twist.

3. Tape the ends of the twisted loop together.

4. Guess what you will have if you cut the loop down the center.

More Practice, page 438, Set C

Least Common Multiple (LCM) and Least Common Denominator (LCD)

Julius cut out several rectangles of colored glass in art class. Each piece was 12 in. by 18 in. What is the smallest square that can be formed with rectangles this size?

12 in.

18 in.

We need to find the smallest number that is a multiple of both 12 and 18. This number is the **least common multiple (LCM)**.

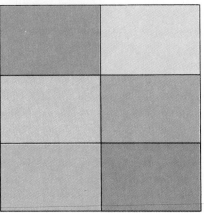

36 in.

36 in.

Multiples of 12:   **12, 24, 36, 48, 60, 72, . . .**
Multiples of 18:   **18, 36, 54, 72, 90, . . .**
Common multiples: **36, 72, . . .**

The least common multiple is 36. The smallest square will be 36 in. on each side.

We can use prime factorizations to find the LCM of two numbers.

$$12 \;\; = 2 \cdot 2 \cdot 3$$
$$18 \;\; = 2 \cdot \;\; 3 \cdot 3$$
$$\text{LCM} = 2 \cdot 2 \cdot 3 \cdot 3 = 36$$

To find the **least common denominator (LCD)** of two fractions, we find the LCM of their denominators.

$$\frac{5}{8}, \frac{7}{12}$$

LCD of 8 and 12 is 24.

We can use the LCD to write equivalent fractions with common denominators.

$$\frac{5}{8} = \frac{15}{24}$$
$$\frac{7}{12} = \frac{14}{24}$$

Warm Up

Give the first six multiples of each number. Then give the LCM.

1. 6 and 8   **2.** 10 and 12   **3.** 9 and 12   **4.** 15 and 25

Use the prime factorizations of each pair of numbers to find the LCM.

5. $12 = 2 \cdot 2 \cdot 3$
$\;\; 20 = 2 \cdot 2 \cdot 5$

6. $18 = 2 \cdot 3 \cdot 3$
$\;\; 20 = 2 \cdot 2 \cdot 5$

7. $40 = 2 \cdot 2 \cdot 2 \cdot 5$
$\;\; 30 = 2 \cdot 3 \cdot 5$

Practice Find the LCM of each group of numbers.

1. 3, 4   **2.** 6, 8   **3.** 4, 8   **4.** 6, 10

5. 2, 8   **6.** 10, 15   **7.** 2, 3   **8.** 8, 12

9. 5, 10   **10.** 9, 10   **11.** 4, 14   **12.** 7, 9

13. 4, 8, 12   **14.** 6, 15, 9   **15.** 8, 16, 20   **16.** 4, 6, 25

Find the LCD for the fractions. Write equivalent fractions using the LCD.

17. $\frac{3}{4}, \frac{1}{3}$ **18.** $\frac{1}{2}, \frac{5}{8}$ **19.** $\frac{3}{8}, \frac{5}{12}$

20. $\frac{1}{10}, \frac{5}{6}$ **21.** $\frac{3}{4}, \frac{7}{16}$ **22.** $\frac{1}{6}, \frac{1}{4}$

23. $\frac{7}{8}, \frac{7}{10}$ **24.** $\frac{4}{9}, \frac{11}{12}$ **25.** $\frac{2}{3}, \frac{3}{10}$

26. $\frac{4}{15}, \frac{9}{20}$ **27.** $\frac{3}{16}, \frac{1}{24}$ **28.** $\frac{1}{6}, \frac{1}{8}$

29. $\frac{5}{8}, \frac{2}{3}$ **30.** $\frac{5}{6}, \frac{7}{10}$ **31.** $\frac{3}{4}, \frac{9}{16}$

32. $\frac{1}{2}, \frac{1}{3}, \frac{1}{6}$ **33.** $\frac{3}{4}, \frac{5}{8}, \frac{7}{12}$ **34.** $\frac{1}{10}, \frac{3}{4}, \frac{3}{5}$

Mixed Applications

35. What is the length of each edge of the smallest possible square formed by placing several rectangles side-by-side if the rectangles are 20 cm long and 15 cm wide?

36. Several rectangles, each measuring 25 cm long and 15 cm wide, are placed side-by-side to form the smallest possible square. How long is each side of the square? How many rectangles are needed to form the square?

THINK MATH

Estimation

Match each fraction with a point on the number line by choosing the correct letter.

| $\frac{3}{4}$ | $\frac{5}{6}$ | $\frac{3}{2}$ | $\frac{1}{3}$ | $\frac{1}{4}$ | $1\frac{3}{8}$ | $2\frac{9}{16}$ | $2\frac{5}{8}$ |

Comparing and Ordering Fractions

Two silos have the same capacity. One silo is $\frac{5}{8}$ full. The other silo is $\frac{7}{12}$ full. Which silo contains more?

We need to decide which fraction is greater.

| Look at the denominators. | Write equivalent fractions with a common denominator. | Compare the numerators. | The fractions compare the same way the numerators compare. |

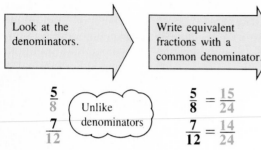

$\frac{5}{8}$ Unlike denominators

$\frac{7}{12}$

$\frac{5}{8} = \frac{15}{24}$

$\frac{7}{12} = \frac{14}{24}$

$15 > 14$

$\frac{15}{24} > \frac{14}{24}$

so $\frac{5}{8} > \frac{7}{12}$

The silo that is $\frac{5}{8}$ full contains more.

To compare mixed numbers, we compare the whole numbers first, then we compare the fractions.

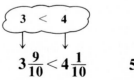

$3 < 4$

$3\frac{9}{10} < 4\frac{1}{10}$　　$5\frac{1}{2} < 5\frac{3}{4}$

Other Examples

$\left.\begin{array}{l} \frac{3}{4} = \frac{15}{20} \\ \frac{7}{10} = \frac{14}{20} \end{array}\right\}$ $\frac{3}{4} > \frac{7}{10}$　　$\left.\begin{array}{l} \frac{1}{6} = \frac{4}{24} \\ \frac{1}{8} = \frac{3}{24} \end{array}\right\}$ $\frac{1}{8} < \frac{1}{6}$　　$\frac{11}{15} > \frac{7}{15}$　　$\frac{3}{4} < 1\frac{1}{10}$

Warm Up

Compare the numbers. Write $>$ or $<$ for each ⬤.

1. $\frac{3}{4}$ ⬤ $\frac{2}{3}$

2. $\frac{3}{2}$ ⬤ $\frac{4}{3}$

3. $\frac{3}{4}$ ⬤ $\frac{7}{9}$

4. $1\frac{6}{8}$ ⬤ $1\frac{7}{9}$

5. $2\frac{3}{4}$ ⬤ $3\frac{7}{8}$

6. $\frac{4}{12}$ ⬤ $\frac{5}{16}$

Practice Compare the fractions. Write $>$ or $<$ for each 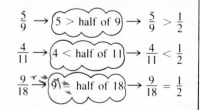.

1. $\frac{1}{2}$ ⬤ $\frac{1}{3}$ 2. $\frac{3}{10}$ ⬤ $\frac{1}{3}$ 3. $\frac{3}{8}$ ⬤ $\frac{2}{5}$ 4. $\frac{5}{6}$ ⬤ $\frac{3}{4}$

5. $\frac{7}{12}$ ⬤ $\frac{8}{15}$ 6. $\frac{3}{7}$ ⬤ $\frac{3}{8}$ 7. $\frac{1}{4}$ ⬤ $\frac{1}{5}$ 8. $\frac{2}{3}$ ⬤ $\frac{9}{10}$

9. $\frac{5}{9}$ ⬤ $\frac{2}{3}$ 10. $\frac{5}{16}$ ⬤ $\frac{1}{4}$ 11. $\frac{7}{10}$ ⬤ $\frac{11}{16}$ 12. $\frac{5}{6}$ ⬤ $\frac{6}{5}$

13. $\frac{17}{20}$ ⬤ $\frac{23}{30}$ 14. $\frac{3}{4}$ ⬤ $\frac{27}{32}$ 15. $\frac{3}{10}$ ⬤ $\frac{33}{100}$ 16. $\frac{1}{25}$ ⬤ $\frac{5}{100}$

Compare the mixed numbers. Write $>$ or $<$ for each ⬤.

17. $3\frac{3}{8}$ ⬤ $3\frac{3}{4}$ 18. $7\frac{9}{10}$ ⬤ $6\frac{9}{10}$ 19. $10\frac{1}{3}$ ⬤ $10\frac{3}{8}$ 20. $16\frac{3}{4}$ ⬤ $16\frac{5}{8}$

21. $37\frac{1}{2}$ ⬤ $37\frac{9}{16}$ 22. $18\frac{5}{6}$ ⬤ $28\frac{3}{4}$ 23. $25\frac{1}{2}$ ⬤ $25\frac{7}{15}$ 24. $14\frac{1}{3}$ ⬤ $14\frac{6}{16}$

List the fractions in order from least to greatest.

25. $\frac{1}{2}$, $\frac{1}{3}$, $\frac{3}{8}$ 26. $1\frac{1}{2}$, $1\frac{1}{4}$, $1\frac{2}{3}$ 27. $\frac{3}{4}$, $\frac{7}{8}$, $\frac{5}{6}$

28. $\frac{9}{10}$, $\frac{3}{4}$, $\frac{15}{16}$ 29. $2\frac{2}{3}$, $2\frac{3}{4}$, $1\frac{7}{8}$ 30. $\frac{7}{12}$, $\frac{9}{16}$, $\frac{13}{20}$

31. $1\frac{4}{8}$, $1\frac{5}{16}$, $1\frac{6}{15}$ 32. $\frac{7}{16}$, $\frac{8}{17}$, $\frac{9}{18}$ 33. $\frac{16}{15}$, $\frac{7}{8}$, $1\frac{1}{2}$

Mixed Applications

34. Two corn silos have the same capacity. One silo is $\frac{3}{4}$ full. The other silo is $\frac{4}{5}$ full. Use $>$ or $<$ to compare the two fractions.

35. Make up a word problem that could be solved by comparing the fractions $\frac{9}{16}$ and $\frac{7}{10}$. Then solve the problem.

THINK MATH

Mental Math

There is an easy way to decide if a fraction is greater than, equal to, or less than $\frac{1}{2}$.

Write $>\frac{1}{2}$, $<\frac{1}{2}$, or $=\frac{1}{2}$ for each fraction.

$\frac{5}{9} \rightarrow \boxed{5 > \text{half of } 9} \rightarrow \frac{5}{9} > \frac{1}{2}$

$\frac{4}{11} \rightarrow \boxed{4 < \text{half of } 11} \rightarrow \frac{4}{11} < \frac{1}{2}$

$\frac{9}{18} \rightarrow \boxed{9 = \text{half of } 18} \rightarrow \frac{9}{18} = \frac{1}{2}$

1. $\frac{7}{16}$ 2. $\frac{9}{15}$ 3. $\frac{11}{21}$ 4. $\frac{15}{32}$ 5. $\frac{7}{12}$

6. $\frac{27}{54}$ 7. $\frac{13}{25}$ 8. $\frac{71}{150}$ 9. $\frac{19}{38}$ 10. $\frac{49}{99}$

More Practice, page 439, Set A

Adding Fractions

A small damaged spot on an antique table was measured. A refinisher used the measurements and cut a piece of wood veneer to restore the table.

What is length A shown in the drawing?

To find length A, we can add the fractions.

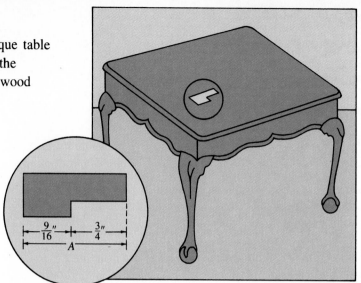

Look at the denominators.	Find the least common denominator (LCD).	Write equivalent fractions with this denominator.	Add the numerators. Write the sum over the common denominator.

$$\frac{9}{16}$$
$$+\frac{3}{4}$$

Unlike denominators

The LCD is 16

$$\frac{9}{16} = \frac{9}{16}$$
$$+\frac{3}{4} = \frac{12}{16}$$

$$\frac{9}{16} = \frac{9}{16}$$
$$+\frac{3}{4} = \frac{12}{16}$$
$$\frac{21}{16} = 1\frac{5}{16}$$

rename

The length of A is $\frac{21}{16}$ or $1\frac{5}{16}$ in.

Other Examples

$$\frac{7}{8} + \frac{5}{8} = \frac{12}{8} = 1\frac{4}{8} = 1\frac{1}{2}$$

$$\frac{3}{4} + \frac{1}{3} = \frac{9}{12} + \frac{4}{12} = \frac{13}{12} = 1\frac{1}{12}$$

$$9\frac{2}{3} = 9\frac{10}{15}$$
$$+7\frac{3}{5} = 7\frac{9}{15}$$
$$16\frac{19}{15} = 17\frac{4}{15}$$

$$16\frac{19}{15} = 16 + 1\frac{4}{15}$$

To add mixed numbers, we add the fractions, then we add the whole numbers.

Warm Up

Give the sums.

1. $\frac{1}{2} + \frac{3}{8}$

2. $\frac{2}{3} + \frac{1}{4}$

3. $\frac{1}{6} + \frac{3}{4}$

4. $\frac{1}{4} + \frac{7}{8}$

Practice Find the sums.

1. $\dfrac{7}{8} + \dfrac{1}{6}$ 2. $\dfrac{1}{2} + \dfrac{3}{5}$ 3. $\dfrac{5}{12} + \dfrac{3}{8}$ 4. $\dfrac{9}{10} + \dfrac{1}{2}$ 5. $\dfrac{3}{8} + \dfrac{13}{16}$

6. $\begin{array}{r} \frac{1}{2} \\ \frac{3}{4} \\ + \frac{7}{8} \\ \hline \end{array}$ 7. $\begin{array}{r} \frac{7}{8} \\ \frac{1}{4} \\ + \frac{1}{3} \\ \hline \end{array}$ 8. $\begin{array}{r} \frac{5}{6} \\ \frac{3}{4} \\ + \frac{1}{2} \\ \hline \end{array}$ 9. $\begin{array}{r} \frac{3}{5} \\ \frac{1}{2} \\ + \frac{3}{4} \\ \hline \end{array}$ 10. $\begin{array}{r} \frac{7}{8} \\ \frac{15}{16} \\ + \frac{3}{4} \\ \hline \end{array}$

11. $\begin{array}{r} 8\frac{1}{2} \\ + 7\frac{1}{8} \\ \hline \end{array}$ 12. $\begin{array}{r} 15\frac{3}{4} \\ + 16\frac{1}{3} \\ \hline \end{array}$ 13. $\begin{array}{r} 29\frac{5}{6} \\ + 56\frac{1}{12} \\ \hline \end{array}$ 14. $\begin{array}{r} 33\frac{3}{10} \\ + 64\frac{1}{3} \\ \hline \end{array}$ 15. $\begin{array}{r} 27\frac{1}{4} \\ + 13\frac{2}{7} \\ \hline \end{array}$

16. $\begin{array}{r} 27\frac{9}{10} \\ 56\frac{1}{3} \\ + 39\frac{3}{5} \\ \hline \end{array}$ 17. $\begin{array}{r} 47\frac{5}{6} \\ 28\frac{3}{8} \\ + 36\frac{3}{4} \\ \hline \end{array}$ 18. $\begin{array}{r} 52\frac{2}{7} \\ 38\frac{1}{2} \\ + 75\frac{5}{6} \\ \hline \end{array}$ 19. $\begin{array}{r} 40\frac{5}{8} \\ 67\frac{9}{10} \\ + 83\frac{1}{6} \\ \hline \end{array}$ 20. $\begin{array}{r} 2\frac{13}{16} \\ \frac{3}{4} \\ + 1\frac{7}{8} \\ \hline \end{array}$

21. $1\frac{3}{8} + 1\frac{9}{16} + \frac{3}{4} + \frac{1}{2}$

22. $3\frac{3}{4} + 5\frac{3}{4} + 1\frac{1}{2} + 1\frac{1}{4}$

23. $16\frac{7}{10} + 23\frac{3}{5} + 12\frac{12}{100}$

24. $8\frac{7}{10} + 8\frac{7}{100} + 8\frac{7}{1,000}$

25. $18\frac{1}{2} + 16\frac{1}{3} + 20\frac{1}{6} + 45$

26. $33\frac{1}{3} + 50 + 66\frac{2}{3} + 75$

Mixed Applications

27. Find the missing dimension on the drawing.

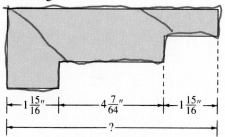

28. A piece of veneer was $\frac{5}{64}''$ longer than the drawing showed it should be. How long was the piece of veneer?

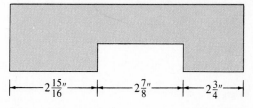

29. Write and solve a word problem that uses the fractions $2\frac{2}{3}$, $1\frac{1}{4}$, and $3\frac{1}{2}$.

30. What is the LCD of these fractions? Find the sum.

$$\frac{1}{2} + \frac{1}{3} + \frac{1}{4} + \frac{1}{5} + \frac{1}{6} + \frac{1}{7} + \frac{1}{8} + \frac{1}{9} + \frac{1}{10}$$

More Practice, page 439, Set B

Subtracting Fractions

Sean used $\frac{1}{3}$ cup (c) of water to make bread.
How much more water is this than the recipe called for?

To find how much more water it is, we can subtract.

| Look at the denominators. | Find the least common denominator | Write equivalent fractions with this denominator. | Subtract the numerators. Write the difference over the common denominator. |

$$\begin{array}{r} \frac{1}{3} \\ -\frac{1}{4} \\ \hline \end{array}$$ 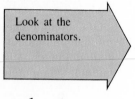 Unlike denominators

The LCD is 12

$$\begin{array}{r} \frac{1}{3} = \frac{4}{12} \\ -\frac{1}{4} = \frac{3}{12} \\ \hline \end{array}$$

$$\begin{array}{r} \frac{1}{3} = \frac{4}{12} \\ -\frac{1}{4} = \frac{3}{12} \\ \hline \frac{1}{12} \end{array}$$

Sean used $\frac{1}{12}$ c more water than the recipe called for.

Other Examples

$$\frac{3}{4} - \frac{2}{5} = \frac{15}{20} - \frac{8}{20} = \frac{7}{20}$$

$$\frac{9}{10} - \frac{3}{10} = \frac{6}{10} = \frac{3}{5}$$

$$\begin{array}{r} 6\frac{2}{3} = 6\frac{8}{12} \\ -1\frac{1}{4} = 1\frac{3}{12} \\ \hline 5\frac{5}{12} \end{array}$$

$$\begin{array}{r} 12\frac{2}{3} \\ -\ 8 \\ \hline 4\frac{2}{3} \end{array}$$

$$\begin{array}{r} 1\frac{3}{5} = 1\frac{24}{40} \\ -\frac{3}{8} = \frac{15}{40} \\ \hline 1\frac{9}{40} \end{array}$$

Warm Up

Find the differences.

1. $\begin{array}{r} \frac{17}{18} \\ -\frac{1}{2} \\ \hline \end{array}$
2. $\begin{array}{r} \frac{5}{16} \\ -\frac{1}{4} \\ \hline \end{array}$
3. $\begin{array}{r} \frac{7}{12} \\ -\frac{1}{3} \\ \hline \end{array}$
4. $\begin{array}{r} 7\frac{3}{4} \\ -4\frac{7}{10} \\ \hline \end{array}$
5. $\begin{array}{r} 5\frac{3}{4} \\ -\ 2 \\ \hline \end{array}$

94

Practice Find the differences.

1. $\begin{array}{r} \frac{2}{3} \\ -\frac{1}{2} \\ \hline \end{array}$

2. $\begin{array}{r} \frac{2}{3} \\ -\frac{1}{6} \\ \hline \end{array}$

3. $\begin{array}{r} \frac{2}{3} \\ -\frac{1}{4} \\ \hline \end{array}$

4. $\begin{array}{r} \frac{13}{18} \\ -\frac{1}{3} \\ \hline \end{array}$

5. $\begin{array}{r} \frac{12}{20} \\ -\frac{1}{4} \\ \hline \end{array}$

6. $\frac{9}{10} - \frac{1}{3}$

7. $\frac{17}{20} - \frac{3}{4}$

8. $\frac{15}{16} - \frac{9}{16}$

9. $\frac{6}{7} - \frac{1}{4}$

10. $\frac{8}{9} - \frac{7}{12}$

11. $\frac{1}{4} - \frac{1}{5}$

12. $\frac{74}{100} - \frac{7}{10}$

13. $\frac{5}{6} - \frac{7}{16}$

14. $\frac{29}{30} - \frac{7}{20}$

15. $\frac{5}{9} - \frac{1}{6}$

Subtract.

16. $\begin{array}{r} 8\frac{2}{3} \\ -4\frac{3}{9} \\ \hline \end{array}$

17. $\begin{array}{r} 7\frac{5}{6} \\ -2\frac{1}{8} \\ \hline \end{array}$

18. $\begin{array}{r} 9\frac{7}{8} \\ -3\frac{1}{3} \\ \hline \end{array}$

19. $\begin{array}{r} 18\frac{3}{4} \\ -15 \\ \hline \end{array}$

20. $\begin{array}{r} 52\frac{7}{10} \\ -13\frac{1}{2} \\ \hline \end{array}$

21. $\begin{array}{r} 4\frac{3}{4} \\ -1\frac{1}{6} \\ \hline \end{array}$

22. $\begin{array}{r} 6\frac{4}{5} \\ -2\frac{2}{3} \\ \hline \end{array}$

23. $\begin{array}{r} 5\frac{1}{2} \\ -3\frac{3}{10} \\ \hline \end{array}$

24. $\begin{array}{r} 69\frac{3}{4} \\ -27\frac{14}{32} \\ \hline \end{array}$

25. $\begin{array}{r} 8\frac{7}{16} \\ -7\frac{1}{4} \\ \hline \end{array}$

26. $37\frac{1}{6} - 21\frac{1}{8}$

27. $11\frac{3}{10} - 7\frac{1}{5}$

28. $35\frac{3}{5} - 27\frac{2}{8}$

29. $50\frac{11}{12} - 37\frac{1}{2}$

30. $1\frac{6}{8} - \frac{4}{9}$

Mixed Applications

31. A recipe requires $3\frac{1}{2}$ c of flour. Louise has $1\frac{1}{4}$ c of flour. How much more flour does she need?

32. A recipe requires $2\frac{1}{2}$ c of milk. Geraldo put in $\frac{3}{4}$ c, and then another $\frac{3}{4}$ c. How much more milk is needed?

33. Make up a word problem that can be solved by finding this difference: $10\frac{9}{10} - 7\frac{1}{2}$.

★ 34. Bill mixed $\frac{1}{4}$ c of sugar and $\frac{1}{2}$ c of milk together. Does Bill have $\frac{3}{4}$ c of liquid when the sugar dissolves in the milk?

SKILLKEEPER

Find the GCF of each pair of numbers.

1. 36, 42
2. 49, 21
3. 41, 17
4. 33, 18
5. 52, 36

Write = or ≠ for each ●.

6. $\frac{7}{9}$ ● $\frac{3}{4}$
7. $\frac{14}{42}$ ● $\frac{16}{48}$
8. $\frac{16}{30}$ ● $\frac{24}{45}$
9. $\frac{12}{20}$ ● $\frac{14}{32}$
10. $\frac{18}{27}$ ● $\frac{16}{24}$

Subtracting Mixed Numbers with Renaming

Patrick Cummings is a biological oceanographer. He dives in the sea to study how organisms live. Last week Patrick had $10\frac{1}{2}$ h of diving time. This week he had $12\frac{1}{4}$ h. How many more hours of diving time did Patrick have this week?

We can subtract to find how much more $12\frac{1}{4}$ h is than $10\frac{1}{2}$ h.

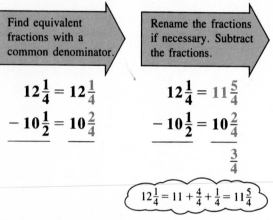

Find equivalent fractions with a common denominator.	Rename the fractions if necessary. Subtract the fractions.	Subtract the whole numbers.
$12\frac{1}{4} = 12\frac{1}{4}$ $-10\frac{1}{2} = 10\frac{2}{4}$	$12\frac{1}{4} = 11\frac{5}{4}$ $-10\frac{1}{2} = 10\frac{2}{4}$ $\frac{3}{4}$	$12\frac{1}{4} = 11\frac{5}{4}$ $-10\frac{1}{2} = 10\frac{2}{4}$ $1\frac{3}{4}$

$$12\frac{1}{4} = 11 + \frac{4}{4} + \frac{1}{4} = 11\frac{5}{4}$$

Patrick had $1\frac{3}{4}$ h more diving time this week.

Other Examples

$10\frac{3}{5} = 10\frac{18}{30} = 9\frac{48}{30}$
$- 6\frac{5}{6} = 6\frac{25}{30} = 6\frac{25}{30}$
$3\frac{23}{30}$

$6 = 5\frac{6}{6}$
$-1\frac{1}{6} = 1\frac{1}{6}$
$4\frac{5}{6}$

$7\frac{1}{8} = 7\frac{1}{8} = 6\frac{9}{8}$
$- \frac{3}{4} = \frac{6}{8} = \frac{6}{8}$
$6\frac{3}{8}$

Warm Up

Find the differences.

1. $9\frac{1}{4}$
  $-2\frac{1}{2}$

2. $16\frac{3}{8}$
  $- 6\frac{2}{3}$

3. 25
  $-17\frac{7}{10}$

4. $12\frac{1}{2}$
  $- 3\frac{1}{3}$

5. $1\frac{1}{8}$
  $- \frac{5}{16}$

6. 60
  $-38\frac{1}{2}$

7. $33\frac{1}{3}$
  $-28\frac{2}{3}$

8. $6\frac{4}{7}$
  $-1\frac{3}{5}$

9. $85\frac{1}{4}$
  $-67\frac{8}{25}$

10. $75\frac{3}{4}$
  $-68\frac{9}{10}$

Practice Subtract.

1. $8\frac{1}{4}$
   $-5\frac{7}{8}$

2. $10\frac{1}{3}$
   $-4\frac{5}{9}$

3. $13\frac{1}{8}$
   $-5\frac{1}{2}$

4. $21\frac{2}{5}$
   $-6\frac{7}{10}$

5. $16\frac{1}{2}$
   $-9\frac{7}{16}$

6. 15
   $-7\frac{7}{8}$

7. $39\frac{5}{6}$
   $-28\frac{7}{8}$

8. $2\frac{1}{10}$
   $-\frac{19}{20}$

9. $2\frac{1}{9}$
   $-1\frac{5}{12}$

10. 100
    $-83\frac{1}{3}$

11. $16\frac{2}{3}$
    $-7\frac{1}{4}$

12. 11
    $-3\frac{27}{100}$

13. $81\frac{1}{5}$
    $-68\frac{7}{8}$

14. $92\frac{1}{2}$
    $-76\frac{2}{3}$

15. $59\frac{3}{16}$
    $-39\frac{3}{4}$

16. $30\frac{1}{4} - 14\frac{2}{3}$

17. $62\frac{7}{10} - 18\frac{3}{4}$

18. $90 - 74\frac{1}{8}$

19. $31\frac{1}{8} - 27\frac{3}{5}$

20. $43\frac{3}{5} - 18\frac{5}{8}$

21. $76 - 58\frac{5}{6}$

22. $105\frac{3}{10} - 78\frac{1}{2}$

23. $66\frac{2}{3} - 18\frac{3}{4}$

24. $78\frac{1}{2} - 15\frac{17}{18}$

Solve. Perform the operations inside the parentheses first.

25. $\left(3\frac{1}{2} + 8\frac{3}{4}\right) - 2\frac{7}{8}$

26. $\left(16 - 6\frac{5}{8}\right) + 8\frac{3}{4}$

27. $8\frac{1}{2} + \left(9\frac{3}{10} - 5\frac{3}{4}\right)$

28. $29 - \left(12\frac{7}{10} + 6\frac{7}{8}\right)$

29. $2 - \left(\frac{1}{2} + \frac{1}{4} + \frac{1}{8}\right)$

30. $\left(50 - 18\frac{2}{3}\right) - 22\frac{1}{2}$

Mixed Applications

31. Patrick worked in the laboratory $8\frac{1}{2}$ h one week and $10\frac{2}{3}$ h the next week. How many more hours did he work the second week than the first week?

32. A charter boat company charges weekly overtime after 40 h. How much over 40 h is the total time for the week?

Day	Hours
Monday	$8\frac{3}{4}$
Tuesday	$8\frac{1}{2}$
Wednesday	$7\frac{3}{4}$
Thursday	$8\frac{2}{3}$
Friday	$9\frac{1}{2}$

33. Make up a word problem using some of the data from the table for Exercise 32. Then solve your problem.

34. **DATA BANK** How much longer is the spiny lobster than the isopod? (See page 429).

Estimating with Fractions

When making estimates with fractions, it often helps to replace a fraction with a simpler, more **compatible** fraction.

Fraction	Think	Lowest-terms
$\dfrac{12}{25}$	About $\dfrac{12}{24}$	$\dfrac{1}{2}$
$\dfrac{5}{16}$	About $\dfrac{5}{15}$	$\dfrac{1}{3}$
$\dfrac{29}{30}$	About $\dfrac{30}{30}$	1
$\dfrac{69}{80}$	About $\dfrac{70}{80}$	$\dfrac{7}{8}$

Give a simpler, lowest-terms fraction for each fraction.

1. $\dfrac{10}{21}$ **2.** $\dfrac{6}{19}$ **3.** $\dfrac{11}{49}$ **4.** $\dfrac{12}{35}$ **5.** $\dfrac{20}{29}$

6. $\dfrac{71}{83}$ **7.** $\dfrac{101}{103}$ **8.** $\dfrac{7}{20}$ **9.** $\dfrac{39}{60}$ **10.** $\dfrac{31}{42}$

11. $\dfrac{16}{33}$ **12.** $\dfrac{60}{77}$ **13.** $\dfrac{24}{74}$ **14.** $\dfrac{24}{47}$ **15.** $\dfrac{19}{58}$

Estimate each sum.

Example $3\dfrac{8}{15}$ about $\dfrac{8}{16}$ or $\dfrac{1}{2} \rightarrow$ $3\dfrac{1}{2} = 3\dfrac{2}{4}$

$\ +5\dfrac{4}{17}$ about $\dfrac{4}{16}$ or $\dfrac{1}{4} \rightarrow +5\dfrac{1}{4} = 5\dfrac{1}{4}$ $8\dfrac{3}{4} \leftarrow$ Estimate

16. $\dfrac{4}{9}$
$+\dfrac{7}{15}$

17. $1\dfrac{7}{27}$
$+3\dfrac{3}{4}$

18. $10\dfrac{9}{30}$
$+12\dfrac{19}{60}$

19. $3\dfrac{43}{60}$
$+7\dfrac{14}{15}$

20. $5\dfrac{6}{25}$
$+8\dfrac{11}{44}$

21. $6\dfrac{1}{6}$
$+8\dfrac{49}{60}$

22. $20\dfrac{12}{49}$
$+30\dfrac{3}{4}$

23. $3\dfrac{19}{20}$
$+2\dfrac{29}{30}$

Estimate each difference.

24. $9\dfrac{16}{31}$
-7

25. 10
$-4\dfrac{19}{60}$

26. $\dfrac{31}{40}$
$-\dfrac{7}{32}$

27. $1\dfrac{14}{16}$
$-\dfrac{34}{40}$

28. $8\dfrac{89}{98}$
$-7\dfrac{1}{10}$

29. $4\dfrac{19}{29}$
$-1\dfrac{10}{37}$

30. $100\dfrac{11}{21}$
$-33\dfrac{14}{27}$

31. $1\dfrac{45}{50}$
$-\dfrac{4}{39}$

PROBLEM SOLVING: Using Data from Drawings

QUESTION
DATA
PLAN
ANSWER
CHECK

Use the data in the drawing for each problem to help you solve the problem.

1. A plumber must bend a piece of tubing twice, allowing $\frac{5}{8}$ in. for each bend. Use the drawing to find the total length of tubing needed.

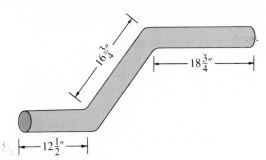

2. A pipe $18\frac{3}{4}$ in. long is threaded for a length of $1\frac{7}{8}$ in. on each end. What is the length of the pipe without threads?

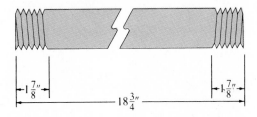

3. An acetylene torch is used to cut a large steel pipe 85 in. long into four pieces of equal length. Each cut takes about $\frac{1}{3}$ of an inch in width. How long is each of the four pieces?

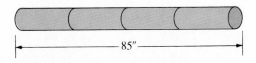

4. The outside diameter (D) of a pipe is $1\frac{1}{2}$ in. The thickness (t) is $\frac{3}{8}$ in. What is the inside diameter (d)?

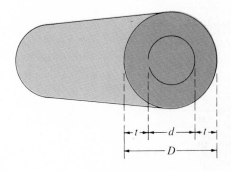

5. A plumber must drill five equally-spaced holes in a piece of wood. The two end holes are the same distance d from the ends. What is the distance d?

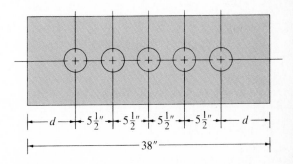

6. Strategy Practice A plumbing contractor employs six plumbers. He assigns the plumbers to work in pairs. How many different pairs of plumbers could work together? Hint: Make an organized list.

Practice: Adding and Subtracting Fractions

Find the sums.

1. $\frac{5}{12} + \frac{1}{3}$

2. $\frac{1}{6} + \frac{2}{3}$

3. $\frac{1}{6} + \frac{2}{6}$

4. $\frac{2}{3} + \frac{3}{4}$

5. $\frac{3}{20} + \frac{1}{4}$

6. $22\frac{3}{8}$
$+ 17\frac{1}{16}$

7. $36\frac{1}{2}$
$+ 9\frac{1}{4}$

8. $53\frac{5}{6}$
$+ 26\frac{2}{3}$

9. $8\frac{5}{8}$
$+ 14\frac{1}{2}$

10. $76\frac{1}{2}$
$+ 24\frac{3}{5}$

11. $33\frac{1}{4}$
$44\frac{1}{2}$
$+ 9\frac{1}{3}$

12. $8\frac{1}{9}$
$10\frac{1}{5}$
$+ 6\frac{2}{3}$

13. $31\frac{1}{10}$
$15\frac{1}{100}$
$+ 8\frac{1}{50}$

14. $31\frac{1}{15}$
$19\frac{3}{10}$
$+ 15\frac{1}{5}$

15. $18\frac{1}{6}$
$14\frac{1}{9}$
$+ 38\frac{5}{12}$

Find the differences.

16. $\frac{5}{8} - \frac{1}{4}$

17. $\frac{11}{10} - \frac{4}{5}$

18. $\frac{3}{10} - \frac{1}{20}$

19. $\frac{3}{5} - \frac{3}{5}$

20. $\frac{11}{12} - \frac{3}{4}$

21. $6\frac{1}{2}$
$- 4\frac{1}{3}$

22. $8\frac{1}{3}$
$- 5\frac{1}{6}$

23. $16\frac{7}{10}$
$- 9\frac{9}{20}$

24. $25\frac{3}{4}$
$- 18$

25. $63\frac{5}{8}$
$- 7\frac{1}{5}$

26. $79\frac{5}{6}$
$- 35\frac{9}{10}$

27. 125
$- 95\frac{3}{4}$

28. $100\frac{1}{100}$
$- 81\frac{1}{10}$

29. $534\frac{7}{15}$
$- 150\frac{4}{5}$

30. $750\frac{7}{15}$
$- 339\frac{3}{10}$

Find the sums or differences.

31. $1\frac{1}{4} - \frac{7}{8}$

32. $2\frac{1}{8} + \frac{12}{16}$

33. $40\frac{1}{2} + 27\frac{3}{4}$

34. $6\frac{1}{5} - \frac{7}{8}$

35. $10\frac{1}{8} - \frac{3}{4}$

36. $\frac{3}{8} + \frac{1}{4}$

37. $\frac{7}{12} - \frac{1}{6}$

38. $\frac{1}{2} + \frac{5}{8}$

39. $\frac{2}{5} - \frac{2}{9}$

40. $\frac{4}{7} + \frac{5}{8}$

41. $8\frac{1}{4}$
$+ 4\frac{1}{2}$

42. $3\frac{4}{8}$
$- 1\frac{15}{16}$

43. 78
$- 31\frac{4}{5}$

44. $430\frac{3}{4}$
$- 199\frac{7}{5}$

45. $231\frac{3}{9}$
$+ 188\frac{7}{8}$

PROBLEM SOLVING: Mixed Practice

QUESTION
DATA
PLAN
ANSWER
CHECK

Solve.

1. Terry had $5\frac{1}{2}$ yards (yd) of fabric left after selling $2\frac{1}{3}$ yd off a bolt. How many yards of fabric were there on the bolt before the $2\frac{1}{3}$ yd were cut off?

2. Monica Li had material to cover a sofa. She had to buy $6\frac{3}{4}$ yd more material. She needed a total of 13 yd. How much material did she have at the start?

3. A pair of pinking shears cost $14.95. When the sales tax was added, the total was $15.85. What was the amount of sales tax?

4. Harry Spinelli worked part time for a dressmaker. He worked a total of $14\frac{1}{4}$ h on Friday and Saturday. On Friday he worked $5\frac{3}{4}$ h. How long did he work on Saturday?

5. Mickey bought 4 yd of fabric that cost $47.80. What was the cost of the fabric per yard?

6. Jay wanted to hem a dress so that the hemline would be $18\frac{1}{4}$ in. from the floor. The hemline is now $15\frac{3}{4}$ in. from the floor. How much must the hemline be raised?

7. Pat bought 4 spools of thread and a thimble that cost $2.00. The total cost was $5.20. What was the cost of each spool of thread?

8. A suit pattern measures $15\frac{1}{4}$ in. from the neckline to the waist. It measures $21\frac{3}{4}$ in. from the waist to the hemline. What is the total measurement from the neckline to the hemline?

9. After cutting out a suit, Zada had $\frac{3}{4}$ yd of fabric left over. She had $3\frac{1}{2}$ yd of fabric to start with. How much fabric did she use to make the suit?

10. **Strategy Practice** The total cost, including tax, of 4 yd of fabric was $20.79. The sales tax was $1.27. What was the price of the fabric per yard?

101

Mixed Skills Practice

Computation
Find the answers.

1. $\begin{array}{r} 12.5 \\ -\,0.756 \end{array}$

2. $\begin{array}{r} 5.3 \\ \times\ 24 \end{array}$

3. $\begin{array}{r} \$250.00 \\ -\ 169.95 \end{array}$

4. $\begin{array}{r} 2,603 \\ -\,1,988 \end{array}$

5. $\frac{3}{8} + \frac{1}{2}$

6. $28\overline{)19,327}$

7. $0.3\overline{)1.44}$

8. $2.5\overline{)32}$

9. $\begin{array}{r} 2\frac{1}{2} \\ +5\frac{3}{4} \end{array}$

10. $\begin{array}{r} 15\frac{1}{3} \\ -\ 9\frac{2}{3} \end{array}$

11. $\begin{array}{r} 23,000 \\ -\,17,685 \end{array}$

12. $\frac{9}{10} - \frac{3}{5}$

13. $\begin{array}{r} \$29.75 \\ 62.50 \\ +\ 18.85 \end{array}$

14. $\begin{array}{r} 5.943 \\ 3.8 \\ +6.77 \end{array}$

15. $\begin{array}{r} \$24.50 \\ \times\ \ 0.06 \end{array}$

16. $\begin{array}{r} \$93.75 \\ 104.58 \\ +\ 62.93 \end{array}$

Mental Math
Write only the answers.

17. $40 + 50 + 60$

18. $(8 \times 5) \times 9$

19. 10×37

20. $150 \div 10$

21. $1,200 - 500$

22. 100×8

23. $240 \div 30$

24. $25 + 75 + 37$

25. 0.1×56

26. $2\frac{1}{2} + \frac{1}{2}$

27. $300 - 99$

28. $300 + 500 + 800$

29. 50×60

30. $3\frac{1}{4} - 3$

31. $16,000 \div 4$

32. $5 \times 29 \times 2$

Estimation
Estimate.

33. $63 + 58 + 59 + 64$

34. 9×79

35. $33\overline{)1,629}$

36. 2.1×6.92

37. 0.5×8.133

38. $8.1\overline{)17.091}$

39. 49×41

40. $0.2\overline{)0.4031}$

41. $\begin{array}{r} 8.73 \\ 3.15 \\ +\ 4.21 \end{array}$

42. $\begin{array}{r} 8\frac{13}{25} \\ +3\frac{4}{9} \end{array}$

43. $\begin{array}{r} 8,244 \\ -\,5,197 \end{array}$

44. $\begin{array}{r} \$7.19 \\ 6.53 \\ +\ \ 2.48 \end{array}$

45. 0.109×80

46. $19\overline{)413.4}$

47. $\begin{array}{r} 37.033 \\ -\,25.188 \end{array}$

48. $\begin{array}{r} 10\frac{31}{40} \\ -\ 3\frac{21}{79} \end{array}$

APPLIED PROBLEM SOLVING

QUESTION
DATA
PLAN
ANSWER
CHECK

Your family has an 8-year-old car. You want to know whether it would be better to buy a new car or to repair the old car and drive it for two more years.

Some Things to Consider

- The old car is driven 40 mi a day and gets an average of 16 mpg with gasoline that costs $1.30/gal.

- A new car would get 24 mpg with gasoline that costs $1.36/gal.

- To make the old car last two more years, repairs that cost $500 and new tires that cost $250 must be bought.

- The new car will cost about $9,500 with the old car used as a trade-in. The car will be paid for in 48 equal monthly payments plus a monthly interest charge of $64.49.

- Your family has decided that it can afford about $325 a month for car payments and gasoline.

Some Questions to Answer

1. How much gasoline is used each month (30 days) for the old car? What is the cost of the gasoline?

2. What would be the gasoline cost per month for a new car? How much would be saved per month on gasoline for the new car?

3. What will be the monthly payment, including interest, for the new car?

4. What will be the total monthly payment, plus gasoline cost, for the new car?

5. If the old car is used for two more years, what will be the total amount that must be spent on the old car for repairs, tires, and gasoline?

What Is Your Decision?

Should the family trade the old car in for a new one, or repair the old car and keep it for two more years?

PROBLEM-SOLVING STRATEGY: Work Backward

QUESTION
DATA
PLAN
ANSWER
CHECK

Try This

The manager of a furniture store added a delivery fee of $25 to the cost of a sofa, multiplied the sum by 2.8 for the mark-up, and added $94 for sales tax. This gave the manager the selling price of $2,460. What was the cost of the sofa?

One way to solve the problem above is to use the strategy called **Work Backward**.

To use this strategy, first show the operations in the order stated in the problem. The chart below shows the steps.

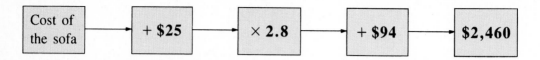

| Cost of the sofa | → | + $25 | → | × 2.8 | → | + $94 | → | $2,460 |

Now work backward using the **inverse** operations.

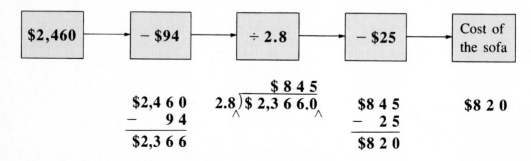

| $2,460 | → | − $94 | → | ÷ 2.8 | → | − $25 | → | Cost of the sofa |

```
                        $ 8 4 5
  $2,4 6 0     2.8)$ 2,3 6 6.0      $8 4 5          $8 2 0
  −     9 4                         −   2 5
  ────────                          ────────
  $2,3 6 6                          $8 2 0
```

The cost of the sofa was $820.

Solve.

1. Atsuko filled his car with 60 L of gasoline. He also spent $1.95 for a can of oil and $0.45 for a tire valve. He spent a total of $23.94. What was the cost of the gasoline per liter?

2. Joan multiplied her birth year by 0.2, then subtracted the number of days in a leap year from the product, and then divided that number by 2. The resulting number was her age in years, 14. What is Joan's birth year?

List all the factors of each number.

1. 20

2. 15

Write the prime factorization of each number.

3. 70

4. 21

5. Which number is composite?

21   31   41

6. Which number is prime?

27   33   53

7. What is the GCF of 18 and 24?

8. What is the LCM of 8 and 10?

Write $=$ or $\neq$ for each ◉.

9. $\frac{7}{8}$ ◉ $\frac{42}{48}$

10. $\frac{5}{6}$ ◉ $\frac{47}{54}$

11. $\frac{2}{3}$ ◉ $\frac{32}{48}$

Write each fraction in lowest terms.

12. $\frac{12}{15}$

13. $\frac{24}{30}$

14. $\frac{14}{28}$

15. $\frac{75}{100}$

16. $\frac{10}{4}$

Write each improper fraction as a whole number or a mixed number.

17. $\frac{18}{5}$

18. $\frac{47}{6}$

19. $\frac{63}{9}$

20. $\frac{35}{3}$

21. $\frac{66}{8}$

Write $>$, $<$, or $=$ for each ◉.

22. $\frac{3}{8}$ ◉ $\frac{2}{5}$

23. $\frac{3}{24}$ ◉ $\frac{2}{16}$

24. $\frac{1}{2}$ ◉ $\frac{1}{3}$

25. $\frac{3}{10}$ ◉ $\frac{3}{9}$

26. $\frac{1}{4}$ ◉ $\frac{2}{7}$

Add or subtract.

27. $\frac{13}{8} - \frac{7}{8}$

28. $\frac{3}{16} + \frac{1}{4}$

29. $1 - \frac{5}{6}$

30. $2\frac{5}{6} + 3\frac{2}{3}$

31. $12\frac{9}{10} - 5\frac{3}{4}$

32.
$$23\frac{1}{2}$$
$$-14\frac{2}{3}$$

33.
$$42\frac{4}{4}$$
$$-29\frac{3}{4}$$

34.
$$12\frac{3}{8}$$
$$7\frac{3}{4}$$
$$+5\frac{1}{2}$$

35.
$$50\frac{3}{10}$$
$$-37\frac{1}{2}$$

36.
$$27\frac{1}{10}$$
$$+19\frac{9}{10}$$

37. A plumber needed a piece of pipe $72\frac{1}{2}$ in. long. He had a piece of pipe that was $68\frac{3}{4}$ in. long. How much too short was the pipe he had?

38. A coupling is used to join a piece of pipe $64\frac{5}{8}$ in. long to another pipe $43\frac{3}{4}$ in. long. The coupling adds $1\frac{1}{4}$ in. to the length. What is the overall length of the pipes, including the coupling?

Factors of 12: **1, 2, 3, 4, 6, 12**

Multiples of 12: **12, 24, 36, 48**

2, 3, 5, 7, 11, . . . are prime.

4, 6, 8, 9, . . . are composite.

0 and **1** are neither prime nor composite.

Equivalent fractions

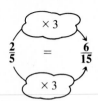

$$\frac{2}{5} = \frac{6}{15}$$

$$\frac{12}{16} = \frac{12 \div 4}{16 \div 4} = \frac{3}{4}$$

$\frac{3}{4}$ is in lowest terms.

$$2\frac{7}{8} = 2\frac{21}{24}$$
$$+ 1\frac{1}{3} = 1\frac{8}{24}$$
$$\overline{ 3\frac{29}{24} = 4\frac{5}{24}}$$

$$6\frac{1}{2} = 6\frac{4}{8} = 5\frac{12}{8}$$
$$- 2\frac{5}{8} = 2\frac{5}{8} = 2\frac{5}{8}$$
$$\overline{\phantom{-2\frac{5}{8}=} 3\frac{7}{8}}$$

List all the factors of each number.

1. 10   **2.** 14   **3.** 13

List the first four multiples of each number.

4. 6   **5.** 8   **6.** 15

Write P (prime) or C (composite) for each number.

7. 21   **8.** 23   **9.** 45

Write the missing numerator.

10. $\frac{3}{4} = \frac{}{20}$ **11.** $\frac{7}{8} = \frac{}{32}$ **12.** $\frac{1}{9} = \frac{}{54}$

Write = or ≠ for each ▒.

13. $\frac{2}{3}$ ▒ $\frac{10}{15}$ **14.** $\frac{1}{2}$ ▒ $\frac{51}{100}$ **15.** $\frac{5}{6}$ ▒ $\frac{50}{60}$

Write each fraction in lowest terms.

16. $\frac{6}{10}$ **17.** $\frac{14}{20}$ **18.** $\frac{24}{32}$

19. $\frac{25}{100}$ **20.** $\frac{10}{15}$ **21.** $\frac{40}{60}$

Add.

22. $\frac{3}{10} + \frac{1}{10}$ **23.** $\frac{1}{2} + \frac{3}{4}$ **24.** $\frac{3}{8} + \frac{1}{3}$

25. $\quad 6\frac{1}{3}$
$\quad + 7\frac{1}{2}$

26. $\quad 12\frac{3}{4}$
$\quad + 9\frac{1}{2}$

27. $\quad 21\frac{7}{8}$
$\quad + 19\frac{3}{4}$

Subtract.

28. $\frac{11}{12} - \frac{7}{12}$ **29.** $\frac{5}{6} - \frac{1}{3}$ **30.** $\frac{9}{10} - \frac{3}{4}$

31. $\quad 16\frac{1}{2}$
$\quad - 8\frac{2}{5}$

32. $\quad 27\frac{1}{3}$
$\quad - 16\frac{1}{2}$

33. $\quad 46\frac{1}{6}$
$\quad - 27\frac{3}{10}$

Using a Calculator with Fractions

You can use a calculator to add or subtract fractions *without using decimals*. To do this, use a calculator with a memory.

To add or subtract two fractions, $\frac{a}{b}$ and $\frac{c}{d}$, we can use the formulas shown at the right.

$$\frac{a}{b} + \frac{c}{d} + \frac{(a \times d) + (b \times c)}{(b \times d)}$$

Add.  $\frac{7}{11} + \frac{2}{15}$

$$\frac{a}{b} - \frac{c}{d} = \frac{(a \times d) - (b \times c)}{(b \times d)}$$

$a = 7$, $b = 11$, $c = 2$, $d = 15$.

Follow these steps to find the sum.

Enter	Press	Display
11×2	$\boxed{=}$ $\boxed{\text{M}^+}$	22.
15×7	$\boxed{+}$ $\boxed{\text{MR}}$ $\boxed{=}$	127. ← Numerator

Enter	Press	Display
11×15	$\boxed{=}$	165. ← Denominator

$$\frac{7}{11} + \frac{2}{15} = \frac{127}{165}$$

To find the difference, follow the same steps but change $\boxed{+}$ to $\boxed{-}$

$$\frac{7}{11} - \frac{2}{15} = \frac{83}{165}$$

Use a calculator to find the sums or differences.

1. $\frac{6}{25} + \frac{8}{9}$ **2.** $\frac{12}{31} + \frac{3}{17}$ **3.** $\frac{9}{29} - \frac{3}{32}$

4. $\frac{13}{18} - \frac{3}{7}$ **5.** $\frac{29}{60} + \frac{15}{43}$ **6.** $\frac{15}{16} - \frac{38}{89}$

7. Check some of your answers by adding or subtracting the usual way.

8. Make up some difficult problems with addition and subtraction of fractions. Find the answers with a calculator.

1. Multiply.

   0.3579×100

   A 3.579   **B** 357.9
   C 35.79   **D** not given

2. Estimate the product.

   72.59×26.7

   A 1,400   **B** 2,100
   C 1,898   **D** not given

3. Find the product.

   113.98×0.25

   A 28.4950   **B** 29.4950
   C 2,825   **D** not given

4. Estimate the amount.

   $\$3,796.75 \div 184$

   A \$17   **B** \$20
   C \$200   **D** not given

5. Find the quotient.

   $567.9 \div 1,000$

   A 56.79   **B** 5.679
   C 0.5679   **D** not given

6. Divide.

   $9\overline{)511.20}$

   A 57   **B** 56.9
   C 5.68   **D** not given

7. Find $388.9 \div 277$ to the nearest tenth.

   A 1.403   **B** 1.41
   C 1.4   **D** not given

8. Find $0.0568 \div 2.7$ to the nearest hundredth.

   A 0.02   **B** 0.021
   C 0.03   **D** not given

9. What is the standard numeral for 7^3?

   A 21   **B** 49
   C 343   **D** not given

10. What is $12 \cdot 12 \cdot 12 \cdot 12 \cdot 12$ in exponential notation?

    A 12^4 **B** 12×5
    C 4^{12} **D** not given

11. What is 87,000 in scientific notation?

    A 87×10^3 **B** 8.7×10^4
    C 8.70×10^2 **D** not given

12. What is the standard numeral for 7.12×10^3?

    A 7,120   **B** 71,300
    C 7,120,000   **D** not given

13. A theater has 1,200 seats. About 0.395 of the seats are occupied. What is an estimate of the number of seats that are occupied?

    A 360   **B** 480
    C 468   **D** not given

14. What is the cost (to the nearest cent) of 11.9 gal of gasoline at \$1.724 per gallon?

    A \$20.51   **B** \$19.52
    C \$20.52   **D** not given

Multiplication and Division of Fractions

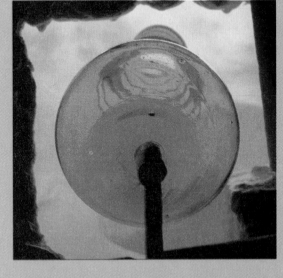

The glassblower dips the blow pipe into the 1,997°F furnace and collects a lump of hot glass called a *gather*. To keep the gather from becoming lopsided and falling off the pipe, the glassblower must rotate the pipe constantly. The gather is then rolled around on a marvering table $\frac{3}{4}$ m long and $\frac{1}{2}$ m wide. The gather has three main ingredients: $\frac{13}{20}$ silica sand, $\frac{4}{20}$ soda ash, and $\frac{3}{20}$ limestone.

The glassblower blows the first bubble with a sharp puff through the pipe. More glass is gathered until there is about $3\frac{1}{4}$ pounds on the pipe. Before the glass is removed from the blow pipe, another pipe called a *punty* is attached to the base of the formed glass. Now the blow pipe can be removed and the edges of the shape can be formed. After the punty is detached with a sharp blow, the shape is ready to cool in a special oven.

Multiplying Fractions

A large plate glass window covers $\frac{3}{4}$ of the length of a wall of a department store. It covers $\frac{2}{3}$ of the height of the wall. What fractional part of the wall does the window cover?

The drawing shows that the window covers $\frac{6}{12}$, or $\frac{1}{2}$, of the wall.

Since we want to find $\frac{2}{3}$ of $\frac{3}{4}$, we can multiply.

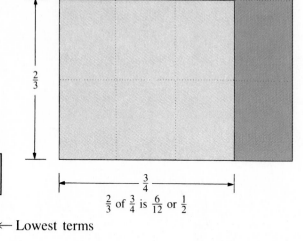

$\frac{2}{3}$ of $\frac{3}{4}$ is $\frac{6}{12}$ or $\frac{1}{2}$

Multiply the numerators.		Multiply the denominators.

$$\frac{2}{3} \times \frac{3}{4} = \frac{6}{\text{▥}} \qquad \frac{2}{3} \times \frac{3}{4} = \frac{6}{12} = \frac{1}{2} \leftarrow \text{Lowest terms}$$

The window covers $\frac{1}{2}$ of the wall.

We can use a shortcut for some problems. We divide a numerator and a denominator by a common factor *before multiplying*.

Long Method   Shortcut

$$\frac{4}{5} \times \frac{7}{8} = \frac{28}{40} = \frac{7}{10} \qquad \frac{\overset{1}{\cancel{4}}}{5} \times \frac{7}{\underset{2}{\cancel{8}}} = \frac{7}{10}$$

Other Examples

$$\frac{\overset{3}{\cancel{9}}}{\underset{2}{\cancel{10}}} \times \frac{\overset{1}{\cancel{5}}}{\underset{4}{\cancel{12}}} = \frac{3}{8} \qquad \frac{\overset{2}{\cancel{6}}}{\underset{1}{\cancel{7}}} \times \frac{\overset{2}{\cancel{14}}}{\underset{5}{\cancel{15}}} = \frac{4}{5} \qquad \frac{3}{2} \times \frac{7}{10} = \frac{21}{20} = 1\frac{1}{20} \qquad \frac{1}{3} \times 18 = \frac{1}{\cancel{3}} \times \frac{\overset{6}{\cancel{18}}}{1} = 6$$

Warm Up

Find the products.

1. $\frac{9}{10} \times \frac{1}{3}$ **2.** $\frac{1}{4} \times \frac{2}{3}$ **3.** $\frac{5}{6} \times \frac{3}{5}$ **4.** $\frac{4}{5} \times \frac{1}{2}$

5. $\frac{5}{8} \times \frac{2}{3}$ **6.** $\frac{1}{6} \times \frac{3}{4}$ **7.** $\frac{4}{3} \times \frac{3}{4}$ **8.** $\frac{3}{8} \times \frac{2}{3}$

9. $\frac{7}{10} \times \frac{5}{6}$ **10.** $\frac{5}{4} \times \frac{7}{8}$ **11.** $\frac{1}{2} \times \frac{1}{3}$ **12.** $\frac{7}{10} \times \frac{8}{10}$

Practice Multiply. Use the shortcut when possible.

1. $\frac{5}{8} \times \frac{2}{3}$ **2.** $\frac{1}{2} \times \frac{3}{5}$ **3.** $\frac{5}{9} \times \frac{3}{5}$ **4.** $\frac{1}{4} \times \frac{1}{4}$

5. $\frac{5}{2} \times \frac{2}{3}$ **6.** $\frac{3}{4} \times \frac{3}{4}$ **7.** $\frac{6}{7} \times \frac{3}{20}$ **8.** $\frac{8}{9} \times \frac{15}{16}$

9. $\frac{7}{8} \times \frac{3}{3}$ **10.** $\frac{4}{3} \times \frac{3}{8}$ **11.** $\frac{9}{10} \times \frac{25}{36}$ **12.** $\frac{1}{10} \times \frac{1}{10}$

13. $\frac{12}{35} \times \frac{7}{24}$ **14.** $\frac{2}{3} \times \frac{8}{12}$ **15.** $\frac{5}{6} \times \frac{6}{5}$ **16.** $\frac{6}{7} \times \frac{7}{16}$

17. $\frac{4}{3} \times \frac{1}{2}$ **18.** $\frac{9}{10} \times \frac{9}{10}$ **19.** $\frac{4}{15} \times \frac{3}{84}$ **20.** $\frac{24}{25} \times \frac{5}{6}$

21. $\frac{1}{24} \times \frac{6}{5}$ **22.** $\frac{8}{3} \times \frac{9}{32}$ **23.** $\frac{6}{1} \times \frac{10}{3}$ **24.** $\frac{17}{2} \times \frac{4}{1}$

25. $\frac{7}{10} \times \frac{5}{3}$ **26.** $\frac{3}{4} \times \frac{12}{9}$ **27.** $\frac{10}{3} \times \frac{2}{3}$ **28.** $\frac{8}{15} \times \frac{9}{4}$

Find the products.

29. $\left(\frac{1}{2} \times \frac{2}{3}\right) \times \frac{3}{4}$ **30.** $\left(\frac{2}{3} \times \frac{1}{6}\right) \times 9$ **31.** $\frac{5}{8} \times \left(\frac{2}{8} \times \frac{12}{5}\right)$ **32.** $\frac{3}{4} \times \left(\frac{3}{4} \times \frac{3}{4}\right)$

Mixed Applications

33. A picture window covers $\frac{5}{8}$ of the height of a wall and $\frac{6}{10}$ of the width of the wall. What part of the whole wall is covered by the picture window?

34. The wall of a room is 20 feet long and 8 feet high. A picture window in the wall is 10 feet long and 4 feet wide. Does the window take up more than $\frac{1}{2}$ the space, less than $\frac{1}{2}$ the space, or just $\frac{1}{2}$ of the space?

SKILLKEEPER

1. $\frac{3}{4} + \frac{2}{3}$ **2.** $\frac{5}{6} - \frac{1}{3}$ **3.** $\frac{7}{9} - \frac{3}{4}$ **4.** $\frac{5}{8} + \frac{2}{3}$ **5.** $\frac{4}{7} + \frac{1}{3}$

6. $5\frac{7}{10} + \frac{2}{3}$ **7.** $8\frac{5}{6} - 5\frac{2}{5}$ **8.** $4\frac{1}{2} - 3\frac{6}{7}$ **9.** $14\frac{1}{8} - 8\frac{5}{6}$ **10.** $10\frac{2}{5} + 7\frac{7}{9}$

11. $6 - 2\frac{17}{20}$ **12.** $8\frac{2}{7} + 3\frac{1}{6}$ **13.** $17\frac{1}{7} - 15\frac{2}{3}$ **14.** $4\frac{5}{36} + 6\frac{1}{9}$ **15.** $13\frac{3}{8} + 10\frac{2}{3}$

16. $7\frac{2}{5} - 4\frac{3}{7}$ **17.** $8\frac{1}{8} - 7\frac{6}{7}$ **18.** $15 - 6\frac{1}{10}$ **19.** $9\frac{4}{5} + 15\frac{1}{3}$ **20.** $34\frac{3}{8} - 9\frac{4}{5}$

21. $3\frac{1}{6} - 2\frac{4}{5}$ **22.** $14\frac{5}{32} + 2\frac{3}{4}$ **23.** $11\frac{4}{6} - \frac{8}{9}$ **24.** $31 - 29\frac{5}{16}$ **25.** $26\frac{2}{3} + 15\frac{2}{5}$

Multiplying with Mixed Numbers

A carpenter laid 20 pieces of wood side-by-side to build a small deck. Each piece of wood was $4\frac{3}{4}$ in. wide. How wide was the deck?

Since each piece has the same width, we can multiply. We can estimate the product by rounding $4\frac{3}{4}$ to 5.

Estimate: $\mathbf{5 \times 20 = 100}$

Write the mixed numbers as improper fractions.	Multiply the fractions.

$$4\frac{3}{4} \times 20 = \frac{19}{4} \times \frac{20}{1} \qquad \frac{19}{\cancel{4}_1} \times \frac{\cancel{20}^5}{1} = \frac{95}{1} = 95$$

The deck was 95 in. wide.
The answer is close to the estimate.

Other Examples

$$2\frac{1}{5} \times 3\frac{1}{2} = \frac{11}{5} \times \frac{7}{2} = \frac{77}{10} = 7\frac{7}{10} \qquad\qquad 6 \times 2\frac{1}{2} = \frac{\cancel{6}^3}{1} \times \frac{5}{\cancel{2}_1} = \frac{15}{1} = 15$$

$$\frac{9}{10} \times 7\frac{2}{3} = \frac{\cancel{9}^3}{10} \times \frac{23}{\cancel{3}_1} = \frac{69}{10} = 6\frac{9}{10} \qquad\qquad 1\frac{3}{4} \times 1\frac{3}{4} = \frac{7}{4} \times \frac{7}{4} = \frac{49}{16} = 3\frac{1}{16}$$

Warm Up

1. $8 \times 2\frac{1}{4}$ **2.** $1\frac{1}{2} \times 6\frac{1}{2}$ **3.** $\frac{9}{10} \times 5$

4. $6\frac{1}{8} \times \frac{6}{7}$ **5.** $1\frac{1}{3} \times 18$ **6.** $8 \times 1\frac{3}{4}$

7. $\frac{2}{3} \times 1\frac{5}{6}$ **8.** $1\frac{9}{10} \times 20$ **9.** $\frac{1}{2} \times 6\frac{2}{3}$

10. $3\frac{1}{2} \times 3\frac{1}{4}$ **11.** $\frac{3}{8} \times 6$ **12.** $1\frac{7}{8} \times \frac{8}{15}$

Practice Find the products.

1. $2\frac{1}{3} \times 6$

2. $\frac{1}{2} \times 8\frac{1}{5}$

3. $10 \times 3\frac{3}{5}$

4. $\frac{3}{4} \times 4\frac{1}{2}$

5. $3\frac{1}{7} \times \frac{14}{33}$

6. $6\frac{2}{3} \times 2\frac{1}{4}$

7. $1\frac{3}{10} \times \frac{5}{6}$

8. $100 \times 2\frac{1}{4}$

9. $1\frac{2}{3} \times 2\frac{1}{2}$

10. $3\frac{1}{4} \times 1\frac{2}{5}$

11. $3\frac{1}{4} \times 1\frac{1}{2}$

12. $2\frac{1}{3} \times 2\frac{1}{2}$

13. $1\frac{1}{4} \times 4\frac{1}{2}$

14. $2\frac{1}{8} \times 1\frac{3}{4}$

15. $\frac{7}{8} \times 2\frac{1}{2}$

16. $3\frac{1}{4} \times \frac{1}{2}$

17. $1\frac{1}{3} \times \frac{3}{4}$

18. $\frac{2}{3} \times 1\frac{1}{2}$

19. $2\frac{1}{2} \times \frac{2}{5}$

20. $\frac{4}{5} \times 1\frac{1}{4}$

21. $10\frac{2}{3} \times 8\frac{1}{4}$

22. $1\frac{3}{10} \times \frac{7}{100}$

23. $\frac{2}{3} \times 12\frac{1}{2}$

24. $\frac{9}{10} \times 6$

25. $1\frac{3}{5} \times \frac{5}{8}$

26. $3 \times 16\frac{2}{3}$

27. $4 \times 3\frac{3}{4}$

28. $2\frac{1}{2} \times \frac{5}{2}$

Perform the operations.

29. $\left(2\frac{1}{2} + 1\frac{1}{2}\right) \times 1\frac{1}{2}$

30. $\left(7 - 5\frac{3}{4}\right) \times 4$

31. $\left(3\frac{1}{3} + 5\frac{2}{3}\right) \times \frac{1}{3}$

32. $1 - \left(\frac{1}{2} \times \frac{2}{5}\right)$

33. $\left(3 \times \frac{1}{2}\right) + \left(5 \times \frac{1}{2}\right)$

34. $\left(9\frac{7}{10} \times 3\right) - 27\frac{1}{2}$

Mixed Applications

35. A carpenter laid 4 pieces of wood side-by-side to build a work bench. Each piece of wood was $6\frac{5}{8}$ in. wide. How wide was the work bench?

36. A screen was made of redwood slats that were $4\frac{1}{2}$ in. wide and $68\frac{3}{4}$ in. long. How wide would 15 slats laid side-by-side be?

★ 37. An adobe-block wall has 20 blocks, each 16 in. long, laid end-to-end. There is $\frac{3}{4}$ in. of mortar between each block. How long is the wall?

38. **DATA BANK** How long is a row of six common bricks laid end-to-end with $\frac{1}{4}$ in. of mortar between each pair of bricks? (See page 430.)

■ THINK MATH ■

Greatest Number Function

The symbol [ ] is used to show the **greatest whole number** that is less than or equal to the number inside the symbol.

$[2\frac{9}{10}] = 2$ $[7.1] = 7$

Give the whole number.

1. $[6\frac{1}{4}]$

2. $[1.8]$

3. $[9\frac{7}{8}]$

4. $[2\frac{1}{4}] + [3\frac{3}{4}]$

5. $[3\frac{1}{4}] \times [2\frac{1}{4}]$

6. $[2\frac{1}{2} + 3\frac{3}{4}]$

Estimating Products: Using Compatible Numbers

An energy specialist for a power company inspected an apartment. It was estimated that about $\frac{1}{6}$ of the utility bill could be cut by conserving energy. If the yearly bill is $1,195, about how much could be saved?

We need to estimate

$\frac{1}{6} \times \$1,195$.

Round $1,195 to $1,200.

$\frac{1}{6} \times \$1,200 = 200$

1,200 is a multiple of 6.

The customer could save about $200 a year.

Other Examples

Estimate $\frac{2}{3}$ of 31.

Round 31 to 30.

$\frac{2}{3} \times 30 = 20$

$\frac{1}{3} \times 30 = 10$
$2 \times 10 = 20$

Estimate $\frac{1}{6}$ of 46.72.

Round 46.72 to 48.

48 is a multiple of 6.

$\frac{1}{6} \times 48 = 8$

Practice Estimate each product.

1. $\frac{1}{4}$ of $15.75

2. $\frac{1}{3}$ of $27.11

3. $\frac{3}{4}$ of $20.33

4. $\frac{1}{5} \times \$9.99$

5. $\frac{1}{2} \times \$68.75$

6. $\frac{2}{3} \times 148.25$

7. $\frac{1}{10} \times 702$

8. $\frac{5}{8} \times 23$

9. $\frac{2}{5} \times 49.5$

10. $\frac{7}{8} \times \$54.95$

11. $\frac{9}{10} \times \$39.75$

12. $\frac{1}{7} \times \$35.27$

Mixed Applications

13. Heating costs could be cut by $\frac{1}{4}$ by turning the thermostat down during the winter. Estimate the savings on a yearly bill of $984.40.

14. DATA HUNT Energy conservation in the home could cut utility expense by about $\frac{1}{5}$. Estimate the monthly and yearly savings for your own household.

114

More Practice, page 440, Set C

Reciprocals

If the product of two numbers is 1, each number is the **reciprocal** of the other.

$$8 \times \frac{1}{8} = \frac{8}{1} \times \frac{1}{8} = 1 \qquad 8 \text{ and } \frac{1}{8} \text{ are reciprocals.}$$

$$2\frac{1}{4} \times \frac{4}{9} = \frac{9}{4} \times \frac{4}{9} = 1 \qquad 2\frac{1}{4} \text{ and } \frac{4}{9} \text{ are reciprocals.}$$

What is the reciprocal of $\frac{7}{8}$?

The reciprocal of $\frac{7}{8}$ is $\frac{8}{7}$.

Check: $\overset{1}{\cancel{7}} \times \overset{1}{\cancel{8}} = \frac{1}{1} = 1$

$\underset{1}{\cancel{8}} \times \underset{1}{\cancel{7}}$

The number line shows the location of some pairs of reciprocals.

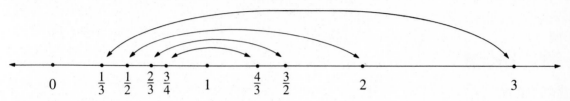

Every number except 0 has a reciprocal. There is no number times 0 that equals 1.

$$0 \times ? = 1$$

The only number that is its own reciprocal is 1.

$$1 \times 1 = 1$$

Give the reciprocal of each number.

1. $\frac{1}{5}$ 　　2. $\frac{2}{3}$ 　　3. $\frac{7}{10}$ 　　4. 3 　　5. $\frac{5}{3}$

6. $1\frac{1}{2}$ 　　7. $2\frac{3}{4}$ 　　8. $\frac{6}{11}$ 　　9. 1 　　10. $\frac{5}{8}$

11. $12\frac{1}{2}$ 　　12. $7\frac{9}{10}$ 　　13. $3\frac{2}{3}$ 　　14. $6\frac{3}{4}$ 　　15. $1\frac{2}{6}$

Give the number for n in each equation. Think about reciprocals.

16. $\frac{3}{5} \times n = 1$ 　　　　17. $\frac{1}{2} \times n = 1$ 　　　　18. $n \times 3\frac{3}{4} = 1$

19. $\frac{7}{9} \times \frac{9}{7} = n$ 　　　　20. $n \times 6\frac{1}{3} = 1$ 　　　　21. $5\frac{3}{4} \times n = 1$

★ 22. $\left(\frac{1}{2} + \frac{1}{3}\right) \times n = 1$ 　　★ 23. $\left(\frac{3}{4} \times \frac{2}{9}\right) \times n = 1$ 　　★ 24. $\left(3\frac{1}{8} - 2\frac{1}{4}\right) \times n = 1$

More Practice, page 440, Set D

Dividing Fractions

Leota wants to make a string of beads that will be 3 in. long. Each bead is $\frac{3}{8}$ in. long.

How many beads does Leota need?

We can measure to see how many times $\frac{3}{8}$ is contained in 3.

We can divide 3 by $\frac{3}{8}$.

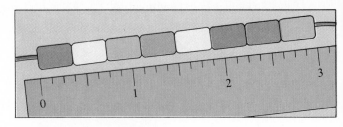

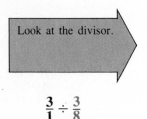 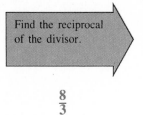

Look at the divisor.	Find the reciprocal of the divisor.	Multiply the dividend by the reciprocal of the divisor.

$$\frac{3}{1} \div \frac{3}{8} \qquad\qquad \frac{8}{3} \qquad\qquad \overset{1}{\cancel{3}} \times \frac{8}{\underset{1}{\cancel{3}}} = \frac{8}{1} = 8$$

Here is why this method of dividing works.

$$\frac{3}{1} \div \frac{3}{8} = \left(\frac{3}{1} \times \frac{8}{3}\right) \div \left(\frac{3}{8} \times \frac{8}{3}\right) \qquad \text{Multiply the divisor and dividend by the reciprocal of the divisor.}$$

$$\frac{3}{1} \div \frac{3}{8} = \left(\frac{3}{1} \times \frac{8}{3}\right) \div 1 \qquad\qquad \text{Divisor is now 1.}$$

$$\frac{3}{1} \div \frac{3}{8} = \frac{3}{1} \times \frac{8}{3} = \frac{24}{3} = 8$$

$\qquad\quad\uparrow\qquad\quad\uparrow$

$\qquad$ Reciprocals

Other Examples

$$1 \div \frac{1}{4} = \frac{1}{1} \times \frac{4}{1} = 4$$

Complex fraction → $\dfrac{\frac{4}{5}}{\frac{1}{2}} = \frac{4}{5} \div \frac{1}{2} = \frac{4}{5} \times \frac{2}{1} = \frac{8}{5} = 1\frac{3}{5}$

$$\frac{9}{10} \div \frac{3}{4} = \overset{3}{\cancel{9}}{\cancel{10}}_{5} \times \overset{2}{\cancel{4}}{\cancel{3}}_{1} = \frac{6}{5} = 1\frac{1}{5}$$

Warm Up

1. $\frac{1}{2} \div \frac{1}{4}$

2. $8 \div \frac{4}{5}$

3. $\frac{2}{3} \div \frac{1}{3}$

4. $\frac{8}{5} \div 2$

5. $\frac{5}{16} \div \frac{5}{8}$

6. $\frac{5}{8} \div \frac{5}{16}$

7. $\frac{3}{1} \div \frac{8}{1}$

8. $\frac{5}{6} \div \frac{10}{12}$

Practice Find the quotients.

1. $\frac{2}{5} \div \frac{1}{10}$

2. $\frac{3}{10} \div \frac{4}{5}$

3. $\frac{2}{3} \div \frac{5}{8}$

4. $\frac{3}{5} \div \frac{3}{4}$

5. $\frac{5}{6} \div \frac{3}{4}$

6. $\frac{2}{3} \div \frac{5}{6}$

7. $\frac{3}{4} \div \frac{3}{4}$

8. $\frac{1}{4} \div \frac{5}{8}$

9. $\frac{4}{5} \div \frac{2}{5}$

10. $\frac{1}{2} \div \frac{1}{10}$

11. $\frac{3}{8} \div \frac{3}{4}$

12. $\frac{1}{3} \div \frac{2}{3}$

13. $\frac{1}{8} \div \frac{1}{6}$

14. $\frac{7}{10} \div \frac{3}{4}$

15. $\frac{3}{10} \div \frac{7}{10}$

16. $\frac{2}{3} \div \frac{1}{2}$

17. $\frac{3}{4} \div \frac{1}{4}$

18. $\frac{7}{12} \div \frac{5}{8}$

19. $\frac{5}{6} \div \frac{1}{12}$

20. $\frac{9}{10} \div \frac{1}{5}$

21. $\dfrac{\frac{3}{8}}{\frac{4}{15}}$

22. $\dfrac{\frac{7}{2}}{3}$

23. $\dfrac{\frac{9}{8}}{\frac{3}{2}}$

24. $\dfrac{15}{\frac{5}{2}}$

Perform the operations.

25. $\left(\frac{3}{4} \div \frac{1}{2}\right) \div \frac{1}{4}$

26. $\left(6 \div \frac{2}{3}\right) \div \frac{1}{2}$

27. $\frac{3}{4} \div \left(\frac{1}{2} \div \frac{1}{4}\right)$

28. $6 \div \left(\frac{2}{3} \div \frac{1}{2}\right)$

29. $\left(\frac{9}{10} \div 3\right) \div \frac{5}{2}$

30. $\frac{9}{10} \div \left(3 \div \frac{5}{2}\right)$

Mixed Applications

31. If Leota strings beads that are $\frac{3}{16}$ in. long for a piece of macrame, how many beads should she use on a length of string that is $\frac{3}{4}$ in. long?

★ 32. Two sizes of beads are alternated to completely fill a necklace 30 in. long. One bead is $\frac{5}{8}$ in. long and costs $0.70. The other bead is $\frac{5}{16}$ in. long and costs $0.55. What is the total cost of the beads for the necklace?

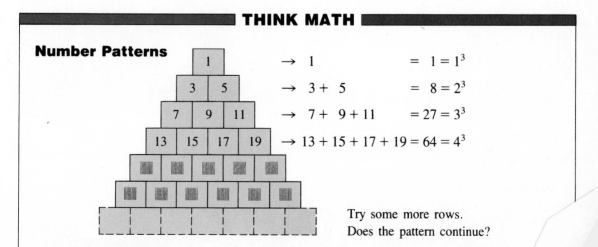

THINK MATH

Number Patterns

$\rightarrow 1 \qquad = 1 = 1^3$

$\rightarrow 3 + 5 \qquad = 8 = 2^3$

$\rightarrow 7 + 9 + 11 \qquad = 27 = 3^3$

$\rightarrow 13 + 15 + 17 + 19 = 64 = 4^3$

Try some more rows.
Does the pattern continue?

More Practice, page 441, Set A

Dividing with Mixed Numbers

Stacy is studying insects for a science project. She learned that a praying mantis is about $4\frac{1}{4}$ in. long and a walking stick is about $2\frac{1}{2}$ in. long. How many times the length of the walking stick is the praying mantis?

Walking stick

To find the number times $2\frac{1}{2}$ that equals $4\frac{1}{4}$, we need to divide $4\frac{1}{4}$ by $2\frac{1}{2}$.

Write mixed numbers or whole numbers as improper fractions.	Divide the fractions.

$$4\frac{1}{4} \div 2\frac{1}{2} = \frac{17}{4} \div \frac{5}{2} \qquad \frac{17}{\overset{}{4}_{2}} \times \frac{\overset{1}{2}}{5} = \frac{17}{10} = 1\frac{7}{10}$$

The praying mantis is $1\frac{7}{10}$ times as long as the walking stick.

Other Examples

$$6 \div 1\frac{2}{3} = \frac{6}{1} \div \frac{5}{3} = \frac{6}{1} \times \frac{3}{5} = \frac{18}{5} = 3\frac{3}{5}$$

$$1\frac{3}{4} \div 7 = \frac{\overset{1}{7}}{4} \times \frac{1}{\underset{1}{7}} = \frac{1}{4}$$

$$2\frac{1}{2} \div \frac{1}{2} = \frac{5}{\underset{1}{2}} \times \frac{\overset{1}{2}}{1} = 5$$

$$12\frac{1}{2} \div 4\frac{1}{2} = \frac{25}{\underset{1}{2}} \times \frac{\overset{1}{2}}{9} = \frac{25}{9} = 2\frac{7}{9}$$

Praying mantis

Warm Up

Find the quotients.

1. $3\frac{2}{3} \div 1\frac{1}{2}$ **2.** $8 \div 2\frac{1}{4}$ **3.** $6\frac{1}{4} \div 1\frac{1}{2}$ **4.** $10\frac{1}{2} \div 4$

5. $25 \div 8\frac{1}{3}$ **6.** $6\frac{7}{8} \div 2\frac{2}{3}$ **7.** $2\frac{9}{10} \div \frac{4}{5}$ **8.** $11 \div 3\frac{1}{7}$

Practice Divide.

1. $4\frac{1}{2} \div 2\frac{3}{4}$ 2. $1\frac{5}{8} \div \frac{5}{6}$ 3. $3\frac{1}{2} \div 1\frac{1}{4}$ 4. $2\frac{1}{2} \div 1\frac{1}{4}$

5. $2\frac{1}{8} \div 1\frac{1}{3}$ 6. $2\frac{1}{4} \div 1\frac{3}{4}$ 7. $5\frac{1}{2} \div 2$ 8. $2 \div \frac{7}{8}$

9. $2 \div 1\frac{1}{4}$ 10. $4\frac{5}{8} \div 1\frac{1}{2}$ 11. $1\frac{3}{8} \div 4\frac{1}{4}$ 12. $6\frac{1}{2} \div 2\frac{2}{3}$

13. $3\frac{1}{4} \div 1\frac{3}{4}$ 14. $\frac{2}{3} \div 2\frac{1}{2}$ 15. $4\frac{1}{3} \div 1\frac{2}{3}$ 16. $3\frac{1}{4} \div 1\frac{2}{3}$

17. $5 \div 2\frac{1}{2}$ 18. $3\frac{5}{8} \div 2\frac{5}{6}$ 19. $1\frac{7}{8} \div \frac{5}{12}$ 20. $1\frac{2}{3} \div 2\frac{3}{4}$

21. $3\frac{1}{3} \div 3$ 22. $10 \div 3\frac{1}{3}$ 23. $16 \div 1\frac{7}{9}$ 24. $\frac{2}{3} \div 4$

Perform the operations.

25. $\left(3\frac{1}{2} + 1\frac{1}{4}\right) \div 2$

26. $\frac{1}{2} \times \left(7 \div 1\frac{3}{4}\right)$

27. $\left(\frac{3}{4} \div \frac{3}{8}\right) \times 2\frac{1}{2}$

28. $\left(6 - 2\frac{2}{3}\right) \div 1\frac{2}{5}$

29. $\left(1\frac{5}{6} + 2\frac{1}{3}\right) \div 1\frac{1}{4}$

30. $\frac{3}{8} \times \left(3\frac{3}{4} \div \frac{15}{16}\right)$

Mixed Applications

31. Stacy found a ladybug that was $\frac{3}{16}$ in. long. She also found a cricket that was $1\frac{1}{8}$ in. long. How many times the ladybug's length was the cricket's length?

32. A grasshopper is $2\frac{5}{8}$ in. long. A katydid is $\frac{1}{4}$ in. longer than the grasshopper. The grasshopper's length is what part of the katydid's length?

33. Write and solve a word problem which can be solved by dividing $12\frac{3}{4}$ by $\frac{7}{8}$.

34. **DATA BANK** How many fleas placed end-to-end would it take to make a length as long as the Goliath beetle? (See page 432.)

SKILLKEEPER

1. $\frac{3}{8} \times \frac{2}{9}$ 2. $3 \times \frac{7}{12}$ 3. $\frac{4}{45} \times \frac{3}{10}$ 4. $\frac{5}{6} \times \frac{11}{12}$ 5. $\frac{1}{24} \times \frac{12}{13}$

6. $\frac{7}{40} \times \frac{15}{56}$ 7. $\frac{9}{20} \times \frac{11}{18}$ 8. $\frac{15}{32} \times \frac{16}{25}$ 9. $\frac{3}{10} \times 5$ 10. $\frac{7}{16} \times \frac{5}{21}$

11. $2\frac{5}{8} \times 3\frac{2}{3}$ 12. $4\frac{1}{6} \times \frac{6}{9}$ 13. $\frac{11}{32} \times 4$ 14. $4\frac{2}{3} \times 5\frac{1}{7}$ 15. $5\frac{3}{32} \times 4\frac{12}{13}$

16. $4\frac{4}{39} \times \frac{1}{16}$ 17. $2\frac{1}{12} \times 7\frac{1}{5}$ 18. $6\frac{1}{4} \times 1\frac{2}{15}$ 19. $\frac{3}{14} \times 2\frac{1}{3}$ 20. $15 \times \frac{23}{45}$

PROBLEM SOLVING: Using Consumer Data

QUESTION
DATA
PLAN
ANSWER
CHECK

The Griffins stopped at a farm market and bought $2\frac{1}{2}$ gal of apple cider. The cider cost $1.80 per gallon. What was the cost of the cider?

Each gallon cost the same. You can find the cost by multiplying. One factor is a *fraction*. The other factor is a *decimal*.

$$2\frac{1}{2} \times \$1.80 = \frac{5}{2} \times \frac{\$1.80}{1} = \frac{\$9.00}{2} = \$4.50$$

The cider cost $4.50.

Solve.

1. Carol Griffin bought $\frac{1}{2}$ dozen brown eggs. The eggs cost $1.42 per dozen. What did Carol pay for the eggs?

2. Dried apricots are sold in $\frac{3}{4}$-pound (lb) packages for $2.25. What is the price of the apricots per pound?

3. Cindy paid $1.65 for $2\frac{1}{2}$ lb of green beans. What was the cost of 1 lb of green beans?

4. Red apples cost 48¢ a pound. Nick bought $1\frac{3}{4}$ lb of apples. How much did he have to pay for them?

5. Pieces of cut watermelon cost 24¢ per pound. What did Willis Griffin pay for a piece of watermelon that weighed $5\frac{3}{4}$ lb?

6. The market sells 6 ears of fresh sweet corn for $1. How much must Stefano pay for $1\frac{1}{2}$ dozen ears of sweet corn?

7. A 5-lb bag of potatoes costs $1.05. A 10-lb bag costs $1.60. What is the cost per pound for each size bag of potatoes?

8. Fresh strawberries cost 79¢ a basket. Fresh cherries are $1.40 per pound. Vanecia bought two baskets of strawberries and $1\frac{3}{4}$ lb of cherries. What did the strawberries cost? What did the cherries cost? What was the total cost?

9. **Strategy Practice** Ellen bought some honey for $1.60 a pound. She spent $2.77 for oranges and $1.33 for bananas. Ellen spent a total of $7.70. How many pounds of honey did she buy? Hint: Work backward.

PROBLEM SOLVING: Using Mental Math

QUESTION
DATA
PLAN
ANSWER
CHECK

Eggs cost 80¢ per dozen. What is the cost of $1\frac{1}{2}$ dozen eggs? You can solve this problem using mental math.

Fresh Eggs   80¢ doz.

Think: Find $80 \times 1\frac{1}{2}$

$80 \times 1 = 80$

$80 \times \frac{1}{2} = 40$

$80 + 40 = 120$

The eggs cost 120¢ or $1.20

Solve each problem. Use mental math whenever possible.

1. The market sold fresh eggs for 80¢ a dozen. How much would $2\frac{1}{2}$ dozen eggs cost?

2. Hal bought $\frac{3}{4}$ dozen ears of sweet corn. How many ears of corn did Hal buy?

3. One pumpkin weighed $8\frac{1}{2}$ pounds. Another weighed $10\frac{1}{2}$ pounds. Margaret bought both pumpkins. What was their total weight?

4. Grapefruit were on sale at 3 for 99¢. How much would 6 grapefruit cost?

5. Roberto bought $8.90 worth of fruit and vegetables. He paid for it with a $10 bill. How much money should he get back?

6. Small apples cost 40¢ a pound. What is the cost of $4\frac{1}{4}$ pounds of the small apples?

7. Peaches weigh about $\frac{1}{2}$ pound each. About how much do 18 peaches weigh?

8. Alicia bought $2\frac{1}{3}$ pounds of green beans at 60¢ a pound. What was the cost of the green beans?

9. Mr. White bought 2 boxes of apples. Their total cost was $12.84. Each box cost the same amount. What was the cost of 1 box of apples?

10. **Strategy Practice** Two large pumpkins weigh a total of 50 pounds. The larger pumpkin weighs 8 pounds more than the smaller pumpkin. What is the weight of each pumpkin?

Writing Decimals for Fractions

A modern dance class has $\frac{19}{25}$ of its students present. A jazz exercise class has $\frac{24}{27}$ of its students present. Which class has the greater part of its students present?

Sometimes it is easier to compare fractions by comparing their decimals.

We can find a decimal for any fraction by dividing the numerator by the denominator.

$$\frac{19}{25} \rightarrow 25\overline{)19.00} \\ \quad\quad \underline{175} \\ \quad\quad\quad 150 \\ \quad\quad\quad \underline{150} \\ \quad\quad\quad\quad 0$$

0.76

Zero remainder

$$\frac{24}{27} \rightarrow 27\overline{)24.000} \\ \quad\quad \underline{216} \\ \quad\quad\quad 240 \\ \quad\quad\quad \underline{216} \\ \quad\quad\quad\quad 240 \\ \quad\quad\quad\quad \underline{216} \\ \quad\quad\quad\quad\quad 24$$

0.888... The digit 8 repeats endlessly.

0.76 is a terminating decimal.

0.888. . . is a repeating decimal.

In a repeating decimal, a bar is marked over the digit or group of digits that repeat.

The jazz exercise class has a greater part of its students present. $0.\overline{8} > 0.76$

Other Examples

$\frac{9}{16} = 0.5625$ $\frac{7}{54} = 0.1296296\ldots = 0.1\overline{296}$

$\frac{15}{8} = 1.875$ $\frac{38}{15} = 2.5333\ldots = 2.5\overline{3}$

Warm Up

Write each repeating decimal using a bar.

1. 0.7272. . .   **2.** 2.65353. . .   **3.** 0.816816. . .   **4.** 3.07720772. . .

Find a decimal for each fraction. Use a bar to show a repeating decimal.

5. $\frac{2}{3}$ **6.** $\frac{1}{8}$ **7.** $\frac{11}{6}$ **8.** $\frac{33}{40}$

Practice Write a decimal for each fraction. Use a bar to show repeating decimals.

1. $\frac{1}{2}$
2. $\frac{2}{5}$
3. $\frac{1}{3}$
4. $\frac{2}{15}$
5. $\frac{3}{11}$

6. $\frac{8}{33}$
7. $\frac{3}{16}$
8. $\frac{3}{2}$
9. $\frac{11}{3}$
10. $\frac{17}{6}$

11. $\frac{11}{18}$
12. $\frac{1}{8}$
13. $\frac{27}{100}$
14. $\frac{27}{99}$
15. $\frac{19}{22}$

16. $\frac{7}{24}$
17. $\frac{7}{9}$
18. $\frac{1}{7}$
19. $\frac{7}{16}$
20. $\frac{15}{12}$

21. $\frac{63}{50}$
22. $\frac{37}{80}$
23. $\frac{31}{48}$
24. $\frac{3}{7}$
25. $\frac{3}{5}$

Compare the fractions by comparing their decimals. Use > or <.

26. $\frac{11}{12}$ ⬤ $\frac{8}{9}$
27. $\frac{10}{11}$ ⬤ $\frac{21}{23}$
28. $\frac{3}{4}$ ⬤ $\frac{17}{24}$
29. $\frac{5}{8}$ ⬤ $\frac{11}{17}$

30. $\frac{9}{14}$ ⬤ $\frac{17}{26}$
31. $\frac{41}{81}$ ⬤ $\frac{3}{7}$
32. $\frac{17}{240}$ ⬤ $\frac{8}{118}$
33. $\frac{1}{3}$ ⬤ $\frac{6}{19}$

Write repeating decimals for the fractions. Look for patterns.

34. $\frac{1}{9}$
35. $\frac{2}{9}$
36. $\frac{5}{9}$
37. $\frac{6}{9}$
38. $\frac{7}{9}$

39. $\frac{8}{9}$
40. $\frac{1}{99}$
41. $\frac{8}{99}$
42. $\frac{17}{99}$
43. $\frac{35}{99}$

44. $\frac{60}{99}$
45. $\frac{89}{99}$
46. $\frac{215}{999}$
47. $\frac{647}{999}$
48. $\frac{3}{999}$

Mixed Applications

49. A dance instructor found that $\frac{15}{18}$ of the students in the morning class were present. The afternoon class had $\frac{17}{25}$ of its students present. Which class had the greater part of its students present?

50. In the morning class of 32 students, $\frac{13}{16}$ of the students attended. In the afternoon class of 24 students, only $\frac{7}{8}$ of the class attended. How many students were absent from either the morning class or the afternoon class?

THINK MATH

Comparing Decimals

Arrange the decimals in order from greatest to least.

0.237   0.$\overline{23}$ 0.23$\overline{7}$ 0.2$\overline{37}$ 0.$\overline{237}$

More Practice, page 441, Set C

Mixed Practice: Fractions

Find the products.

1. $\frac{1}{4} \times \frac{1}{5}$

2. $\frac{3}{4} \times \frac{4}{3}$

3. $2 \times \frac{3}{8}$

4. $\frac{2}{3} \times 45$

5. $\frac{11}{12} \times \frac{4}{3}$

6. $\frac{3}{4} \times \frac{1}{2}$

7. $\frac{1}{2} \times \frac{4}{5}$

8. $\frac{3}{5} \times \frac{10}{6}$

9. $\frac{7}{3} \times \frac{9}{8}$

10. $\frac{7}{15} \times \frac{3}{8}$

11. $\frac{2}{5} \times \frac{1}{4}$

12. $\frac{3}{5} \times \frac{5}{9}$

Find the quotients.

13. $\frac{3}{4} \div \frac{1}{2}$

14. $\frac{7}{6} \div \frac{7}{8}$

15. $\frac{5}{6} \div \frac{1}{8}$

16. $\frac{3}{4} \div 9$

17. $\frac{5}{8} \div 10$

18. $\frac{7}{8} \div \frac{1}{4}$

19. $\frac{1}{3} \div \frac{4}{5}$

20. $1 \div \frac{7}{6}$

21. $\frac{8}{3} \div \frac{5}{4}$

22. $\frac{9}{10} \div \frac{3}{8}$

23. $\frac{4}{9} \div \frac{2}{3}$

24. $\frac{2}{3} \div \frac{2}{5}$

Multiply or divide.

25. $\frac{1}{16} \times 8$

26. $0 \times \frac{5}{6}$

27. $\frac{3}{8} \div \frac{4}{9}$

28. $\frac{5}{8} \div \frac{1}{3}$

29. $\frac{8}{25} \times \frac{5}{6}$

30. $\frac{3}{4} \div \frac{4}{15}$

31. $1\frac{1}{4} \times \frac{1}{3}$

32. $\frac{2}{3} \times 2\frac{3}{4}$

33. $2\frac{1}{3} \div \frac{1}{6}$

34. $\frac{1}{4} \div 3\frac{1}{2}$

35. $\frac{7}{8} \times 1\frac{5}{9}$

36. $10 \times 3\frac{5}{6}$

Add, subtract, multiply, or divide.

37. $\begin{array}{r} 2\frac{5}{6} \\ + 6\frac{1}{3} \\ \hline \end{array}$

38. $\begin{array}{r} 5\frac{3}{4} \\ + 7\frac{1}{2} \\ \hline \end{array}$

39. $\begin{array}{r} 28\frac{1}{2} \\ - 9\frac{7}{12} \\ \hline \end{array}$

40. $\begin{array}{r} 35\frac{1}{2} \\ - 18\frac{1}{8} \\ \hline \end{array}$

41. $3 \times 4\frac{1}{6}$

42. $\frac{9}{25} \times 2\frac{1}{4}$

43. $3\frac{9}{10} \div 4\frac{1}{3}$

44. $4\frac{1}{2} \div 18$

45. $\begin{array}{r} 46\frac{1}{4} \\ + 87\frac{1}{3} \\ \hline \end{array}$

46. $\begin{array}{r} 63\frac{1}{2} \\ - 29\frac{3}{10} \\ \hline \end{array}$

47. $\begin{array}{r} 46\frac{1}{2} \\ + 98\frac{7}{8} \\ \hline \end{array}$

48. $\begin{array}{r} 57\frac{5}{6} \\ - 29\frac{7}{8} \\ \hline \end{array}$

49. $2\frac{3}{4} \div \frac{1}{2}$

50. $4\frac{1}{2} \times 3\frac{1}{3}$

51. $8 \times 9\frac{3}{4}$

52. $2\frac{1}{3} \div 5\frac{1}{4}$

PROBLEM SOLVING: Using Data from a Map

QUESTION
DATA
PLAN
ANSWER
CHECK

Switzerland is a small, mountainous country in central Europe. The map shows the larger cities and the roads.

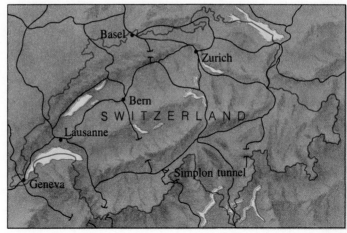

$\frac{1}{4}$ inch represents 15 miles

On the map, $\frac{1}{4}$ in. represents 15 mi. You can use this fact to find distances between points shown on the map.

Solve.

1. The road distance between Geneva and Lausanne is $\frac{3}{4}$ in. on the map. How many times is $\frac{1}{4}$ contained in $\frac{3}{4}$? How many miles is it from Geneva to Lausanne?

2. The map distance from Geneva to Bern is $1\frac{1}{4}$ in. How many times is $\frac{1}{4}$ contained in $1\frac{1}{4}$? How many miles is it from Geneva to Bern?

3. The map shows a road from Geneva to Lausanne to Basel that is about $3\frac{3}{4}$ in. long. How many miles is this?

4. The distance of a straight line on the map is about $1\frac{3}{4}$ in. from Lausanne to Zurich. How many miles does this represent?

5. From Bern to the Simplon Tunnel near the Italian border is a distance of about 60 mi along a highway. What is the map distance for the highway?

6. The road distance from Basel to Zurich on the map is about $\frac{5}{6}$ in. How many times is $\frac{1}{4}$ contained in $\frac{5}{6}$? How many miles is it from Basel to Zurich?

7. On the map, the east-west length of Switzerland is about $3\frac{1}{2}$ in. How many miles is the east-west distance?

8. The air distance from Geneva to Zurich is 150 mi. How many inches are needed to show this distance on the map?

★ 9. How many miles is it completely around the border of Switzerland? Estimate first, then measure the map to find the distance.

10. **Strategy Practice** Zurich, the largest Swiss city, has 10,000 more than twice the population of Basel. The two cities have a total population of 565,000. What is the population of each city?

125

PROBLEM-SOLVING STRATEGY: Draw a Picture

QUESTION
DATA
PLAN
ANSWER
CHECK

Try This

A tractor is pulling two trailers. The tractor is $\frac{1}{2}$ as long as the first trailer. The second trailer is as long as the tractor and the first trailer combined. The total length of the tractor and the two trailers is 18 m. What is the length of the tractor and each trailer?

A good strategy to use to help you solve the problem is called **Draw a Picture**. You can draw a picture and label it with the data given in the problem. Your picture should help you see what you must do to solve the problem.

Data	**Picture**	**Conclusion**
The tractor is $\frac{1}{2}$ as long as the first trailer.	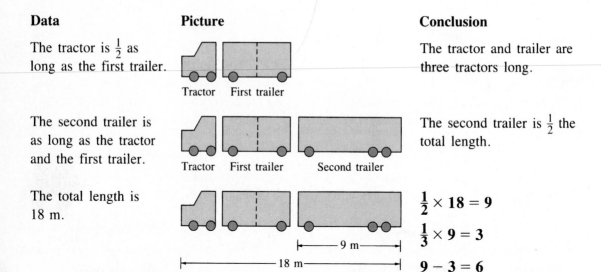	The tractor and trailer are three tractors long.
The second trailer is as long as the tractor and the first trailer.		The second trailer is $\frac{1}{2}$ the total length.
The total length is 18 m.		$\frac{1}{2} \times 18 = 9$ $\frac{1}{3} \times 9 = 3$ $9 - 3 = 6$

The tractor is 3 m long. The trailers are 6 m and 9 m long.

Solve.

1. Alicia's little brother has a wooden toy train with an engine, a freight car, and a caboose. The caboose is $\frac{1}{2}$ as long as the freight car and the freight car is $1\frac{1}{2}$ times as long as the engine. The engine is 16 cm long. What is the length of the freight car and the caboose?

2. Ed Lazar caught only one fish. He described his catch like this: "The head of the fish was 10 cm long. The tail was as long as the head plus $\frac{1}{2}$ of the body. The body was as long as the head and the tail together." How long was Ed's fish?

Multiply.

1. $\frac{4}{5} \times \frac{7}{8}$

2. $\frac{1}{2} \times \frac{4}{5}$

3. $\frac{6}{10} \times \frac{5}{3}$

4. $\frac{3}{4} \times \frac{5}{6}$

5. $\frac{2}{3} \times 15$

6. $10 \times \frac{2}{5}$

7. $\frac{5}{8} \times 48$

8. $\frac{9}{10} \times 200$

9. $1\frac{1}{2} \times 12$

10. $2\frac{2}{3} \times 1\frac{7}{8}$

11. $2\frac{3}{4} \times 20$

12. $6\frac{1}{2} \times 5$

Estimate each product.

13. $\frac{1}{4}$ of $27\frac{1}{2}$

14. $\frac{1}{2}$ of $89\frac{3}{4}$

15. $\frac{2}{3}$ of $21\frac{1}{8}$

16. $\frac{3}{8}$ of $23.58

Give the reciprocal of each number.

17. $\frac{5}{8}$

18. 4

19. $2\frac{3}{10}$

20. $\frac{1}{16}$

Divide.

21. $\frac{7}{8} \div \frac{3}{4}$

22. $\frac{9}{10} \div \frac{3}{2}$

23. $2 \div \frac{1}{4}$

24. $\frac{8}{15} \div \frac{2}{3}$

25. $9 \div 1\frac{1}{2}$

26. $3\frac{1}{3} \div \frac{1}{3}$

27. $6\frac{3}{4} \div 3$

28. $8\frac{1}{2} \div 1\frac{1}{2}$

29. $\frac{15}{16} \div 3\frac{3}{4}$

30. $100 \div 3\frac{1}{3}$

31. $7 \div \frac{7}{8}$

32. $88 \div 3\frac{1}{7}$

Write each number as a repeating decimal or a terminating decimal.

33. $\frac{7}{25}$

34. $\frac{1}{6}$

35. $\frac{7}{24}$

36. $\frac{13}{30}$

37. $0.333\ldots$

38. $1.2555\ldots$

39. $0.718718\ldots$

40. $0.60101\ldots$

41. Duvall bought $3\frac{3}{4}$ lb of apples that cost 48¢ a pound. What was the cost of the apples?

42. Jerry had 24 lb of dried apricots to put into bags. He put $\frac{3}{4}$ lb in each bag. How many bags of apricots would the 24 lb make?

Multiply the numerators.
Multiply the denominators.

Shortcut

$\frac{2}{5} \times \frac{5}{8} = \frac{10}{40} = \frac{1}{4}$ $\frac{\cancel{2}^{1}}{\cancel{5}_{1}} \times \frac{\cancel{5}^{1}}{\cancel{8}_{4}} = \frac{1}{4}$

$3\frac{1}{2} \times 6$
$\downarrow \qquad \downarrow$
$\qquad \quad 3$
$\frac{7}{\cancel{2}_{1}} \times \frac{\cancel{6}}{1} = \frac{21}{1} = 21$

$1\frac{2}{3} \times 2\frac{1}{2} = \frac{5}{3} \times \frac{5}{2} = \frac{25}{6} = 4\frac{1}{6}$

Multiply.

1. $\frac{3}{8} \times \frac{5}{6}$
2. $\frac{3}{2} \times \frac{7}{15}$
3. $\frac{2}{3} \times \frac{3}{5}$
4. $\frac{3}{10} \times \frac{5}{8}$
5. $\frac{12}{5} \times \frac{5}{6}$
6. $\frac{8}{9} \times \frac{27}{1}$
7. $2\frac{1}{2} \times 8$
8. $5 \times 3\frac{2}{5}$
9. $\frac{1}{2} \times 4\frac{3}{8}$
10. $1\frac{1}{5} \times 1\frac{1}{2}$
11. $2\frac{2}{3} \times 1\frac{7}{8}$
12. $6\frac{2}{3} \times 3$

Estimate $\frac{1}{8}$ of **65.**

Round 65 to 64.

$\frac{1}{8}$ of $64 = \frac{1}{8} \times 64 = 8$

$\frac{1}{8}$ of 65 is about 8.

Estimate the products.

13. $\frac{1}{2}$ of 11
14. $\frac{1}{6}$ of 36
15. $\frac{2}{3} \times 8.5$
16. $\frac{3}{10} \times 21$
17. $\frac{1}{8} \times 33$
18. $\frac{3}{4} \times 17$

$\frac{5}{8} \div \frac{3}{4} = \frac{5}{\cancel{8}_{2}} \times \frac{\cancel{4}^{1}}{3} = \frac{5}{6}$
$\qquad \uparrow \quad \uparrow$
$\qquad \text{reciprocals}$

$2\frac{1}{2} \div 1\frac{1}{8} = \frac{5}{2} \div \frac{9}{8}$

$\qquad = \frac{5}{\cancel{2}_{1}} \times \frac{\cancel{8}^{4}}{9} = \frac{20}{9} = 2\frac{2}{9}$

Divide.

19. $\frac{3}{4} \div \frac{1}{2}$
20. $\frac{9}{10} \div \frac{3}{5}$
21. $\frac{4}{1} \div \frac{3}{4}$
22. $1\frac{1}{2} \div 3$
23. $3 \div 1\frac{1}{2}$
24. $1\frac{3}{8} \div \frac{5}{32}$
25. $3\frac{2}{3} \div 2\frac{3}{4}$
26. $12 \div 3\frac{3}{4}$
27. $16 \div \frac{2}{3}$

$$\frac{1}{6} \to 6 \overline{)\begin{array}{l} 0.1\,6\,6\ldots = 1.\overline{6} \\ 1.0\,0\,0 \end{array}}$$
$$\begin{array}{r} 6 \\ \hline 4\,0 \\ 3\,6 \\ \hline 4 \end{array}$$

Repeating
decimal

6 repeats

Write a decimal for each fraction.

28. $\frac{4}{9}$
29. $\frac{3}{20}$
30. $\frac{17}{18}$
31. $\frac{11}{6}$
32. $\frac{23}{40}$
33. $\frac{13}{5}$

Shape Perception

Study the patterns in the table below.

Shape	Length of each side	Number of small triangles	Part shaded	Part not shaded
	1 unit	1	1	0
	2 units	4	$\frac{3}{4}$	$\frac{1}{4}$
	3 units	9	$\frac{6}{9}=\frac{2}{3}$	$\frac{3}{9}=\frac{1}{3}$
	4 units	16	$\frac{10}{16}=\frac{5}{8}$	$\frac{6}{16}=\frac{3}{8}$

1. How is the number of small triangles related to the number of units of length of each side of the triangle?

2. Extend the table for triangles with sides that are 5, 6, and 7 units long.

3. Are the fractions for the part shaded (1, $\frac{3}{4}$, $\frac{2}{3}$, $\frac{5}{8}$, . . . ,) increasing or decreasing in size as the number of small triangles increase?

4. Are the fractions for the part unshaded (0, $\frac{1}{4}$, $\frac{1}{3}$, $\frac{3}{8}$, . . . ,) increasing or decreasing in size as the number of small triangles increase?

5. If the large shape contained a very large number of small triangles shaded in the pattern above, about what part of the triangles would be shaded?

1. Estimate the product.

2.953 × 28.59

A 56   **B** 84
C 90   **D** not given

2. Multiply.

2,194.52 × 3.7

A 8,119.724   **B** 811.9724
C 8,000   **D** not given

3. Estimate the quotient.

32.7 ÷ 8.92

A 4   **B** 3.7
C 3   **D** not given

4. Divide.

0.58)2.088

A 3.5   **B** 3.6
C 0.035   **D** not given

5. Multiply.

$5^2 \cdot 4^3$

A 1,600   **B** 400
C 120   **D** not given

6. What is the product of 125 × 200 in scientific notation?

A 25,000   **B** 2.5×10^3
C 2.5×10^4 **D** not given

7. What is the prime factorization of 220?

A $3 \cdot 25^3$ **B** $3^3 \cdot 5^5$
C $3 \cdot 5^2$ **D** not given

8. What is the GCF of 54 and 117?

A 3   **B** 9
C 54   **D** not given

9. Find the missing numerator.

$\frac{27}{30} = \frac{\blacksquare}{10}$

A 3   **B** 9
C 81   **D** not given

10. What is $\frac{84}{120}$ in lowest terms?

A $\frac{7}{10}$ **B** $\frac{3}{7}$
C $\frac{21}{30}$ **D** not given

11. What is the mixed number for $\frac{62}{7}$?

A $8\frac{8}{7}$ **B** $8\frac{6}{7}$
C $9\frac{6}{7}$ **D** not given

12. Add.

$2\frac{3}{4} + 1\frac{5}{8} + 6\frac{2}{3}$

A $10\frac{1}{8}$ **B** $10\frac{1}{4}$
C $11\frac{1}{24}$ **D** not given

13. Babette bought 7 calculator batteries for a total of $20.23. What was the cost of each battery?

A $3.99   **B** $2.89
C $2.99   **D** not given

14. Chad worked $9\frac{1}{2}$ h Monday and $7\frac{3}{4}$ h on Wednesday. How many more hours did he work on Monday than on Wednesday?

A $1\frac{1}{2}$ h   **B** $2\frac{1}{4}$ h
C $2\frac{3}{4}$ h   **D** not given

There are over 3,000 different languages used throughout the world today. A language that could be spoken and understood by everyone in the world would make it easier to exchange ideas and gain understanding. In 1887 *Esperanto* was created for that purpose. About 8 million people now speak Esperanto. Some people believe Esperanto could replace the six official languages in the United Nations— Arabic, Chinese, English, French, Spanish, and Russian.

French used to be the leading world language. Now English is used throughout the world by almost 400 million speakers: 4 times the number of people who speak French. Although English is shared by people who need to communicate in a second language, from air traffic controllers in Amsterdam to zoologists in Zaire, it is not the language spoken by the greatest number of people. People who speak Mandarin Chinese outnumber English speakers by approximately 2 to 1.

Evaluating Expressions

Wallace Jenne restores and repairs clocks.
He makes a table of the movements of the
gears before he begins work on a clock.
One clock has a large spur gear that makes
1 revolution while its smaller pinion makes
4 revolutions.

If the spur gear makes r
revolutions, the pinion makes
$4 \cdot r$ or $4r$ revolutions.

$4r$ is an **algebraic expression**.

The letter r is a **variable**. To
evaluate an expression,
we substitute a number for the
variable and perform the operations.

Let $r = 6$.
$4 \cdot 6 = 24$

Revolutions	
Spur	Pinion
1	4
2	8
3	12
4	16

Spur gear
and pinion

Other Examples

$100 - y$
Let $y = 30$.
$100 - 30 = 70$

$\dfrac{3k}{4}$
Let $k = 8$.
$\dfrac{3 \cdot 8}{4} = 6$

$\dfrac{h}{2} + 1$
Let $h = 16$.
$\dfrac{16}{2} + 1 = 9$

To evaluate an expression with two or more
variables, we substitute a number for each
variable.

$(a - 2b) + 4$
Let $a = 20$ and let $b = 3$.
$(20 - 2 \cdot 3) + 4 = (20 - 6) + 4 = 18$

Warm Up

Evaluate each expression. Substitute 6 for each variable.

1. $23c$ **2.** $1 + j$ **3.** $6r - 3$ **4.** $\dfrac{12}{y} + 4$ **5.** $\dfrac{10 - t}{2}$

Evaluate each expression.

6. $z - 9$ if
$z = 16$

7. $6(h - 3)$ if
$h = 10$

8. $\dfrac{5s}{2}$ if
$s = 14$

9. $2d - e$ if
$d = 9$ and
$e = 10$

10. $\dfrac{m - 4}{n}$ if
$m = 25$ and
$n = 3$

Practice Evaluate each expression for $d = 10$ and $t = 3$.

1. $7 + d$ 2. $6t$ 3. $d - 9$ 4. $\dfrac{27}{t}$

5. $50 - 4d$ 6. $\dfrac{d}{2}$ 7. $\dfrac{8t}{6}$ 8. $\dfrac{4+d}{7}$

9. $3(t + 2)$ 10. $10d - 75$ 11. $\dfrac{30}{t} - 6$ 12. $\dfrac{30 - 6}{t}$

Evaluate each expression for $n = 8$ and $s = 6$.

13. $n + s$ 14. ns 15. $n - s$ 16. $\dfrac{4s}{n}$

17. $(n + 3) - s$ 18. $\dfrac{n + 4}{s}$ 19. $\dfrac{6n}{s}$ 20. $3(n + s)$

21. $3n + s$ 22. $\dfrac{n}{s + 2}$ 23. $\dfrac{ns}{12}$ 24. $\dfrac{2s + n}{5}$

Copy and complete each table by evaluating the expressions.

	y	$15y - 1$		r	$\dfrac{r}{12} + 2$		s	$\dfrac{s - 3}{2}$
25.	1		31.	12		37.	7	
26.	2		32.	0		38.	13	
27.	3		33.	24		39.	21	
28.	5		34.	144		40.	57	
29.	10		35.	96		41.	95	
30.	20		36.	108		42.	201	

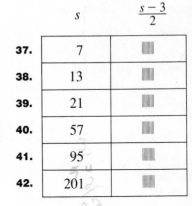

Copy and complete each table by evaluating the expressions.

	x	y	$3x - y$		k	s	$29k - 15s$
43.	2	1		47.	16	18	
44.	5	9		48.	38	12	
45.	9	5		49.	166	271	
46.	10	19		50.	30	58	

More Practice, page 441, Set D

Writing Addition and Subtraction Expressions

The Buckskins have lost a certain number of games (g). They have won 8 more games than they have lost. What expression represents the number of games won?

Variable

$g \leftarrow$ Number of games lost

Algebraic expression

$g + 8 \leftarrow$ Number of games won

Other Examples

Phrase	Variable	Algebraic expression
3 **more than** a number	y	$y + 3$
A number **decreased** by 5	s	$s - 5$
A number **increased** by 10	n	$n + 10$
12 **less than** a number	t	$t - 12$
The **sum** of 8 and a number	c	$8 + c$
$4 **plus** a number of dollars	x	$x + 4$
100 **minus** a number	k	$100 - k$
The **remainder** when 7 is **subtracted** from a number	z	$z - 7$

Warm Up

Choose the expression for each phrase.

1. 2 less than a number n

  A $n + 2$
  B $n - 2$
  C $2 - n$

2. A number j increased by 8

  A $j - 8$
  B $j + 8$
  C $8 - j$

3. 15 decreased by a number h

  A $h - 15$
  B $15 + h$
  C $15 - h$

Give the expression for each phrase.

4. 20 less than a number r

5. 25 more than a number v

6. A number p increased by 37

7. A number d minus 14

8. The sum of 16 and a number n

9. 80 decreased by a number y

134

Practice Write an expression for each phrase.

1. A number f increased by 40

2. 1 less than a number n

3. The sum of 48 and a number m

4. A number t minus 10

5. The difference when a number r is subtracted from 1,000

6. The result of adding a number y to 15

7. A number x plus 44

8. A number z decreased by 17

9. The remainder when 19 is subtracted from a number b

10. The money left from $20 after spending d dollars

11. The remainder when a number n is taken from 206

12. $18 more than a number of dollars j

13. 30 decreased by a number w

14. The total when a number z is added to 64

Mixed Applications Write an expression for each problem.

15. Larry Bird scored f field goals. He made 4 more free throws than field goals. What expression represents the number of free throws?

16. Parrish and Bird scored a total of 62 points. Bird scored n of these points. What expression shows the points for Parrish?

17. The Bears have played x games so far this season. They have lost 25 of the games. What expression represents the number of games they have won this season?

18. The Bears played 82 games in a season. There were g games played at home and the remainder were away games. What expression represents the number of away games?

SKILLKEEPER

1. $\frac{3}{8} \div \frac{5}{6}$

2. $\frac{7}{10} \div \frac{2}{5}$

3. $8 \div \frac{2}{3}$

4. $\frac{2}{9} \div \frac{1}{3}$

5. $\frac{4}{15} \div \frac{2}{3}$

6. $\frac{18}{22} \div \frac{3}{4}$

7. $\frac{5}{6} \div 25$

8. $\frac{8}{21} \div \frac{4}{7}$

9. $\frac{7}{36} \div \frac{1}{6}$

10. $\frac{2}{3} \div 4$

11. $3\frac{2}{3} \div \frac{1}{9}$

12. $5\frac{1}{4} \div 3\frac{1}{2}$

13. $\frac{5}{6} \div 6\frac{2}{3}$

14. $1\frac{7}{18} \div 1\frac{1}{9}$

15. $8 \div 3\frac{1}{5}$

16. $5\frac{1}{4} \div 6\frac{3}{10}$

17. $4\frac{1}{6} \div 5$

18. $1\frac{2}{7} \div \frac{3}{14}$

19. $\frac{2}{3} \div 7\frac{1}{3}$

20. $1\frac{5}{27} \div 1\frac{7}{9}$

Addition and Subtraction Equations

The Hoover Dam is about 188 m wider at the base than it is at the top. The base is 201 m wide. How wide is the dam at the top?

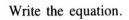

We can solve the problem by writing and solving an **equation**.

Let $t =$ the width at the top.

$t + 188 =$ width at the base

Write the equation. $t + 188 = 201$

Subtract the same number from each side of the equation. $t + 188 - 188 = 201 - 188$

Simplify. $t = 13$

Substitute the value of the variable in the original equation. $13 + 188 = 201$

It checks.

The dam is about 13 m wide at the top.

Other Examples

To solve a subtraction equation, we *add* the same number to each side.

$r - 23 = 59$
$r - 23 + 23 = 59 + 23$
$r = 82$
$82 - 23 = 59$ Check

$2.4 + y = 5$
$2.4 - 2.4 + y = 5 - 2.4$
$y = 2.6$
$2.4 + 2.6 = 5.0$ Check

Warm Up

Solve the equations. Show each step.

1. $y - 15 = 25$

2. $k + 9 = 21$

3. $11 + n = 40$

4. $s - 35 = 48$

5. $2.6 + z = 7.1$

6. $x + 8 = 20$

Practice Solve the equations.

1. $b - 15 = 8$ **2.** $c - 12 = 41$ **3.** $n + 18 = 24$ **4.** $a + 27 = 60$

5. $r + 35 = 72$ **6.** $k - 17 = 15$ **7.** $y - 56 = 7$ **8.** $x + 29 = 36$

9. $z + 64 = 100$ **10.** $20 + s = 42$ **11.** $j - 33 = 2$ **12.** $t + 30 = 48$

13. $a - 24 = 9$ **14.** $h + 17 = 17$ **15.** $46 + p = 60$ **16.** $x - 8 = 14$

17. $55 + n = 81$ **18.** $26 + x = 93$ **19.** $m - 39 = 67$ **20.** $w + 1 = 71$

21. $46 + y = 91$ **22.** $v - 5.0 = 6.3$ **23.** $z + 0.6 = 1.3$ **24.** $2.9 + p = 10.7$

25. $d + 8.3 = 15.3$ **26.** $g - \frac{3}{4} = \frac{1}{2}$ **27.** $1\frac{3}{4} + x = 1\frac{15}{16}$ **28.** $f - \frac{2}{3} = 2\frac{1}{2}$

Solve the equations. Use a calculator.

29. $x + 96,784 = 123,476$ **30.** $r - 19,768 = 4,876$ **31.** $88,888 + d = 99,999$

Mixed Applications

32. The height of the Hoover Dam is 221 m. The height is 158 m less than the length of the top of the dam. What is the length of the top? Solve the equation. $t - 158 = 221$

33. The Dartmouth Dam in Australia is about 177 m high. This height is about 56 m less than the height of the Chivor Dam in Colombia. What is the height of the Chivor Dam? Solve the equation. $h - 56 = 177$

34. A generator is rated at 95,000 kilowatts (kW). This is 12,500 kW more than a smaller generator that is rated at k kilowatts. What is the rating of the smaller generator? Solve the equation. $k + 12,500 = 95,000$

35. **DATA BANK** How much greater is the height of the Mica Dam in Canada than the height of the Hungry Horse Dam in the United States? (See page 431.)

THINK MATH

Calculator Number Patterns

Find the number for n in each equation.

Write the next five equations in this pattern.

$8 \times 1 + 1 = n$
$8 \times 12 + 2 = n$
$8 \times 123 + 3 = n$
$8 \times 1,234 + 4 = n$

PROBLEM SOLVING: Using the 5-Point Checklist

| QUESTION |
| DATA |
| PLAN |
| ANSWER |
| CHECK |

To Solve a Problem

1. Understand the QUESTION
2. Find the needed DATA
3. PLAN what to do
4. Find the ANSWER
5. CHECK back

Rhett ate a cheddar cheese sandwich and drank a glass of milk. The sandwich and the milk had a total of 505 calories. The milk had 180 calories. How many calories were there in the sandwich?

You can use the 5-Point Checklist as you write and solve an equation for the problem above.

1. Understand the QUESTION
You need to find the number of calories in the sandwich.

Choose a variable for the unknown number.

Let c = the number of calories in the sandwich.

2. Find the needed DATA
The total was 505 calories.
The milk had 180 calories.

$$\begin{matrix} c & 180 & 505 \\ \uparrow & \uparrow & \uparrow \\ \text{Sandwich} & \text{Milk} & \text{Total} \end{matrix}$$

3. PLAN what to do
Write an equation.

$$c + 180 = 505$$

4. Find the ANSWER
Solve the equation.

$$c + 180 = 505$$
$$c + 180 - 180 = 505 - 180$$
$$c = 325$$

5. CHECK back
Substitute 325 for c.

$$325 + 180 = 505 \quad \text{It checks.}$$

The sandwich had 325 calories.

Write and solve an equation for each problem. Use the 5-Point Checklist.

1. An avocado has 276 calories more than a pear. An avocado has 380 calories. How many calories does a pear have?

Let p = the number of calories in a pear.
$p + 276 = $ ▓

2. If 60 is subtracted from the number of calories in a bagel, the difference is the number of calories in a muffin. How many calories are there in a bagel if there are 120 calories in a muffin?

Let b = the number of calories in a bagel.

138

Write and solve an equation for each problem. Use the 5-Point Checklist.

1. If 8 is added to the number of calories in a boiled potato, the sum is the number of calories in $\frac{1}{2}$ c of cooked navy beans. The beans have 112 calories. How many calories are there in the potato?

2. If 21 is subtracted from the number of calories in a banana, the difference is the number of calories in an apple. An apple has 80 calories. How many calories does a banana have?

3. A serving of tuna has 23 g of fat. This is 4 g more fat than a serving of salmon has. How many grams of fat are there in a serving of salmon?

4. Tuna packed in water has 182 calories less than tuna packed in oil. There are 144 calories in tuna packed in water. How many calories are there in tuna packed in oil?

5. If 70 calories are added to the number of calories in one hard roll, the sum is the same as the number of calories in one cup of cream of mushroom soup. If the sum is 214 calories, what is the number of calories in one hard roll?

6. There are 120 calories in one cup of low-fat milk. Beth ate two pieces of toast and drank one cup of low-fat milk. This was a total of 325 calories. How many calories were there in the toast?

7. A cup of applesauce has 230 calories. If 190 is subtracted from the number of calories in a cup of raisins, the difference is the number of calories in a cup of applesauce. How many calories are there in a cup of raisins?

8. **Strategy Practice** Angie stacked 220 oranges to make a display. Each layer of oranges was in the shape of a triangle with the same number of oranges on each side. The top layer had a single orange. How many layers of oranges were there in the display? Hint: Draw a picture.

Writing Multiplication and Division Expressions

The Lambert glacier in Antarctica is about 3 times as long as the Peter Monas glacier in Greenland. What algebraic expression represents the length of the Lambert glacier?

$x \leftarrow$ Length of Peter Monas glacier

$3x \leftarrow$ Length of Lambert glacier

Other Examples

Phrase	Variable	Expression
5 **times** a number	y	$5y$
The **product** of a number and 10	n	$10n$
$\frac{3}{4}$ **of** a number	z	$\frac{3}{4}z$
A number **times** 4	k	$4k$
12 **divided by** a number	t	$\frac{12}{t}$ or $12 \div t$
A number **divided by** 12	s	$\frac{s}{12}$ or $s \div 12$

Warm Up

Choose the expression for each phrase.

1. The quotient of a number s divided by 10

   A $\frac{10}{s}$ **B** $\frac{s}{10}$ **C** $10s$

2. 9 times a number w

   A $9 + w$ **B** $w \div 9$ **C** $9w$

3. 24 divided by a number d

   A $\frac{24}{d}$ **B** $24d$ **C** $\frac{d}{24}$

4. 2 more than a number x times 3

   A $3x + 2$ **B** $2x + 3$ **C** $2 + 3 + x$

Give the expression for each phrase.

5. A number k divided by 4

6. The product of a number n and 3

7. 100 divided by r

8. y multiplied by 12

9. The quotient when 27 is divided by z

10. b times 15

Practice Write an expression for each phrase.

1. A number n divided by 4

2. 6 times a number z

3. The result of dividing p by 5

4. $\frac{2}{3}$ of a number w

5. A number j tripled

6. 50 divided by a number x

7. 32 multiplied by a number z

8. 100 over a number t

9. A number v divided by 2

10. 12 more than a number y

11. 16 times a number e

12. 36 divided by a number q

13. 5 less than a number n

14. 100 times a number c

15. A number n divided by 8

16. $\frac{1}{4}$ of a number y plus 23

17. 100 less than 4 times a number p

18. 2 subtracted from z divided by 5

19. The product of 9 times a number s increased by 7

20. The quotient of a number n divided by 12

21. The sum of a number k and 7 divided by 8

22. A number p subtracted from the quotient of 2 divided by 7

Mixed Applications

23. The Novaya Zemlya glacier in the U.S.S.R. is 2 times as long as the Recovery glacier in Antarctica. What is an expression for the length of the Novaya Zemlya glacier?

24. The area of the Malaspina glacier in Alaska is 2.8 times the area of the Jostedal glacier in Norway. What is an expression for the area of the Jostedal glacier?

THINK MATH

Evaluating an Expression

Evaluate this expression.

What is interesting about the value of this expression?

$25 \cdot (4m + 13) + a - 365 + 40$
Let m = your birth month (Jan.= 1, Feb.= 2, . . .).
Let a = your age in years.

Multiplication and Division Equations

Gray whales migrate 6,000 mi in about 16 weeks. How many miles do they travel per week?

We could solve the problem using simple arithmetic. We can also solve it by using an equation.

Let d = the number of miles per week.

$16d$ = total number of miles

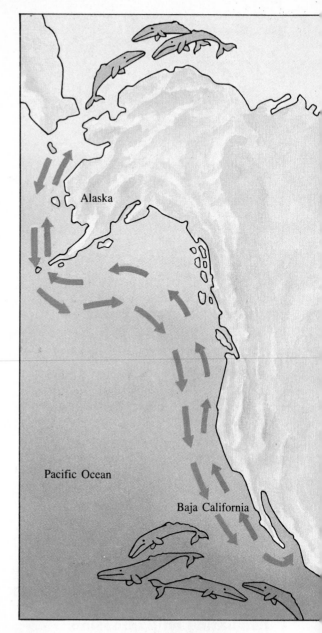

Alaska

Pacific Ocean

Baja California

Write the equation.	$16d = 6,000$
Divide each side by the same number.	$\dfrac{16d}{16} = \dfrac{6,000}{16}$
Simplify.	$d = 375$
Substitute the value of the variable in the original equation.	$16 \cdot 375 = 6,000$

It checks.

Gray whales travel about 375 mi per week.

Other Examples

To solve a division equation, we *multiply* each side of an equation by the same number.

$$\frac{n}{9} = 5 \qquad\qquad \frac{t}{20} = 15$$

$$\frac{n}{9} \cdot 9 = 5 \cdot 9 \qquad \frac{t}{20} \cdot 20 = 15 \cdot 20$$

$$n = 45 \qquad\qquad t = 300$$

$$\frac{45}{9} = 5 \text{ Check} \qquad \frac{300}{20} = 15 \text{ Check}$$

Warm Up

Solve the equations. Show each step.

1. $2t = 20$
2. $\dfrac{n}{6} = 7$
3. $7d = 140$
4. $\dfrac{a}{10} = 12$

5. $\dfrac{s}{3} = 25$
6. $9n = 108$
7. $\dfrac{j}{12} = 6$
8. $24x = 120$

Practice Solve the equations.

1. $9y = 72$ 2. $5r = 45$ 3. $\frac{n}{3} = 8$ 4. $\frac{s}{8} = 12$

5. $8z = 128$ 6. $10m = 100$ 7. $\frac{w}{2} = 46$ 8. $\frac{h}{10} = 7$

9. $30y = 210$ 10. $\frac{b}{17} = 4$ 11. $25e = 200$ 12. $\frac{c}{7} = 7$

13. $60f = 600$ 14. $\frac{r}{19} = 9$ 15. $13g = 91$ 16. $\frac{n}{13} = 25$

17. $4n = 64$ 18. $\frac{s}{6} = 30$ 19. $\frac{x}{1.5} = 3$ 20. $0.6y = 12$

Solve the equations. You may need to add, subtract, multiply, or divide.

21. $d - 23 = 17$ 22. $\frac{y}{18} = 3$ 23. $40s = 360$

24. $w + 35 = 90$ 25. $k - 29 = 75$ 26. $\frac{u}{11} = 13$

27. $18n = 126$ 28. $\frac{v}{6} = 55$ 29. $z - 45 = 45$

Mixed Applications

30. In 11 weeks a gray whale traveled 5,599 mi. How far did the whale travel per week? Write and solve an equation.

31. To find the speed at which a whale travels, you can divide the distance traveled by the time traveled. What distance must a whale travel in 72 h to average 3 miles per hour (mph)? Write and solve an equation.

SKILLKEEPER

Solve.

1. $33 + w = 97$ 2. $r - 28 = 113$ 3. $210 + x = 507$ 4. $t - 53 = 34$

5. $y + 44 = 1,406$ 6. $16 + n = 49$ 7. $w - 36 = 9$ 8. $x - 1,019 = 3,506$

9. $z - 0.7 = 5.2$ 10. $19.5 + r = 23.1$ 11. $t - 3.14 = 67.8$ 12. $0.02 + n = 13.3$

13. $0.013 + y = 0.020$ 14. $x - 24.8 = 33.5$ 15. $r - 0.103 = 0.2$ 16. $w + 5.002 = 7$

17. $\frac{3}{4} + t = 1\frac{1}{12}$ 18. $x + 1\frac{2}{9} = 2\frac{5}{36}$ 19. $y - \frac{2}{3} = \frac{29}{30}$

20. $m - 1\frac{1}{3} = 3\frac{3}{4}$ 21. $t - \frac{1}{7} = 3\frac{2}{21}$ 22. $3\frac{1}{24} + w = 5\frac{1}{4}$

Two-Step Equations

To repair a sprinkler system, Dave bought a section of pipe that was 229 cm long. He cut off 3 pieces of equal length and had 1 piece 25 cm long left over. What was the length of each of the 3 pieces?

We can write and solve an equation for this problem.

Let c = the length of each piece.

$3c$ = length of 3 pieces

$3c + 25$ = total length of the pipe

Write the equation.	$3c + 25 = 229$
Subtract the same number from each side.	$3c + 25 - 25 = 229 - 25$
Simplify.	$3c = 204$
Divide each side by the same number.	$\dfrac{3c}{3} = \dfrac{204}{3}$
Simplify.	$c = 68$

$$3 \cdot 68 + 25 = 204 + 25 = 229$$

Each piece was 68 cm long.   It checks.

Other Examples

$$\frac{d}{6} - 3 = 2$$

$$\frac{d}{6} - 3 + 3 = 2 + 3$$

$$\frac{d}{6} = 5$$

$$\frac{d}{6} \cdot 6 = 5 \cdot 6$$

$$d = 30$$

$$\frac{30}{6} - 3 = 5 - 3 = 2 \quad \text{Check}$$

$$7d - 1 = 34$$

$$7d - 1 + 1 = 34 + 1$$

$$7d = 35$$

$$\frac{7d}{7} = \frac{35}{7}$$

$$d = 5$$

$$7 \times 5 - 1 = 35 - 1 = 34 \quad \text{Check}$$

Warm Up

Solve the equations. Show each step.

1. $4x + 5 = 13$ **2.** $3n - 2 = 16$ **3.** $\dfrac{y}{2} + 1 = 3$ **4.** $\dfrac{h}{5} - 7 = 1$

Practice Solve the equations.

1. $3y - 3 = 24$

2. $\dfrac{d}{12} + 4 = 7$

3. $7n - 19 = 44$

4. $2r + 4 = 20$

5. $\dfrac{k}{5} - 1 = 1$

6. $\dfrac{j}{3} + 8 = 11$

7. $5y - 7 = 18$

8. $12t + 4 = 100$

9. $\dfrac{p}{21} + 9 = 11$

10. $\dfrac{b}{11} - 2 = 1$

11. $85a - 35 = 50$

12. $\dfrac{n}{8} + 7 = 7$

13. $4b + 15 = 27$

14. $\dfrac{e}{6} - 4 = 4$

15. $7s - 5 = 51$

16. $8f + 8 = 8$

17. $15g - 20 = 25$

18. $\dfrac{j}{15} + 7 = 10$

19. $\dfrac{w}{2} - 9 = 6$

20. $\dfrac{z}{5} - 3.1 = 59$

21. $6v - 2\dfrac{1}{4} = 39\dfrac{3}{4}$

22. $\dfrac{t}{3} - 0.2 = 0.6$

23. $7x - \dfrac{2}{5} = 48\dfrac{3}{5}$

24. $\dfrac{u}{12} + 1.6 = 1.7$

Use a calculator to solve these equations. Check each solution.

25. $36t - 780 = 42{,}420$

26. $75y + 668 = 16{,}343$

27. $\dfrac{n}{27} - 100 = 215$

28. $\dfrac{k}{60} + 56 = 87$

29. $729z - 10{,}438 = 31{,}115$

30. $\dfrac{m}{229} + 742 = 755$

Mixed Applications

31. Dave had $20. He bought 3 sprinkler heads and had $2 left. How much did each sprinkler head cost?

    Let s = the cost of each sprinkler head.

    Solve the equation. $3s + 2 = 20$

32. It is 8 m from the water outlet to the first sprinkler head. Then there are 6 equally-spaced sprinkler heads. The whole system is 38 m long. How far apart are the sprinkler heads? Choose the correct equation and solve it to find the distance.

    Let d = the distance apart.

    A $5d + 8 = 38$ **B** $5d - 8 = 38$

More Practice, page 442, Set C

PROBLEM SOLVING: Writing and Solving Equations

QUESTION
DATA
PLAN
ANSWER
CHECK

Ken and May Yamamoto bought living room furniture. The total cost with tax and interest was $2,250. They made a down payment of $450. The balance was to be paid in 8 equal payments. How much was each payment?

To solve the problem, you can write and solve a two-step equation.

Let p = the amount of each payment.

$8p$ = amount for 8 payments

$8p + 450$ = total cost

Equation: $8p + 450 = 2,250$

$$8p + 450 - 450 = 2,250 - 450$$

$$8p = 1,800$$

$$\frac{8p}{8} = \frac{1,800}{8}$$

$$p = 225$$

Check: $8 \times 225 + 450 = 1,800 + 450 = 2,250$

Each payment was $225.

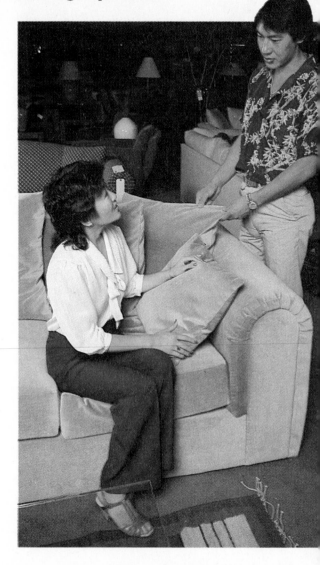

Write and solve an equation for each problem.

1. A certain number is divided by 6 and 17 is added to the quotient. The result is 21. What is the number?

Let n = the number.

2. If 15 is subtracted from 8 times a certain number, the difference is 57. What is the number?

Let n = the number.

3. A number is multiplied by 7 and then 36 is added to the product. The sum is 106. What is the number?

4. A number is divided by 4 and then 19 is subtracted from the quotient. The difference is 2. What is the number?

Write and solve an equation for each problem.

1. A certain number is multiplied by 7 and 11 is added to the product. The total is 67. What is the number?

2. When 9 is subtracted from the quotient of a number divided by 3, the difference is 8. What is the number?

3. Luke bought 5 T-shirts. Each T-shirt cost the same amount. The sales tax on the shirts was $1. Altogether Luke paid $21. What was the cost of each shirt?

4. Jeri runs the same distance 5 days a week. On Saturday she runs 15 km and she does not run on Sunday. If Jeri runs a total of 60 km a week, how far does she run on each of the 5 days?

5. Tonia drove the same distance each hour for 3 h. Then she drove 38 km farther. The total distance she drove was 293 km. What distance did she drive in each of the first 3 h?

6. Anita started a savings account with $25. How much must she put in the account each week in order to have a total of $145 at the end of 8 weeks?

7. Dirk repaid a loan in 12 equal payments plus a down payment of $180. Altogether he paid $2,160. How much was each of the equal payments?

8. Diane bought 6 cans of cat food. She had a coupon that was worth 25¢ off one can of cat food. The cat food cost $2.27 altogether. What was the cost of each can without the coupon?

9. There are 10 homerooms. One homeroom has 23 students, and one homeroom has 26 students. The 8 remaining homerooms each have the same number of students. There are 273 students in homerooms. How many are there in each of the 8 homerooms?

10. Romero worked 40 h one week for a certain number of dollars per hour. He also earned $36 in overtime pay by working over 40 h. His total pay was $676. How many dollars per hour did he earn for each of the 40 h?

11. Suzanne pays the same amount each month for her co-op apartment, plus a yearly maintenance fee of $600. Suzanne pays $6,000 per year altogether. How much does she pay each month?

12. **Strategy Practice** Van gave this puzzle problem to his math class. "I am thinking of a number. First multiply my number by 7. Then divide my number by 7. Now add the two results. You should get 500." What is Van's number?

147

PROBLEM SOLVING: Using Formulas

QUESTION
DATA
PLAN
ANSWER
CHECK

The volume of air a person can exhale after taking a deep breath is called the *vital capacity* of the lungs. You can use a formula to find the vital capacity.

$$V = 0.04\,h - 0.012\,a - 2.69$$

V = volume in liters
h = height in centimeters
a = age in years

What would be the vital capacity (V) of a person who is 165 cm tall (h) and 15 years old (a)?

Write the formula. $\qquad$ $V = 0.04\,h - 0.012\,a - 2.69$

Substitute the given
numbers in the formula. $\qquad$ $V = (0.04 \times 165) - (0.012 \times 15) - 2.69$

Perform the operations $\qquad$ $V = 6.6 - 0.18 - 2.69$
in the formula. $\qquad\qquad$ $V = 3.73$

The vital capacity would be about 3.7 L.

Copy and complete each table for the formula given.

1. 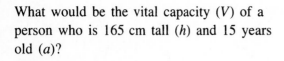 $H = 8 + \dfrac{18 - a}{2}$

H = hours of sleep
a = age in years
$\quad(a \le 18)$

Hours of sleep needed to age 18

Age	2	10	14	18
Hours	▨	▨	▨	▨

2. $P = S - C$

P = profit
S = selling price
C = cost

Profit

Selling price	$84	$2,300	$25,000	$229,575
Cost	$67	$1,675	$14,900	$176,898
Profit	▨	▨	▨	▨

3. $B = \dfrac{(220 - a) \times 4}{5}$

B = beats per minute
a = age in years

Highest heartbeat rate for exercise

Age	10	15	20	40	70
Beats/min					

4. $F = \$0.75 + (\$0.60\,d)$

F = taxicab fare
d = distance in kilometers

Taxicab fare

Distance	2	1	5	10	8
Fare					

5. $C = 52 + 37(m - 1)$

C = cost in cents
m = length of call
in minutes

Telephone call cost

Minutes	4	11	10	20	30
Cost					

6. $W = \dfrac{4(h - 150)}{5} + 50$

W = weight in kilograms
h = height in centimeters

Ideal weight

Height	200	180	165	160	150
Weight					

Use a formula given above for problems 7 and 8.

7. Lana had to take a taxi to work one morning. The distance was 4.5 km. What was the fare?

8. Jones is 220 cm tall. What is the ideal weight for this height?

9. **DATA HUNT** What is your vital capacity? Use the formula on page 148.

10. **Strategy Practice** Wilma made a telephone call that cost $4.22. How many minutes long was the call? Hint: Use the telephone call formula and work backward.

PROBLEM-SOLVING STRATEGY: Make a Table

QUESTION
DATA
PLAN
ANSWER
CHECK

Try This

A car and a truck start from the same point and travel along the same route. The truck starts first and travels 80 km before the car starts. The truck averages 72 kilometers per hour (km/h) and the car averages 88 km/h. How many hours will it take the car to catch up with the truck?

To solve a problem like the one above, it helps to **Make a Table** using the data given in the problem. Then you will be able to add to the table to solve the problem.

Start the table with the given data.

	Start	1 h	
Truck	80 km	152 km	
Car	0 km	88 km	

Now add to the table until you solve the problem.

	Start	1 h	2 h	3 h	4 h	5 h
Truck	80 km	152 km	224 km	296 km	368 km	440 km
Car	0 km	88 km	176 km	264 km	352 km	440 km

The table shows that after 5 h the truck and car will have traveled the same distance. It will take 5 h for the car to catch up with the truck.

Solve.

1. Two empty tanks are being filled with water. Tank I starts filling 3 min before Tank II. Tank I fills at the rate of 175 L/min and Tank II fills at the rate of 250 L/min. How long after Tank II begins filling will the two tanks contain the same amount of water?

2. At the start of an experiment on plant growth, plant A was 6 cm tall and plant B was 3 cm tall. Plant A was not fed nutrients and grew 0.4 cm a day. Plant B was fed nutrients and grew 0.8 cm a day. How many days was it until plant B was 1 cm taller than plant A?

150

Evaluate each expression for $b = 8$ and $g = 2$.

1. $b + 9$

2. $3g$

3. $10 - b$

4. $g + 9$

5. $8b - 60$

6. $5g - 6$

7. $\dfrac{b}{g}$

8. $5g - b$

9. $bg - 16$

10. $g(b - 3)$

Write an expression for each phrase.

11. The sum of n and 17

12. 6 less than a number y

Use addition or subtraction to solve each equation.

13. $x - 9 = 6$

14. $y + 12 = 20$

15. $n - 11 = 3$

16. $13 + r = 31$

17. $x - 7 = 7$

18. $x - 3 = 9$

Write an expression for each phrase.

19. 10 times a number t

20. A number r divided by 5

Use multiplication or division to solve each equation.

21. $6t = 42$

22. $\dfrac{t}{5} = 8$

23. $9t = 207$

24. $\dfrac{w}{8} = 13$

25. $17t = 85$

26. $\dfrac{t}{9} = 13$

Solve each two-step equation.

27. $3n - 7 = 14$

28. $\dfrac{k}{2} + 11 = 17$

29. $4z + 25 = 61$

30. When 18 is added to a certain number the sum is 45. What is the number?

31. Jamie earns d dollars an hour. If she works 9 h, she gets $144. How much does she earn each hour?

32. Isi multiplied the number of problems he got right by 5 and then subtracted 12 for the problems he missed. His score was 73. How many problems did he get right?

33. Find the cost of a 10-minute phone call using the formula $C = 21 + 13(m - 1)$. Let $C =$ the cost in cents. Let $m =$ the length of the call in minutes.

Evaluate each expression for $n = 10$ and $x = 8$.

1. $n + 3$	**2.** $x - 5$	**3.** $2 \cdot n$
4. $3x$	**5.** $\frac{n}{2}$	**6.** $\frac{x}{2} + 7$
7. $x + n$	**8.** $n - x$	**9.** xn

$$3n \qquad n = 4$$
$$\uparrow \text{ variable} \qquad \uparrow \text{ value}$$

Substitute. $\quad 3 \times 4 = 12$

3 more	$n + 3$
3 less	$n - 3$
3 times	$3n$
Divided by 3	$\frac{n}{3}$

Write an expression for each phrase.

10. 4 more than a number x

11. 12 less than a number y

12. The product of a number s and 7

13. A number z divided by 6

14. The quotient of a number n divided by 2

15. The number b added to 35

Add or subtract the same number on both sides.

$$n - 5 = 13$$
$$n - 5 + 5 = 13 + 5$$
$$n = 18$$

Solve the equations.

16. $x + 12 = 20$	**17.** $y - 6 = 15$
18. $8r = 56$	**19.** $\frac{n}{7} = 21$
20. $z - 20 = 66$	**21.** $15k = 60$

Multiply or divide the same number on both sides.

$$\frac{x}{4} = 9$$
$$\frac{x}{4} \cdot 4 = 9 \cdot 4$$
$$x = 36$$

Add or subtract, then multiply or divide.

Solve the equations.

22. $3x + 4 = 22$	**23.** $\frac{y}{5} - 1 = 6$
24. $2n - 3 = 17$	**25.** $\frac{m}{4} + 7 = 10$

Sequences

A **sequence** is a set of numbers given in a specific order, usually according to a pattern called a **rule**.

2, 5, 8, 11, 14, . . . , 3 n − 1, . . .

The first **term** of the sequence above is 2, the second term is 5, and the nth term is $3n - 1$.

The rule for this sequence is **nth term = $3n - 1$.**

1st	2nd	3rd	4th	5th	nth
2,	5,	8,	11,	14,	$3n - 1$,

Using the rule, we can find other terms in the sequence.

6th term	20th term	100th term
$3 \times 6 - 1 = 17$	$3 \times 20 - 1 = 59$	$3 \times 100 - 1 = 299$

Write the next four terms for each sequence.

1. 1, 4, 7, 10, . . . , $3n - 2$, . . .

2. 1, 4, 9, 16, . . . , n^2, . . .

3. 0, 2, 6, 12, . . . , $n \cdot (n - 1)$, . . .

4. 1, 6, 11, 16, . . . , $5n - 4$, . . .

5. $\dfrac{1}{2}, \dfrac{2}{3}, \dfrac{3}{4}, \dfrac{4}{5}, \cdots, \dfrac{n}{n+1}, \cdots$

6. 3, 7, 13, 21, . . . , $n^2 + n + 1$, . . .

Write the first six terms of the sequence whose nth term is given.

7. $2n - 1$

8. $5n - 2$

9. $\dfrac{n}{2}$

10. n^3

11. $2n^2 - 1$

12. $\dfrac{n(n+1)}{2}$

Write the rule for the nth term for each sequence.

13. 4, 8, 12, 16, . . .

14. 4, 7, 12, 19 . . .

15. 2, 6, 12, 20, . . .

16. 100, 95, 90, 85, . . .

1. Which pair of numbers is relatively prime?

   A 9 and 22   **B** 14 and 21
   c 9 and 33   **D** not given

2. What is the LCM of 7 and 63 and 105?

   A 105   **B** 525
   c 315   **D** not given

3. What is the LCD of $\frac{3}{4}$ and $\frac{3}{10}$?

   A 20   **B** 40
   c 10   **D** not given

Add, subtract, multiply, or divide.

4. $22\frac{7}{10} + 29\frac{3}{40}$

   A $51\frac{27}{28}$ **B** $52\frac{1}{28}$

   c $51\frac{55}{56}$ **D** not given

5. $28\frac{5}{6} - 12\frac{7}{16}$

   A $16\frac{1}{5}$ **B** $16\frac{1}{8}$

   c $16\frac{1}{2}$ **D** not given

6. $42\frac{5}{12} - 18\frac{7}{8}$

   A $24\frac{13}{24}$ **B** $24\frac{1}{2}$

   c $23\frac{13}{24}$ **D** not given

7. $\frac{7}{12} \times \frac{2}{3}$

   A $\frac{7}{18}$ **B** $\frac{7}{24}$

   c $\frac{21}{24}$ **D** not given

8. $12 \times 6\frac{2}{3}$

   A 80   **B** $72\frac{2}{3}$
   c $80\frac{2}{3}$ **D** not given

9. $15 \div 2\frac{2}{3}$

   A $5\frac{8}{45}$ **B** $5\frac{5}{8}$

   c $7\frac{1}{2}$ **D** not given

10. Estimate $\frac{3}{4}$ of $24.36.

    A $15   **B** $18
    c $20   **D** not given

11. Find n. $7\frac{3}{4} \times n = 1$

    A $\frac{4}{31}$ **B** 1

    c $\frac{3}{28}$ **D** not given

12. What is the decimal for $\frac{7}{12}$?

    A 0.584   **B** 0.6
    c 0.58   **D** not given

13. Three lengths of pipe measure $1\frac{5}{8}$ ft, $3\frac{1}{2}$ ft, and $17\frac{1}{4}$ ft. What is the total of the three measurements?

    A $21\frac{3}{8}$ ft   **B** $22\frac{3}{8}$ ft

    c $21\frac{1}{4}$ ft   **D** not given

14. A fly is $\frac{7}{16}$ in. long. A water bug is $1\frac{7}{8}$ in. long. How many times the length of the fly is the water bug?

    A $4\frac{2}{7}$ **B** $1\frac{13}{14}$

    c $2\frac{5}{16}$ **D** not given

7

Measurement: Metric Units

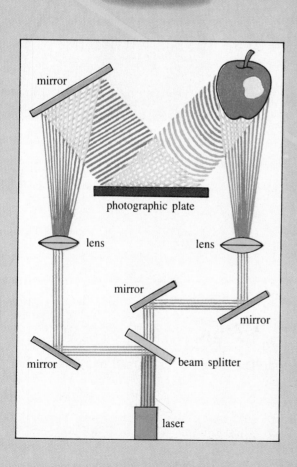

If you have ever seen a *hologram*, you have probably seen the photograph of the future. Holography is now in the same pioneering stage that photography was a century ago.

To make a hologram, laser light of 2 milliwatts or more is split into two beams. The first light beam travels to a photographic plate measuring 102 mm by 127 mm. The second beam bounces off the object being photographed and then collides with the first beam on the photographic plate. After the plate is developed, the first beam is directed through the back of the plate and a three-dimensional image of the photograph becomes visible. The image is so accurate that a hologram of a powerful camera lens 20 cm in diameter can magnify just as well as the lens itself.

Holograms can also be used for storage. A square hologram measuring less than 13 cm on a side is supposed to be able to store all the books in the world!

Units of Length

The forest service plants thousands of trees each year. A young tree is about 1 **meter (m)** tall.

The meter is the basic unit of length in the metric system. Other units of length are related to the meter.

Unit	Symbol	Relation to the meter
kilometer	km	1,000 m
hectometer	hm	100 m
dekameter	dam	10 m
meter	m	1 m
decimeter	dm	0.1 m
centimeter	cm	0.01 m
millimeter	mm	0.001 m

A pine needle is about 10 **centimeters (cm)** long and about 1 **millimeter (mm)** thick.

1 millimeter

0 1 2 3 4 5 6 7 8 9 10
Centimeters

Warm Up

Give the missing units.

1. The length of a hiking trail is 12 ▨.

2. The height of a tall tree is 66 ▨.

3. The diameter of a wild berry is 7 ▨.

4. The thickness of a small tree limb is 2 ▨.

Give the missing numbers.

5. 1 m = ▨ cm

6. 1 cm = ▨ mm

7. 1 hm = ▨ m

8. 0.001 km = ▨ m

Compare the measurements. Write >, <, or = for each ▨.

9. 1 m ▨ 10 cm

10. 100 mm ▨ 1 cm

11. 0.1 km ▨ 100 m

12. 0.1 cm ▨ 1 dm

Practice Write the missing units. Use km, m, cm, or mm.

1. A pine cone is 15 ▥ long.

2. The distance across a lake is 2 ▥.

3. A leaf stem is 2 ▥ thick.

4. An oak tree is 23 ▥ tall.

5. A shallow creek is 30 ▥ deep.

6. A tree stump has a diameter of 1.5 ▥.

Write the missing numbers.

7. 100 cm = ▥ m

8. 1 dm = ▥ cm

9. 10 mm = ▥ cm

10. 1 km = ▥ m

11. 1,000 mm = ▥ m

12. 1 hm = ▥ m

13. 1 m = ▥ mm

14. 1 dm = ▥ m

15. 10 m = ▥ dam

16. 0.1 m = ▥ dm

17. 1 mm = ▥ m

18. 0.01 m = ▥ cm

19. 1 m = ▥ km

20. 1 dm = ▥ mm

21. 1 mm = ▥ cm

22. 1 km = ▥ hm

23. 1 m = ▥ dam

24. 1 dam = ▥ km

Compare the measurements. Write >, <, or = for each ▥.

25. 1 cm ▥ 10 mm

26. 100 m ▥ 1 km

27. 100 cm ▥ 10 m

28. 100 mm ▥ 1 m

29. 10 hm ▥ 10 km

30. 10 dm ▥ 1 m

31. 1,000 km ▥ 1,000 mm

32. 10 mm ▥ 1 cm

33. 1 dam ▥ 1 dm

34. 0.01 m ▥ 1 cm

35. 0.001 km ▥ 10 m

36. 10 mm ▥ 0.01 m

SKILLKEEPER

Solve.

1. $9p = 45$

2. $37x = 148$

3. $\frac{r}{10} = 4$

4. $12n = 48$

5. $\frac{b}{9} = 9$

6. $7y = 560$

7. $12x = 108$

8. $\frac{z}{15} = 1$

9. $\frac{p}{9} = 20$

10. $\frac{a}{7} = 30$

11. $70g = 420$

12. $60h = 120$

13. $\frac{x}{5} = 12$

14. $\frac{n}{5} = 30$

15. $50t = 3,500$

16. $30x = 210$

More Practice, page 442, Set D

Changing Units of Length

Design engineers draw the designs for new devices or structures. The engineers must be able to express measurements in different units.

To change from one metric unit to another, we multiply or divide by a power of ten.

km	hm	dam	m	dm	cm	mm

42.0 mm
 4.2 cm
0.42 dm
0.042 m

We *multiply* to change from a larger unit to a smaller unit.

Meters to centimeters

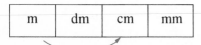

$\times 100$ **5.43 m = 543 cm**

Kilometers to meters

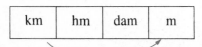

$\times 1,000$ **5.3 km = 5,300 m**

Annex two zeros.

We *divide* to change a smaller unit to a larger unit.

Millimeters to centimeters

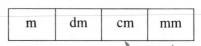

$\div 10$ **5 mm = 0.5 cm**

Meters to kilometers

$\div 1,000$ **6,500 m = 6.5 km**

Warm Up

Give the missing numbers.

1. 5.8 m = ▒ cm

2. 52 cm = ▒ mm

3. 532 mm = ▒ m

4. 80.9 m = ▒ km

5. 17.5 km = ▒ m

6. 2.5 m = ▒ cm

Practice Write the missing numbers.

1.

km	hm	dam	m	dm	cm	mm

5.836 km = ▦ m

2.

km	hm	dam	m	dm	cm	mm

3,653 m = ▦ km

3. 53 cm = ▦ m

4. 4 m = ▦ km

5. 3 m = ▦ cm

6. 284 mm = ▦ m

7. 42 cm = ▦ mm

8. 2.5 km = ▦ m

9. 4.1 cm = ▦ m

10. 250 cm = ▦ m

11. 4,500 m = ▦ km

12. 720 m = ▦ km

13. 4,523 mm = ▦ m

14. 25.4 km = ▦ m

15. 5.2 cm = ▦ dm

16. 0.005 m = ▦ mm

17. 0.07 km = ▦ m

Write the missing units.

18. 2.37 m = 237 ▦

19. 9,250 m = 9.250 ▦

20. 345 mm = 34.5 ▦

21. 847 cm = 8.47 ▦

22. 15 km = 15,000 ▦

23. 5,209 mm = 5.209 ▦

24. 2,894 mm = 2.894 ▦

25. 1.06 m = 1,060 ▦

26. 6.4 m = 640 ▦

Mixed Applications

27. The windows on a model for a passenger train are spaced every 0.6 cm. Write this measurement in millimeters, decimeters, and meters.

28. On a design blueprint, each letter in the word "SCHEMATIC" is 8 mm wide. The space between each letter is 4 mm wide. How many centimeters long is the word?

▌ THINK MATH ▐

Shape Perception

The pencils form six small squares. Remove two pencils to form four squares of the same size. All remaining pencils must be part of a complete square.

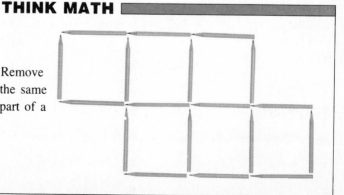

More Practice, page 443, Set A

Capacity

It takes about 1 **liter (L)** of water to refine 100 **milliliters (mL)** of oil. Liters and milliliters are units of liquid measure, or **capacity**.

Unit	Symbol	Relation to the liter
kiloliter	kL	1,000 L
hectoliter	hL	100 L
dekaliter	daL	10 L
liter	L	1 L
deciliter	dL	0.1 L
centiliter	cL	0.01 L
milliliter	mL	0.001 L

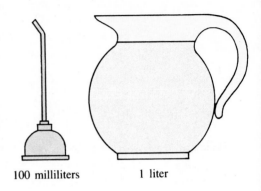

100 milliliters   1 liter

The most commonly used units of capacity are the kiloliter, the liter, and the milliliter.

To change from one unit of capacity to another, we multiply or divide by a power of 10.

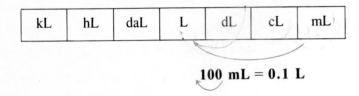

kL	hL	daL	L	dL	cL	mL

100 mL = 0.1 L

Give the missing units.

1. The capacity of a gasoline tank is about 75 ▧.

2. The capacity of a perfume bottle is about 45 ▧.

3. The capacity of a juice glass is about 150 ▧.

4. The capacity of a railroad tank car is about 100 ▧.

Give the missing numbers.

5. 1 mL = ▧ L

6. 1 L = ▧ kL

7. 1 dL = ▧ L

8. 1,000 mL = ▧ L

9. 1 L = ▧ mL

10. 1,000 L = ▧ kL

11. 500 mL = ▧ L

12. 250 L = ▧ hL

13. 4.5 L = ▧ mL

14. 725 L = ▧ kL

15. 3.25 L = ▧ mL

16. 4,600 mL = ▧ L

More Practice, page 443, Set B

PROBLEM SOLVING: Mixed Practice

QUESTION
DATA
PLAN
ANSWER
CHECK

Solve.

1. Sarah drinks 5 glasses of water every day. Each glass holds 375 mL. How many liters of water does Sarah drink each day?

2. It takes 4,500 L of water to manufacture 1 t of cement. How many kiloliters of water is this?

3. Gene uses 3.5 L of water on his house plants each week. How many milliliters of water is this per day?

4. A washing machine uses 170 L of water per load of clothes. How many kiloliters of water are used to wash 3 loads of clothes a week for 1 year (52 weeks)?

5. Powdered eggs are made by removing the water from the eggs. One medium egg contains 33 mL of water. How many liters of water must be removed from 50 eggs to make a box of powdered eggs?

6. Mara uses a garden hose to wash her car. When the water is fully on, it flows at a rate of 27.3 L per minute. At this rate, how much water is used in 15 min?

7. To produce one can of vegetables, 40 L of water are used. The production of 1 t of steel uses 500 times this amount of water. How many kiloliters of water are needed to produce 1 t of steel?

★ **8.** A shower without a flow restrictor used 18.9 L of water per minute. After the flow restrictor was installed, the shower used 11.3 L per minute. How much water will the flow restrictor save in 30 days if 3 people each take one 4-minute shower daily?

9. Each member of a family of 4 uses an average of 130 L of water daily. How many kiloliters of water does the family use during 1 year (365 days)?

10. **Strategy Practice** Two empty tanks are being filled with water. The first tank fills at a rate of 60 L per minute for 2 min before the water to the second tank is turned on. The second tank fills at a rate of 80 L per minute. How many minutes will it be until the second tank has the same amount of water as the first tank? Hint: Make a table.

Units of Weight

A white rhinoceros may weigh about 3,200 **kilograms (kg)**. What is its weight in **grams (g)**?

The kilogram, the gram, and the milligram are the most commonly used units of weight.

To change from a larger unit of weight to a smaller unit of weight, we multiply by a power of 10.

Unit	Symbol	Relation to the gram
metric ton	t	1,000 kg
kilogram	kg	1,000 g
hectogram	hg	100 g
dekagram	dag	10 g
gram	g	1 g
decigram	dg	0.1 g
centigram	cg	0.01 g
milligram	mg	0.001 g

kg	hg	dag	g	dg	cg	mg

3,200 kg = 3,200,000 g

The rhinoceros weighs about 3,200,000 g.

The capacity and the weight of pure water have a simple relation.

1 L of water weighs 1 kg.
1 mL of water weighs 1 g.

Write the missing units. Use mg, g, kg, or t.

1. The weight of a truck is 4.5 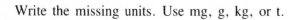.

2. The weight of a snowflake is 2 .

3. The weight of a loaf of bread is 454 .

4. The weight of a bicycle is 14 .

Write the missing numbers.

5. 1 g = ▓ kg

6. 1 kg = ▓ t

7. 1 mg = ▓ g

8. 2,000 g = ▓ kg

9. 4 g = ▓ mg

10. 5,000 kg = ▓ t

11. 500 g = ▓ kg

12. 2,500 kg = ▓ t

13. 4.2 t = ▓ kg

14. 5.2 kg = ▓ g

15. 475.5 g = ▓ kg

16. 3.25 g = ▓ mg

Give the weight of each amount of water.

17. 250 mL

18. 5 L

19. 16 mL

20. 14.8 L

162

More Practice, page 443, Set C

PROBLEM SOLVING: Using Data from a Table

QUESTION
DATA
PLAN
ANSWER
CHECK

A zoo veterinarian records the weights of animals to make sure they are in good health.

Animal Weights

Animal	1984	1985
Cheetah	33.7 kg	35.2 kg
Alligator	67.5 kg	65.9 kg
Elephant	6.37 t	6.39 t
Gorilla	202.5 kg	197.3 kg
Monkey	2.7 kg	2.8 kg
Chimpanzee	68.5 kg	70.3 kg

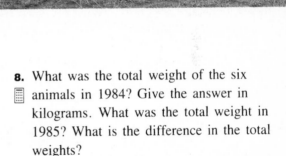

Solve.

1. Did the alligator gain or lose weight during the year? How much?

2. How many kilograms did the chimpanzee gain? How many grams is this?

3. In 1984 which animal weighed about one half as much as the chimpanzee?

4. What is the 1985 weight of the elephant, in kilograms?

5. How much did the elephant gain during the year? Give the answer in kilograms.

6. Which animal lost more weight during the year, the gorilla or the alligator? How much more did it lose?

7. The average weight of a Helena's hummingbird is about 0.002 kg. How many grams is this?

8. What was the total weight of the six animals in 1984? Give the answer in kilograms. What was the total weight in 1985? What is the difference in the total weights?

9. **DATA BANK** If you could whip your weight in wildcats, how many wildcats could you whip? Use your weight and round the answer to the nearest whole number. (See page 430.)

10. **Strategy Practice** The zoo gift shop has four posters on display. There is one poster of rodents, one of amphibians, one of cats, and one of a koala. How many different ways can the posters be arranged in a row if the poster of the rodents is never placed next to the poster of the koala?

163

Temperature

Common temperatures are often given in **degrees Celsius (°C).**

In scientific work, temperatures may be given in **Kelvin (K).**

The two thermometers show how Celsius and Kelvin temperatures are related.

Kelvin temperature begins at **absolute zero,** ⁻273.15°C.

Celsius = Kelvin − 273.15

C = K − 273.15   K = C + 273.15

Silver melts at 1,233.65 K. What is this temperature on the Celsius scale?

C = 1,233.65 − 273.15 = 960.50

The Celsius temperature is 960.5°C.

A moderate oven temperature is 175°C. What is the Kelvin temperature?

K = 175 + 273.15 = 448.15

The Kelvin temperature is 448.15 K.

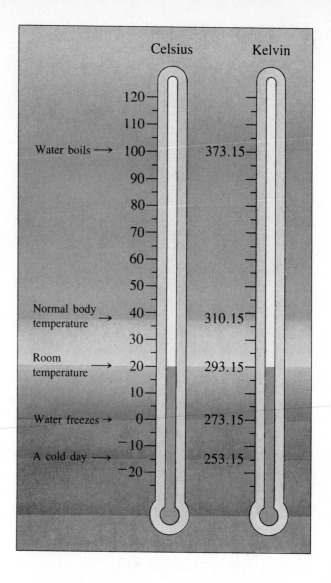

Practice Give each temperature in degrees Celsius.

1. Normal body temperature **2.** Boiling point of water **3.** Freezing point of water

4. Absolute zero **5.** 277.15 K **6.** 298.15 K

7. 357.65 K **8.** 289.45 K **9.** 393.15 K

Give the Kelvin temperature.

10. Freezing point of water **11.** Normal body temperature **12.** Boiling point of water

13. 14°C **14.** ⁻15°C **15.** 33°C

16. 120°C **17.** 2°C **18.** 79°C

164

More Practice, page 443, Set D

Units of Time

One of the longest table tennis rallies ever recorded was in 1936. It lasted 2 h and 12 min. How many minutes is this?

Since we want to change from a large unit to a smaller unit, we multiply.

$$2 \times 60 = 120$$

↑ Hours   ↑ Minutes/hour   ↑ Minutes

Add the extra minutes. **120 + 12 = 132**

The rally lasted 132 min.

Units of Time

1,000 milliseconds (ms)	= **1 second (s)**
60 seconds	= **1 minute (min)**
60 minutes	= **1 hour (h)**
24 hours	= **1 day**
7 days	= **1 week (wk)**
12 months	= **1 year (yr)**
365 days*	= **1 year**
100 years	= **1 century**

*leap year = 366 days

Other Examples

How many weeks are there in 41 days?

41 days = **5** weeks and **6** days

```
      5  ← Weeks
   7)41
     35
   ────
      6  ← Extra days
```

Practice Give the missing numbers.

1. 7 min = ▦ s
2. 5 h = ▦ min
3. 4 s = ▦ ms

4. 120 h = ▦ days
5. 3,000 ms = ▦ s
6. 4 h 15 min = ▦ min

7. 4 wk 3 days = ▦ days
8. 8 min 3.5 s = ▦ s
9. 145 min = ▦ h ▦ min

10. 9 yr = ▦ months
11. 40 s = ▦ min
12. 90 min = ▦ h

13. One of the longest recorded kite flights was 169 h. How many days and hours did it fly?

14. If a person has watched about 17,000 h of television, how many years and days is this?

SKILLKEEPER

Write the missing numbers.

1. 29 cm = ▦ m
2. 3L = ▦ kL
3. 5 mg = ▦ g

4. 0.5 cm = ▦ mm
5. 4,000 mL = ▦ L
6. 3.62 km = ▦ mm

7. 2 kL = ▦ L
8. 8.6 cm = ▦ dm
9. 7,200 kg = ▦ t

More Practice, page 444, Set A

Elapsed Time

Patrice is flying from Los Angeles to Seattle. She will depart at 7:50 a.m. Pacific Standard Time (PST) and will arrive at 10:10 a.m. (PST). How long is the flight from Los Angeles to Seattle?

The difference between the departure time and the arrival time is the **elapsed time.** To find the elapsed time, we subtract.

$$\begin{array}{r} \overset{9}{\cancel{10}} \text{ h } \overset{70}{\cancel{10}} \text{ min} \\ - 7 \text{ h } 50 \text{ min} \\ \hline 2 \text{ h } 20 \text{ min} \end{array}$$

> Regroup 1 h to 60 min.

The flight is 2 h 20 min long.

Other Examples

We can solve time problems mentally.

Depart	9:15 a.m.
Arrive	2:30 p.m.
Elapsed time	?

> Depart at 9:15 a.m.
> 5 h later is 2:15 p.m.
> 15 min later 2:30 p.m.

The elapsed time is 5 h 15 min.

Depart	10:30 p.m.
Arrive	?
Elapsed time	7 h 10 min

> Depart at 10:30 p.m.
> 7 h later is 5:30 a.m.
> 10 min later is 5:40 a.m.

The arrival time is 5:40 a.m.

Practice Copy and complete the table.

	Depart (PST)	Arrive (PST)	Elapsed Time
1.	8:00 a.m.	11:15 a.m.	
2.	8:30 a.m.	3:30 p.m.	
3.	1:20 p.m.	4:05 p.m.	
4.	10:15 a.m.	3:10 p.m.	
5.	9:30 a.m.		2 h 15 min
6.	11:25 a.m.		4 h 20 min
7.		5:45 p.m.	6 h 10 min
8.		3:00 a.m.	5 h 25 min

PROBLEM SOLVING: Mixed Practice

QUESTION
DATA
PLAN
ANSWER
CHECK

Solve.

1. A bicycle trip began at 3:45 p.m. and ended at 5:15 p.m. How long did it last?

2. Nora does yard work for $4.50 per hour. She worked from 9:30 a.m. to 1:30 p.m. How much did she earn?

3. Jade worked on a school report from 4:45 p.m. until 6:00 p.m. on Monday, from 7:20 p.m. until 8:50 p.m. on Tuesday, and from 7:05 p.m. until 9:45 p.m. on Wednesday. How many hours were spent on the report?

4. Ray and Perry are planning a hiking trip that will take about 6 h and 30 min. They want to finish the hike by sunset, which is at 6:45 p.m. What is the latest time they should begin their hike?

5. Jake slept 10 h and 30 min last night. He awoke at 7:20 a.m. What time did he go to sleep?

6. Jan is a computer technologist. She charges $28 per hour from 9:00 a.m. until 5:00 p.m. and $35 per hour at any other time. She worked from 10:00 a.m. until 6:00 p.m. What did she charge for this job?

7. A package was mailed by special express at 4:20 p.m. It arrived at its destination at 10:40 a.m. the next day. If both times were in the same zone, how long was the package en route?

★ 8. Phon worked from 9:00 a.m. until 5:00 p.m. with a lunch break from 11:45 to 12:30, and two 20-minute rest breaks. How many hours did Phon work?

9. **Strategy Practice** Estelle works on the West Coast and wants to call her business partner, Martha, on the East Coast. Martha goes to lunch every day at 11:20 a.m. The business call will take at least 30 min. It is 3 h later on the East Coast than on the West Coast. What is the latest time Estelle can make the call to talk to Martha before her lunch time?

Precision in Measurement

Measurements are never exact. The two bolts both measure 4 cm when measured *to the nearest centimeter*. The actual length of the bolts is between 3.5 cm and 4.5 cm. The **greatest possible error (GPE)** is 0.5 cm.

When measured *to the nearest millimeter*, the top bolt is 43 mm and the bottom bolt is 39 mm. The GPE for these measurements is 0.5 mm.

Measuring to the nearest millimeter is more **precise** than measuring to the nearest centimeter.

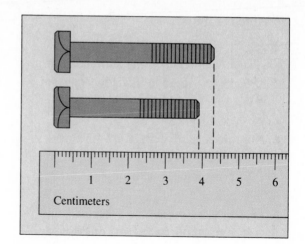

The smaller the unit of measure, the more precise the measurement.

The GPE in a measurement is $\frac{1}{2}$ or 0.5 of the smallest unit used in the measurement.

43 mm is more precise than 4 cm. 43 mm and 4.3 cm have the same precision because the smallest unit in each measurement is 0.1 of a centimeter, or 1 mm.

Measurements are sometimes reported as ± the GPE.

Reported measure		GPE	Actual length is between
25 cm	±	0.5 cm	24.5 cm and 25.5 cm
8.3 km	±	0.05 km	8.25 km and 8.35 km
3.04 m	±	0.005 m	3.035 m and 3.045 m

Warm Up

State which measurement is more precise. Give the GPE of each measurement.

1. 9 m, 9.2 m

2. 18.2 km, 12.34 km

3. 6.26 m, 626 cm

4. 5 cm, 3.726 m

5. 23 cm, 23 dm

6. 1 mm, 0.1 mm

Practice State which measurement is more precise.

1. 4 cm, 4 m   **2.** 5.2 km, 52 km   **3.** 6.3 mm, 6.32 mm   **4.** 33.5 km, 34 km

Give the GPE of each measurement.

5. 38 cm   **6.** 12 mm   **7.** 8.2 m   **8.** 31.3 km

Copy and complete the table.

	Measurement	Precision	GPE	Actual Length Is Between
	47 cm	To the nearest centimeter	0.5 cm	46.5 cm, 47.5 cm
9.	4.8 m	To the nearest ▓▓▓	?	?
10.	17.03 km	To the nearest ▓▓▓	?	?
11.	486 mm	To the nearest ▓▓▓	?	?
12.	3.9 cm	To the nearest ▓▓▓	?	?
13.	49 m	To the nearest ▓▓▓	?	?
14.	16.04 m	To the nearest ▓▓▓	?	?
15.	3.5 km	To the nearest ▓▓▓	?	?

Mixed Applications

16. The length of a bolt is 62.4 mm. What is the range of the actual length of this measurement?

17. An inspector checks the depth of tread on new tires. The tread is supposed to measure 0.6 cm ± 0.05 cm. Will tread that measures 0.58 cm pass an inspection?

THINK MATH

How well can you estimate lengths?

First estimate, then find the actual length.

Find the difference between your estimate and the actual measure.

	Estimate	Measure	Difference
Width of a desk (cm)			
Your height (cm)			
Room length (m)			
Room width (m)			
Chalkboard length (m)			

Mixed Skills Practice

Computation
Find the answers.

1. $\frac{2}{3} \times \frac{3}{8}$

2. $8 \div 1\frac{1}{2}$

3. $4.3\overline{)115.24}$

4. $87\overline{)7,569}$

5. $12\frac{1}{2}$
$-7\frac{3}{4}$

6. 260
$\times 0.8$

7. $\$200.00$
-167.75

8. 7.09
$\times 0.3$

9. $6\frac{3}{8}$
$+5\frac{7}{8}$

10. $63,000$
$-37,584$

11. $\$93.75$
44.87
$+63.99$

12. 0.49
0.772
$+0.834$

13. Solve.
$x - 15 = 6$

14. Solve.
$7x = 98$

15. Solve.
$3x - 1 = 23$

16. Solve.
$\frac{x}{3} = 8$

Mental Math
Write only the answers.

17. $82 \div 10$

18. $\frac{1}{3} \times 15$

19. 26×100

20. 0.1×200

21. $3,200 \div 40$

22. $\frac{1}{2} + 3 + \frac{1}{2}$

23. $300 - 199$

24. $60 + 70 + 40$

25. $\frac{1}{6} \times 42$

26. $4 \times 5\frac{1}{2}$

27. 750×0.01

28. $82.7 \div 10$

29. 40×40

30. $7\frac{3}{4} - 6$

31. $2 \times 5 \times 5 \times 8$

32. $4\frac{1}{4} + 2\frac{3}{4}$

Estimation
Estimate.

33. 9.2×3.8

34. $6.2\overline{)372.41}$

35. $\frac{1}{4} \times \$23.95$

36. $0.43\overline{)26.17}$

37. $8,602$
$-1,518$

38. 6.19
8.33
$+4.59$

39. 842
327
$+544$

40. $12\frac{19}{40}$
$-7\frac{7}{15}$

41. 6×0.1993

42. $\frac{2}{5} \times \$49.95$

43. 69×4.09

44. $43 + 39 + 38 + 41$

45. $\frac{1}{6} \times \$31.15$

46. 0.211×0.297

47. 11×58.5

48. $\$609.44$
-197.66

170

APPLIED PROBLEM SOLVING

QUESTION
DATA
PLAN
ANSWER
CHECK

You are in charge of scheduling an intramural basketball tournament for your school. You need to decide when teams will play their tournament games.

Some Things to Consider

- There are 8 teams in the tournament.

- There are 3 basketball courts that can be used for the game.

- The tournament is a single elimination tournament. A team which loses a game is out of the tournament.

- You want to allow 1 hour for lunch when no teams play.

- The tournament is to be held and completed on one Saturday.

- A winning team must have at least 1 hour of rest before playing again.

- It takes a maximum of 75 minutes (1 hour 15 minutes) to play a game.

- The games cannot begin before 8:30 a.m.

- The final game of the tournament should be completed by 5:45 p.m.

Some Questions to Answer

Use the Tournament Schedule at the right to help you make your decisions.

1. How many games must be played in the tournament?

2. How many games could be played at the same time for the opening round of the tournament?

3. What is the latest time the last game could start to end the tournament on time?

4. What time would you plan for the lunch hour?

Tournament Schedule

What Is Your Decision?

What are the times you would assign for each of the games of the tournament?

171

PROBLEM-SOLVING STRATEGY: Solve a Simpler Problem

QUESTION
DATA
PLAN
ANSWER
CHECK

Try This

The average yearly rainfall in the Mississippi Delta, based on the last 30 yr, is 141.9 cm per year. This year the rainfall totaled 154.3 cm. What is the average annual rainfall for the last 31-year period?

When you are not sure what you need to do to solve a problem, it may help to use the strategy called **Solve a Simpler Problem.** Set up and solve a simpler problem, then use the same steps you used for the simpler problem to solve the harder problem.

A Simpler Problem

The average annual rainfall for the past 2 yr was 25 cm per year. This year the rainfall was 10 cm. What is the average rainfall for the last 3 yr?

Now use the same steps to solve the harder problem.

The average rainfall is 142.3 cm.

Solving the Simpler Problem

$2 \times 25 = 50$ Rainfall for 2 yr
$50 + 10 = 60$ Rainfall for 3 yr
$60 \div 3 = 20$ Average rainfall for 3 yr

$30 \times 141.9 = 4,257.0$ Total for 30 yr
$4,257.0 + 154.3 = 4,411.3$ Total for 31 yr
$4,411.3 \div 31 = 142.3$ Average for 31 yr

Solve.

1. Lynn bowled 9 games and made an average score of 143 pins per game. She bowled one more game and made a score of 173. What is her average score for the 10 games?

2. Gary keeps a record of his test scores. On 11 tests he had an average score of 83.2. On the 12th test he had a score of 94. What is his new average for the 12 tests? How much did he increase his test average with the 12th test?

172

Write the missing numbers.

1. 1 m = ▦ cm

2. 1 cm = ▦ mm

3. 1 km = ▦ m

Compare the measurements. Write >, <, or = for each ▦

4. 60 mm ▦ 2 cm

5. 2 dam ▦ 0.5 km

6. 0.02 cm ▦ 0.2 mm

Write the missing numbers.

7. 1,000 mm = ▦ m

8. 0.01 m = ▦ cm

9. 250 m = ▦ km

10. 5.2 cm = ▦ mm

11. 3 km = ▦ m

12. 34 mm = ▦ cm

13. 6 L = ▦ mL

14. 500 mL = ▦ L

15. 3,000 L = ▦ kL

16. 4 g = ▦ mg

17. 5.3 kg = ▦ g

18. 430 g = ▦ kg

19. 1 kg = ▦ g

20. 10 dg = ▦ g

21. 2,000 g = ▦ kg

22. 37°C = ▦ K

23. 297.15 K = ▦ C

24. ⁻52°C = ▦ K

25. 2,400s = ▦ min

26. 19 d = ▦ wk ▦ days

27. 84 min = ▦ h ▦ min

Write the missing times.

28. Depart   10:20 a.m.
Arrive   1:15 p.m.
Elapsed
time   ▦ h ▦ min

29. Depart   ▦ a.m.
Arrive   4:30 p.m.
Elapsed
time   7 h 30 min

30. Depart   9:00 p.m.
Arrive   ▦ a.m.
Elapsed
time   5 h 45 min

Give the GPE of each measurement.

31. 37.2 mm

32. 16 km

33. 9.56 cm

Solve.

34. A melon has a weight of 0.72 kg. How many grams is this?

35. A photograph is 7.5 cm wide. How many millimeters is this?

36. Pam bought 6 cans of tomato juice, each with 350 mL of juice. How many liters of juice are in the 6 cans?

37. Javier left home at 11:45 a.m. and arrived at a friend's house at 3:15 p.m. How long did the trip take?

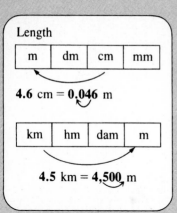

Length

m	dm	cm	mm

4.6 cm = 0.046 m

km	hm	dam	m

4.5 km = 4,500 m

Write the missing numbers.

1. 267 mm = ▦ cm

2. 0.6 m = ▦ cm

3. 527 km = ▦ m

4. 67 cm = ▦ m

5. 45 mm = ▦ cm

6. 0.28 m = ▦ mm

Capacity

1 L = 1,000 mL
1 mL = 0.001 L
236 mL = 0.236 L

7. 380 mL = ▦ L

8. 0.3 L = ▦ mL

9. 5 L = ▦ mL

10. 4.3 L = ▦ mL

11. 9 mL = ▦ L

12. 5,640 mL = ▦ L

Weight

1 kg = 1,000 g
1 g = 0.001 kg
35 g = 0.035 kg

13. 7 kg = ▦ g

14. 0.68 kg = ▦ g

15. 7,280 g = ▦ kg

16. 75 g = ▦ kg

17. 3.6 kg = ▦ g

18. 2.05 kg = ▦ g

Depart   10:30 a.m.
Arrive   2:00 p.m.

10:30 a.m. to **1:30 p.m.**
↓
3 h

1:30 p.m. to **2:00 p.m.**
↓
30 min

Elapsed time   **3 h 30 min**

Write the missing times.

19. 30 min = ▦ s

20. 120 min = ▦ h

21. 35 days = ▦ w

22. 27 w = ▦ days

23. Depart   ▦
Arrive   2:00 p.m.
Elapsed time   5 h 20 min

24. Depart   9:00 a.m.
Arrive   ▦
Elapsed time   8 h 10 min

25. Depart   8:40 a.m.
Arrive   2:00 p.m.
Elapsed time   ▦

26. Depart   9:00 a.m.
Arrive   5:10 p.m.
Elapsed time   ▦

Reading an Airline Flight Schedule

The airline flight schedule at the right shows information about all flights from Houston, Texas to Los Angeles, California.

The first line of the table contains this information:

7:00 a I   Leave 7:00 a.m. (CST) from Houston Intercontinental

10:11 a L   Arrive 10:11 a.m. (PST) at Los Angeles International

CO 903   Airline, flight number 903

FYBQM   Classes of service available: F = first class, Y = tourist, etc.

D9S   Type of airplane (DC-9)

ML   Kind of meal: S = snack

S   Stops en route; 0 means nonstop.

Freq. Leave Arrive Flight Class Eq ML S

To **LOS ANGELES, CALIF.** PST from **HOUSTON, TEXAS** CST

  B-BUR (Burbank)   H-HOU (Houston)
  G-LGB (Long Beach)   I-IAH (Houston
  L-LAX (International)   Intercontinental)
  O-ONT (Ontario)
  Also see Long Beach, Calif.

Freq.	LEAVE		ARRIVE		FLIGHT	CLASS	EQ	ML	S
	7:00a	I	10:11a	L	CO 903	FYBQM	D9S	S	2
	3:15a	H	10:40a	B RC	31	CYB	D9S	B	1
X7	8:45a	H	10:00a	L MC	860	C	D98	S	0
	10:05a	I	12:21p	L CO	791	FYBQM	D9S	L	1
	10:15a	I	11:39a	L CO	59	FYBQM	D10	B	0
	10:15a	I	11:51a	L PA	705	FYBM	72S	L	0
	11:45a	I	1:00p	L EA	45	FYBML	727	L	0
	12:30p	I	1:54p	L CO	53	FYBQM	D10	L	0
	12:30p	I	2:00p	L PA	709	FYBM	72S	L	0
	12:45p	H	2:00p	L MC	862	C	D98	S	0
X67	1:00p	H	3:00p	L WN	852	S	737		1
67	1:00p	H	3:00p	L WN	52	K	737		1
	1:45p	H	4:17p	B RC	707	CYB	D9S	S	1
	3:30p	I	4:55p	L CO	499	FYBQM	72S	S	0
	3:40p	I	5:10p	L PA	410	FYBM	72S	D	0
X6	4:15p	I	5:40p	L EA	43	FYBML	727	D	0
	4:45p	H	6:00p	L MC	864	C	D98	S	0
X6	4:45p	H	6:59p	L RC	824	CYB	D9S	D	1
	5:45p	I	6:59p	L CO	351	FYBQM	72S	D	0
	7:10p	H	9:25p	B RC	828	CYB	D9S	D	1
	7:40p	I	10:00p	O CO	145	FYBQM	72S	S	1
	7:55p	I	9:19p	L CO	55	FYBQM	D10	D	0
	7:55p	I	9:25p	L PA	719	FnYnBM	72S	D	0

Use the table above to answer the questions.

1. You have a 10:15 flight leaving Houston for Los Angeles. You are flying PA. What is your flight number? What time (PST) will you arrive in Los Angeles?

2. Mr. Rosen wants to get the earliest nonstop flight from Houston to Los Angeles. Which flight number is this? How many hours does this flight take?

3. Mrs. Hawkins is scheduled to fly on Flight 791. What time does her flight leave? Will she be served breakfast (B), lunch (L), or dinner (D) on the way?

4. The symbol X6 means "except Saturday" and X7 means "except Sunday." Which flight flies every day except Saturday and Sunday?

5. Suppose you fly EA Flight 45 to Los Angeles. While en route you notice that the time on your watch (CST) is 1:15 p.m. How much more flying time is left until you will arrive in Los Angeles?

6. What is the latest time you can leave Houston and arrive in Los Angeles no later than 7:00 p.m. PST? Which flight is it and how long is the flying time?

1. What is $\frac{75}{120}$ in lowest terms?

   A $\frac{3}{25}$ **B** $\frac{15}{25}$

   C $\frac{5}{8}$ **D** not given

2. What is the mixed number for $\frac{65}{12}$?

   A $4\frac{12}{17}$ **B** $5\frac{5}{12}$

   C $5\frac{4}{12}$ **D** not given

3. What is the LCM of 12, 28, and 42?

   A 252   **B** 84

   C 42   **D** not given

Find the sums.

4. $\frac{7}{8} + \frac{3}{4} + \frac{5}{16}$

   A $\frac{15}{16}$ **B** $1\frac{3}{4}$

   C $1\frac{15}{16}$ **D** not given

5. $19\frac{1}{2} + 15\frac{5}{6} + 67\frac{2}{3}$

   A $103\frac{5}{6}$ **B** $102\frac{5}{6}$

   C 102   **D** not given

6. Subtract.

   $\frac{7}{8} - \frac{3}{16}$

   A $\frac{11}{16}$ **B** $\frac{6}{16}$

   C $\frac{1}{2}$ **D** not given

7. If $a = 8$ and $b = 10$, what is $6a - 3b$?

   A 18   **B** 6

   C 78   **D** not given

8. Give the expression for 20 more than a number n.

   A $n - 20$ **B** $20 - n$

   C $20\,n$ **D** not given

9. Give the expression for 10 times a number t.

   A $t + 10$ **B** $10 - t$

   C $10\,t$ **D** not given

Solve.

10. $y + 92 = 573$

    A $y = 665$ **B** $y = 481$

    C $y = 491$ **D** not given

11. $x - 29 = 106$

    A $x = 135$ **B** $x = 125$

    C $x = 77$ **D** not given

12. $15x = 375$

    A $x = 5{,}675$ **B** $x = 25$

    C $x = 360$ **D** not given

13. A recipe requires $4\frac{3}{4}$ c of flour. There is $2\frac{1}{2}$ c of flour. How much more flour is needed?

    A $2\frac{1}{4}$ c   **B** $3\frac{1}{4}$ c

    C $2\frac{1}{2}$ c   **D** not given

14. Will bought 3 gal of milk for $3.90. What was the cost per gallon? Which equation shows this problem?

    A $3m = \$3.90$ **B** $\$3.90 - m = 3$

    C $m \div 3 = \$3.90$ **D** not given

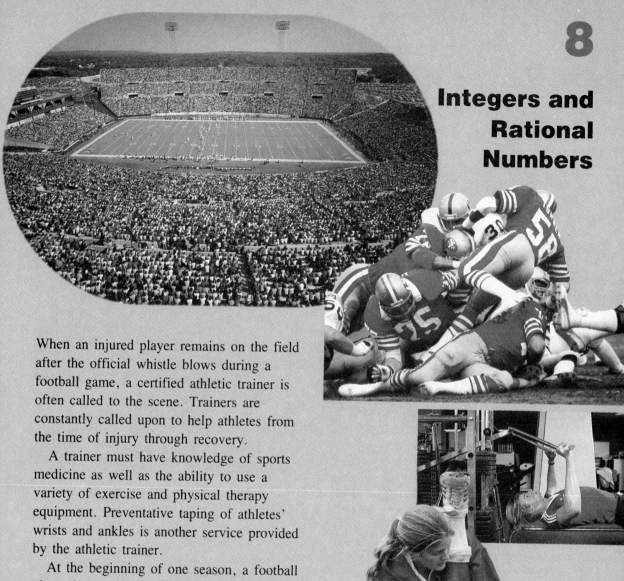

8

Integers and Rational Numbers

When an injured player remains on the field after the official whistle blows during a football game, a certified athletic trainer is often called to the scene. Trainers are constantly called upon to help athletes from the time of injury through recovery.

A trainer must have knowledge of sports medicine as well as the ability to use a variety of exercise and physical therapy equipment. Preventative taping of athletes' wrists and ankles is another service provided by the athletic trainer.

At the beginning of one season, a football player had a right quadriceps strength that registered 98% on a machine readout. After an injury during a game, the reading was down 29 percentage points. The strength of the player's muscle will have to rise 21 points before the trainer allows the player to return to the game. While the player recovers, the trainer will prescibe a program of whirlpool baths, exercise on a stationary bicycle, and ice packs. The player could miss as much as 2 weeks out of the 14-week playing season.

Positive and Negative Numbers

A surveyor measured the distance above and below the foundation level, or **grade level**, of a building site. The surveyor used **positive** and **negative** numbers to record the measurements.

$^+$**4** (**positive** four) means **4** ft **above** grade level.

$^-$**4** (**negative** four) means **4** ft **below** grade level.

0 means exactly at grade level.

Positive and negative whole numbers are called **integers**. The integer 0 is neither positive nor negative.

Positive and negative fractions are called **rational numbers**.

Integers and rational numbers can be shown by points on the number line.

Negative   Positive

$$^-2 \quad ^-1\tfrac{3}{4} \quad ^-1\tfrac{1}{2} \quad ^-1\tfrac{1}{4} \quad ^-1 \quad ^-\tfrac{3}{4} \quad ^-\tfrac{1}{2} \quad ^-\tfrac{1}{4} \quad 0 \quad \tfrac{1}{4} \quad \tfrac{1}{2} \quad \tfrac{3}{4} \quad 1 \quad 1\tfrac{1}{4} \quad 1\tfrac{1}{2} \quad 1\tfrac{3}{4} \quad 2$$

Each integer and each rational number has an **opposite**, or **additive inverse**. The **Opposites Property** gives an important relation between pairs of opposites.

2 is the opposite of $^-2$.	$2 + {}^-2 = 0$
$^-\tfrac{1}{4}$ is the opposite of $\tfrac{1}{4}$.	$^-\tfrac{1}{4} + \tfrac{1}{4} = 0$
0 is the opposite of 0.	$0 + 0 = 0$
$^-0.3$ is the opposite of 0.3.	$^-0.3 + 0.3 = 0$

> **The Opposites Property**
>
> The sum of any number and its opposite is zero.

The usual basic properties for addition and multiplication also apply to integers and rational numbers.

<table>
<tr><td colspan="2">Zero and One Properties</td><td colspan="2">Commutative Properties</td></tr>
</table>

Zero and One Properties

$$a + 0 = a$$
$$a \cdot 1 = a$$

Commutative Properties

$$a + b = b + a$$
$$a \cdot b = b \cdot a$$

Associative Properties

$$a + (b + c) = (a + b) + c$$
$$a \cdot (b \cdot c) = (a \cdot b) \cdot c$$

Distributive Property

$$a \cdot (b + c) = a \cdot b + a \cdot c$$

Practice Write the opposite of each number.

1. 9
2. $^-3$
3. $^-8$
4. $^-10$
5. 20

6. $^-1$
7. $^-25$
8. 14
9. 0
10. $^-11$

11. 40
12. $^-15$
13. $^-100$
14. 300
15. 2

16. $\frac{1}{2}$
17. $^-2.5$
18. $\frac{^-1}{10}$
19. 5.4
20. $\frac{^-7}{8}$

Write the missing numbers. Use the opposites property.

Example: $7 + \text{▥} = 0$

$$7 + {}^-7 = 0$$

21. $6 + {}^-6 = \text{▥}$
22. $1 + \text{▥} = 0$
23. $\text{▥} + {}^-7 = 0$

24. $^-11 + \text{▥} = 0$
25. $\text{▥} + 8 = 0$
26. $\text{▥} + {}^-9 = 0$

27. $^-15 + 15 = \text{▥}$
28. $67 + \text{▥} = 0$
29. $\text{▥} + 14 = 0$

30. $\frac{^-3}{4} + \frac{3}{4} = \text{▥}$
31. $^-5.1 + \text{▥} = 0$
32. $\frac{^-8}{3} + \text{▥} = 0$

33. $6.15 + \text{▥} = 0$
34. $0 + \text{▥} = 0$
35. $^-1,000 + \text{▥} = 0$

Tell which basic property each statement shows.

36. $^-8 + 0 = {}^-8$
37. $\frac{^-1}{2} + \frac{1}{4} = \frac{1}{4} + \frac{^-1}{2}$
38. $2({}^-3 + 4) = 2 \cdot {}^-3 + 2 \cdot 4$

39. $\frac{^-5}{8} \cdot 1 = \frac{^-5}{8}$
40. $^-6 + ({}^-4 + 10) = ({}^-6 + {}^-4) + 10$
41. $^-3 \cdot 7 = 7 \cdot {}^-3$

More Practice, page 444, Set C

Adding Integers

Jay owed Ruth $2. Jay earned $5 and paid Ruth. How much money does Jay have?

We can use a number line to add the integers and find how much money Jay has. We use ⁻2 for owing $2 and 5 for earning $5.

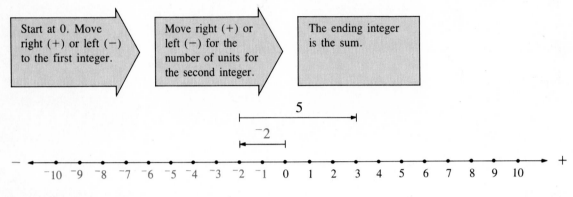

$$^-2 + 5 = 3$$

Jay has $3 after paying Ruth.

Other Examples

$$3 + {}^-6 = {}^-3 \qquad {}^-2 + {}^-3 = {}^-5 \qquad 4 + 1 = 5$$

Warm Up

Give the addition fact shown.

1.

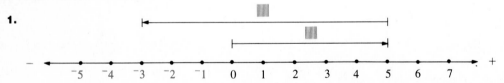

2.

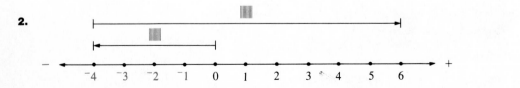

Give the sums. Use a number line.

3. ⁻5 + 4

4. ⁻4 + ⁻3

5. ⁻1 + 8

6. ⁻9 + 10

7. ⁻3 + ⁻7

8. 7 + ⁻6

9. ⁻6 + ⁻5

10. 8 + ⁻10

Practice Find the sums. Use a number line if necessary.

1. $5 + {}^-1$ **2.** $4 + {}^-3$ **3.** ${}^-2 + 6$ **4.** $2 + {}^-5$

5. $1 + {}^-4$ **6.** $9 + {}^-5$ **7.** ${}^-4 + {}^-3$ **8.** ${}^-1 + {}^-5$

9. $3 + 7$ **10.** $8 + {}^-8$ **11.** $7 + {}^-10$ **12.** ${}^-9 + 6$

13. ${}^-3 + {}^-4$ **14.** $10 + {}^-1$ **15.** $6 + {}^-9$ **16.** $4 + {}^-8$

Find the sums.

Example: ${}^-2 + 4 + {}^-3 = {}^-1$

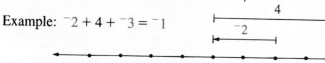
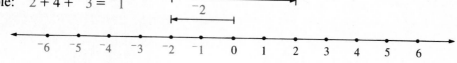

17. $2 + {}^-7 + {}^-1$ **18.** ${}^-3 + {}^-5 + 6$ **19.** $6 + {}^-5 + {}^-1$ **20.** $7 + {}^-7 + 5$

21. ${}^-1 + {}^-3 + {}^-2$ **22.** $4 + {}^-8 + {}^-2$ **23.** ${}^-6 + {}^-3 + 10$ **24.** $7 + {}^-11 + {}^-4$

25. ${}^-8 + 12 + {}^-12$ **26.** ${}^-3 + {}^-1 + 0$ **27.** $8 + {}^-6 + 4$ **28.** ${}^-10 + 8 + {}^-3$

29. ${}^-2 + {}^-2 + 4$ **30.** $9 + {}^-13 + {}^-7$ **31.** ${}^-10 + 1 + {}^-5$ **32.** ${}^-4 + {}^-5 + {}^-6$

Mixed Applications

33. Terry owed Len $5. Then she borrowed $3 more from Len. How much does Terry owe Len? Write an addition fact for the problem using negative integers for "owing" and "borrowing."

34. Ted owed Judy $10. He paid Judy $6. Now how much does Ted owe Judy? Write an addition fact for the problem using negative integers for "owing."

━━━ **THINK MATH** ━━━

Adding Integers on a Calculator

Calculators with a $\boxed{+/-}$ (change sign) key can be used to add integers.

Example: Find ${}^-63 + 47$.

Enter	Press	Display
63	$\boxed{+/-}$ $\boxed{+}$	${}^-63$
47	$\boxed{=}$	${}^-16$

Find the sums.

1. ${}^-58 + {}^-29$ **2.** $96 + {}^-337$

3. $106 + {}^-79$ **4.** ${}^-266 + {}^-877$

5. ${}^-121 + 508$ **6.** ${}^-404 + {}^-955$

7. ${}^-500 + 748$ **8.** $381 + {}^-295$

9. $823 + {}^-672$ **10.** ${}^-770 + {}^-459$

More Practice, page 445, Set A

181

Subtracting Integers

The top of a tree is 12 m above ground
level. The main root of the tree goes to a
depth of 5 m below ground level ($^-5$).
What is the difference between the height of
the tree and the depth of the main root?

To find the difference, we subtract.

$12 - {}^-5 = ?$ (What number added
to $^-5$ equals 12?)

Since $17 + {}^-5 = 12$, then $12 - {}^-5 = 17$.

There is a difference of 17 m between the
top of the tree and the bottom of the main
root.

To *subtract* any integer, we can *add* its
opposite.

$9 - 3 = 9 + {}^-3 = 6$

opposites

$5 - 7 = 5 + {}^-7 = {}^-2$

opposites

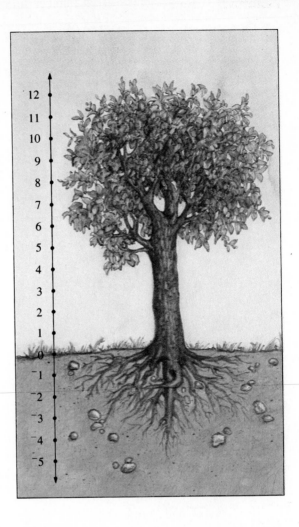

Other Examples

$0 - 6 = 0 + {}^-6 = {}^-6$ $^-2 - {}^-3 = {}^-2 + 3 = 1$

$^-5 - 4 = {}^-5 + {}^-4 = {}^-9$ $7 - {}^-3 = 7 + 3 = 10$

Warm Up

Subtract.

1. $2 - 4$ **2.** $^-3 - 2$ **3.** $6 - {}^-3$ **4.** $^-8 - 5$

5. $7 - 10$ **6.** $^-8 - 4$ **7.** $0 - {}^-2$ **8.** $^-1 - 5$

9. $^-1 - 6$ **10.** $^-6 - {}^-6$ **11.** $8 - 3$ **12.** $^-8 - 0$

Practice Subtract.

1. $4 - {}^-3$
2. $10 - {}^-8$
3. $1 - 5$
4. ${}^-6 - {}^-5$

5. ${}^-7 - 4$
6. ${}^-11 - {}^+12$
7. ${}^-9 - {}^+7$
8. $3 - 11$

9. ${}^-1 - {}^+2$
10. $0 - {}^-6$
11. $25 - {}^-10$
12. $14 - 6$

13. ${}^-13 - {}^+14$
14. $7 - {}^-5$
15. ${}^-9 - 1$
16. $8 - {}^-7$

17. ${}^-4 + 4$
18. ${}^-15 - {}^+6$
19. $3 - 12$
20. $11 - {}^-9$

21. ${}^-9 - {}^+7$
22. ${}^-6 - 9$
23. ${}^-19 - 0$
24. ${}^-99 - 1$

25. ${}^-14 - 2$
26. ${}^-7 - {}^+5$
27. $0 - {}^-3$
28. $1 - 13$

29. $18 - {}^-9$
30. ${}^-6 - 6$
31. ${}^-16 - {}^-9$
32. ${}^-8 - {}^+14$

33. $23 - 33$
34. $1 - {}^-1$
35. ${}^-5 + {}^-12$
36. $16 - {}^+8$

37. ${}^-3 - 0$
38. ${}^-11 - 7$
39. $5 - {}^-6$
40. $12 - 18$

41. ${}^-4 - 9$
42. $15 - {}^-5$
43. $6 + 13$
44. ${}^-17 - {}^+10$

Perform the operations inside the parentheses first.

45. $(3 - 8) + {}^-4$
46. ${}^-4 + (6 - 9)$
47. $(1 - 2) - 3$
48. $(9 + 15) + {}^-4$

49. $({}^-1 - {}^-2) - {}^-3$
50. $(11 + {}^+4) - 15$
51. $({}^-2 - {}^-3) - {}^-4$
52. $(9 - 8) - 7$

53. $10 + ({}^-2 - {}^-7)$
54. $(7 + {}^-9) - {}^-6$
55. $({}^-12 + {}^-6) - {}^+8$
56. $(5 - 6) - 7$

Mixed Applications

57. The top of a tree is 15 m above ground level. The roots reach 9 m below ground level (${}^-9$). What is the difference between the height of the tree and the depth of the roots?

58. Write a word problem that could be solved by finding this difference: $10 - {}^-4$.

Solve your problem.

183

Practice: Adding and Subtracting Integers

Add.

1. $7 + {}^-9$
2. ${}^-5 + {}^-5$
3. $9 + {}^-11$
4. $2 + {}^-12$

5. ${}^-4 + 4$
6. ${}^-1 + {}^-9$
7. ${}^-5 + 10$
8. ${}^-4 + {}^-6$

9. ${}^-2 + 7$
10. ${}^-3 + {}^-5$
11. $6 + {}^-5$
12. ${}^-7 + 0$

13. ${}^-8 + 12$
14. $9 + {}^-13$
15. ${}^-10 + 1$
16. ${}^-6 + 13$

Subtract.

17. $2 - 8$
18. $9 - {}^+5$
19. ${}^-6 - 7$
20. $15 - {}^-20$

21. $12 - {}^-3$
22. ${}^-4 - {}^-6$
23. ${}^-4 - {}^+9$
24. $9 - {}^-9$

25. $0 - {}^+5$
26. ${}^-3 - {}^+3$
27. $2 - {}^+8$
28. ${}^-7 - 9$

29. ${}^-4 - 0$
30. ${}^-20 - {}^+10$
31. $10 - 16$
32. ${}^-6 - {}^-5$

Add or subtract.

33. $16 - 9$
34. $3 + {}^-10$
35. ${}^-9 + 8$
36. ${}^-4 + 1$

37. ${}^-5 + {}^-8$
38. $11 - {}^-4$
39. ${}^-14 + 7$
40. $50 - 60$

41. ${}^-1 + {}^-8$
42. ${}^-10 + {}^+20$
43. ${}^-9 - 0$
44. $0 - {}^+11$

45. ${}^-3 + 11$
46. $2 + {}^-16$
47. ${}^-1 - 5$
48. ${}^-9 + {}^-8$

Perform the operations inside parentheses first.

49. $8 + (6 - 7)$
50. ${}^-2 + (3 + 4)$
51. $({}^-1 + 5) - 6$
52. $10 + ({}^-2 + {}^-8)$

53. ${}^-5 - (8 + {}^-4)$
54. $12 + ({}^-6 + {}^-2)$
55. $({}^-2 - {}^-2) - {}^-2$
56. $6 - (7 + 8)$

57. $({}^-9 + 4) + 5$
58. $100 - (80 + {}^-50)$
59. $(14 + {}^-1) + {}^-9$
60. ${}^-8 - ({}^-8 + 7)$

61. $({}^-2 - {}^-5) - 9$
62. $1 - (2 + 3)$
63. $7 - (6 - 5)$
64. $(9 - 15) + {}^-4$

PROBLEM SOLVING: Choosing a Calculation Method

| QUESTION |
| DATA |
| PLAN |
| ANSWER |
| CHECK |

Your choice!
- **Pencil-Paper**
- **Mental Math**
- **Estimation**
- **Calculator**

You may use any of these methods to solve the problems, but use each method at least once.

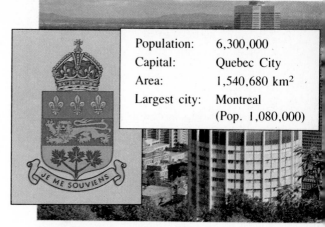

Population:	6,300,000
Capital:	Quebec City
Area:	1,540,680 km²
Largest city:	Montreal (Pop. 1,080,000)

City of Montreal, Canada

Solve.

1. In Quebec City the lowest morning temperature was ⁻14°C. By 1 p.m. the temperature has risen 9°C. What was the temperature at 1 p.m.?

2. The high temperature for a December day in Montreal was 5°C. At night the temperature dropped 11° from the high temperature. What was the temperature at night?

3. The highest March temperature in Montreal was 2°C. The lowest temperature was ⁻6°C. Find the difference between the temperatures.

4. The lowest recorded temperature in Quebec is ⁻54°C. The highest recorded temperature is 40°C. What is the difference between the temperatures?

5. About $\frac{4}{5}$ of the population of Quebec has French ancestors. About how many people in Quebec have French ancestors?

6. Which fraction, $\frac{1}{4}$, $\frac{1}{6}$, or $\frac{3}{5}$, best shows the part of the population of Quebec living in Montreal?

7. The French explorer Champlain founded Quebec City in 1608. Today the population of Quebec City is about 0.028 times the population of Montreal. What is the population of Quebec City?

8. If the area of Quebec is divided by 2 and 181,849 km² is subtracted from the quotient, the result is the area of Texas. What is the area of Texas?

9. The population of the province of Quebec is 849,300 less than the population of New York City. What is the population of New York City?

10. **Strategy Practice** During an 8-year period, an area of Quebec averaged 89 cm of precipitation per year. The next year that area had 103 cm of precipitation. What was the average precipitation for the 9-year period? Hint: Solve a simpler problem.

Multiplying Integers

The number of students at Ida Wells High School is decreasing at a rate of 20 students per year. If this rate continues, how many less students will there be at Ida Wells High School 4 years from now?

We can use this problem to show the rules for multiplying integers.

$$4 \cdot {}^-20 = {}^-80$$

↑	↑	↑
Years from now (+)	Decreasing rate (−)	Decrease in students (−)

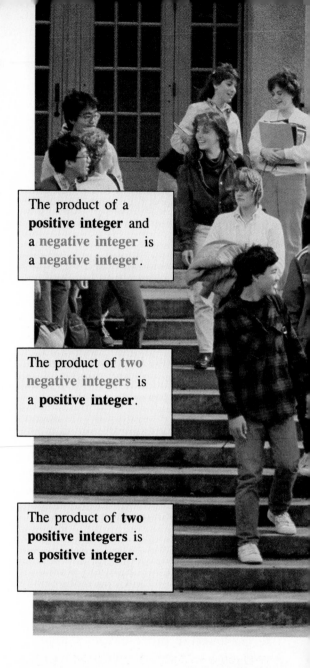

The product of a **positive integer** and a negative integer is a negative integer.

There will be 80 less students at the school 4 years from now.

How many more students were there at the school 3 years ago?

$${}^-3 \cdot {}^-20 = 60$$

↑	↑	↑
Years ago (−)	Decreasing rate (−)	Increase in students (+)

The product of two negative integers is a **positive integer**.

There were 60 more students at the school 3 years ago.

Since positive integers are the same as whole numbers greater than zero, we already know how to multiply two positive integers.

The product of two **positive integers** is a **positive integer**.

Other Examples

$${}^-7 \cdot 0 = 0 \qquad (3 \cdot 7) \cdot {}^-2 = {}^-42 \qquad ({}^-4)^3 = ({}^-4 \cdot {}^-4) \cdot {}^-4 = {}^-64$$

Warm Up

Multiply.

1. $8 \cdot {}^-3$ **2.** ${}^-4 \cdot {}^-7$ **3.** ${}^-9 \cdot 5$ **4.** ${}^-10 \cdot {}^-2$

5. $(6 \cdot {}^-2) \cdot {}^-1$ **6.** ${}^-3 \cdot ({}^-3 \cdot 3)$ **7.** $({}^-2)^3$ **8.** $({}^-1)^4$

186

Practice Multiply.

1. $^-7 \cdot ^-6$
2. $3 \cdot ^-10$
3. $6 \cdot 8$
4. $^-8 \cdot ^-8$

5. $^-9 \cdot ^-3$
6. $4 \cdot 9$
7. $^-3 \cdot ^-3$
8. $7 \cdot 5$

9. $^-8 \cdot 6$
10. $6 \cdot 1$
11. $9 \cdot 0$
12. $^-4 \cdot ^-4$

13. $^-5 \cdot ^-5$
14. $^-3 \cdot ^-12$
15. $^-2 \cdot 15$
16. $8 \cdot ^-9$

17. $^-2 \cdot ^-50$
18. $4 \cdot ^-16$
19. $^-8 \cdot 15$
20. $^-10 \cdot ^-10$

21. $5 \cdot ^-3$
22. $^-8 \cdot ^-4$
23. $^-2 \cdot 4$
24. $^-1 \cdot 1$

25. $14 \cdot ^-2$
26. $^-9 \cdot 7$
27. $5 \cdot 9$
28. $^-10 \cdot ^-6$

29. $3 \cdot ^-40$
30. $^-60 \cdot ^-4$
31. $^-8 \cdot ^-6$
32. $12 \cdot ^-2$

Find the products.

33. $(^-2 \cdot ^-3) \cdot 4$
34. $^-5 \cdot (2 \cdot 5)$
35. $^-6 \cdot (^-1 \cdot ^-4)$

36. $8 \cdot 2 \cdot 2$
37. $^-3 \cdot ^-5 \cdot ^-2$
38. $^-1 \cdot ^-1 \cdot 9$

39. $^-6 \cdot ^-3 \cdot ^-1$
40. $^-2 \cdot ^-2 \cdot ^-3 \cdot ^-3$
41. $^-5 \cdot 2 \cdot ^-2 \cdot ^-5$

Find the integer for each power.

42. $(^-5)^3$
43. $(^-3)^2$
44. $(2)^4$
45. $(^-1)^5$

Mixed Applications

46. The number of students at Pequot School is increasing at a rate of 16 students per year. How many less students were there at the school 3 years ago? Use positive and negative integers to solve the problem.

47. There are 362 students at Webb Jr. High School today. The number of students at the school is decreasing by 13 students per year. How many less students will there be at Webb School 5 years from now? How many students were there at Webb School 5 years ago?

THINK MATH

Estimation

Make an estimate of each sum. Then find the exact sum.

1. $^-72 + ^-29 + 201$
2. $27 + ^-28 + 69 + ^-101$
3. $^-38 + 49 + ^-63$
4. $^-52 + ^-71 + 43 + 68$
5. $^-19 + ^-42 + ^-53 + 90$
6. $^-88 + 121 + ^-33$
7. $243 + 259 + ^-604$
8. $59 + ^-66 + ^-41 + 32$

Dividing Integers

Over a 5-day period, the stock market index changed by ⁻30 points. What was the average change in the index per day?

To find the average change, we divide.

⁻30 ÷ 5 = ?

> What number times 5 equals ⁻30?

Since 5 · ⁻6 = ⁻30, then ⁻30 ÷ 5 = ⁻6.

The index changed by an average of ⁻6 points per day.

$$12 ÷ 4 = 3 \text{ because } 3 · 4 = 12.$$
$$⁻20 ÷ ⁻5 = 4 \text{ because } 4 · ⁻5 = ⁻20.$$

> The quotient of two **positive integers** or two negative integers is **positive**.

$$⁻18 ÷ 6 = ⁻3 \text{ because } ⁻3 · 6 = ⁻18.$$
$$21 ÷ ⁻3 = ⁻7 \text{ because } ⁻7 · ⁻3 = 21.$$

> If one integer is **positive** and the other integer is negative, their quotient is negative.

Other Examples

126 ÷ ⁻14 = ⁻9   0 ÷ ⁻7 = 0 $\frac{⁻16}{⁻4} = ⁻16 ÷ ⁻4 = 4$ Historic stock certificates

Warm Up

Divide.

1. ⁻32 ÷ 8   **2.** 18 ÷ 3   **3.** ⁻72 ÷ ⁻8   **4.** ⁻7 ÷ ⁻7

5. 48 ÷ ⁻8   **6.** ⁻28 ÷ 7   **7.** ⁻35 ÷ ⁻5   **8.** 63 ÷ 7

9. $\frac{9}{⁻3}$ **10.** $\frac{⁻45}{9}$ **11.** $\frac{⁻27}{⁻9}$ **12.** $\frac{50}{⁻10}$

Practice Find the quotients.

1. $18 \div {}^-9$
2. ${}^-25 \div 5$
3. ${}^-6 \div {}^-3$
4. $14 \div 2$

5. $24 \div 3$
6. $20 \div {}^-4$
7. $32 \div 8$
8. ${}^-24 \div {}^-6$

9. ${}^-15 \div 5$
10. ${}^-9 \div {}^-3$
11. ${}^-7 \div {}^-1$
12. $28 \div 4$

13. ${}^-30 \div 6$
14. $72 \div 9$
15. ${}^-81 \div 9$
16. ${}^-1 \div {}^-1$

17. ${}^-36 \div 9$
18. $0 \div {}^-4$
19. ${}^-40 \div {}^-10$
20. $48 \div {}^-12$

21. ${}^-60 \div {}^-3$
22. ${}^-84 \div 7$
23. $100 \div {}^-25$
24. ${}^-105 \div {}^-35$

25. $\dfrac{{}^-24}{{}^-8}$
26. $\dfrac{6}{3}$
27. $\dfrac{21}{{}^-7}$
28. $\dfrac{{}^-30}{5}$

29. $\dfrac{54}{6}$
30. $\dfrac{81}{{}^-9}$
31. $\dfrac{42}{{}^-6}$
32. $\dfrac{63}{{}^-9}$

33. $\dfrac{{}^-8}{{}^-1}$
34. $\dfrac{{}^-56}{{}^-7}$
35. $\dfrac{40}{{}^-4}$
36. $\dfrac{{}^-75}{15}$

Perform the operations inside the parentheses first.

37. $({}^-18 \div 6) + 7$
38. $(10 - 16) \div {}^-2$
39. $({}^-8 \cdot 3) \div {}^-6$

40. $({}^-9 + {}^-6) \div {}^-5$
41. ${}^-7 + (20 \div {}^-4)$
42. ${}^-64 \div ({}^-2 \cdot 4)$

43. $\dfrac{({}^-9 + {}^-3)}{{}^-4}$
44. $\dfrac{({}^-4 \cdot {}^-8)}{2}$
45. $\dfrac{(9 - 5)}{(5 - 9)}$

Mixed Applications

46. During a 14-day period, the stock market index changed ${}^-28$ points. What was the average change in the index per day?

47. A stock had a price of \$74 a share. In 5 days the stock changed by ${}^+\$1$, ${}^-\$2$, ${}^-\$2$, ${}^+3$, ${}^+\$1$. What was the price of a share after 5 days?

Mixed Practice

Find the sums.

1. $7 + {}^-5$
2. ${}^-8 + {}^-6$
3. ${}^-9 + 3$
4. $12 + {}^-15$

5. ${}^-10 + 4$
6. $0 + {}^-13$
7. $21 + {}^-16$
8. ${}^-8 + {}^-9$

9. ${}^-20 + 17$
10. ${}^-11 + 6$
11. ${}^-5 + {}^-9$
12. $17 + {}^-17$

13. ${}^-40 + 30$
14. $23 + {}^-27$
15. $14 + {}^-3$
16. ${}^-9 + {}^-16$

Find the differences.

17. $3 - {}^-5$
18. $8 - 12$
19. $5 - {}^-1$
20. ${}^-6 - 4$

21. $0 - {}^-8$
22. ${}^-10 - {}^-2$
23. $7 - {}^-7$
24. ${}^-8 - {}^-5$

25. $19 - 8$
26. ${}^-4 - 8$
27. ${}^-11 - 4$
28. $13 - 20$

29. ${}^-5 - {}^-15$
30. ${}^-50 - {}^-25$
31. ${}^-16 - 0$
32. $1 - {}^-7$

Find the products.

33. $6 \cdot {}^-8$
34. ${}^-9 \cdot 3$
35. ${}^-7 \cdot {}^-5$
36. $8 \cdot {}^-7$

37. ${}^-10 \cdot {}^-10$
38. ${}^-1 \cdot {}^-8$
39. ${}^-16 \cdot 0$
40. ${}^-12 \cdot {}^-8$

41. $5 \cdot {}^-4$
42. $11 \cdot 3$
43. ${}^-9 \cdot 9$
44. $15 \cdot {}^-3$

45. ${}^-4 \cdot {}^-9$
46. ${}^-17 \cdot 0$
47. ${}^-6 \cdot {}^-60$
48. ${}^-3 \cdot 20$

Find the quotients.

49. ${}^-21 \div 7$
50. ${}^-12 \div {}^-12$
51. ${}^-27 \div {}^-3$
52. $42 \div 6$

53. ${}^-64 \div {}^-8$
54. ${}^-30 \div 5$
55. $40 \div {}^-8$
56. ${}^-49 \div 7$

57. ${}^-4 \div {}^-1$
58. $36 \div {}^-9$
59. $0 \div {}^-5$
60. ${}^-16 \div 4$

61. $56 \div {}^-7$
62. ${}^-120 \div 20$
63. $91 \div {}^-7$
64. ${}^-85 \div {}^-17$

Perform the operations inside parentheses first.

65. $(3 + {}^-7) + 2$
66. $(8 \cdot {}^-2) + 9$
67. $20 - ({}^-10 \div 2)$
68. $({}^-3 \cdot 10) \div 5$

69. $({}^-2 \cdot 2) \cdot {}^-5$
70. $(36 \div {}^-4) + 10$
71. ${}^-4 \cdot (6 - 9)$
72. $(24 \div 3) + {}^-8$

73. $15 - (3 \cdot {}^-2)$
74. $(5 \cdot {}^-3) - (6 \cdot {}^-2)$
75. $({}^-16 \div {}^-8) \div {}^-2$
76. $(3 \cdot {}^-9) + 7$

190

Evaluating Integer Expressions

A large tank has 8,000 L of water in it now. It is being filled at a rate of 100 L each minute. How much water was in the tank 8 minutes *ago*?

You can evaluate the expression

$$8,000 + 100t$$

where t is the time in minutes to solve the problem.

Since the time was 8 minutes ago, let $t = {}^-8$. Replace t with ${}^-8$ in the expression.

$$8,000 + 100 \cdot {}^-8 = 8,000 + {}^-800$$
$$= 7,200$$

There were 7,200 L in the tank 8 min ago.

Other Examples

Evaluate each expression. Let $a = {}^-2$, $b = 6$, and $c = {}^-5$.

$3a + 1$

$\dfrac{{}^-5b}{2}$

$2a + c$

$3 \cdot {}^-2 + 1 = {}^-6 + 1 = {}^-5$

$\dfrac{{}^-5 \cdot 6}{2} = \dfrac{{}^-30}{2} = {}^-15$

$2 \cdot {}^-2 + {}^-5 = {}^-4 + {}^-5 = {}^-9$

Practice Evaluate each expression. Let $a = {}^-7$, $b = 3$, and $c = {}^-10$.

1. $9b$
2. $b \div 8$
3. $\dfrac{c}{{}^-2}$
4. $2a - 6$
5. $\dfrac{{}^-30}{b}$
6. $3c + {}^-5$
7. $\dfrac{9 - b}{{}^-3}$
8. $2(c + 3)$
9. $\dfrac{6a}{21}$
10. $\dfrac{c}{10} + 1$
11. $(a \div {}^-7) \times {}^-7$
12. $b({}^-5 + 2)$
13. $\dfrac{2c}{5}$
14. $5a + 40$
15. $20 - 7b$
16. ${}^-8b - 15$
17. $a - c$
18. bc
19. $3b + a$
20. $a - 3b$
21. $\dfrac{a + b}{2}$
22. $(a - b) + c$
23. $\dfrac{4b}{a - c}$
24. $\dfrac{b - c}{c - b}$
25. $10b + 3c$
26. $5b + c$
27. $(b - a) + c$
28. $\dfrac{7c}{a}$
★29. $a^2 + b^2$
★30. $a^2 - b^2$
★31. $c^2 + b$
★32. $b^2 - a$

More Practice, page 446, Set A

One-Step Equations

The lowest temperature of the day was at 6:00 a.m. The temperature rose 13° during the day to reach a high temperature of 5°C. What was the lowest temperature that day?

We can solve an equation for the problem and use the same steps we used for whole number equations.

Let t = the lowest temperature.

Equation	$t + 13 = 5$
Subtract the same number from each side.	$t + 13 - 13 = 5 - 13$
Simplify.	$t = {}^-8$
Check.	${}^-8 + 13 = 5$

The lowest temperature was ${}^-8$°C.

Other Examples

Subtraction equation

$n - 9 = {}^-11$
$n - 9 + 9 = {}^-11 + 9$
$n = {}^-2$
Check:
${}^-2 - 9 = {}^-11$

Multiplication equation

${}^-8y = 56$
$\dfrac{{}^-8y}{{}^-8} = \dfrac{56}{{}^-8}$
$y = {}^-7$
Check:
${}^-8 \cdot {}^-7 = 56$

Division equation

$\dfrac{s}{7} = {}^-6$
$\dfrac{s}{7} \cdot 7 = {}^-6 \cdot 7$
$s = {}^-42$
Check:
$\dfrac{{}^-42}{7} = {}^-6$

Warm Up

Solve.

1. $n + 5 = 4$ **2.** $x - 6 = {}^-2$ **3.** $10y = 80$ **4.** ${}^-12y = {}^-36$

5. $\dfrac{m}{8} = {}^-3$ **6.** $\dfrac{n}{10} = {}^-9$ **7.** $y + 7 = {}^-9$ **8.** $r + 2 = {}^-3$

Practice Solve each addition and subtraction equation.

1. $d - 6 = {}^-5$

2. $f + {}^-5 = 10$

3. $g + 8 = {}^-6$

4. $t + 2 = 7$

5. $r + 8 = 0$

6. $x + 16 = 7$

7. $n + 6 = 5$

8. $y + {}^-4 = {}^-7$

9. $j - 14 = 6$

10. $t + 7 = 0$

11. $a - 11 = 6$

12. $h + 12 = 2$

13. $w + 16 = 13$

14. $p - 7 = 27$

Solve each multiplication and division equation.

15. $6t = {}^-18$

16. $\frac{u}{16} = {}^-2$

17. ${}^-2n = {}^-10$

18. $8w = 56$

19. $\frac{e}{{}^-13} = {}^-4$

20. $\frac{a}{9} = 4$

21. ${}^-2y = 2$

22. $\frac{x}{2} = {}^-19$

23. $3z = 42$

24. ${}^-7x = 70$

25. $\frac{s}{25} = 4$

26. ${}^-5g = 75$

Solve.

27. $p + {}^-7 = {}^-10$

28. $\frac{c}{{}^-1} = 12$

29. $m - {}^-5 = {}^-5$

30. $15s = {}^-60$

31. $\frac{m}{{}^-4} = 14$

32. $g + 14 = 3$

33. $\frac{f}{{}^-5} = 60$

34. ${}^-4k = {}^-44$

35. $\frac{v}{11} = 11$

36. $w + 17 = {}^-8$

37. $\frac{b}{{}^-12} = {}^-8$

38. $j - 6 = {}^-7$

Mixed Applications

39. The temperature rose 11° to reach a high temperature of ${}^-6°C$. What was the low temperature? Let $t =$ the low temperature.

$t + 11 = {}^-6$

40. The temperature dropped 8° from the high temperature to reach a low temperature of ${}^-3°C$. What was the high temperature? Let $h =$ the high temperature.

$h - 8 = {}^-3$

More Practice, page 446, Set B

PROBLEM SOLVING: Writing and Solving Equations

QUESTION
DATA
PLAN
ANSWER
CHECK

Greg thought of an integer. He said, "If I multiply the integer by 4, I will get ⁻36." What is Greg's integer?

To find the integer, we can write and solve an equation.

Let **n** = Greg's integer.

Then **4n** = 4 times Greg's integer.

Equation	$4n = {}^-36$
Divide each side by 4.	$\dfrac{4n}{4} = \dfrac{{}^-36}{4}$
Simplify.	$n = {}^-9$
Check.	$4 \cdot {}^-9 = {}^-36$

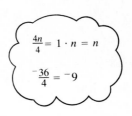

$$\frac{4n}{4} = 1 \cdot n = n$$

$$\frac{{}^-36}{4} = {}^-9$$

Greg's integer is ⁻9

Write and solve an equation for each problem.

1. Kim said, "I thought of an integer. I multiplied it by ⁻5 and the product was 30." What is Kim's integer? Let k = Kim's integer.

2. Peri said, "I thought of an integer. I divided it by 3. The quotient was ⁻8." What was Peri's integer? Let p = Peri's integer.

3. Michelle thought of a number. She said, "I added 9 to my number and got ⁻5 as the sum." What is Michelle's number?

4. Raul said, "If you multiply my number by 6 you should get ⁻48." What is Raul's number?

5. Lee chose an integer and then divided it by 5. The quotient was ⁻5. What integer did Lee choose?

6. Bill said, "If I had 20¢ less than what I have now, I would owe someone 11¢." How much money does Bill have?

7. Hideo gave his brother 75¢. He then had 60¢ left. How much money did Hideo have at first?

8. If ⁻8 is added to Donna's year of birth, the sum is 1968. 1968 is her brother's year of birth. What is Donna's year of birth?

Time Line

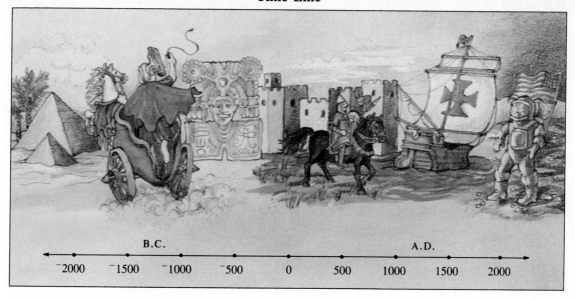

Write and solve an equation for each problem.
Positive numbers represent years A.D. Negative numbers represent years B.C.

1. If 2,275 is added to the year the city of Rome was founded, the sum is 1492, the year Columbus discovered America. In what year was Rome founded?

2. If the year for the beginning of the Mayan civilization is multiplied by 5, the product is ⁻2,500, the date of the building of the Great Pyramids of Egypt. What is the year of the beginning of the Mayan civilization?

3. Bob subtracted his birth year of 1972 from George Washington's birth year and got an answer of ⁻240. What is the year of George Washington's birth?

4. If 2,305 is subtracted from the year man first landed on the moon, the difference is ⁻336, the year Alexander the Great came into power. What year did man first land on the moon?

5. If the year of the Battle of Hastings is divided by ⁻41 the quotient is ⁻26. In what year was the Battle of Hastings?

6. Milly subtracted her birth year of 1972 from Mozart's birth year and got an answer of ⁻216. What was Mozart's birth year?

7. **DATA HUNT** Make up a problem about a historical date like the ones on this page. Write and solve an equation for the problem.

8. **Strategy Practice** Lupe chose a negative integer. She multiplied it by itself and then added twice the integer she chose to the product. The sum was 99. What is Lupe's number?

Adding and Subtracting Rational Numbers

The change of the price of a share of stock was $^-\frac{3}{8}$ one day. The next day the change was $^+\frac{3}{4}$.

What was the total change in price for the two days? To find the total change in price, we can add.

Look at the denominators.	Find the least common denominator.	Write equivalent fractions with this denominator.	Add the numerators Write the sum over the common denominator.
$^-\frac{3}{8} + \frac{3}{4}$	LCD = 8	$^-\frac{3}{8} + \frac{6}{8}$	$\frac{^-3 + 6}{8} = \frac{3}{8}$

The total change was $\frac{3}{8}$. The stock was up a total of $\frac{3}{8}$.

To subtract rational numbers, add the opposite of the number subtracted.

$$\frac{1}{3} - \frac{1}{2} = \frac{2}{6} - \frac{3}{6} = \frac{2}{6} + \frac{^-3}{6} = \frac{^-1}{6}$$

$$\underset{\text{opposites}}{\uparrow \qquad \uparrow}$$

$$^-\frac{3}{5} + \frac{^-1}{5} = \frac{^-4}{5} \qquad\qquad ^-\frac{1}{6} - \frac{3}{6} = \frac{^-1}{6} + \frac{^-3}{6} = \frac{^-4}{6} = \frac{^-2}{3}$$

$$^-0.9 + 0.5 = {^-}0.4 \qquad\qquad 1.8 - {^-}2.0 = 1.8 + 2.0 = 3.8$$

Warm Up

Find the sums.

1. $\frac{7}{8} + \frac{^-3}{8}$

2. $\frac{^-1}{7} + \frac{4}{7}$

3. $^-\frac{3}{4} + \frac{^-5}{8}$

4. $^-\frac{9}{10} + \frac{7}{20}$

5. $0.6 + {^-}0.4$

6. $^-1.5 + {^-}0.5$

7. $0.56 + {^-}0.41$

8. $^-2.77 + {^-}1.23$

Find the differences.

9. $^-\frac{2}{5} - \frac{4}{5}$

10. $\frac{1}{8} - \frac{5}{8}$

11. $^-\frac{2}{3} - \frac{^-2}{5}$

12. $^-\frac{6}{10} - \frac{11}{15}$

13. $0.7 - 0.9$

14. $5.0 - {^-}3.2$

15. $^-0.83 - 0.09$

16. $1 - {^-}2.5$

196

Practice Find the sums.

1. $\dfrac{5}{8} + {}^-\dfrac{3}{8}$

2. ${}^-\dfrac{7}{10} + \dfrac{3}{10}$

3. ${}^-\dfrac{1}{6} + {}^-\dfrac{5}{6}$

4. $\dfrac{2}{7} + {}^-\dfrac{3}{7}$

5. ${}^-\dfrac{1}{2} + \dfrac{2}{3}$

6. ${}^-\dfrac{8}{10} + {}^-\dfrac{3}{5}$

7. $\dfrac{2}{3} + {}^-\dfrac{1}{4}$

8. ${}^-\dfrac{4}{9} + {}^-\dfrac{3}{4}$

9. ${}^-0.4 + 0.7$

10. $1.5 + {}^-0.8$

11. ${}^-3.2 + {}^-1.5$

12. $10 + {}^-6.9$

13. $2\dfrac{1}{2} + {}^-\dfrac{1}{2}$

14. ${}^-\dfrac{7}{8} + 1$

15. ${}^-\dfrac{5}{3} + \dfrac{2}{3}$

16. ${}^-3 + 2\dfrac{2}{3}$

Find the differences.

17. $\dfrac{7}{10} - \dfrac{9}{10}$

18. ${}^-\dfrac{2}{5} - \dfrac{3}{5}$

19. $\dfrac{4}{9} - {}^-\dfrac{3}{9}$

20. ${}^-\dfrac{1}{8} - {}^-\dfrac{7}{8}$

21. $\dfrac{2}{5} - {}^-\dfrac{1}{2}$

22. $\dfrac{1}{4} - \dfrac{3}{8}$

23. ${}^-\dfrac{7}{10} - {}^-\dfrac{5}{6}$

24. $\dfrac{5}{8} - \dfrac{9}{10}$

25. $0.9 - {}^-0.3$

26. ${}^-0.3 - 0.5$

27. $3.7 - 2.9$

28. $0.9 - 1.0$

29. $1 - 1\dfrac{3}{4}$

30. ${}^-1 - \dfrac{2}{3}$

31. $2\dfrac{7}{8} - {}^-\dfrac{1}{8}$

32. $4\dfrac{3}{4} - 5$

Mixed Applications

33. The price of a share of stock closed "up" $1\frac{3}{4}$ on Monday. The stock closed "down" $1\frac{1}{4}$ on Tuesday. What was the total change in the price for the two days? Show this by adding two rational numbers.

34. A stock was selling for $\$12\frac{1}{2}$ a share. At the end of the day the change in price was $^-1\frac{1}{4}$. What was the price at the end of the day?

35. The stock of Ace Company was selling for $\$23\frac{1}{4}$ a share. The stock of Baker Company was selling for $\$16\frac{3}{4}$ per share. How much more did one share of Ace Company stock cost?

36. Write a word problem that could be solved by using this subtraction: $0.50 - 0.75$. Solve your problem.

More Practice, page 446, Set C

Multiplying and Dividing Rational Numbers

Harold planned a diet to lose $2\frac{1}{2}$ lbs ($^-2\frac{1}{2}$) in a week. He was able to lose only $\frac{4}{5}$ of that amount. How many pounds did Harold lose?

To find part of a number, we can multiply.

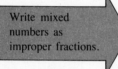 

| Write mixed numbers as improper fractions. | Multiply the numerators. | Multiply the denominators. |

$$\frac{4}{5} \times {^-}2\frac{1}{2} = \frac{4}{5} \times \frac{^-5}{2} \qquad \frac{4}{5} \times \frac{^-5}{2} = \frac{^-20}{} \qquad \frac{4}{5} \times \frac{^-5}{2} = \frac{^-20}{10} = {^-}2$$

The product is $^-2$
Harold lost 2 lbs.

Two rational numbers are **reciprocals** if their product is 1.

The reciprocal of $\frac{^-2}{3}$ is $\frac{^-3}{2}$ because
$\frac{^-2}{3} \times \frac{^-3}{2} = \frac{6}{6} = 1$

The reciprocal of $\frac{^-7}{4}$ is $\frac{^-4}{7}$ because
$\frac{^-7}{4} \times \frac{^-4}{7} = \frac{28}{28} = 1$

To divide two rational numbers, we can multiply by the reciprocal of the divisor.

$$\frac{3}{5} \div \frac{^-7}{10} = \frac{3}{5} \times \frac{^-10}{7} = \frac{^-30}{35} = \frac{^-6}{7} \qquad \frac{^-5}{8} \div \frac{^-3}{4} = \frac{^-5}{8} \times \frac{^-4}{3} = \frac{20}{24} = \frac{5}{6}$$

| If two rational numbers are **both positive** or **both negative**, then their product (quotient) is **positive**. | If one rational number is **positive** and the other is **negative**, then their product (quotient) is **negative**. |

Other Examples

Find $^-2.5 \times 0.7$.

$$
\begin{array}{r}
-2.5 \\
\times\ \ 0.7 \\
\hline
-1.75
\end{array}
$$

Find $6.72 \div {^-}2.1$

$$
\begin{array}{r}
^-3.2 \\
^-2.1\overline{)6.72} \\
6.3 \\
\hline
42 \\
42 \\
\hline
0
\end{array}
$$

Warm Up

Find the products and quotients.

1. $\frac{^-1}{2} \times \frac{4}{9}$ **2.** $^-0.3 \times {^-}0.4$ **3.** $\frac{^-9}{10} \div \frac{2}{3}$ **4.** $5\overline{)^-9.25}$

Practice Find the products.

1. $\frac{2}{5} \cdot \frac{-5}{8}$

2. $\frac{-3}{8} \cdot \frac{4}{3}$

3. $\frac{5}{6} \cdot \frac{3}{10}$

4. $\frac{1}{2} \cdot {}^-12$

5. $\frac{-1}{4} \cdot \frac{-1}{2}$

6. ${}^-4 \cdot \frac{3}{4}$

7. $\frac{-3}{8} \cdot \frac{-8}{3}$

8. $\frac{-3}{4} \cdot \frac{5}{6}$

9. $2\frac{1}{4} \cdot 8$

10. $1\frac{1}{2} \cdot {}^-6$

11. ${}^-2\frac{1}{5} \cdot 1\frac{1}{2}$

12. $\frac{-9}{10} \cdot {}^-2\frac{2}{3}$

13. $0.7 \cdot {}^-0.3$

14. ${}^-3.4 \cdot 21$

15. ${}^-8.3 \cdot 0.26$

16. ${}^-5.7 \cdot {}^-4.9$

Find the quotients.

17. $\frac{4}{5} \div \frac{2}{3}$

18. $\frac{5}{6} \div \frac{-1}{2}$

19. $\frac{-2}{3} \div \frac{-3}{4}$

20. $\frac{-3}{5} \div \frac{3}{5}$

21. $2 \div \frac{-3}{4}$

22. $1 \div \frac{-1}{2}$

23. $\frac{-1}{4} \div \frac{-5}{8}$

24. $\frac{-9}{10} \div 3$

25. $1\frac{2}{3} \div \frac{1}{2}$

26. ${}^-2\frac{7}{8} \div 4$

27. ${}^-10 \div {}^-3\frac{1}{3}$

28. $2\frac{1}{2} \div {}^-1\frac{1}{4}$

29. ${}^-3.2 \div 4$

30. $0.335 \div {}^-0.5$

31. ${}^-1.42 \div {}^-0.4$

32. $4.62 \div {}^-6$

Find the number for *n* in each equation.

33. $\left(\frac{3}{4} + \frac{1}{2}\right) \div {}^-2 = n$

34. $\left(\frac{2}{3} \div \frac{1}{2}\right) + \left(\frac{-1}{3} \div \frac{1}{2}\right) = n$

35. $\left(\frac{1}{4} \cdot \frac{-5}{7}\right) \div \frac{5}{8} = n$

36. $\left(\frac{9}{10} - \frac{1}{5}\right) \div \frac{-7}{8} = n$

37. $\left(\frac{3}{4} \cdot \frac{5}{6}\right) \div \frac{-2}{3} = n$

38. $\left(\frac{2}{3} + \frac{-3}{4}\right) \cdot {}^-12 = n$

Mixed Applications

39. Jody lost 12 lb (${}^-12$) in $2\frac{1}{3}$ months. What was Jody's average loss in weight per month?

40. Mary gained $1\frac{3}{4}$ lb the first week, lost 2 lb (${}^-2$) the next week and gained $1\frac{1}{2}$ lb the next week. What was Mary's average gain or loss in weight per week?

More Practice, page 446, Set D

Comparing and Ordering Rational Numbers

The average January temperature in a grassland area is $^-1$°C. The January temperature for a coniferous forest is $^-12$°C. Which area has the lower average temperature?

We can think of the number line to compare the temperatures.

$^-12 < ^-1$ because $^-12$ is to the left of $^-1$.

The coniferous forest has the lower average temperature. $0 > ^-10$ because 0 is to the right of $^-10$. $\frac{1}{2} > ^-\frac{1}{4}$ because $\frac{1}{2}$ is to the right of $^-\frac{1}{4}$.

We can use repeated inequality symbols to compare and order three or more numbers.

$^-3 < ^-2 < 0$ means $^-3 < ^-2$ **and** $^-2 < 0$.

$^-2$ is **between** $^-3$ and **0**.

$\frac{1}{2} > ^-\frac{1}{2} > ^-\frac{3}{4}$ means $\frac{1}{2} > ^-\frac{1}{2}$ and $^-\frac{1}{2} > ^-\frac{3}{4}$. $^-\frac{1}{2}$ is between $\frac{1}{2}$ and $^-\frac{3}{4}$.

Practice Write $>$ or $<$ for each 〰.

1. $^-6$ 〰 $^-4$

2. $^-1$ 〰 3

3. 11 〰 9

4. $^-3$ 〰 $^-5$

5. $^-8$ 〰 $^-12$

6. $^-10$ 〰 $^-4$

7. 0 〰 5

8. 0 〰 $^-6$

9. $^-\frac{3}{7}$ 〰 $^-\frac{2}{7}$

10. $^-\frac{7}{8}$ 〰 $^-\frac{1}{5}$

11. $\frac{1}{3}$ 〰 $^-\frac{1}{3}$

12. 5.3 〰 5.4

Use repeated inequality symbols to order the numbers.

13. $^-1, 4, ^-7$

14. $6, ^-3, 9$

15. $^-11, ^-10, ^-20$

16. $0, ^-1, 1$

17. $5, ^-14, ^-8$

18. $^-4, ^-11, ^-2$

19. $\frac{1}{3}, \frac{3}{4}, ^-\frac{1}{2}$

20. $1.1, ^-2.4, ^-1.8$

21. $^-\frac{3}{10}, ^-\frac{1}{2}, ^-1$

Mixed Applications

22. Which of these two areas has the higher average January temperature? Tundra, $^-24$°C; Grassland, 12°C. Write an inequality using these numbers.

23. DATA BANK Which continent has the biome with the lowest winter temperature, Africa or Asia? (See page 430.)

Absolute Value

We can think of the **absolute value** of a number
as the number of units it is from 0 on the number line.

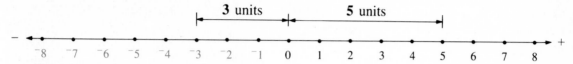

$^-3$ is **3** units from **0**. **5** is **5** units from **0**.

The absolute value of $^-3$ is **3**. We write: $|^-3| = 3$

The absolute value of **5** is **5**. $|5| = 5$

The absolute value of any number is either positive or zero.

$$|0| = 0 \qquad |2 - 6| = 4 \qquad |6 + ^-2| = 4 \qquad |^-9 + 6| = 3 \qquad |0 - ^-7| = 7$$

The absolute value of the difference of two numbers is the
distance between the points for the number on a number line.

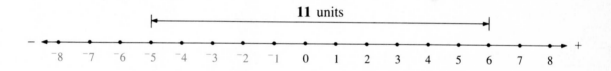

$$|^-4 - 7| = |^-4 + ^-7| = |^-11| = 11 \qquad |7 - ^-4| = |7 + 4| = |11| = 11$$

Practice Find the absolute value.

1. $|6|$ 2. $|^-5|$ 3. $|^-10|$ 4. $|1|$ 5. $|^-16|$

6. $|^-2|$ 7. $|^-3|$ 8. $|11|$ 9. $\left|^-\dfrac{5}{8}\right|$ 10. $\left|^-\dfrac{8}{15}\right|$

11. $|6 + ^-5|$ 12. $|^-9 + 2|$ 13. $|^-12 + ^-4|$ 14. $|11 + ^-7|$ 15. $|^-19 + 20|$

16. $\left|\dfrac{4}{5} + ^-\dfrac{4}{5}\right|$ 17. $\left|^-\dfrac{4}{5} - \dfrac{9}{10}\right|$ 18. $\left|^-\dfrac{3}{8} - \dfrac{1}{4}\right|$ 19. $|^-1.0 - 0.51|$ 20. $|2.1 - 5.3|$

21. How many units is $^-15$ from $^-23$ on the
number line? Use absolute value to find
the answer.

★ 22. Write two possible integers for x.
$$|x - ^-2| = 7$$

More Practice, page 447, Set A

201

Two-Step Equations: Rational Numbers

The temperature was 0°C at 6:00 a.m. The temperature changed the same number of degrees each hour for 4 h. The fifth hour the temperature rose 3° to reach ⁻5°C. How many degrees did the temperature change per hour during the first 4 h?

We can write and solve an equation for the problem.

Let d = the number of degrees of change per hour.

Equation $\qquad\qquad\qquad 4d + 3 = {}^-5$

Subtract 3 from each side. $\quad 4d + 3 - 3 = {}^-5 - 3$

Simplify. $\qquad\qquad\qquad\qquad\quad 4d = {}^-8$

Divide each side by 4. $\qquad\qquad \dfrac{4d}{4} = \dfrac{{}^-8}{4}$

Simplify. $\qquad\qquad\qquad\qquad\quad d = {}^-2$

Check. $\qquad 4 \cdot {}^-2 + 3 = {}^-8 + 3 = {}^-5$

The temperature changed ⁻2°C per hour during the first 4 h.

Other Examples

$$2y - 7 = {}^-2$$
$$2y - 7 + 7 = {}^-2 + 7$$
$$2y = 5$$
$$\frac{2y}{2} = \frac{5}{2}$$
$$y = \frac{5}{2} \quad \text{Check:}$$
$$2 \cdot \frac{5}{2} - 7 = 5 - 7 = {}^-2$$

$$\frac{k}{6} - 0.5 = {}^-2.0$$
$$\frac{k}{6} - 0.5 + 0.5 = {}^-2.0 + 0.5$$
$$\frac{k}{6} = {}^-1.5$$
$$\frac{k}{6} \cdot 6 = {}^-1.5 \cdot 6 \quad \text{Check:}$$
$$k = {}^-9.0 \qquad \frac{{}^-9.0}{6} - 0.5 = {}^-1.5 - 0.5 = {}^-2.0$$

Warm Up

Solve.

1. $5c + 7 = 17$

2. $2n + 7 = {}^-3$

3. ${}^-4z - 8 = 12$

4. $3h - 10 = {}^-25$

5. $\dfrac{d}{4} + 1 = {}^-5$

6. $\dfrac{p}{3} - 5 = 4$

7. $2r + 0.7 = 0.5$

8. $2n + \dfrac{7}{4} = \dfrac{{}^-1}{4}$

202

Practice Solve.

1. $7y - 6 = 29$

2. $6s + 17 = 5$

3. $\frac{d}{2} - 4 = 2$

4. $\frac{z}{3} + 7 = 4$

5. $^-2t + 14 = 24$

6. $\frac{v}{7} + 1 = ^-8$

7. $8v - 19 = ^-3$

8. $\frac{z}{7} + 3 = 5$

9. $20c - 1 = 99$

10. $9n - 7 = ^-34$

11. $3b + 19 = 1$

12. $\frac{a}{5} + 2 = ^-3$

13. $\frac{r}{3} + 3 = ^-3$

14. $6k - ^-10 = 46$

15. $9g - 15 = ^-51$

16. $\frac{h}{^-4} - 6 = 2$

17. $^-2f - 6 = 6$

18. $\frac{m}{10} - 10 = ^-6$

19. $7n - 20 = 15$

20. $^-8x + 9 = 57$

21. $^-1r + 9 = 6$

22. $\frac{k}{^-2} + ^-4 = ^-9$

23. $\frac{w}{8} + 6 = 8$

24. $3y + 12 = 0$

25. $9m + 17 = ^-64$

26. $7c - 3 = ^-31$

27. $\frac{i}{5} - 7 = 0$

28. $\frac{p}{12} + 3 = 1$

29. $^-4y - 6 = ^-26$

30. $6z + 10 = 46$

31. $3x + \frac{7}{8} = ^-2\frac{1}{8}$

32. $0.4x - 1.5 = ^-3.9$

33. $2x + \frac{1}{8} = ^-\frac{3}{8}$

34. $\frac{x}{2} - \frac{1}{2} = ^-\frac{3}{4}$

35. $11d + ^-\frac{5}{7} = \frac{6}{7}$

36. $\frac{1}{2}z + \frac{1}{2} = ^-\frac{1}{2}$

Solve. 🖩

37. $837y + 65,000 = 551$

38. $^-5x - 783 = 3,417$

39. $\frac{n}{49} + 977 = 1,076$

Mixed Applications

40. If the present temperature is divided by 2 and 3 is subtracted from the quotient, the result is $^-2$. What is the present temperature? Let $t =$ the present temperature.

$$\frac{t}{2} - 3 = ^-2$$

41. A temperature of 0°C changed by the same number of degrees each hour for 5 h. The change in temperature the sixth hour was $^-2°$. The temperature was then $^-17°$C. How many degrees per hour did the temperature change in the first 5 h? Let $t =$ the number of degrees change per hour.

$$5t + ^-2 = ^-17$$

Graphing Equations

The location of point P is given by the **ordered pair** of numbers ($^-5$, 3).

To locate P, start at the **origin** (0, 0). Count 5 units left on the **horizontal**, or **x-axis**. Then count up 3 units parallel to the **vertical**, or **y-axis**.

The **coordinates** of P are ($^-$**5, 3**).

The order of the numbers is important.

Point Q has coordinates (**3**, $^-$**5**).

          3 units right   5 units down

To **graph**, or **plot**, a point for an ordered pair of numbers, mark a dot on the grid that corresponds to the ordered pair of numbers.

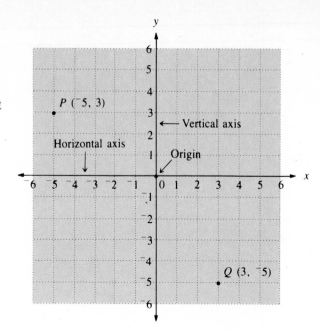

To draw a graph of the equation $y = x + 4$, follow the steps below.

1. Make a **table of values** for x and y. Choose values for x. Then find the corresponding values for y.

2. Plot the points for the ordered pairs of numbers in the table of values. All of the points appear to lie on a line.

3. Draw a line through the points. The line is the graph of the equation $y = x + 4$.

4. The coordinates (x, y) of any point on the line will give a true statement when substituted for x and y in the equation.

The point ($^-1$, 3) is a point on the line $y = x + 4$ because $3 = {}^-1 + 4$.

Table of Values for $y = x + 4$

x	2	0	$^-2$	$^-3$	$^-4$	$^-6$
y	6	4	2	1	0	$^-2$

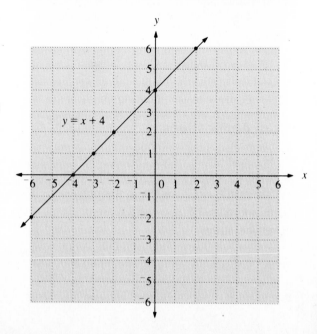

Practice Give the coordinates of each point.

1. A 2. B 3. C

4. D 5. I 6. J

7. K 8. L 9. Q

10. R 11. S 12. T

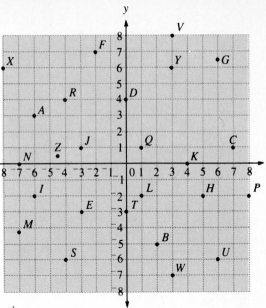

Give the letter of the point for each ordered pair of numbers.

13. $(3, 6)$ 14. $(^-7, 0)$ 15. $(8, ^-2)$

16. $(^-8, 6)$ 17. $(5, ^-2)$ 18. $(^-3, ^-3)$

19. $(^-2, 7)$ 20. $(3, ^-7)$ 21. $(6, ^-6)$

22. $(6, 6.5)$ 23. $\left(^-4\frac{1}{2}, \frac{1}{2}\right)$ 24. $\left(^-7, ^-4\frac{1}{4}\right)$

Copy and complete each table. Then graph each equation.

25. $y = x - 2$

x	$^-4$	$^-3$	$^-2$	$^-1$	0	1	2	3
y								

26. $y = x + 3$

x	4	3	2	0	$^-1$	$^-2$	$^-3$	$^-4$
y								

27. $y = \frac{x}{2}$

x	6	4	2	0	$^-8$	$^-6$	$^-4$	$^-2$
y								

28. $y = 2x + 1$

x	$^-3$	$^-2$	$^-1$	0	1	2	3	4
y								

29. $y = 3 - x$

x	6	5	3	1	0	$^-1$	$^-2$	$^-3$
y								

30. $y = 5 - 2x$

x	6	5	4	2	1	0	$^-1$	$^-2$
y								

Make a table of values for each equation. Then graph each equation.

31. $y = x + 5$ 32. $y = 2x + ^-3$ 33. $y = 1 - x$

34. $y = 4 - x$ 35. $y = 2(x - 1)$ 36. $y = 2x + 2$

37. $y = 3x - 2$ 38. $y = ^-x$ ★ 39. $y = |x|$

More Practice, page 447, Set C

Graphing Pairs of Equations

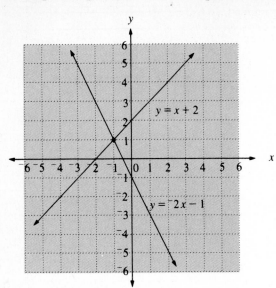

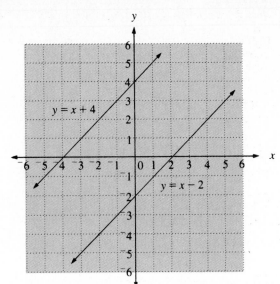

The two lines appear to intersect at Point P with coordinates $(-1, 1)$. To check, substitute $(-1, 1)$ in each equation.

$y = x + 2$	$y = {}^-2x - 1$
$1 = {}^-1 + 2$	$1 = {}^-2 \cdot {}^-1 - 1$
True	True

The graphs of the equations $y = x + 4$ and $y = x - 2$ do not intersect. The two lines are **parallel**.

Warm Up

1. Copy and complete each table of values.

$y = x - 2$

x	4	2	0	$^-2$	$^-4$
y					

$y = 4 - x$

x	4	2	0	$^-2$	$^-4$
y					

2. Graph the equations $y = x - 2$ and $y = 4 - x$.

3. Do the graphs of the two lines in exercise 2 intersect? What is the point of intersection? Check by substituting values for x and y in each equation.

Practice Copy and complete each table of values. Graph each pair of equations. Give the coordinates of the point of intersection if the lines intersect.

1. $y = x + 3$

x	$^-4$	$^-2$	0	2	4
y	▓	▓	▓	▓	▓

$y = {}^-2x$

x	$^-4$	$^-2$	0	2	4
y	▓	▓	▓	▓	▓

2. $y = 2x - 1$

x	$^-1$	1	3	5	6
y	▓	▓	▓	▓	▓

$y = 5 - x$

x	$^-1$	1	3	4	5
y	▓	▓	▓	▓	▓

3. $y = 3x$

x	$^-3$	$^-2$	$^-1$	0	1
y	▓	▓	▓	▓	▓

$y = 3x - 4$

x	$^-3$	$^-2$	$^-1$	0	1
y	▓	▓	▓	▓	▓

4. $y = x$

x	$^-4$	$^-2$	0	2	4
y	▓	▓	▓	▓	▓

$y = {}^-x$

x	$^-4$	$^-2$	0	2	4
y	▓	▓	▓	▓	▓

Graph each pair of equations. If the lines intersect, give the coordinates of the point of intersection.

5. $y = x - 1$
$y = 3 - x$

6. $y = 2x + 3$
$y = x + 1$

7. $y = 4x - 4$
$y = 2x - 2$

8. $y = x + 2$
$y = x - 2$

9. $y = \frac{x}{2} + 3$
$y = {}^-3x - 4$

10. $y = 6 - x$
$y = x + 6$

11. Graph the lines whose equations are $y = 3x - 2$ and $y = 3 - x$. Estimate the coordinates of the point of intersection. What is the exact point of intersection?

★ **12.** Graph the three lines with equations $y = 4 - \frac{x}{2}$, $y = 2x - 6$, and $y = {}^-3x - 1$ on the same coordinate grid. Find the coordinates of the three points of intersection.

207

Negative Exponents

Study the patterns of exponents for the powers of 10 and the powers of 2.

Powers of 10

$10^4 = 10,000$	$10^0 = 1$
$10^3 = 1,000$	$10^{-1} = \frac{1}{10}$
$10^2 = 100$	$10^{-2} = \frac{1}{100}$
$10^1 = 10$	$10^{-3} = \frac{1}{1,000}$

Powers of 2

$2^4 = 16$	$2^0 = 1$
$2^3 = 8$	$2^{-1} = \frac{1}{2}$
$2^2 = 4$	$2^{-2} = \frac{1}{4}$
$2^1 = 2$	$2^{-3} = \frac{1}{8}$

Each power of 10 is $\frac{1}{10}$ as large as the power of 10 before it.

Each power of 2 is $\frac{1}{2}$ as large as the power of 2 before it.

$$10^{-1} = \frac{1}{10^1} = \frac{1}{10} \qquad 10^{-2} = \frac{1}{10^2} = \frac{1}{100} \qquad 2^{-1} = \frac{1}{2^1} = \frac{1}{2} \qquad 2^{-2} = \frac{1}{2^2} = \frac{1}{4}$$

Other Examples

$$5^{-3} = \frac{1}{5^3} \qquad 3^{-4} = \frac{1}{3^4} \qquad 9^{-1} = \frac{1}{9^1}$$

Practice Write each power with a positive exponent.

1. 3^{-3}
2. 6^{-4}
3. 10^{-5}
4. 2^{-6}
5. 4^{-1}

6. 8^{-7}
7. 2^{-5}
8. 7^{-1}
9. 6^{-6}
10. 3^{-4}

Write each power with a negative exponent.

11. $\frac{1}{7^2}$
12. $\frac{1}{10^7}$
13. $\frac{1}{5^4}$
14. $\frac{1}{9^3}$
15. $\frac{1}{16^1}$

16. $\frac{1}{4^4}$
17. $\frac{1}{20^1}$
18. $\frac{1}{8^3}$
19. $\frac{1}{2^{10}}$
20. $\frac{1}{3^3}$

Write each decimal as a power of 10. Example: $0.001 = \frac{1}{1,000} = \frac{1}{10^3} = 10^{-3}$

21. 0.1
22. 0.01
23. 100
24. 0.0001
25. $10,000$

26. 0.00001
27. $1,000$
28. $1,000,000$
29. 0.000001
30. 0.0000001

Scientific Notation for Small Numbers

A chemist collected 0.000325 L of liquid for an experiment. **Scientific notation** was used to record the amount.

$$3.25 \times 10^{-4} \text{ L}$$

A number from 1 to 10   A power of 10

$0.000325 = 3.25 \times 10^{-4}$ because

$$0.000325 = \frac{3.25}{10,000}$$

$$= 3.25 \times \frac{1}{10^4}$$

$$= 3.25 \times 10^{-4}$$

Study the shortcuts below.

$0.000325 \quad = \quad 3.25 \quad \times \quad 10^{-4}$

Shift 4 places right   Negative exponent

$0.0000062 \quad = \quad 6.2 \quad \times \quad 10^{-6}$

Shift 6 places right   Negative exponent

To write a decimal for a number in scientific notation, we reverse the steps above.

$1.76 \quad \times \quad 10^{-3} \quad = \quad 0.00176$

Shift 3 places left

$8.9 \quad \times \quad 10^{-5} \quad = \quad 0.000089$

Shift 5 places left

Practice Write in scientific notation.

1. 0.0027
2. 0.00085
3. 0.0000068
4. 0.0426
5. 0.00000029
6. 0.662
7. 0.000048
8. 0.00000007
9. 0.0000376

Write the decimals.

10. 3.81×10^{-3}
11. 1.06×10^{-4}
12. 6.5×10^{-2}
13. 9.77×10^{-6}
14. 4.0×10^{-10}
15. 7.44×10^{-5}
16. 5.1×10^{-1}
17. 1.88×10^{-7}
18. 8.0×10^{-12}

More Practice, page 448, Set A

PROBLEM-SOLVING STRATEGY: Find a Pattern

QUESTION
DATA
PLAN
ANSWER
CHECK

Try This

There are 8 players in a one-on-one basketball tournament. Each player must play each other player one game. How many games will be played in the tournament?

To solve a problem like the one above, you may use the strategy called **Find a Pattern** to help you see what you must do.

Brent found this pattern.

Player 1 must play the 7 other players for 7 games.

Player 2 must then play the remaining 6 players for 6 more games.

Player 3 must then play the remaining players for 5 more games. And so on.

There is a pattern in the number of games.

$7 + 6 + 5 + 4 + 3 + 2 + 1 = 28$

There will be 28 games.

Blythe thought about the problem another way.

Each of the 8 players play 7 other players.

$8 \times 7 = 56$

But it takes 2 players for each game, so I need to divide by 2.

$56 \div 2 = 28$ There will be 28 games.

Solve.

1. Berry made a string design in art class. The design had 12 pins equally spaced around a circle. Each pin was connected to each of the other pins with a string. How many pieces of string were used to make the design?

2. There were 16 men and 16 women at a dance. Each man danced one dance with each woman. Every person danced in every dance. How many different couples danced together? How many dances were danced?

210

Add, subtract, multiply, or divide.

1. $6 + {}^-4$

2. ${}^-8 + {}^-2$

3. ${}^-7 \cdot 3$

4. ${}^-20 \div 5$

5. $3 - {}^-2$

6. $3 - 8$

7. ${}^-12 + 9$

8. ${}^-8 \cdot {}^-7$

9. $\frac{3}{4} + \frac{{}^-3}{4}$

10. $\frac{{}^-2}{5} \cdot \frac{1}{2}$

11. $\frac{1}{10} - \frac{3}{10}$

12. $4.8 \div {}^-6$

Evaluate each expression. Let $a = {}^-7$ and $b = 5$.

13. $2a + 1$

14. ${}^-3b$

15. $a - b$

16. $4b - a$

Solve each equation.

17. $y + 5 = {}^-3$

18. $x - 9 = 2$

19. $t + 6 = {}^-30$

20. $5n = {}^-45$

21. $\frac{n}{3} = {}^-1$

22. $2c - \frac{4}{5} = \frac{1}{5}$

Compare the numbers. Write $>$ or $<$ for each ◉.

23. ${}^-2$ ◉ 3

24. ${}^-7$ ◉ ${}^-9$

25. 1 ◉ ${}^-10$

26. ${}^-\frac{1}{2}$ ◉ ${}^-\frac{4}{7}$

Give the absolute values.

27. $|{}^-8|$

28. $|0|$

29. $|{}^-6 + 4|$

30. $\left|\frac{3}{8} - \frac{7}{8}\right|$

31. Copy and complete the table of values for the equation $y = 2x - 1$. Then draw the graph of the equation.

x	5	3	2	0	1	⁻2	⁻3	⁻4
y								

32. Graph the equations $y = x + 4$ and $y = 2 - x$ on the same coordinate axis. Then give the coordinates of the point of intersection of the graph of the lines.

Write in scientific notation.

33. 0.00092

34. 0.123

35. 0.0000005

Write and solve equations for problems 36 and 37.

36. Katie chose an integer and subtracted 6 from it. The difference was ${}^-4$. What was the integer?

37. Heather said, "I thought of an integer. I multiplied it by 8 and then added 5. The sum was ${}^-27$." What integer did Heather think of?

$2 + {}^-3 = {}^-1$

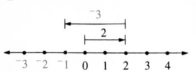

$$\begin{array}{ccccccccc} {}^-3 & {}^-2 & {}^-1 & 0 & 1 & 2 & 3 & 4 \end{array}$$

To subtract a number, *add* its opposite.

${}^-8 - 4 = {}^-8 + {}^-4 = {}^-12$

+ times + = +
+ times − = −
− times + = −
− times − = +
+ divided by + = +
− divided by + = −
+ divided by − = −
− divided by − = +

$3z - 4 = {}^-19$
$3z - 4 + 4 = {}^-19 + 4$
$3z = {}^-15$
$\dfrac{3z}{3} = \dfrac{{}^-15}{3}$
$z = {}^-5$

$y = x + 4$

If $x = 4$ then $y = 4 + 4 = 8$.

Add or subtract.

1. $5 + {}^-4$ **2.** ${}^-9 + 3$ **3.** ${}^-2 + {}^-6$

4. ${}^-1 - 4$ **5.** $7 - {}^-2$ **6.** ${}^-6 - {}^-8$

7. $8 + {}^-11$ **8.** ${}^-3 - 10$ **9.** ${}^-12 - {}^-9$

10. ${}^-9 + {}^-4$ **11.** $2 - 7$ **12.** ${}^-13 + 15$

Multiply or divide.

13. $7 \cdot {}^-5$ **14.** ${}^-4 \cdot 4$ **15.** ${}^-6 \cdot {}^-8$

16. ${}^-32 \div 8$ **17.** ${}^-40 \div {}^-10$ **18.** $21 \div {}^-3$

19. $9 \cdot 6$ **20.** ${}^-36 \div {}^-4$ **21.** ${}^-1 \cdot {}^-1$

22. ${}^-42 \div 7$ **23.** $8 \cdot {}^-9$ **24.** ${}^-63 \div {}^-9$

Copy and solve the equations.

25. $x - 7 = {}^-13$ **26.** $y + 6 = {}^-9$
$\quad x - 7 + 7 = {}^-13 + 7$ $\quad y + 6 - 6 = {}^-9 - 6$

27. $2t - 3 = {}^-11$ **28.** $\dfrac{n}{2} + 6 = 2$
$\quad 2t - 3 + 3 = {}^-11 + 3$ $\quad \dfrac{n}{2} + 6 - 6 = 2 - 6$

29. Copy and complete the table of values for the equation $y = x + 4$. Then graph the equation.

x	4	2	0	${}^-1$	${}^-3$	${}^-4$	${}^-5$	${}^-6$
y								

Graphs of Inequalities

The examples below show graphs of sentences that use the
words "is less than" and "is greater than."

A. 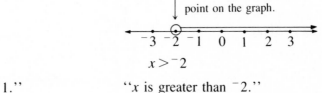 Shows that ⁻1 is a
point on the graph.

$x \leq {}^-1$

"x is less than or equal to ⁻1."

B. Shows that ⁻2 is not a
point on the graph.

$x > {}^-2$

"x is greater than ⁻2."

C.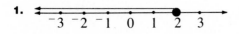

$x < 2$ and $x > {}^-2$

"x is less than 2 and
x is greater than ⁻2."

D.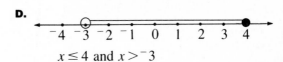

$x \leq 4$ and $x > {}^-3$

"x is less than or equal to 4 and x is
greater than ⁻3."

Write an inequality for each graph.

1.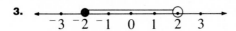

2.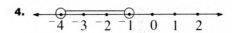

3.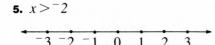

4.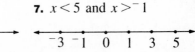

Make a graph of each inequality.

5. $x > {}^-2$

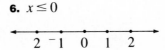

6. $x \leq 0$

7. $x < 5$ and $x > {}^-1$

8. $x \leq 0$ and $x \geq {}^-3$

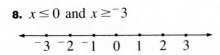

9. $x > \frac{{}^-3}{2}$ and $x \leq \frac{{}^-1}{2}$

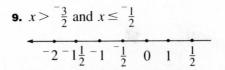

★10. $x < {}^-2$ or $x > 2$

11. Write an inequality of your own.
Draw a graph of your inequality.

213

Find the products.

1. $\frac{7}{12} \times \frac{6}{21}$

A $\frac{1}{9}$ B $\frac{1}{6}$

C $\frac{1}{8}$ D not given

2. $7\frac{2}{3} \times 2\frac{5}{8}$

A $14\frac{5}{12}$ B $14\frac{5}{24}$

C $20\frac{1}{8}$ D not given

3. What is $\frac{5}{6}$ of 54?

A 45   B 36

C 50   D not given

4. What is the reciprocal of $3\frac{3}{4}$?

A $4\frac{4}{3}$ B $\frac{4}{15}$

C $\frac{15}{4}$ D not given

5. Find the quotient.

$6\frac{7}{8} \div 3\frac{2}{3}$

A $1\frac{7}{8}$ B $2\frac{5}{16}$

C $1\frac{3}{4}$ D not given

6. What is the decimal for $\frac{3}{20}$?

A $6.\overline{6}$ B $0.1\overline{5}$

C 0.15   D not given

7. Which is correct?

A 0.01 m > 1 cm   B 5.2 cm = 0.52 m

C 2 km > 240 m   D not given

Write the missing number.

8. 9.56 kL = ▨ L

A 956   B 0.956

C 95.6   D not given

9. 526 g = ▨ mg

A 526,000   B 52.6

C 5,260   D not given

10. 75 s = ▨ min

A 4,500   B $3\frac{1}{8}$

C $1\frac{1}{4}$ D not given

11. What is 75°C in Kelvin temperature?

A 198.15 K   B 348.15 K

C 272.4 K   D not given

12. What is the elapsed time from 11:45 a.m. to 3:30 p.m.?

A 4 h 15 min   B 4 h 45 min

C 3 h 45 min   D not given

13. Mushrooms cost $1.34 per pound. What would be the cost of $2\frac{1}{2}$ lb of mushrooms?

A $3.35   B $3.02

C $2.68   D not given

14. A moderate oven temperature is 175°C. Water boils at 100°C. How much greater is the oven temperature?

A 275°   B 150°

C 75°   D not given

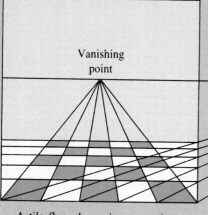

A tile floor drawn in perspective

Geometry

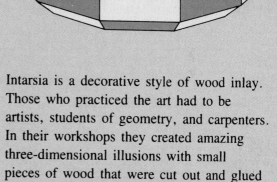

Intarsia is a decorative style of wood inlay. Those who practiced the art had to be artists, students of geometry, and carpenters. In their workshops they created amazing three-dimensional illusions with small pieces of wood that were cut out and glued on a backboard. In 1478 there were over 80 intarsia workshops in Florence, Italy.

To create the illusions, the rules of perspective had to be followed. One example of intarsia that is 500 years old shows an open cupboard with books, tools, and a polyhedron with 72 sides. Another example shows a dodecahedron made of 12 pentagons. There are pyramids made of 5 equilateral triangles projecting from each pentagon. Great skill and knowledge of geometry was required to create these masterpieces.

Basic Geometric Figures

The world is filled with objects that remind us of geometric figures. Some figures or shapes are seen so often that they have been given names and descriptions.

We think of a **point** as a position in space with no length, width, or thickness.

P
.

Symbol: *P*

A **segment** is two points on a line and all the points on the line between them.

X ———————————————— Y

Symbol: $\overline{XY}$

We think of a **line** as a straight path of points that goes on endlessly in both directions.

Symbol: $\overleftrightarrow{PQ}$

A **ray** is a part of a line that has one endpoint and extends endlessly in one direction.

Symbol: $\overrightarrow{OP}$

We think of a **plane** as a flat surface.

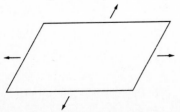

An **angle** is formed by two rays from the same endpoint or vertex.

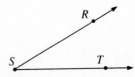

Symbol: $\angle RST$ or $\angle S$

216

Draw and label each figure.

1. $\overleftrightarrow{AB}$

2. $\overrightarrow{RS}$

3. $\angle DEF$

4. $\overline{MN}$

5. $\angle GHI$

6. $\overrightarrow{JK}$

Use the figure at the right for exercises 7–10.

7. Name three lines.

8. Name two rays from point D.

9. On what two lines is point E?

10. Name a point that is on $\overleftrightarrow{EF}$ and $\overleftrightarrow{FD}$.

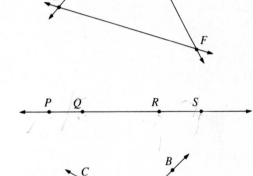

11. Points P, Q, R, and S are four points on a line. Name all the segments which have pairs of these points as endpoints.

12. The three rays from point Q form three different angles. Name each angle.

13. How many different angles are formed by the four rays from point P? Name each angle.

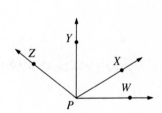

Study each drawing. Then name a geometric figure to complete the statement.

14. If three points are not on the same line, then exactly one __?__ contains the points.

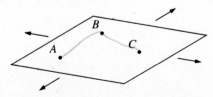

15. If two different planes intersect, then their points of intersection form a __?__ .

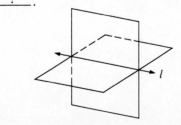

Angle Measure

A **protractor** can be used to measure angles. The unit of angle measure is the **degree** (°).

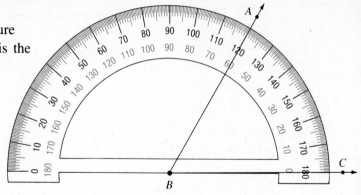

The measure of angle ABC is 60 degrees.

$$m\angle ABC = 60°$$

Angles are named according to their measures.

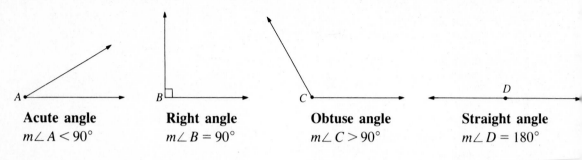

Acute angle	Right angle	Obtuse angle	Straight angle
$m\angle A < 90°$	$m\angle B = 90°$	$m\angle C > 90°$	$m\angle D = 180°$

Two angles are **complementary** if their measures have a sum of 90°.

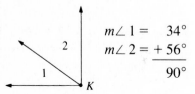

$$m\angle 1 = 34°$$
$$m\angle 2 = \underline{+56°}$$
$$90°$$

∠1 and ∠2 are complementary angles.

Two angles are **supplementary** if their measures have a sum of 180°.

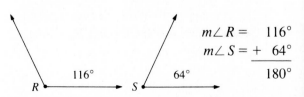

$$m\angle R = 116°$$
$$m\angle S = \underline{+64°}$$
$$180°$$

∠R and ∠S are supplementary angles.

Warm Up

State if the angle is acute, right, obtuse, or straight.

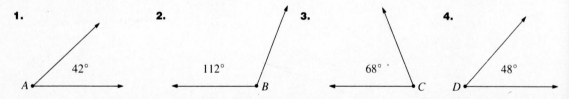

1. 42° A

2. 112° B

3. 68° C

4. 48° D

5. Which angles above are complementary?   **6.** Which angles above are supplementary?

218

Practice Use the figure at the right to name the following angles.

1. Two right angles

2. A straight angle

3. An obtuse angle

4. Two acute angles

5. A pair of complementary angles

6. All pairs of supplementary angles

7. The measure of $\angle DBE$

8. The measure of $\angle ABE$

9. The measure of $\angle DBC$

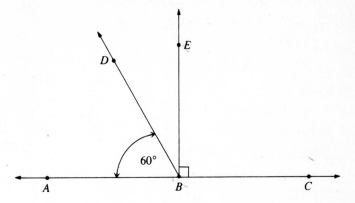

Give the measure of a complement to the given angle.

10. $m\angle A = 32°$ 11. $m\angle B = 51°$ 12. $m\angle C = 73°$

13. $m\angle D = 84°$ 14. $m\angle E = 67°$ 15. $m\angle F = 45°$

Give the measure of a supplement to the given angle.

16. $m\angle G = 100°$ 17. $m\angle H = 77°$ 18. $m\angle I = 160°$

19. $m\angle J = 90°$ 20. $m\angle K = 3°$ 21. $m\angle L = 138°$

22. What is the degree measure of x?

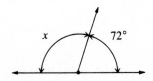

★ 23. The measure of $\angle 1$ is twice the measure of $\angle 2$. What is the measure of each angle?

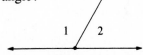

Parallel Lines and Perpendicular Lines

Some pairs of lines have special names.

Parallel lines are lines in the same plane that do not intersect.

Line *a* is parallel to line *b*.
Symbol: $a \| b$

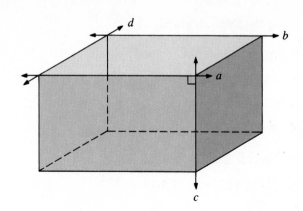

Perpendicular lines are two lines that intersect to form right angles.

Line *a* is perpendicular to line *c*.
Symbol: $a \perp c$

Skew lines are lines in space that are not parallel and do not intersect.

Lines *b* and *c* are skew lines.

A **transversal** is a line that intersects two or more lines.

Line *d* is a transversal of lines *a* and *b*.

We can use a **compass** and a **straightedge** to construct perpendicular lines and parallel lines.

Constructing Perpendicular Lines

Step 1

Draw line *a*. Mark point *P*. Mark points *R* and *S* with *P* as the center.

Step 2

Locate *Q* with the compass point at *R* and at *S*.

Step 3

Draw $\overleftrightarrow{PQ}$. $\overleftrightarrow{PQ} \perp a$

Constructing Parallel Lines

Step 1

Draw line *b*. Mark point *M* on line *b*.

Step 2

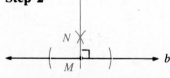

Construct $\overleftrightarrow{MN} \perp b$.

Step 3

Mark point *H* on $\overleftrightarrow{MN}$. Construct $c \perp \overleftrightarrow{HN}$. $c \| b$

Use the figure at the right for exercises 1–7.
$r \parallel s$, $q \perp r$, and $q \perp s$

1. Name three right angles.

2. Name two transversals of lines r and s.

3. Name two transversals of lines t and q.

4. What is the measure of $\angle 1$?

5. What other angles have the same measure as $\angle 1$?

6. What is the measure of $\angle 9$?

7. What is the measure of $\angle 6$?

8. Draw line k and construct a line through J perpendicular to line k.

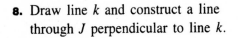

9. Draw line s and construct a line t parallel to line s.

10. Draw $\overrightarrow{PS}$ and construct a ray from point P so that a right angle is formed.

11. Construct a **square**. All angles are right angles and all sides have the same length.

THINK MATH

Shape Perception

In which figure are the red lines straight *and* parallel?

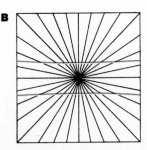
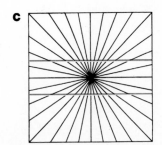

A   B   C

Triangles

Triangles have three **sides**, three **vertices**, and three **angles**.

$\triangle ABC$

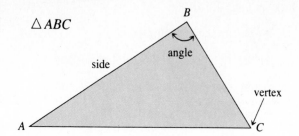

Sides: $\overline{AB}, \overline{BC}, \overline{AC}$

Vertices: A, B, C

Angles: $\angle A, \angle B, \angle C$

Triangles are named according to the lengths of their sides.

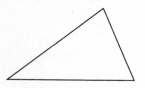

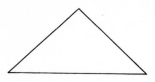

Scalene triangle
No two sides have the same length.

Isosceles triangle
Two sides have the same length.

Equilateral triangle
All sides have the same length.

Triangles are also named according to the size of their angles.

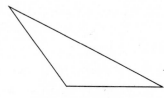

Right triangle
One right angle

Acute triangle
All angles acute

Obtuse triangle
One obtuse angle

The sum of the measures of the angles of any triangle is 180°.

$$50° + 20° + 110° = 180°$$

Warm Up

1. Name $\triangle SRT$.

2. Find the measure of $\angle R$.

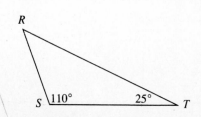

Practice Name each triangle according to the length of its sides.

1.
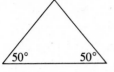
5 cm   10 cm
10 cm

2.

8 m   8 m
8 m

3.
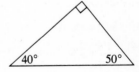
7 cm   9 cm
8 cm

Name each triangle according to the measure of its angles.

4.
60°
80°   40°

5.

45°
100°   35°

6.
40°   50°

Find the measure of the third angle in each triangle.

7.
50°   50°

8.
66°
24°

9.
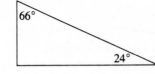
28°   22°

10.
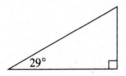
29°

11.

40°
15°

12.
60°
60°

13. In right △*ABC*, ∠*C* is the right angle. What is the sum of the measures of angles *A* and *B*? How are angles *A* and *B* related?

14. DATA HUNT Draw a large triangle. What is the measure of each angle to the nearest whole degree? Add the measures of the angles. What is their sum?

THINK MATH

Angle Estimation

Estimate the measure of each of the angles in each triangle.

Check your estimates by measuring the angles.

1.
A   B

2.
F
D   E

3.
I
G   H

4.
L
J   K

Polygons

A **polygon** is a closed geometric figure whose sides are segments. A polygon is named according to the number of its sides.

Polygon	Number of sides
Triangle	3
Quadrilateral	4
Pentagon	5
Hexagon	6

Polygon	Number of sides
Heptagon	7
Octagon	8
Nonagon	9
Decagon	10

All the sides of a **regular polygon** have the same length. All its angles have the same measure.

To find the sum (s) of the measures of the angles of a polygon, we can divide a polygon into triangles by using **diagonals** from one vertex.

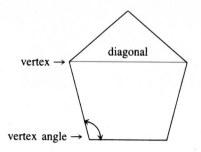

Quadrilateral
4 sides
2 triangles
$s = 2 \times 180° = 360°$

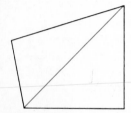

Pentagon
5 sides
3 triangles
$s = 3 \times 180° = 540°$

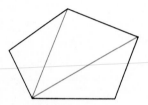

Hexagon
6 sides
4 triangles
$s = 4 \times 180° = 720°$

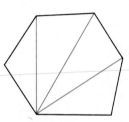

We can use a formula to find the sum of the measures of the angles of a polygon of n sides. $s = (n - 2) \times 180°$

Warm Up

1. Find the degree measure of x.

2. Find the sum of the measures of the angles of this regular polygon.

224

Practice Name each polygon. Find the sum of the measures of the angles.

1.
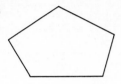

2.
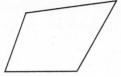

3.

4.
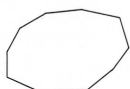

5.
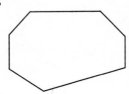

6.
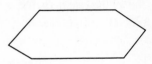

Find the degree measure of x in each polygon.

7.
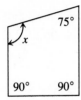

75°
x
90°   90°

8.

120°
120°   110°
x
90°

9.
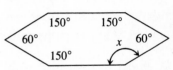

150°   150°
60°   60°
150° x

10.

x
76° 76°

11.
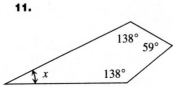

138°
59°
x 138°

12.
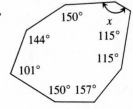

150° x
144°   115°
115°
101°
150° 157°

13. What is the measure of each angle of a regular pentagon?

14. What is the measure of each angle of a regular decagon?

15. What is the measure of each angle of a regular octagon?

★ 16. What is the measure of each tip of the star in the regular pentagon below?

x

225

Circles

The photograph of the watch shows several **circles**. The circles have the same center. They are called **concentric circles**.

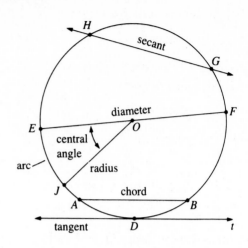

A **circle** is all the points in a plane that are the same distance from one point called the **center**. Point O is the center of circle O.

A **chord** is a segment with its endpoints on the circle. $\overline{AB}$ and $\overline{EF}$ are chords.

A **diameter** is a chord that passes through the center of the circle. $\overline{EF}$ is a diameter.

Line t is a **tangent** line. It intersects the circle at just one point.

A **radius** is a segment from the center of the circle to a point on the circle. $\overline{OE}$, $\overline{OF}$, and $\overline{OJ}$ are radii.

A **central angle** has its vertex at the center of a circle. $\angle JOE$ and $\angle JOF$ are central angles.

An **arc** is a part of a circle. $\overset{\frown}{EJ}$ (or $\overset{\frown}{JE}$) is the shorter arc with endpoints J and E.

Line GH is a **secant** line. It intersects the circle at two points.

Warm Up

The two circles in the figure are concentric circles with center at O.

1. Name the diameter of the large circle.

2. Name the diameter of the small circle.

3. If the length of $\overline{AB}$ is 12 cm, how long is the radius of the large circle?

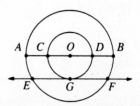

4. Is $\overleftrightarrow{EF}$ a secant or a tangent of the large circle?

5. Is $\overleftrightarrow{EF}$ a secant or a tangent of the small circle?

226

Practice Use circle *P* for exercises 1–7.

1. Name a diameter of the circle.

2. Name three radii of the circle.

3. Name two chords of the circle.

4. Name two central angles of the circle.

5. Name two arcs with *S* as one end. $\overset{\frown}{ST}$, $\overset{\frown}{SM}$ are examples.

6. Name a tangent line.

7. Name a secant line.

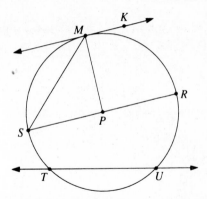

8. Use the method shown below to construct a regular hexagon in a circle.

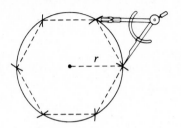

9. What is the measure of each central angle of the regular hexagon below?

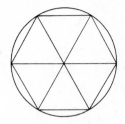

10. Use the construction of exercise 8 to draw an equilateral triangle in a circle.

★ 11. Draw a circle with center *P*. Mark points *A* and *B* on the circle so that $\overline{AB}$ is not a diameter. Draw $\triangle ABP$. What kind of triangle is it?

THINK MATH

Shape Perception

Use a compass to make a copy of this figure.

Shade all regions that are inside at least four different circles.

Congruent Segments and Angles

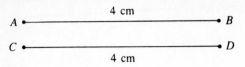

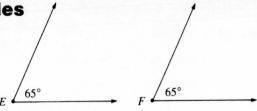

Congruent segments have the same length.

$\overline{AB}$ is **congruent** to $\overline{CD}$.

$\overline{AB} \cong \overline{CD}$

Congruent angles have the same measure.

$\angle E$ is **congruent** to $\angle F$.

$\angle E \cong \angle F$

We can construct congruent segments or angles using a compass and a straightedge. Construct a segment congruent to $\overline{PQ}$.

Step 1	**Step 2**	**Step 3**

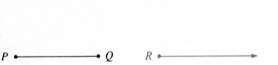

Draw a ray from R.	Open the compass to the length of $\overline{PQ}$.	Use the opening from P to Q to mark S. $\overline{PQ} \cong \overline{RS}$

Construct an angle congruent to $\angle A$.

Step 1	**Step 2**	**Step 3**

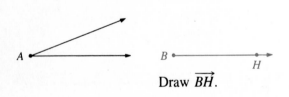

Draw $\overrightarrow{BH}$.	Draw any arc with center at point A.	Draw another arc with the same radius from point B.

Step 4	**Step 5**	**Step 6**

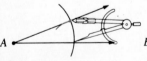 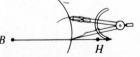 

Draw an arc to measure the opening of $\angle A$.	Use the same opening to draw an arc from $\overrightarrow{BH}$.	Draw $\overrightarrow{BF}$. $\angle A \cong \angle B$

228

Construct the **perpendicular bisector** of a segment.

Step 1

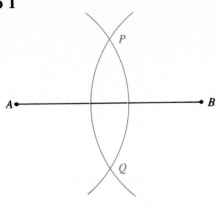

Draw arcs with centers at A and B. Label the points of intersection P and Q.

Step 2

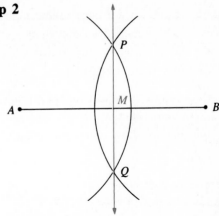

Draw $\overleftrightarrow{PQ}$ intersecting $\overline{AB}$ at M. $\overleftrightarrow{PQ}$ is the perpendicular bisector of $\overline{AB}$. $\overline{AM} \cong \overline{MB}$ M is the midpoint of $\overline{AB}$.

Bisect an angle.

Step 1

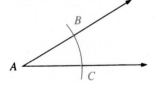

Draw $\overarc{BC}$ with center at A.

Step 2

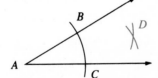

Draw arcs with centers at B and C to locate D.

Step 3

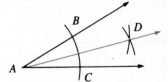

Draw $\overrightarrow{AD}$. $\overrightarrow{AD}$ bisects $\angle A$. $\angle BAD \cong \angle DAC$

1. Draw $\overline{AB}$. Construct a segment congruent to $\overline{AB}$.

2. Draw $\angle ABC$. Construct an angle congruent to $\angle ABC$.

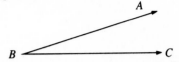

3. Draw a segment. Construct a perpendicular bisector of the segment.

4. Draw an angle. Then bisect the angle.

5. Draw any triangle. Construct the bisector of each of the three angles of the triangle.

6. Draw an acute triangle. Construct the perpendicular bisector of each side of the triangle.

Congruent Triangles

When two triangles are **congruent**, their vertices can be matched so that their matching sides are congruent and their matching angles are congruent.

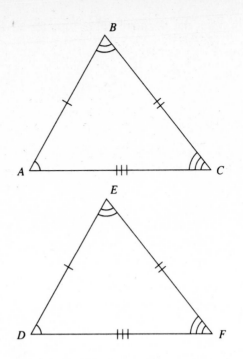

The same number of slash marks on sides show congruent segments. The same number of arcs in angles show congruent angles.

$$\overline{AB} \cong \overline{DE} \qquad \angle A \cong \angle D$$
$$\overline{BC} \cong \overline{EF} \qquad \angle B \cong \angle E$$
$$\overline{AC} \cong \overline{DF} \qquad \angle C \cong \angle F$$

If three sides of one triangle are congruent to three sides of another triangle, then the triangles are congruent. This is called **side-side-side (SSS) congruence**.

$\triangle ABC$ is congruent to $\triangle DEF$.

$\triangle ABC \cong \triangle DEF$

Use SSS congruence to construct a triangle congruent to $\triangle PRQ$.

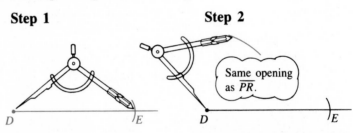

Step 1

Construct $\overline{DE} = \overline{PQ}$.

Step 2

Same opening as $\overline{PR}$.

Draw an arc with center D.

Step 3

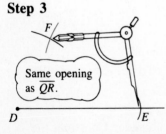

Same opening as $\overline{QR}$.

Draw an arc with center E to locate F.

Step 4

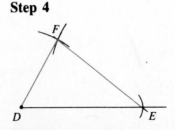

Draw $\overline{DF}$ and $\overline{EF}$.

$\triangle DFE = \triangle PRQ$

List the pairs of congruent sides and angles for each pair
of congruent triangles. Use ≅ to show congruence.

1.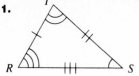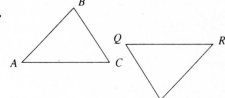

2.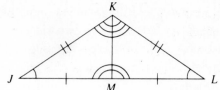

Write a statement of congruence for each pair of congruent triangles.

3.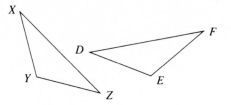

4.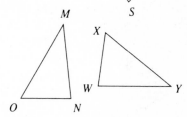

5.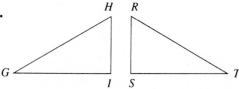

6.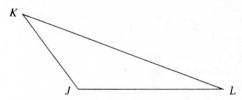

7. Trace △XYZ. Then construct a triangle
congruent to it.

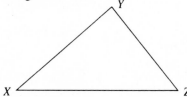

8. Trace △JKL. Then construct a triangle
congruent to it.

SAS and ASA Congruence

If two sides and the included angle of one triangle are congruent to two sides and the included angle of another triangle, the two triangles are congruent. This is called **side-angle-side (SAS) congruence**.

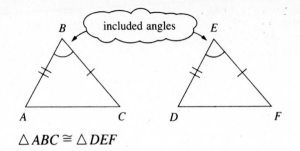

$\triangle ABC \cong \triangle DEF$

Use SAS congruence to construct a triangle congruent to $\triangle XYZ$.

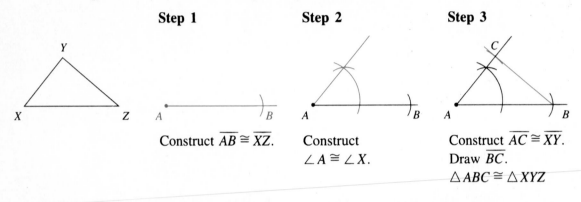

Step 1

Construct $\overline{AB} \cong \overline{XZ}$.

Step 2

Construct $\angle A \cong \angle X$.

Step 3

Construct $\overline{AC} \cong \overline{XY}$. Draw $\overline{BC}$.

$\triangle ABC \cong \triangle XYZ$

If two angles and the included side of one triangle are congruent to two angles and the included side of a second triangle, the two triangles are congruent. This is called **angle-side-angle (ASA) congruence**.

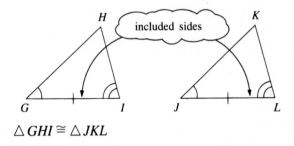

$\triangle GHI \cong \triangle JKL$

Use ASA congruence to construct a triangle congruent to $\triangle ABC$.

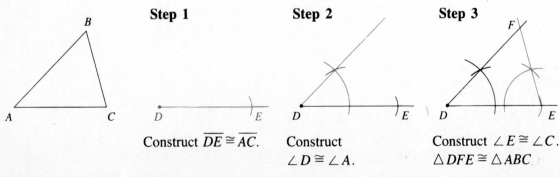

Step 1

Construct $\overline{DE} \cong \overline{AC}$.

Step 2

Construct $\angle D \cong \angle A$.

Step 3

Construct $\angle E \cong \angle C$.

$\triangle DFE \cong \triangle ABC$

232

State if the triangles have SSS, SAS, or ASA congruence.

1.

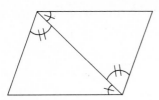

2.

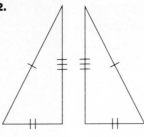

3.

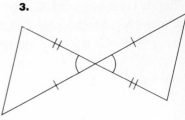

4.

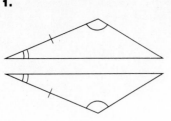

5.

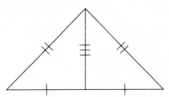

6.

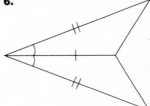

7. Trace $\triangle MNO$. Use SAS congruence to construct a triangle congruent to $\triangle MNO$.

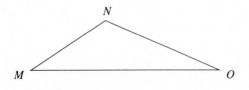

8. Trace $\triangle JKL$. Use ASA congruence to construct a triangle congruent to $\triangle JKL$.

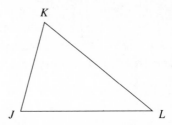

9. Construct a triangle with sides congruent to the three segments below.

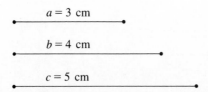

$a = 3$ cm

$b = 4$ cm

$c = 5$ cm

10. Construct a triangle with two sides and the included angle congruent to the sides and the angle below.

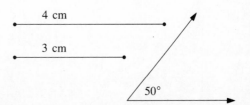

4 cm

3 cm

50°

Symmetry and Polygons

The dotted line on the butterfly divides it into two identical parts. The dividing line is called a **line of symmetry.**

Some polygons have more than one line of symmetry. Some polygons have no lines of symmetry.

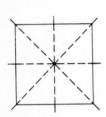   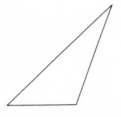   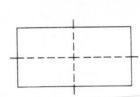   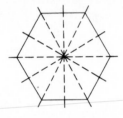

Square
Four lines
of symmetry

Scalene triangle
No lines
of symmetry

Rectangle
Two lines
of symmetry

Regular hexagon
Six lines
of symmetry

Warm Up

Is the dotted line a line of symmetry for each polygon?

1.
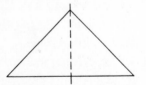

2.
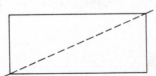

3.
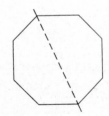

4.
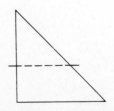

5.
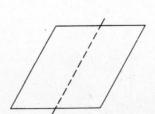

6.
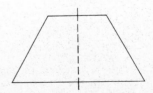

Practice How many lines of symmetry does each polygon have?

1.

Equilateral triangle

2.

Regular pentagon

3.

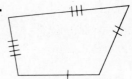

Quadrilateral

4.

Rhombus

5.

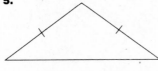

Isosceles triangle

6.

Isosceles trapezoid

Trace or sketch each figure in exercises 7–12.
Then draw all lines of symmetry for each figure.

7.

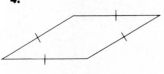

8.

9.

10.

11.

12.

THINK MATH

Optical Illusions

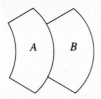

Is region *A* smaller than region *B*?

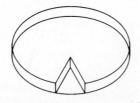

To find the missing piece of cake, turn the picture 180°.

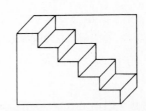

Stare at the stair steps. Which way is "up the stairs"?

235

PROBLEM·SOLVING STRATEGY: Use Logical Reasoning

QUESTION
DATA
PLAN
ANSWER
CHECK

Try This

Amir, Lisa, Joel, and Mary are each active in a different sport. Their sports are running, golf, tennis, and bowling. Lisa is the sister of the tennis player. Mary's sport does not use a ball. Joel once made a "hole in one" in his sport. Which sport does each person play?

To solve a problem like the one above, you cannot use the operations of arithmetic. Instead you must follow the strategy called **Use Logical Reasoning** to draw reasonable conclusions.

Make a table. Fill in the facts you know.

> Lisa is not the tennis player.

> Joel is the golfer because of the "hole in one."

	Amir	Lisa	Joel	Mary
Golf	no	no	yes	no
Tennis		no	no	
Bowling			no	
Running			no	

> Mary must be the runner since no ball is used.

	Amir	Lisa	Joel	Mary
Golf	no	no	yes	no
Tennis		no	no	no
Bowling			no	no
Running	no	no	no	yes

> Now we can conclude that Lisa must be the bowler. Therefore Amir is the tennis player.

	Amir	Lisa	Joel	Mary
Golf	no	no	yes	no
Tennis	yes	no	no	no
Bowling	no	yes	no	no
Running	no	no	no	yes

Joel plays golf, Mary is the runner, Lisa is a bowler, and Amir plays tennis.

Solve.

1. Sally, Tom, and Laura went from home to school on a skateboard, a moped, and a bicycle. The bicycle rider was a girl. Sally had to stop for gasoline. How did each person get to school?

2. Ned has a dog, a bird, a fish, and a cat. Their names are Bud, Dot, Perk, and Sam. The bird talks to Perk and Dot. Sam cannot walk or fly. Perk runs from the dog. What is each animal's name?

1. Is ∠R right, acute, or obtuse?

2. Give the measure of a supplement of ∠R.

3. Give the measure of a complement of ∠R.

4. Is △ABC right, acute, or obtuse?

5. Is △ABC scalene, isosceles, or equilateral?

6. What is the degree measure of ∠x?

7. Name polygon DEFG.

8. What is the sum of the angles of polygon DEFG?

9. What is the degree measure of ∠y?

10. Draw a line s. Mark point P on s. Construct line t ⊥ s at P.

11. Draw a line r. Construct a line parallel to line r.

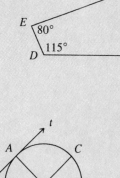

In exercises 12–15, name each part of the circle.

12. $\overline{AB}$

13. line t

14. $\overline{OC}$

15. ∠BOC

State if the triangles have SSS, SAS, or ASA congruence.

16.

17.

18.

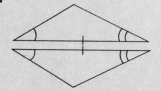 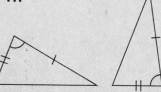 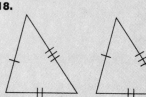

Give the number of lines of symmetry of each figure.

19.

20.

21.

Equilateral triangle   Square   Rectangle

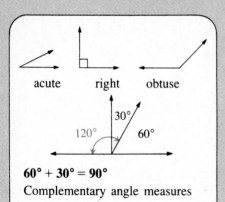

acute   right   obtuse

60° + 30° = 90°
Complementary angle measures

120° + 60° = 180°
Supplementary angle measures

1. Is ∠R acute, obtuse, or right?

2. What kind of angle is ∠S?

3. What kind of angle is ∠T?

4. Give the measure of a complement of ∠R.

5. Give the measure of a supplement of ∠T.

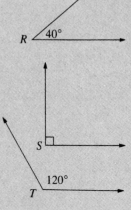

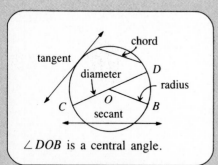

The sum of the angle measures equals 180°.

6. Is △ABC scalene, equilateral, or isosceles?

7. Give the measure of ∠C.

8. Is △ABC acute, right, or obtuse?

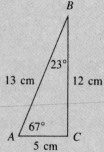

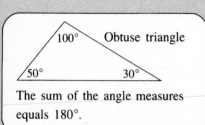

∠DOB is a central angle.

In exercises 9–14, name each part of the circle.

9. $\overline{CD}$

10. $\overline{OB}$

11. line s

12. line t

13. $\overline{AB}$

14. ∠BOC

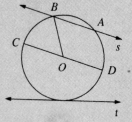

SSS: Three sides congruent

SAS: Two sides and included angle congruent

ASA: Two angles and included side congruent

State if the triangles have SSS, SAS, or ASA congruence.

15.

16.

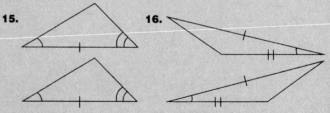

Constructing a Regular Pentagon

Step 1 Draw a large circle with perpendicular diameters $\overline{AB}$ and $\overline{CD}$.

Step 2 Bisect $\overline{OB}$ at point M.

Step 3 Open compass to $\overline{CM}$. With center at M, mark arc at N.

Step 4 With center at C, open compass to $\overline{CN}$. Mark $\overset{\frown}{NH}$.

Step 5 With the same compass opening, mark arcs of equal lengths at G, F, and E.

Step 6 Draw regular pentagon $CEFGH$.

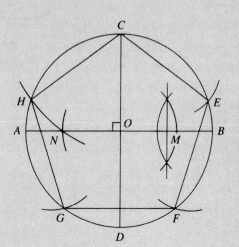

Use the construction for a regular pentagon to make some designs of your own.

Construct a regular decagon. Hint: Construct a regular pentagon in a circle. Then construct the perpendicular bisectors of the sides of the pentagon.

1. Which expression represents a number t decreased by 92?

   A $t + 92$ **B** $92 - t$
   C $t - 92$ **D** not given

Solve.

2. $\frac{x}{4} = 124$

   A $x = 31$ **B** $x = 372$
   C $x = 496$ **D** not given

3. $34 + y = 93$

   A $y = 59$ **B** $y = 61$
   C $y = 127$ **D** not given

4. $p - 12 = 156$

   A $p = 144$ **B** $p = 168$
   C $p = 13$ **D** not given

5. $16\,z = 848$

   A $z = 13{,}568$ **B** $z = 53$
   C $z = 864$ **D** not given

6. If $m = 16$, what is $20 - \frac{m}{4}$?

   A 64   **B** 1
   C 16   **D** not given

7. Which is correct?

   A $^-3 < {}^-5 < {}^-4$ **B** $32 > {}^-12 < {}^-3$
   C $14 < {}^-15 < {}^-27$ **D** not given

8. Add.

   $^-5 + {}^-20 + 7$

   A 32   **B** $^-32$
   C $^-18$ **D** not given

9. Find the difference.

   $(12 - {}^-2) - 7$

   A 3   **B** 7
   C $^-7$ **D** not given

10. Find the product.

    $^-12 \cdot {}^-13$

    A $^-156$ **B** $^-146$
    C 146   **D** not given

11. Divide.

    $\dfrac{^-117}{13}$

    A $^-9$ **B** 9
    C $^-12$ **D** not given

12. If $c = {}^-12$, what is $3\,c + {}^-2$?

    A 34   **B** $^-38$
    C 38   **D** not given

13. Shawna had $28. She bought 4 tickets to a concert and had $4 left. What was the cost of each ticket? Which equation shows this problem?

    A $4\,b + 4 = 28$ **B** $4\,b = 28$
    C $4\,b - 4 = 28$ **D** not given

14. If the present temperature is divided by 5 and 7 is subtracted from that number, the result will be $^-3$. What is the present temperature?

    A $^-20°C$ **B** $15°C$
    C $20°C$ **D** not given

Ratio and Proportion

In 1545 King Henry VIII watched as the warship *Mary Rose* sank into the murky waters near Portsmouth, England. In 1982 the 40-meter-long hull of the *Mary Rose* was raised to the surface. Its recovery was the climax of a 15-year project costing $7 million.

Much of the recovery work was done by hundreds of divers under the direction of an underwater archeologist. Scuba divers, even in shallow water, can only stay underwater a few hours at a time. They average only 4 h of work a day, as compared to the 8 h averaged by land archeological excavators.

The *Mary Rose* was 12 m underwater. All that could be seen of her were two lines of oak posts jutting out of the muddy seabed. It took 5 years to confirm the identity and position of the ship. After 2 more years, the divers established the condition of the ship.

The exploration and removal of over 17,000 artifacts and the raising of the hull required hundreds of thousands of dives. The diving hours in 1 year totaled 4,212.

Ratio

This concrete mix uses 1 part water for every 2 parts of cement.

A **ratio** can be used to compare the parts of water to the parts of cement. There are three ways to write the ratio of water to cement:

1 to **2**   **1:2** $\dfrac{1}{2}$ ← Parts of water
                              ← Parts of cement

Each example above is read "1 to 2."

The ratio of cement to water is 2 to 1.

$\dfrac{2}{1}$ ← Parts of cement
  ← Parts of water

This means that when 2 parts of water are used, 4 parts of cement should be used.

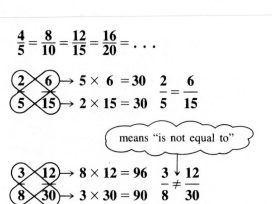

Concrete Mix Formula

4 parts sand
5 parts gravel
2 parts cement
1 part water

$\dfrac{1}{2}$ and $\dfrac{2}{4}$ are **equal ratios**. $\dfrac{1}{2} = \dfrac{2}{4}$

We can find equal ratios by thinking about equivalent fractions. Two ratios are equal if, and only if, their **cross products** are equal.

A statement that two ratios are equal is called a **proportion**.

$$\frac{4}{5} = \frac{8}{10} = \frac{12}{15} = \frac{16}{20} = \cdots$$

$$\begin{array}{l} 2 \times 6 \to 5 \times 6 = 30 \\ 5 \times 15 \to 2 \times 15 = 30 \end{array} \quad \frac{2}{5} = \frac{6}{15}$$

means "is not equal to"

$$\begin{array}{l} 3 \times 12 \to 8 \times 12 = 96 \\ 8 \times 30 \to 3 \times 30 = 90 \end{array} \quad \frac{3}{8} \neq \frac{12}{30}$$

Warm Up

Use the concrete mix formula to give each ratio three different ways.

1. Water to sand   **2.** Cement to gravel   **3.** Gravel to water   **4.** Sand to gravel

Write = or ≠ for each ⦀. Use cross products to decide.

5. $\dfrac{9}{12}$ ⦀ $\dfrac{3}{4}$ **6.** $\dfrac{8}{10}$ ⦀ $\dfrac{12}{15}$ **7.** $\dfrac{18}{8}$ ⦀ $\dfrac{10}{4}$ **8.** $\dfrac{1}{3}$ ⦀ $\dfrac{17}{51}$

Practice Write each ratio two other ways.

1. 7 to 10   **2.** 3:5   **3.** $\frac{2}{9}$ **4.** 5:4

5. $\frac{11}{15}$ **6.** 1 to 100   **7.** $\frac{3}{10}$ **8.** $\frac{1}{1,000}$

9. 8 to 5   **10.** 6:7   **11.** 4 to 1   **12.** $\frac{9}{10}$

Write = or ≠ for each ▓. Use cross products to decide.

13. $\frac{3}{9}$ ▓ $\frac{7}{21}$ **14.** $\frac{2}{3}$ ▓ $\frac{12}{15}$ **15.** $\frac{8}{7}$ ▓ $\frac{64}{49}$ **16.** $\frac{10}{16}$ ▓ $\frac{5}{8}$

17. $\frac{3}{16}$ ▓ $\frac{4}{18}$ **18.** $\frac{5}{2}$ ▓ $\frac{35}{14}$ **19.** $\frac{12}{30}$ ▓ $\frac{16}{40}$ **20.** $\frac{1}{3}$ ▓ $\frac{33}{100}$

21. $\frac{9}{10}$ ▓ $\frac{90}{100}$ **22.** $\frac{3}{4}$ ▓ $\frac{24}{32}$ **23.** $\frac{17}{34}$ ▓ $\frac{14}{28}$ **24.** $\frac{45}{54}$ ▓ $\frac{35}{40}$

Write the next three ratios in each pattern.

25. $\frac{2}{3} = \frac{4}{6} = \frac{6}{9} = \frac{▓}{▓} = \frac{▓}{▓} = \frac{▓}{▓}$

26. 3 to 5, 6 to 10, 9 to 15, ▓, ▓, ▓

27. 3:1, 6:2, 9:3, ▓, ▓, ▓

28. $\frac{128}{32} = \frac{64}{16} = \frac{32}{8} = \frac{▓}{▓} = \frac{▓}{▓} = \frac{▓}{▓}$

29. 7 to 3, 14 to 6, 21 to 9, ▓, ▓, ▓

30. $\frac{9}{10} = \frac{18}{20} = \frac{27}{30} = \frac{▓}{▓} = \frac{▓}{▓} = \frac{▓}{▓}$

Write a proportion. Use two of the ratios for each exercise.

31. $\frac{6}{8}, \frac{24}{40}, \frac{18}{24}$ **32.** $\frac{1}{8}, \frac{4}{9}, \frac{12}{27}$ **33.** $\frac{14}{18}, \frac{6}{9}, \frac{21}{27}$ **34.** $\frac{25}{40}, \frac{3}{5}, \frac{21}{35}$

Mixed Applications

Use the concrete mix formula on page 242 for problems 35–38.

35. What is the ratio of the parts of cement to the parts of sand for the concrete mix?

36. What is the ratio of the parts of cement to all the parts of the concrete mix?

37. Brian Johnson used 3 buckets of water to mix concrete. How many buckets of each of the other materials are needed for the concrete?

38. If only 1 bucket of cement were used for concrete mix, how many buckets of each of the other materials should be used to make the mix?

More Practice, page 448, Set C

Rate

The Booster Club raised money by washing windows. They charged $12 for a job that took 4 hours. What was the rate per hour?

A **rate** is a ratio comparing two different units. To find the rate, we can write a ratio of dollars to hours and then find a simpler ratio with a denominator of 1.

$$\frac{\$12}{4\ h} = \frac{\$3}{1\ h} = \$3/h$$ ⟨ 3 dollars per hour ⟩

The rate was 3 dollars per hour.

Trish ran 200 m in 25 s. What was her running rate in meters per second?

$$\frac{200\ m}{25\ s} = \frac{8\ m}{1\ s} = 8\ m/s$$

Trish's running rate was 8 m/s.

Other Examples

$$\frac{176\ km}{2\ h} = 88\ km/h \qquad \frac{\$26}{4\ h} = \$6.50/h \qquad \frac{\$2.96}{8\ L} = \$0.37/L$$

Practice Simplify each rate.

1. $\dfrac{\$42}{6\ h}$

2. $\dfrac{90\ km}{10\ L}$

3. $\dfrac{1{,}000\ words}{4\ min}$

4. $\dfrac{68\ cm}{4\ s}$

5. $\dfrac{2{,}400\ km}{4\ h}$

6. $\dfrac{28\ days}{4\ weeks}$

7. $\dfrac{48\ people}{24\ cars}$

8. $\dfrac{18\ players}{2\ teams}$

9. $\dfrac{275\ min}{5\ classes}$

10. $\dfrac{120\ problems}{48\ min}$

11. $\dfrac{650\ students}{26\ teachers}$

12. $\dfrac{100\ revolutions}{3\ min}$

13. It took Trish 64 s to run 400 m. What was her running rate in meters per second?

14. Brad lowered his window washing rate to $2.75/h. What should he charge for a job that takes 3.2 h?

More Practice, page 449, Set A

PROBLEM SOLVING: Mixed Practice

QUESTION
DATA
PLAN
ANSWER
CHECK

Solve.

1. Janice typed 432 words in 9 min. What is her typing rate in words per minute?

2. Saul read 30 pages in 40 min. What is Saul's reading rate in pages per minute?

3. Talia read 45 pages of a book in 54 min. How many minutes did it take her to read 1 page?

4. A babysitter charged $7 for 4 h. What is the rate for babysitting?

5. When driving on a freeway, a car traveled 7.5 km on 1 L of gasoline. How far could the car be driven on the freeway on 40 L of gasoline?

6. Harry drove 260 km in 5 h. At what rate, in km/h, did Harry drive?

7. An auto mechanic charged $75 for labor that took 3 h. What is the hourly rate for labor?

8. The pilot of a jet plane announced to the passengers that the plane would cruise at 960 km/h. How far would the plane travel in 3.5 h at that rate?

9. Charo read a book in 6 h. The book was 384 pages long. What was Charo's reading rate in pages per hour?

★ 10. A baseball announcer said that the pitcher was throwing the ball at a rate of 144 km/h. What is this rate in meters per second?

11. A record time for running 1,500 m is 3 min 31.36 s. What is the running rate in meters per second?

12. **Strategy Practice** Artie, Bruno, Kit, and Jasper went camping. Each person took a different kind of light—a candle, matches, a flashlight, and a lantern. Bruno did not have the matches. Artie needed oil for his light. Jasper borrowed the matches to start his light. What kind of light did each person have? Hint: Use logical reasoning.

Unit Prices

The price for *one* unit of an item is called the **unit price**.

UNIT PRICE: ?

APPLE JUICE
1.40 L
$1.26

UNIT PRICE: ?

APPLE JUICE
1.80 L
$1.53

What is the unit price of each bottle of apple juice? Which bottle costs less per unit?

Write a ratio of the price to the number of units.	Divide the price by the number of units.	Write the unit price.

$$\frac{\$1.26}{1.4 \text{ L}} \qquad \$1.26 \div 1.4 = \$0.90 \qquad \$0.90/\text{L}$$

$$\frac{\$1.53}{1.8 \text{ L}} \qquad \$1.53 \div 1.8 = \$0.85 \qquad \$0.85/\text{L}$$

The 1.8-liter bottle costs less per unit.

Other Examples

Grapefruit: **4** for **$1.08**

Unit price $= \dfrac{\$1.08}{4} =$ **$0.27/grapefruit**

Fresh grapes: **$1.35** for **0.45** kg

Unit price $= \dfrac{\$1.35}{0.45 \text{ kg}} =$ **$3/kg**

Warm Up

Give the unit price.

1. 1.5 L for $3.30

2. $2.17 for 0.7 kg

3. 24 cans for $23.28

4. 0.6 kg for $1.40

5. 24 packages for $16.32

6. 2.5 L for $9.95

Practice Find the unit price. Use a calculator if possible. 🖩

1.

Unit price	?
Potatoes: 4.5 kg for	$0.90

2.

Unit price	?
Luncheon meat: 0.07 kg for	$0.49

3.

Unit price	?
Cereal: 0.5 kg for	$1.09

4.

Unit price	?
Applesauce: 0.67 kg for	$0.79

5.

Unit price	?
Yogurt: 0.25 kg for	$0.53

6.

Unit price	?
Peanut butter: 0.45 kg for	$1.62

7.

Unit price	?
Toothpaste: 0.25 kg for	$1.59

8.

Unit price	?
Fresh carrots: 1.8 kg for	$1.00

9.

Unit price	?
Sunflower seeds: 0.2 kg for	$0.79

Find the unit price of each item.
Then tell which size has the lower unit price.

10. Melons
  A 2 for $0.79
  B 3 for $1.00

11. Pet food
  A 5 cans for $1.55
  B 3 cans for $0.99

12. Cheese slices
  A 12 slices for $1.20
  B 18 slices for $1.62

13. Cottage cheese
  A 0.45 kg for $0.72
  B 0.9 kg for $1.53

14. Bread
  A 0.45 kg for $0.45
  B 0.66 kg for $0.78

15. Raisins
  A 0.45 kg for $1.98
  B 0.2 kg for $0.79

Mixed Applications

16. Fish fillets cost $6.60/kg. What is the cost of 0.45 kg of fish fillets?

17. Fresh cauliflower cost $1.76/kg. What is the cost of a head of cauliflower that weighs 0.65 kg?

18. Bananas were priced at $0.78/kg. Edla bought some for $2.73. How many kilograms of bananas did she buy?

19. DATA HUNT Find three different sizes of the same item and the cost of each item. Find the unit price of each item. Which size has the lowest unit price?

Solving Proportions

Jonathan wears contact lenses. He cleans them with a saline solution made with 112 mL of distilled water and 4 g of salt. Jonathan has 7 g of salt left. How much water does he need to make a saline solution with 7 g of salt?

Since the ratio of water to salt will be the same, we can use a **proportion** to solve the problem.

Let w = the amount of water needed.

Write the proportion.

$$\text{Water (mL)} \rightarrow \frac{w}{7} = \frac{112}{4} \leftarrow \text{Salt (g)}$$

Find the cross products. $4w = 784$

Solve the multiplication equation. $w = 196$

Jonathan needs 196 mL of water for 7 g of salt.

Other Examples

$\dfrac{6}{8} = \dfrac{n}{60}$ $\dfrac{2}{5} = \dfrac{11}{t}$ $\dfrac{7}{t} = \dfrac{21}{42}$

$8n = 360$ $2t = 55$ $21t = 294$

$n = 45$ $t = 27.5$ $t = 14$

Warm Up

Solve each proportion.

1. $\dfrac{5}{10} = \dfrac{9}{n}$ **2.** $\dfrac{2}{5} = \dfrac{x}{70}$ **3.** $\dfrac{2}{3} = \dfrac{n}{10}$ **4.** $\dfrac{9}{15} = \dfrac{10}{p}$

248

Practice Solve each proportion.

1. $\frac{2}{3} = \frac{24}{n}$

2. $\frac{2}{5} = \frac{x}{60}$

3. $\frac{9}{12} = \frac{3}{n}$

4. $\frac{3}{7} = \frac{t}{42}$

5. $\frac{3}{8} = \frac{n}{72}$

6. $\frac{4}{5} = \frac{36}{n}$

7. $\frac{1}{6} = \frac{a}{84}$

8. $\frac{3}{2} = \frac{15}{n}$

9. $\frac{4}{11} = \frac{20}{x}$

10. $\frac{7}{3} = \frac{n}{18}$

11. $\frac{6}{7} = \frac{n}{63}$

12. $\frac{37}{100} = \frac{n}{215}$

13. $\frac{9}{10} = \frac{n}{22}$

14. $\frac{3}{5} = \frac{8}{t}$

15. $\frac{4}{9} = \frac{10}{n}$

16. $\frac{11}{12} = \frac{x}{16}$

17. $\frac{7}{15} = \frac{1}{n}$

18. $\frac{5}{4} = \frac{n}{30}$

19. $\frac{17}{68} = \frac{b}{4}$

20. $\frac{1}{6} = \frac{n}{400}$

21. $\frac{6}{13} = \frac{x}{78}$

22. $\frac{2}{1} = \frac{15}{n}$

23. $\frac{3}{1,000} = \frac{p}{3,500}$

24. $\frac{13}{18} = \frac{n}{72}$

Mixed Applications

Write and solve a proportion for each problem.

25. Jonathan poured out 560 mL of distilled water. How many grams of salt should he add to the water if it takes 1 g of salt for every 28 mL of water? Let n = the grams of salt to be added.

26. It takes 112 mL of water and 4 g of salt to make a saline solution. Wendy used 145 mL of water and 5 g of salt to make a solution. How much greater or less was the amount of water than was needed? Let n = the amount of water needed.

27. **DATA BANK** The "saltiness," or *salinity*, of water is the ratio of grams of salt in the water to the volume of water. About how many times greater is the salinity of the Great Salt Lake than the salinity of the Pacific Ocean? (See page 432.)

PROBLEM SOLVING: Writing and Solving Proportions

QUESTION
DATA
PLAN
ANSWER
CHECK

Your heart will circulate about 48 L of blood every 10 min while you are seated at your desk. How many liters of blood would your heart circulate during a class period of 55 min?

Since the heart circulates the same amount of blood every 10 min, you can write and solve a proportion.

Let n = the number of liters of blood circulated in 55 min.

$$\begin{array}{l} \text{Minutes} \rightarrow \\ \text{Liters} \rightarrow \end{array} \frac{10}{48} = \frac{55}{n}$$

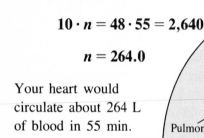

$$10 \cdot n = 48 \cdot 55 = 2{,}640$$

$$n = 264.0$$

Your heart would circulate about 264 L of blood in 55 min.

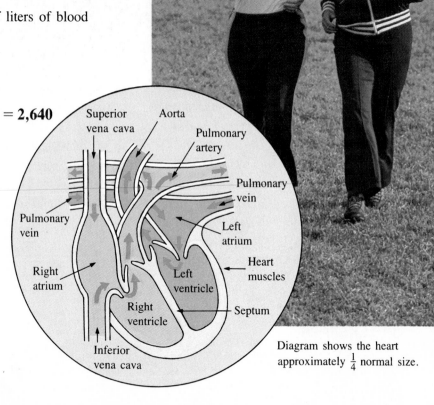

Superior vena cava
Aorta
Pulmonary artery
Pulmonary vein
Pulmonary vein
Left atrium
Right atrium
Left ventricle
Heart muscles
Right ventricle
Septum
Inferior vena cava

Diagram shows the heart approximately $\frac{1}{4}$ normal size.

Write and solve a proportion for each problem.

1. If your heart beats 16 times in 10 s, about how many times would it beat in 1 min?
   Let b = the number of heart beats in 1 min.

2. There are 750 registered voters in one precinct. In a primary election, 64 out of 100 registered voters actually voted. How many persons in the precinct voted?
   Let v = the number of people who voted.

5. One 0.25-liter serving of milk contains about 170 calories. How many calories are there in a 1.89-liter carton of milk?

6. Most airlines expect that out of 85 people who have reserved tickets for a flight, 7 people will not show up. If a flight has 340 reserved tickets, about how many people will be "no shows?"

7. A public opinion poll found that 5 out of 8 people in a community wanted an exercise course. If there are 10,000 people in the community, about how many of them want an exercise course? How many do not want an exercise course?

8. A bicycle wheel must make 13 revolutions to roll 25 m. How many revolutions must the wheel make to travel 1,000 m or 1 km?

9. A 52-gram weight tied to a spring stretches the spring 1.3 cm. How many grams would it take to stretch the spring 3 cm?

★ 10. A candle was 28 cm long. After burning for 20 min, the candle was 25.5 cm long. How many minutes would the candle burn from the time it was lit until the time it was used up?

3. In a sample from a lake, a biologist found that 3 out of 25 fish were bass. The biologist estimates that the lake contains about 6,000 fish. About how many bass should the biologist estimate are in the lake?

4. Marta drove her car about 132 km on 11 L of gasoline. She is planning a trip of 440 km. About how many liters of gasoline should she expect to use?

11. **Strategy Practice** Rosemary ran a 10-kilometer race. She ran the first kilometer in 5.0 min. After that, each kilometer took 0.2 min longer than the one before. What was the total time it took Rosemary to run the race?

251

Similar Triangles

Sam constructed a triangle with sides that were 2 cm, 3 cm, and 4 cm long. Then he constructed another triangle with sides that were three times as long as the sides of the first triangle. He noticed that the two triangles had the *same shape* but *not the same size*.

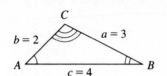

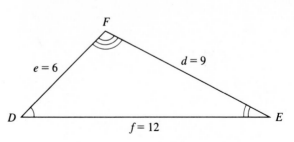

$\triangle ABC$ **is similar to** $\triangle DEF$.
$\triangle ABC \sim \triangle DEF$

Two triangles are similar if the corresponding angles are congruent to each other and if the ratios of the lengths of corresponding sides are equal.

$\angle A \cong \angle D, \quad \angle B \cong \angle E, \quad \angle C \cong \angle F$

$\dfrac{a}{d} = \dfrac{3}{9} = \dfrac{1}{3}, \qquad \dfrac{b}{e} = \dfrac{2}{6} = \dfrac{1}{3}, \qquad \dfrac{c}{f} = \dfrac{4}{12} = \dfrac{1}{3}$

Other Examples

$\triangle MNP \sim \triangle HKG$ What is length f?

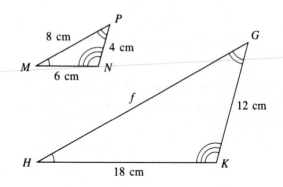

$\dfrac{f}{8} = \dfrac{12}{4}$ Ratios of lengths of corresponding sides

$4f = 96$

$f = 24$

Warm Up

1. $\triangle ABC \sim \triangle DEF$ Find length f.

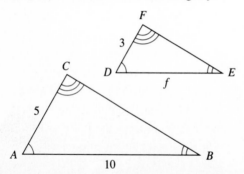

2. $\triangle RST \sim \triangle XYZ$ Find length s.

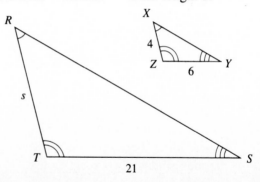

Practice Each pair of triangles is similar. Find length x for each pair.

1.

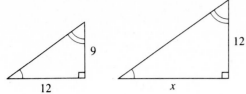

2.

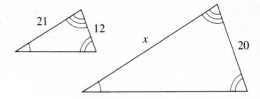

3.

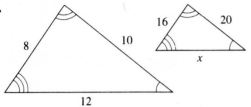

4.

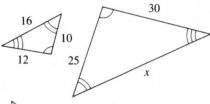

5.

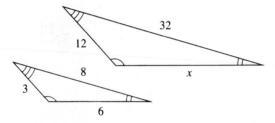

6.

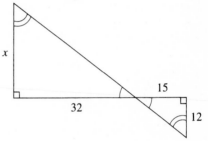

7. $\triangle RST \sim \triangle UVW$. What is length v? What are the degree measures of x and y?

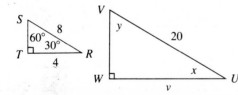

8. $\triangle ABC \sim \triangle AEF$. Find the lengths of $\overline{AB}$ and $\overline{EF}$.

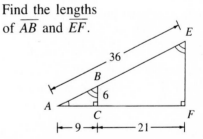

THINK MATH

Shape Perception

List the triangles in the figure that are similar to $\triangle ABC$.

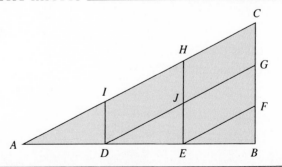

PROBLEM SOLVING: Using Data from a Drawing

QUESTION
DATA
PLAN
ANSWER
CHECK

A person 1.8 m tall casts a shadow of 2.4 m at the same time that a tower casts a shadow of 36 m. What is the height of the tower?

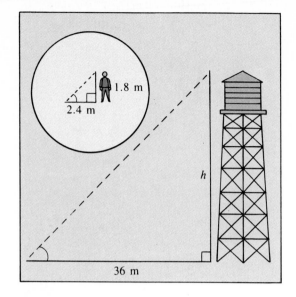

The two triangles in the picture are similar. We can write and solve a proportion to find the height (h) of the tower.

$$\frac{h}{1.8} = \frac{36}{2.4}$$

$$2.4\,h = 64.8$$

$$h = 27$$

The height of the tower is 27 m.

Solve.

The triangles in each problem are similar.

1. A person 1.6 m tall casts a shadow of 4.0 m at the same time that a flag pole casts a shadow of 42 m. What is the height (h) of the pole?

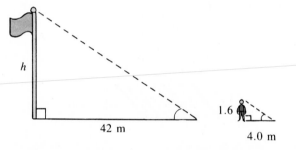

2. To find the distance (d) across the river, Diana sighted from point E, across A, to point C. Then she found the lengths of $\overline{AB}$, $\overline{AD}$, and $\overline{DE}$. What is the distance (d) across the river?

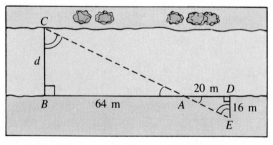

3. What is the vertical height (h) of the playground slide?

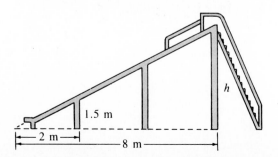

4. Tammy is 1.6 m tall. Her father is 2.0 m tall. Her father casts a shadow of 5 m. How long would Tammy's shadow (d) be?

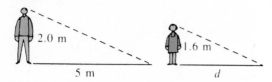

2.0 m
5 m
1.6 m
d

5. What is the height (h) of the kite?

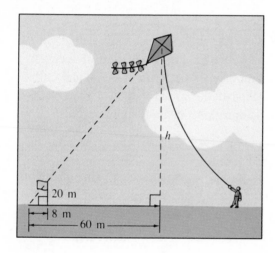

20 m
8 m
60 m
h

6. What is the distance (d) across the lake? What is the total distance around △PQR?

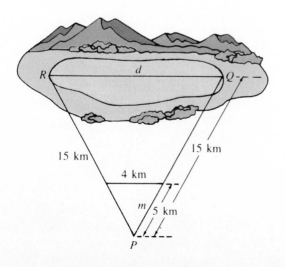

R
d
Q
15 km
15 km
4 km
m
5 km
P

7. David is 1.9 m tall. He stood 0.8 m from a mirror and could see the top of a building in the mirror. It is 72 m from the mirror to the base of the building. What is the height (h) of the building?

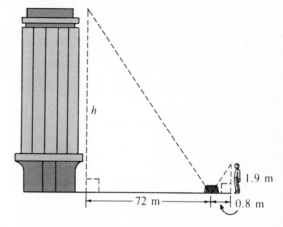

h
72 m
1.9 m
0.8 m

★ **8.** A concrete wheelchair ramp slopes upward 35 cm for each 2 m of its length. What is the total rise of the ramp if the total length along the ramp is 8.4 m?

9. **DATA HUNT** Choose a tall object at your school or near your home. Find the height of the object by using the "shadow method" of problem 1, and the "mirror method" of problem 7. What is the difference in the heights using the two methods?

10. **Strategy Practice** Edward's shadow is 600 cm long when Andrew's shadow is 720 cm long. Andrew is 30 cm taller than Edward. How tall is each person? Hint: Draw a picture.

Scale and Proportion

Scale: 2 cm : 480 m

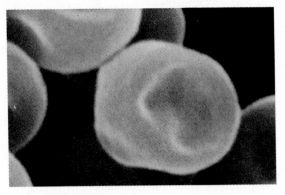

Scale: 2,800 mm : 1 mm   Enlarged 2,800×

The width of a field in an aerial photograph is 2 cm wide. The actual field is 480 m wide. What is the actual length of the field if it is 1.5 cm long in the photograph?

The photograph shows all dimensions reduced in the same ratio or **scale**.

The scale for the photograph is 2 cm : 480 m.

Let l = the actual length of the field.

Photograph width (cm) →
Actual width (m) →
$$\frac{2}{480} = \frac{1.5}{l}$$
$$2\,l = 720$$
$$l = 360$$

The field is 360 m long.

The microscope photograph of a cell is 2,800 times larger than the actual cell. What is the actual length of the cell if it is 42 mm long in the photograph?

Let d = the actual length of the cell.

Photograph length (mm) →
Actual length (mm) →
$$\frac{42 \text{ mm}}{d} = \frac{2,800}{1}$$
$$2,800\,d = 42$$
$$d = \frac{42}{2,800}$$
$$d = 0.015$$

The actual length of the cell is 0.015 mm.

Warm Up

Give the actual length between the two points.

1.

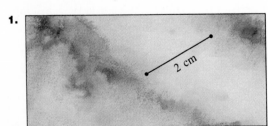

2 cm

Scale: 3 cm : 50 km

2.

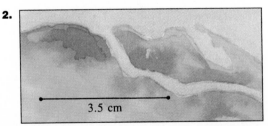

3.5 cm

Scale: 5 cm : 360 m

Practice

Use the map and the scale to find the actual direct distance, to the nearest kilometer, between the cities in Florida. Use a metric ruler to measure the map distances to the nearest tenth of a centimeter.

1. West Palm Beach to Fort Myers

2. West Palm Beach to Miami

3. Fort Lauderdale to Key West

4. Fort Myers to Key West

5. Fort Lauderdale to Naples

6. Fort Myers to Miami

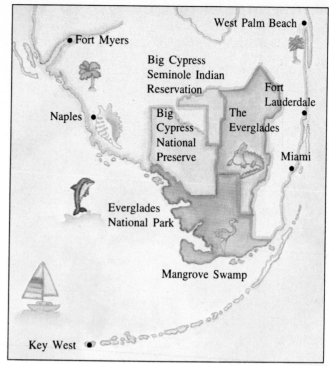

Scale: 3 cm : 85 km

Mixed Applications

Think of enlargements to solve these problems.

7. An electron microscope was used to make a photograph of a mumps virus. The virus was enlarged 45,600 times in the photograph. The diameter of the virus in the photograph was 32 mm. What is the actual diameter of the virus, to the nearest ten-thousandth of a millimeter?

8. A virus measures 0.0004 mm. How many times must the cell be magnified for it to measure 42 mm in a photograph?

9. Use the data in the drawing below to make up a problem.

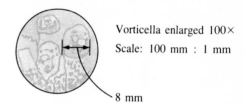

Vorticella enlarged 100×
Scale: 100 mm : 1 mm

8 mm

10. A polio virus was magnified 290,000 times by an electron microscope. In the photograph the virus has a diameter of 8 mm. An influenza virus is magnified 36,000 times and has a diameter of 22 mm. How many times larger is the actual diameter of the influenza virus than the actual diameter of the polio virus? Round your answer to the nearest whole number.

The Tangent Ratio

The sides of right $\triangle ABC$ have special names.

Side a is **opposite** $\angle A$.
Side b is **adjacent to** $\angle A$.
Side c is the **hypotenuse**.

The hypotenuse is always opposite the right angle.

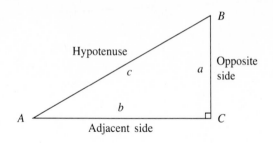

The three triangles below are similar triangles. Each triangle has an acute angle of 32°.

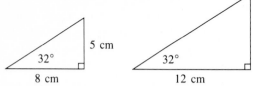

In each triangle, the ratio of the length of the opposite side to the length of the adjacent side is the same number.

$$\frac{5}{8} = \frac{7.5}{12} = \frac{10}{16} = 0.625$$

This special ratio is called the **tangent ratio**.

$$\frac{\text{Opposite side}}{\text{Adjacent side}}$$

tan 32° = 0.625   We read: "Tangent of 32° equals 0.625."

Other Examples

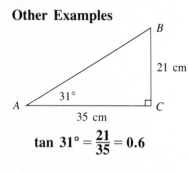

$$\tan 31° = \frac{21}{35} = 0.6$$

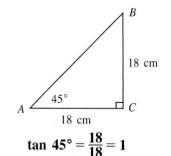

$$\tan 45° = \frac{18}{18} = 1$$

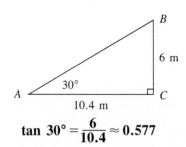

$$\tan 30° = \frac{6}{10.4} \approx 0.577$$

Warm Up

Give the tangent of $\angle A$ to the nearest thousandth.

1.

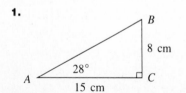

2.

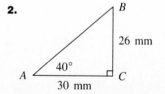

3.

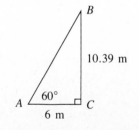

258

Practice Find tan A to the nearest thousandth.

1.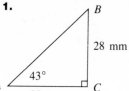

28 mm 43° 30 mm

2.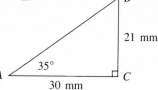

21 mm 35° 30 mm

3.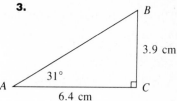

3.9 cm 31° 6.4 cm

4.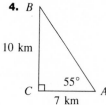

10 km 55° 7 km

5.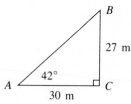

5.6 cm 6.0 cm 47°

6.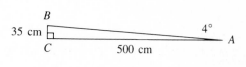

35 cm 4° 500 cm

7.

2.87 cm 60° 4.97 cm

8.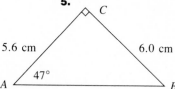

27 m 42° 30 m

9.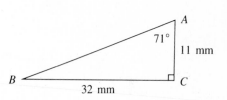

71° 11 mm 32 mm

Mixed Applications

10. A ladder rests against a building 8 m above the ground. The base of the ladder is 2 m from the building so that the ladder forms an angle of 76° with the ground. What is tan 76°? Make and label a drawing.

11. A freeway exit ramp slopes downward 5°. In a horizontal distance of 100 m, the ramp drops a vertical distance of 8.7 m. What is tan 5°? Make and label a drawing.

Table of Tangent Ratios

Some calculators and computers have been programmed to give the tangent ratio for any angle.

A table of tangent ratios has also been made for easy reference.

The table gives tangent ratios rounded to the nearest thousandth.

To find tan 62°

Enter	Press	Display
62	**tan**	1.8807265

Angle	Tangent	Angle	Tangent	Angle	Tangent	Angle	Tangent	Angle	Tangent
0°	0.000	20°	0.364	40°	0.839	60°	1.732	80°	5.671
1°	0.017	21°	0.384	41°	0.869	61°	1.804	81°	6.314
2°	0.035	22°	0.404	42°	0.900	62°	1.881	82°	7.115
3°	0.052	23°	0.424	43°	0.933	63°	1.963	83°	8.144
4°	0.070	24°	0.445	44°	0.966	64°	2.050	84°	9.514
5°	0.087	25°	0.466	45°	1.000	65°	2.145	85°	11.430
6°	0.105	26°	0.488	46°	1.036	66°	2.246	86°	14.301
7°	0.123	27°	0.510	47°	1.072	67°	2.356	87°	19.081
8°	0.141	28°	0.532	48°	1.111	68°	2.475	88°	28.636
9°	0.158	29°	0.554	49°	1.150	69°	2.605	89°	57.290
10°	0.176	30°	0.577	50°	1.192	70°	2.748	90°	—
11°	0.194	31°	0.601	51°	1.235	71°	2.904		
12°	0.213	32°	0.625	52°	1.280	72°	3.078		
13°	0.231	33°	0.649	53°	1.327	73°	3.271		
14°	0.249	34°	0.675	54°	1.376	74°	3.487		
15°	0.268	35°	0.700	55°	1.428	75°	3.732		
16°	0.287	36°	0.727	56°	1.483	76°	4.011		
17°	0.306	37°	0.754	57°	1.540	77°	4.332		
18°	0.325	38°	0.781	58°	1.600	78°	4.705		
19°	0.344	39°	0.810	59°	1.664	79°	5.145		

Practice Use the table to find each tangent ratio.

1. tan 13°   **2.** tan 50°   **3.** tan 80°   **4.** tan 15°

5. tan 41°   **6.** tan 45°   **7.** tan 10°   **8.** tan 23°

9. tan 53°   **10.** tan 3°   **11.** tan 65°   **12.** tan 78°

Find the degree measure for $\angle A$.

13. tan $A \approx 0.404$ **14.** tan $A \approx 0.933$ **15.** tan $A \approx 2.475$ **16.** tan $A \approx 9.514$

17. tan $A \approx 1.327$ **18.** tan $A \approx 8.144$ **19.** tan $A \approx 2.356$ **20.** tan $A \approx 19.081$

PROBLEM SOLVING: Using Data from a Table

QUESTION
DATA
PLAN
ANSWER
CHECK

From a point on the ground 80 m in front of a building, the angle to the top of the building measures 42°. What is the height of the building?

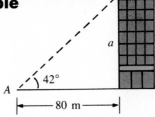

To find the height, you can write and solve an equation using the tangent ratio.

Use the table of tangent ratios on page 260 to find tan 42°.

Tangent ratio equation $\dfrac{a}{80} = \tan 42°$

Substitute tan 42°. $\dfrac{a}{80} = 0.900$

Solve the division equation. $80 \cdot \dfrac{a}{80} = 80 \cdot 0.900$

$a = 72.00$

The height of the building is 72 m.

Use the table of tangent ratios on page 260 to solve these problems.

1. A guy wire is stretched from the top of a vertical pole to a point on the ground 6 m from the base of the pole. The wire makes an angle of 84° with the ground. What is the height of the pole?

2. The top of a ladder reaches to a height of 8 m on the side of a building when the bottom of the ladder is 2 m from the building. What is the tangent of the angle that the ladder forms with the ground? What is the degree measure of the angle?

3. An airplane climbs at a constant angle of 8° at takeoff. How high above the ground is the plane when it is 1,000 m from the takeoff point?

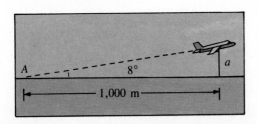

4. Makiko is 1.7 m tall. Makiko's shadow is 3.3 m long. What is the measure of the angle between the sun's rays and the ground at this moment?

5. The gable of a building forms an isosceles triangle. The base of the triangle is 16 m long. The roof makes an angle of 25° with the base. What is the height of the gable?

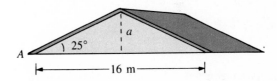

6. **Strategy Practice** Maggie hiked 7.2 km east in a straight line from camp. Then she turned and hiked 3.5 km due north. At what angle to the north-south direction should she walk in order to walk directly back to camp? Hint: Draw and label a picture.

261

Mixed Skills Practice

Computation
Find the answers.

1. $\begin{array}{r} 23.5 \\ \times 18 \\ \hline \end{array}$

2. $\begin{array}{r} 162 \\ \times 59 \\ \hline \end{array}$

3. $\begin{array}{r} \$64.00 \\ -27.58 \\ \hline \end{array}$

4. $\begin{array}{r} \$23.48 \\ 16.50 \\ +37.95 \\ \hline \end{array}$

5. $0.9\overline{)3.105}$

6. $3\frac{1}{2} \div \frac{7}{8}$

7. $92\overline{)34,142}$

8. $\frac{5}{8} \times \frac{2}{3}$

9. $\begin{array}{r} 2\frac{1}{2} \\ +5\frac{1}{4} \\ \hline \end{array}$

10. $\begin{array}{r} 20 \\ -12\frac{3}{8} \\ \hline \end{array}$

11. $\begin{array}{r} 3.77 \\ \times 0.34 \\ \hline \end{array}$

12. $\begin{array}{r} 12.013 \\ -7.746 \\ \hline \end{array}$

13. Solve.
$x + 19 = 9$

14. Solve.
$\frac{x}{5} - 3 = 2$

15. Solve.
$2x + 1 = {}^{-}11$

16. Solve.
$x - \frac{2}{5} = 1\frac{1}{2}$

Mental Math
Write only the answers.

17. 7×400

18. $\frac{1}{4} \times 28$

19. $50 + 80 + 50 + 20$

20. $4,500 \div 90$

21. $2,400 \div 300$

22. $400 - 99$

23. $700 + 500 + 800$

24. $\frac{2}{3} \times 60$

25. $2 \times 5\frac{1}{2}$

26. 0.01×380

27. $1.6 \div 4$

28. $8\frac{3}{4} + 1\frac{1}{4}$

29. ${}^{-}2 \times 8$

30. ${}^{-}7 \times {}^{-}9$

31. $(8 \times {}^{-}3) \div {}^{-}4$

32. $({}^{-}7 + 5) \times 6$

Estimation
Estimate.

33. 216×4.13

34. $79\overline{)1,762}$

35. $78.6\overline{)39.224}$

36. $\frac{1}{3} \times \$29.75$

37. 3.7×8.4

38. $2.93\overline{)16.44}$

39. $18 + 23 + 20 + 19$

40. $28\frac{9}{19} + 15\frac{3}{11}$

41. 50.3×6.29

42. 0.78×0.593

43. 0.976×1.015

44. $\frac{1}{8} \times \$319.77$

45. $\begin{array}{r} 553 \\ 224 \\ +636 \\ \hline \end{array}$

46. $\begin{array}{r} 82,149 \\ -76,953 \\ \hline \end{array}$

47. $\begin{array}{r} \$3.98 \\ 4.19 \\ 6.22 \\ +5.75 \\ \hline \end{array}$

48. $\begin{array}{r} 9.071 \\ -3.584 \\ \hline \end{array}$

APPLIED PROBLEM SOLVING

QUESTION
DATA
PLAN
ANSWER
CHECK

You are helping a marine biologist estimate the number of fish in a lake. You will use a "capture-recapture" plan to decide on the estimate.

Some Things to Consider

- You capture 200 fish and mark all of them with a special dye. Then you put the fish back in the lake.

- At a later time you capture samples of fish and record how many have the special dye mark.

- You use a proportion to estimate the total number of fish.

Sample	Number of fish in a sample	Number with special mark
A	50	1
B	80	2
C	100	3
D	60	1
E	40	0
F	70	1

Some Questions to Answer

1. Using sample A, what would be your estimate of the number of fish in the lake?

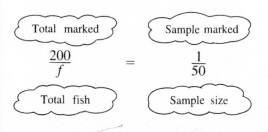

$$\frac{200}{f} = \frac{1}{50}$$

Total marked — Sample marked
Total fish — Sample size

2. What is your estimate of the total number of fish using sample B?

3. What is your estimate of the total number of fish using sample C?

4. Using sample D, what is an estimate of the total number of fish?

What Is Your Decision?

What estimate would you give for the number of fish in the lake?

PROBLEM SOLVING: Using the Strategies

QUESTION
DATA
PLAN
ANSWER
CHECK

Problem–Solving Strategies

✔ Guess and Check   ✔ Make a Table

✔ Choose the Operations   ✔ Solve a Simpler Problem

✔ Make an Organized List   ✔ Find a Pattern

✔ Work Backward   ✔ Use Logical Reasoning

✔ Draw a Picture

You have learned to use different strategies to solve some of the problems in this book.

1. Norma and Helen are orienteering. Norma walks 3 km east, 4 km north, 10 km west, 5 km south, and 3 km east to the end of the course. Helen walks 5 km north, 6 km east, 8 km south, 4 km west, and 2 km north. How far and in what direction must Helen now walk to reach the end of the course?

2. Joaquin said, "My telephone number is alphabetical and each of the ten digits 0 through 9 is used one time." The first three digits are eight, five, and four. What are the next seven digits?

3. Jesse, Bob, Josh, and Jonah were each born under different signs of the zodiac. Their signs are Aquarius, Pisces, Leo, and Scorpio. Josh is neither Scorpio nor Pisces. Jesse is not Pisces. The name of the Aquarius does not start with the letter B. The teacher is a Leo. Josh, Jesse, and Bob are students. What is each person's zodiac sign?

4. Lita's airplane flight leaves at 9:05 a.m. She wants to be at the airport $\frac{1}{2}$ h before. It will take her about 50 min to get to the airport. She needs 45 min to get dressed and have breakfast. At what time should she set her alarm clock?

Write = or ≠ for each 🌀. Use cross products to decide.

1. $\frac{3}{4}$ 🌀 $\frac{12}{16}$

2. $\frac{2}{3}$ 🌀 $\frac{12}{15}$

3. $\frac{8}{14}$ 🌀 $\frac{6}{10}$

4. $\frac{15}{18}$ 🌀 $\frac{20}{24}$

Simplify each rate.

5. $\frac{85 \text{ m}}{5 \text{ s}}$

6. $\frac{\$2.40}{10 \text{ min}}$

7. $\frac{88 \text{ km}}{11 \text{ L}}$

8. $\frac{240 \text{ revolutions}}{8 \text{ minutes}}$

Find each unit price.

9. 1.2 kg for $6.00

10. 0.25 L for $0.80

Solve each proportion.

11. $\frac{2}{9} = \frac{n}{45}$

12. $\frac{3}{8} = \frac{15}{n}$

13. $\frac{1}{18} = \frac{n}{72}$

14. $\frac{5}{3} = \frac{n}{18}$

Find length x in each pair of similar figures.

15.

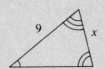

16.
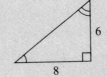

Write the missing numbers.

17. Grand Rapids to Lansing: 🌀 km

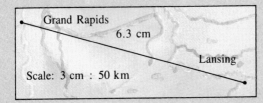

Grand Rapids
6.3 cm
Lansing
Scale: 3 cm : 50 km

18. Cell magnified 1,500 times
Actual length: 🌀 mm

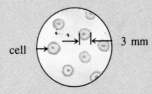

cell   3 mm

19. Find tan A.

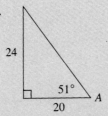

24
51°
20
A

20. What is length a?

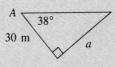

A 38°
30 m
a

21. About 5 of every 12 people order wheat bread. Out of 180 people, how many would order wheat bread?

22. About 3 out of every 8 people called will buy insurance. If 120 people are called, how many will buy insurance?

Three ways to write ratios

3 to 4 **3:4** $\frac{3}{4}$

$\begin{array}{l} 2 \quad 8 \\ 5 \quad 20 \end{array}$ → $\begin{array}{l} 5 \times 8 = 40 \\ 2 \times 20 = 40 \end{array}$ $\frac{2}{5} = \frac{8}{20}$

$\begin{array}{l} 8 \quad 3 \\ 12 \quad 4 \end{array}$ → $\begin{array}{l} 12 \times 3 = 36 \\ 8 \times 4 = 32 \end{array}$ $\frac{8}{12} \neq \frac{3}{4}$

Write each ratio as a fraction.

1. 6 to 10   **2.** 8:15   **3.** 3 to 1

Write = or ≠ for each ◉. Use cross products to decide.

4. $\frac{2}{9}$ ◉ $\frac{10}{45}$ **5.** $\frac{5}{3}$ ◉ $\frac{15}{12}$ **6.** $\frac{10}{8}$ ◉ $\frac{15}{12}$

7. $\frac{18}{4}$ ◉ $\frac{9}{2}$ **8.** $\frac{3}{10}$ ◉ $\frac{33}{100}$ **9.** $\frac{6}{9}$ ◉ $\frac{14}{21}$

---

100 km in 2 h

$\frac{100 \text{ km}}{2 \text{ h}} = \frac{100 \text{ km} \div 2}{2 \text{ h} \div 2} = \frac{50 \text{ km}}{1 \text{ h}}$

$\frac{50 \text{ km}}{1 \text{ h}} = 50 \text{ km/h}$ ⟵ Rate

Simplify each rate.

10. $\frac{250 \text{ m}}{50 \text{ s}}$ **11.** $\frac{640 \text{ words}}{4 \text{ min}}$ **12.** $\frac{63 \text{ days}}{9 \text{ wk}}$

---

5 L for $2.50

$\frac{\$2.50}{5 \text{ L}} = \$0.50/\text{L}$ ⟵ Unit price

Find each unit price.

13. 0.5 L for $1.20   **14.** 0.1 kg for $0.60

15. 3 cans for $0.78   **16.** 0.75 L for $3

$\frac{3}{8} = \frac{n}{40}$

$8n = 120$

$\frac{8n}{8} = \frac{120}{8}$

$n = 15$

Solve each proportion.

17. $\frac{4}{9} = \frac{n}{27}$ **18.** $\frac{8}{3} = \frac{40}{n}$

19. $\frac{8}{10} = \frac{n}{60}$ **20.** $\frac{1}{12} = \frac{9}{n}$

21. $\frac{3}{2} = \frac{9}{n}$ **22.** $\frac{11}{12} = \frac{n}{60}$

$\frac{8}{10} = \frac{4}{x}$

$8x = 40$

$x = 5$

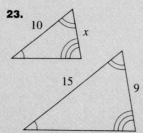

Find length x in each pair of similar triangles.

23.

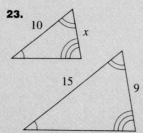

24.

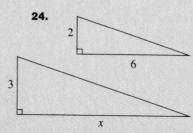

Compound Proportions

The band members of Wilbur Middle School organized a car wash to raise money for new uniforms. It took 20 min for 8 students to wash 3 cars. At this rate, how many cars could 16 students wash in 30 min?

You may be able to solve this problem using logical reasoning. The steps below will help you.

Use the data to identify inputs and outputs.

Inputs: Number of students, number of minutes
Outputs: Number of cars washed

1. Make a table of inputs and outputs.

First input	8 students, 20 min
First output	3 cars
Second input	16 students, 30 min
Second output	n cars

2. Write a compound proportion.

$$\frac{\text{Product of First inputs}}{\text{First output}} = \frac{\text{Product of Second outputs}}{\text{Second output}}$$

3. Solve the proportion.

n = number of cars by 16 students in 30 min

$$\frac{8 \cdot 20}{3} = \frac{16 \cdot 30}{n}$$

$$\frac{160}{3} = \frac{480}{n}$$

$$160\,n = 1{,}440$$

$$n = 9$$

Sixteen students could wash 9 cars in 30 min.

Write and solve a compound proportion for each problem.

1. If 10 students can wash 3 cars in 5 min, how many cars can 12 students wash in 25 min?

2. If 3 robots can assemble 7 motors in 10 min, how many motors can 12 robots assemble in 20 min?

3. If 2 painters can paint 3 houses in 6 days, how many houses would be painted by 3 painters in 4 days?

4. If a hen and a half lays an egg and a half in a day and a half, how many eggs would 6 hens lay in 1 day?

Write the missing numbers.

1. 27,956 m = ▓ km

   A 27.956   **B** 0.27956
   C 279.56   **D** not given

2. 95 mL = ▓ g of water

   A 9.5   **B** 950
   C 95   **D** not given

3. 3 h 12 min = ▓ s

   A 2,160   **B** 900
   C 11,520   **D** not given

4. What is the capacity of a cocoa mug?

   A about 225 L   **B** about 225 kL
   C about 225 mL   **D** not given

5. At what temperature does water freeze?

   A ⁻20° C   **B** 0° C
   C 32° C   **D** not given

6. Which measurement is most precise?

   A 16 mm   **B** 16.3 mm
   C 16 cm   **D** not given

7. What is the symbol for parallel lines?

   A ∥   **B** ↔
   C ⊥   **D** not given

8. What is the name of a triangle with two sides the same length?

   A obtuse   **B** vertex
   C isosceles   **D** not given

9. What is the sum of the measures of the angles in any quadrilateral?

   A 180°   **B** 540°
   C 720°   **D** not given

10. What is the measure of the central angle x?

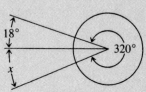

   A 360°   **B** 22°
   C 338°   **D** not given

11. What is the name of a line that intersects a circle at two points?

   A arc   **B** secant
   C tangent   **D** not given

12. How many lines of symmetry does a square have?

   A 2   **B** 3
   C 4   **D** not given

13. If three sides of one triangle are congruent to three sides of another triangle, what type of congruence is this?

   A ASA   **B** SSS
   C SAS   **D** not given

14. One day, Dotty did yard work from 9:15 a.m. to noon. Then she worked as a service station attendant from 1:45 to 5:15 p.m. How many hours did she work?

   A $5\frac{1}{4}$ h   **B** $6\frac{1}{4}$ h
   C $5\frac{3}{4}$ h   **D** not given

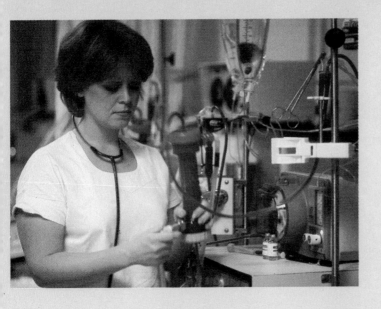

11

Percent

The blood moving through your veins and arteries is part of a complex system that feeds every cell in your body. Your body probably holds from 3.3 to 3.8 liters of blood.

Blood is made up of solid and liquid substances. The liquid part, a yellowish fluid called *plasma*, is mostly water. Blood is 55 to 65 percent plasma. There are solid substances in the plasma that make up the rest of the volume: red blood cells, white blood cells, and platelets. The red blood cells give blood its color.

Blood can be transferred from one body to another. The Red Cross, an organization founded to help people in distress, keeps blood in storage units called blood banks. Some hospitals have their own blood banks.

Blood banks were first set up during World War II. One of the founders of the American Red Cross Blood Bank was Dr. Charles Drew, a medical doctor who did research on blood plasma. He also did research on the separation of blood into its various components and on the preservation of blood. His efforts during World War II saved many lives.

Percent

In the Daniel A. Payne
High School Band,
35 out of 100 members
are trombone players.

The part of the band that is the trombone section
can be described in several ways.

Ratio: **35** out of **100** members are trombone players.

Fraction: $\frac{35}{100}$ of the members are trombone players.

Decimal: **0.35** of the members are trombone players.

A percent can also be used.

Percent means **per hundred**.
The symbol for percent is %.

35% of the band members are trombone players.

Other Examples

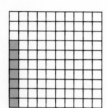

Fraction: $\frac{7}{100}$
Decimal: **0.07**
Percent: **7%**

Fraction: $\frac{62}{100}$
Decimal: **0.62**
Percent: **62%**

Fraction: $\frac{100}{100}$
Decimal: **1.00**
Percent: **100%**

Practice Write a fraction, a decimal, and a percent for the part of each region that is shaded.

1.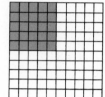
2.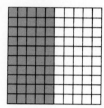
3.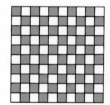
4.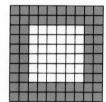

What percent of each region is shaded?

5.
6.
7.
8.

Copy and complete the table.

	Ratio	Fraction	Decimal	Percent
9.	7 out of 100			
10.	37 to 100			
11.	61 out of 100			
12.	79 for every 100			
13.	23 per 100			
14.	11 to 100			
15.	1 for every 100			
16.	99 to 100			

Mixed Applications

17. In a college band, 17 of 100 members play wind instruments. What percent of the band plays wind instruments?

18. Only 2 out of 100 band members were absent at the last practice. What percent of the members were absent?

19. In a 100-member band, 27 of the members got new uniforms last year. What percent of the band does not have new uniforms?

20. The Montclair Junior High Drum and Bugle Corps has 100 members. There are 67 bugle players and the rest are drummers. What percent of the members are drummers?

Percents and Decimals

A single serving of cereal contains 10% of the amount of protein adults need daily. What is the decimal for this percent?

Remember, percent means per hundred.

$$10\% = \frac{10}{100} = 0.10$$

Dividing by 100 shifts the decimal point 2 places to the left.

The cereal supplies 0.10 of the recommended daily allowance.

One serving of cereal provides about 0.06 of the amount of iron adults need. What is the percent for this decimal?

To write a percent for a decimal, shift the decimal point 2 places to the right.

$0.06 = 6\%$

Other Examples

$0.64 = 64\%$ $0.075 = 7.5\%$ $0.2 = 20\%$

$12.5\% = 0.125$ $2\% = 0.02$ $33.3\% = 0.333$

Warm Up

Give each percent as a decimal.

1. 74%   **2.** 19%   **3.** 40%   **4.** 8.4%

Give each decimal as a percent.

5. 0.48   **6.** 0.54   **7.** 0.3   **8.** 0.085

272

Practice Write each percent as a decimal.

1. 83% 2. 17% 3. 66% 4. 25% 5. 9%

6. 78% 7. 41% 8. 23% 9. 16% 10. 3%

11. 4.5% 12. 7.2% 13. 5% 14. 133% 15. 42%

Write each decimal as a percent.

16. 0.75 17. 0.38 18. 0.07 19. 0.65 20. 0.16

21. 0.5 22. 0.08 23. 0.09 24. 0.18 25. 0.6

26. 0.384 27. 0.266 28. 0.8 29. 0.155 30. 0.322

Mixed Applications

31. A glass of milk provides about 30% of the amount of calcium adults need daily. What decimal part is 30%?

32. A single serving of hot wheat cereal supplies 0.08 of the recommended daily amount of iron. What percent of the daily amount is this?

33. A pancake supplies about one percent of the daily amount of vitamin A. What is the decimal for this percent?

34. **DATA BANK** What percent of the recommended daily allowance for vitamin B-2 does one vitamin tablet supply? What is the decimal for this percent? (See page 431.)

SKILLKEEPER

Write = or ≠ for each ratio. Use cross products to decide.

1. $\frac{45}{54}$ ⬤ $\frac{35}{40}$ 2. $\frac{12}{30}$ ⬤ $\frac{15}{40}$ 3. $\frac{9}{4}$ ⬤ $\frac{27}{12}$ 4. $\frac{10}{16}$ ⬤ $\frac{25}{40}$ 5. $\frac{17}{34}$ ⬤ $\frac{14}{28}$

6. $\frac{12}{16}$ ⬤ $\frac{24}{32}$ 7. $\frac{2}{3}$ ⬤ $\frac{12}{15}$ 8. $\frac{7}{21}$ ⬤ $\frac{3}{9}$ 9. $\frac{12}{16}$ ⬤ $\frac{21}{28}$ 10. $\frac{3}{8}$ ⬤ $\frac{24}{72}$

11. $\frac{4}{5}$ ⬤ $\frac{21}{27}$ 12. $\frac{3}{5}$ ⬤ $\frac{57}{95}$ 13. $\frac{7}{8}$ ⬤ $\frac{50}{60}$ 14. $\frac{6}{8}$ ⬤ $\frac{63}{84}$ 15. $\frac{9}{12}$ ⬤ $\frac{51}{68}$

16. $\frac{2}{3}$ ⬤ $\frac{24}{39}$ 17. $\frac{9}{15}$ ⬤ $\frac{24}{40}$ 18. $\frac{2}{5}$ ⬤ $\frac{25}{70}$ 19. $\frac{6}{8}$ ⬤ $\frac{45}{60}$ 20. $\frac{4}{10}$ ⬤ $\frac{14}{35}$

Percents and Fractions

By the age of 8, girls reach about $\frac{2}{5}$ of their adult weight. What percent of their adult weight is this?

To give a percent for a fraction, we find an equivalent fraction with a denominator of 100.

$$\frac{2}{5} = \frac{2 \times 20}{5 \times 20} = \frac{40}{100} = 40\%$$

We can also divide to find a decimal for the fraction.

$$\begin{array}{r} 0.4\,0 \\ 5\,\overline{)2.0\,0} \\ 2\,0 \\ \hline 0 \\ 0 \\ \hline 0 \end{array} \rightarrow 0.40 = 40\%$$

Girls reach about 40% of their adult weight by the age of 8.

Other Examples

What is the fraction for 45%?

$$45\% = \frac{45}{100} = \frac{9}{20}$$

What percent is $\frac{5}{8}$?

$$\begin{array}{r} 0.62\frac{4}{8} \\ 8\,\overline{)5.00} \end{array} \rightarrow 0.62\frac{1}{2} = 62\frac{1}{2}\% = 62.5\%$$

$62\frac{1}{2}\%$ rounded to the nearest whole percent is 63%.

Warm Up

Give the percent for each fraction.

1. $\frac{3}{10}$ **2.** $\frac{7}{50}$ **3.** $\frac{1}{6}$ **4.** $\frac{7}{12}$

Give the lowest-terms fraction for each percent.

5. 75%   **6.** 22%   **7.** 25%   **8.** 64%

274

Practice Write the percent for each fraction.

1. $\frac{4}{10}$
2. $\frac{9}{20}$
3. $\frac{7}{100}$
4. $\frac{1}{50}$
5. $\frac{7}{25}$

6. $\frac{3}{50}$
7. $\frac{3}{25}$
8. $\frac{3}{20}$
9. $\frac{5}{12}$
10. $\frac{5}{6}$

11. $\frac{1}{9}$
12. $\frac{3}{15}$
13. $\frac{5}{24}$
14. $\frac{7}{36}$
15. $\frac{5}{9}$

Copy and complete the tables.

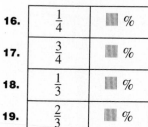

	Fraction	Percent
16.	$\frac{1}{4}$	▨ %
17.	$\frac{3}{4}$	▨ %
18.	$\frac{1}{3}$	▨ %
19.	$\frac{2}{3}$	▨ %

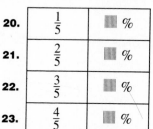

	Fraction	Percent
20.	$\frac{1}{5}$	▨ %
21.	$\frac{2}{5}$	▨ %
22.	$\frac{3}{5}$	▨ %
23.	$\frac{4}{5}$	▨ %

	Fraction	Percent
24.	$\frac{1}{8}$	▨ %
25.	$\frac{3}{8}$	▨ %
26.	$\frac{5}{8}$	▨ %
27.	$\frac{7}{8}$	▨ %

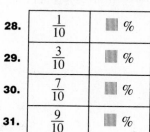

	Fraction	Percent
28.	$\frac{1}{10}$	▨ %
29.	$\frac{3}{10}$	▨ %
30.	$\frac{7}{10}$	▨ %
31.	$\frac{9}{10}$	▨ %

Write the lowest-terms fraction for each percent.

32. 70%
33. 25%
34. 15%
35. $87\frac{1}{2}\%$
36. $12\frac{1}{2}\%$

Write the percent for each fraction. Round to the nearest whole percent. ▨

37. $\frac{73}{87}$
38. $\frac{56}{95}$
39. $\frac{261}{375}$
40. $\frac{45}{214}$
41. $\frac{319}{500}$

42. By the age of 14, boys reach about $\frac{2}{3}$ of their adult weight. What percent of their adult weight is this?

43. By the age of 12, girls reach about $\frac{88}{135}$ of their adult weight. What percent (to the nearest whole percent) of their adult weight is this?

More Practice, page 449, Set D

275

Large and Small Percents

The graphs show the money raised by a fund drive during one month. Each square shows 1% of the fund.

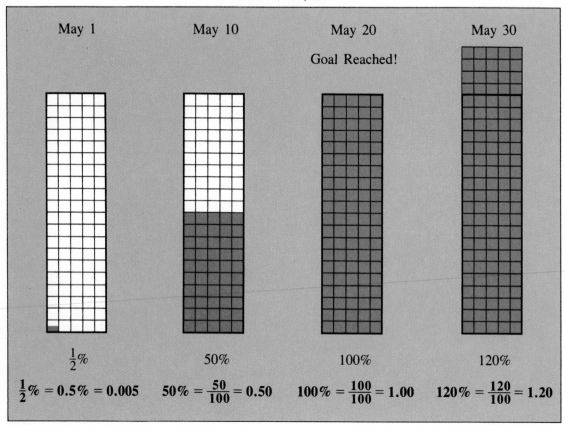

Performing Arts Center Fund Drive
Goal: $100,000

May 1	May 10	May 20	May 30
		Goal Reached!	
$\frac{1}{2}\%$	50%	100%	120%

$\frac{1}{2}\% = 0.5\% = 0.005$ $50\% = \frac{50}{100} = 0.50$ $100\% = \frac{100}{100} = 1.00$ $120\% = \frac{120}{100} = 1.20$

Other Examples

$250\% = \frac{250}{100} = 2.50$ $3\frac{1}{4}\% = 3.25\% = \frac{3.25}{100} = 0.0325$ $0.1\% = \frac{0.1}{100} = 0.001$

Warm Up

Give the decimal for each percent.

1. 110%   **2.** $\frac{3}{4}\%$ **3.** 0.8%   **4.** 3.8%   **5.** 1,000%

Give the percent for each decimal.

6. 0.002   **7.** 0.085   **8.** 3.50   **9.** 60.0   **10.** 0.0005

276

Practice Write each percent as a decimal.

1. 225%   **2.** 150%   **3.** $5\frac{1}{2}\%$ **4.** 4.25%   **5.** 500%

6. $3\frac{3}{4}\%$ **7.** 510%   **8.** 1,500%   **9.** $2\frac{1}{2}\%$ **10.** 5.4%

11. 300%   **12.** 33.3%   **13.** $\frac{1}{4}\%$ **14.** 725%   **15.** 0.2%

Write each decimal as a percent.

16. 3.0   **17.** 4.25   **18.** 0.003   **19.** 5.6   **20.** 0.0025

21. 0.045   **22.** 8.7   **23.** 1   **24.** 1.25   **25.** 0.004

26. 2   **27.** 0.072   **28.** 3.18   **29.** 0.185   **30.** 4.2

Write each fraction as a percent.

31. $\frac{150}{100}$ **32.** $\frac{387}{100}$ **33.** $\frac{5}{4}$ **34.** $\frac{7}{2}$ **35.** $\frac{11}{10}$

36. $\frac{0.3}{100}$ **37.** $\frac{8}{5}$ **38.** $\frac{266}{100}$ **39.** $\frac{5.25}{100}$ **40.** $\frac{9}{4}$

Write each fraction as a percent. Round to the nearest hundredth of a percent. 🖩

41. $\frac{3}{500}$ **42.** $\frac{18}{2,700}$ **43.** $\frac{84}{90}$ **44.** $\frac{1}{160}$ **45.** $\frac{318}{149}$

Mixed Applications

46. A fund drive reached 175% of its goal. What is this percent as a decimal?

★ **47.** Julia O'Neill gave $10.00 to the fund drive. What percent of $100,000 did she contribute?

THINK MATH

Space Perception

A block is made of 100 cubes.
The six outer faces of the block are blue.

What percent of the small cubes have:

1. one blue face?   **2.** two blue faces?
3. three blue faces?   **4.** no blue faces?

Finding a Percent of a Number

A building code limits window area in a building to 20% of the building's floor area. What is the greatest window area allowed in a building with 2,800 square meters (m^2) of floor area?

To find 20% of 2,800, we multiply. We can use either a decimal or a fraction for the percent.

Decimal

$$20\% = 0.20 \rightarrow \begin{array}{r} 2{,}8\,0\,0 \\ \times \quad 0.2\,0 \\ \hline 5\,6\,0.0\,0 \end{array}$$

Fraction

$$20\% = \frac{20}{100} = \frac{1}{5} \rightarrow \frac{1}{5} \times \frac{2{,}800}{1} = 560$$

The building can have no more than 560 m^2 of window area.

Other Examples

Find 6.5% of 350.

$0.065 \times 350 = 22.75$

Find 25% of 36.

$\frac{1}{4} \times 36 = 9$

What is 200% of 120?

$2.00 \times 120 = 240.00$

Warm Up

Give the percent of each number. Use a decimal for the percent.

1. 12% of 125

2. 7% of 18

3. 135% of 1,000

4. 13% of 55

5. 7.8% of 21

6. 2.5% of 75

Give the percent of each number. Use a lowest-terms fraction for the percent.

7. 50% of 76

8. $33\frac{1}{3}$% of 117

9. 60% of 400

10. 25% of 92

11. 90% of 40

12. $33\frac{1}{3}$% of 500

278

Practice Find the percent of each number. Use a decimal for the percent.

1. 18% of 65　　**2.** 14% of 36　　**3.** 65% of 230　　**4.** 35% of 92

5. 7% of 180　　**6.** 45% of 1,000　　**7.** 23.5% of 18　　**8.** 15.5% of 30

9. 7.3% of 50　　**10.** 140% of 80　　**11.** 112% of 300　　**12.** 270% of 45

Find the percent of each number. Use a lowest-terms fraction for the percent.

13. 25% of 48　　**14.** 10% of 230　　**15.** 40% of 95　　**16.** 75% of 36

17. 80% of 200　　**18.** 50% of 450　　**19.** 30% of 60　　**20.** $33\frac{1}{3}$% of 18

21. 20% of 55　　**22.** 90% of 30　　**23.** $12\frac{1}{2}$% of 32　　**24.** $66\frac{2}{3}$% of 54

Find the percent of each number.

25. 28% of 84　　**26.** 15% of 105　　**27.** 75% of 84　　**28.** 16.3% of 37

29. 64.3% of 200　　**30.** 30% of 9.3　　**31.** 145% of 300　　**32.** 9.8% of 32

33. 2% of 650　　**34.** 400% of 28　　**35.** 260% of 75　　**36.** 325% of 90

Mixed Applications

37. A building code in another city allows a window area that is 18% of a building's floor area. How much window area is allowed in a building with 980 m² of floor area?

38. A building has 3 floors. Each floor has an area of 400 m². A building code allows a window area that is 25.5% of the building's floor area. How much window area is allowed in the building?

39. Use the graphs below to decide which shopping center rents the greatest amount of floor area.

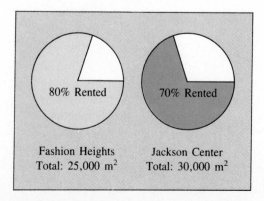

Fashion Heights
Total: 25,000 m²

Jackson Center
Total: 30,000 m²

40. A building with 1,580 m² of floor area has a window area of 302 m². The building code allows the window area to be 20% of the floor area. How many square meters above or below code is the window area?

41. This problem has missing data. Make up the needed data, then solve the problem.

An office building rented 20% of its floor area for shops. How many square meters of floor area are used for shops?

Finding Simple Interest

Kyle borrowed $300 for 6 months to buy mountain climbing equipment. The **interest rate** is 16% per year. How much is the **interest**? What is the amount to be repaid?

To find the interest, we can use the formula $I = PRT$.

Interest (I): Charge for use of money
Principal (P): Amount loaned or saved

$P = \$300,\ R = 0.16,$
$\quad T = 0.5$ **yr (6 months)**
$I = \$300 \times 0.16 \times 0.5$
$I = \$24$ The interest is $24.

Rate (R): A percent
Time (T): Length of time money is used
Amount (A): Principal plus interest

$A = P + I$
$A = \$300 + \$24$
$A = \$324$ The amount is $324.

Other Examples

Find the interest and the amount on a principal of $4,000 at 12% per year for 18 months.

$I = PRT$
$I = \$4,000 \times 0.12 \times 1.5 = \$720$

$A = P + I$
$A = \$4,000 + \$720 = \$4,720$

The interest is $720. The amount is $4,720.

Practice Find the interest and the amount.

1. $P = \$1,000$
   $R = 15\%$ per year
   $T = 3$ yr

2. $P = \$800$
   $R = 11\%$ per year
   $T = 2$ yr

3. $P = \$2,500$
   $R = 13\%$ per year
   $T = 4$ yr

4. $P = \$600$
   $R = 9\%$ per year
   $T = 6$ months

5. $P = \$3,000$
   $R = 12.5\%$ per year
   $T = 3$ yr

6. $P = \$900$
   $R = 16\%$ per year
   $T = 3$ months

7. $P = \$750$
   $R = 10\frac{1}{2}\%$ per year
   $T = 6$ yr

8. $P = \$20,000$
   $R = 14\%$ per year
   $T = 6.5$ yr

9. $P = \$12,000$
   $R = 12\frac{3}{4}\%$ per year
   $T = 18$ months

280

More Practice, page 450, Set C

PROBLEM SOLVING: Using Interest Formulas

QUESTION
DATA
PLAN
ANSWER
CHECK

Solve.

1. The Greene family borrowed $4,000 to pay for their car. The loan was for 3 yr. The interest rate was 11% per year. What is the interest they must pay?

2. Travis Steck put $4,325 in a savings account 5 yr ago. The interest rate on the account was 8% per year. How much interest did he earn?

3. Ms. Veaner borrowed $7,500. The loan is for 4 yr at a rate of 15% per year. What is the interest? What is the total amount she must repay?

4. Dana Klein has $1,320 in savings, earning 12% per year. How much interest will it earn in 4 yr and 6 months?

5. The Shimizas borrowed $800 for 3 months at a rate of 16% to buy a new refrigerator. What is the total amount the Shimizas must repay?

6. Keith bought a 6-month certificate of deposit for $5,000. The yearly interest rate on the certificate is 14%. How much will the certificate be worth in 6 months?

7. Steve White has had $1,000 in a savings account for 5 yr at 7% interest per year. He plans to use the interest earned in the account to buy a television set. How much more does he need to buy a TV which costs $425?

8. Mr. Stoddard has $2,200 in savings at a rate of 10.5% per year. Ms. Roth has $1,800 in savings at 16% per year. What will be the savings account balance on each amount after 3 yr?

9. Read the advertisements. How much interest will you earn on $3,000 for 1 yr in each account?

> **Fed Savings**
> Invest $3,000 for 1 year
> at 7% interest.

> **Northern Savings**
> Invest Here!
> All accounts earn
> 8% interest per year.

10. Mr. Ahtone put $13,750 in a money market fund for 2 months. The yearly rate of interest for this time was 8.36%. How much interest did the money earn? What was the amount at the end of 2 months?

11. **Strategy Practice** Mindy, Rodrigo, Biff, and Bren won the first four prizes in a contest. One winner's prize was put in a savings account. First prize was a car. Second prize was a trip to Hawaii. Fourth prize was a video game. Rodrigo needed time off from work to use his prize. Mindy won third prize. Bren did not need a license to use his prize. Name the prize each person won.

Finding the Percent One Number Is of Another

A community center is offering classes in signing for the hearing impaired. The class size is limited to 30 people. 24 people are taking the class. What percent of the class is filled?

To solve the problem, we can find the percent for the ratio of the two numbers.

Ratio: **24** out of **30** people $\rightarrow \dfrac{24}{30}$

Percent: $\dfrac{24}{30} = 0.80 = 80\%$

80% of the class is filled.

Check:
80% of $30 = 0.80 \times 30 = 24$

percent

American Sign Language

Other Examples

What percent of 8 is 12?

$\dfrac{12}{8} = 1.5 = 150\%$

16 is what percent of 4?

$\dfrac{16}{4} = 4.00 = 400\%$

7 is what percent of 15?

$\dfrac{7}{15} \approx 0.4666 \approx 46.7\% \leftarrow$ Nearest tenth

What percent of 9 is 2?

$\dfrac{2}{9} = 22\dfrac{2}{9}\%$

Warm Up

Find each percent.

1. What percent of 25 is 15?

2. What percent of 48 is 3?

3. 22 is what percent of 132?

4. 40 is what percent of 50?

5. 1 out of 50 is what percent?

6. 12 is what percent of 16?

Practice Find the percents.

1. What percent of 30 is 18?

2. What percent of 65 is 13?

3. What percent is 65 out of 325?

4. What percent is 21 out of 30?

5. 1 is what percent of 40?

6. 4 is what percent of 25?

7. What percent of 10 is 9?

8. What percent of 75 is 15?

9. 48 is what percent of 32?

10. 52 is what percent of 65?

11. What percent is 8 out of 400?

12. What percent of 86 is 215?

13. What percent is 6 out of 48?

14. 720 is what percent of 400?

15. 18 is what percent of 360?

16. What percent is 6 out of 80?

17. What percent of 66 is 22?

18. What percent is 21 out of 56?

Use your calculator to find the percents. Round to the nearest tenth of a percent. 🖩

19. 83 is what percent of 141?

20. 567 is what percent of 823?

21. What percent of 94 is 67.5?

22. What percent of 16.5 is 7?

23. 372 is what percent of 250?

24. What percent of 94 is 368?

Mixed Applications

25. The size of a pottery class is limited to 15 people. 9 people have signed up for the pottery class. What percent of the class limit is this?

26. A swimming class is limited to 20 people. 45 people have signed up. What percent of the limited class size is the number of people who have signed up?

★ 27. There are three cooking classes offered. Each class is limited to 25 students. The Chinese cooking class has 23 students, the Italian cooking class has 18 students, and the French cooking class is full. What percent of the total possible number of students are enrolled?

28. The recreation center offers 84 classes limited to 30 students each. The actual enrollment is 2,420 students. What percent of the total possible enrollment is the actual enrollment?

More Practice, page 450, Set D

283

Estimation and Percent

Out of 40 questions on an American history test, 31 are about Colonial life. Estimate the percent of the questions that are about Colonial life.

$\frac{31}{40}$ is about $\frac{30}{40}$

$\frac{30}{40} = \frac{3}{4} = 75\%$

About 75% of the questions are about Colonial life.

On a science test, $8\frac{1}{3}\%$ of the 84 questions are on the solar system. Estimate the number of questions on the solar system.

$8\frac{1}{3}\%$ is about **8%**

84 is about **80**

8% of 80 = ?

$0.08 \times 80 = 6.4$

There are about 6 questions on the solar system.

William Penn making a treaty with the Indians.

Other Examples

19 out of 58 is about what percent?

$\frac{19}{58}$ is about $\frac{20}{60}$

$\frac{20}{60} = \frac{1}{3} = 33\frac{1}{3}\%$

19 out of 58 is about 33%.

38% of 195

38% is about **40%**

195 is about **200**

$0.40 \times 200 = 80$

38% of 195 is about 80.

Warm Up

Estimate the percent of the number.

1. 38 out of 51 is about what percent?

2. About what percent of 147 is 102?

3. About what percent is 62 out of 118?

4. About what percent of 587 is 199?

5. 32% of 90

6. 73% of 36

7. 17.9% of 149

8. $91\frac{1}{2}\%$ of 32

284

Practice Estimate the percent for each ratio.

1. 14 out of 21

2. 16 to 29

3. 61 out of 79

4. 59 out of 121

5. 38 to 118

6. 24 to 97

7. 27 to 88

8. 70 out of 60

9. 16 to 162

10. $\frac{199}{298}$

11. $\frac{148}{302}$

12. $\frac{121}{152}$

Estimate the number.

13. 19% of 80

14. 49% of 129

15. 32% of 66

16. 16.9% of 120

17. 26% of 28

18. 11% of 388

19. 18% of 85

20. $83\frac{1}{3}$% of 42

21. 142% of 125

22. 24% of 360

23. 55.2% of 250

24. 74% of 200

25. 39% of 135

26. 9% of 57

27. $54\frac{1}{2}$% of 8,720

28. 76% of 3,975

29. 21% of 5,130

30. $66\frac{2}{3}$% of 2,750

Mixed Applications

31. Rona was absent from school 4 out of 19 days last month. About what percent of the days was she absent?

32. Jim's total score on 5 exams was 420 out of 490 points. About what percent was Jim's total score?

33. The history test has about 88% of 41 questions on the southern Indian tribes. Estimate the number of questions on the southern Indians.

34. Dumar got 72 out of 81 questions correct on the first test. On the second test, he got 29 out of 42 questions correct. On which test did Dumar get the higher percentage of questions correct? Use estimation.

THINK MATH

Mental Math

Find 15% of $46 mentally.

> 10% of $46 is $4.60.
> 5% of $46 is $\frac{1}{2}$ of $4.60 or $2.30. So
> 15% of $46 is $4.60 + $2.30, or $6.90.

15% of $46 is $6.90.

Solve these problems mentally.

1. Find 15% of $18.

2. Find 5% of $72.

3. Find 20% of $68.

4. Find 5% of $85.

5. Find 15% of $350.

6. Find 20% of $2,084.

Percent of Increase or Decrease

A restaurant served an average of 120 meals per day in September. During October the average number of meals per day increased to 138. What was the increase in the number of meals? What was the **percent of increase**?

To find the percent of increase, we find the percent for the ratio of increase to the first amount.

First amount = **120**
Second amount = **138**

Increase = second amount − first amount

$$= 138 - 120 = 18$$

$$\frac{\text{Increase}}{\text{First amount}} = \frac{18}{120} = 15\%$$

The number of meals increased by an average of 18 per day. The percent of increase was 15%.

A shipment of seafood cost a restaurant $850. The next shipment of the same quantity of seafood cost only $782. What was the decrease in cost? What was the **percent of decrease**?

First amount = **$850**
Second amount = **$782**

Decrease = first amount − second amount

$$= \$850 - 782 = \$68$$

$$\frac{\text{Decrease}}{\text{First amount}} = \frac{\$68}{\$850} = 0.08 = 8\%$$

The cost decreased by $68. The percent of decrease was 8%.

Practice Copy and complete the tables.

	First amount	Second amount	Increase	Percent increase
1.	60	80		
2.	75	93		
3.	64	72		
4.	192	312		
5.	363	726		

	First amount	Second amount	Decrease	Percent decrease
6.	145	87		
7.	150	132		
8.	284	213		
9.	150	78		
10.	32	20		

PROBLEM SOLVING: Using Data from a Monthly Statement

QUESTION
DATA
PLAN
ANSWER
CHECK

The Harris family charged $74.94 on their credit card last month. When they receive the monthly statement, they will make a payment of $25. The interest charge is $1\frac{1}{2}\%$ of the unpaid balance per month. What is the interest charge and the new balance?

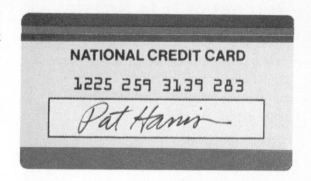

NATIONAL CREDIT CARD

1225 259 3139 283

Pat Harris

Find the unpaid balance.

```
 $7 4.9 4   Purchases
- 2 5.0 0   Payment
 $4 9.9 4   Unpaid balance
```

Find the interest on the unpaid balance.

```
   $4 9.9 4    Unpaid balance
  × 0.0 1 5    Interest rate
    2 4 9 7 0
    4 9 9 4
  $0.7 4 9 1 0  Interest
    $0.7 5      Interest rounded to the nearest cent
```

Find the new balance.

```
   $4 9.9 4    Unpaid balance
 +   0.7 5     Interest
   $5 0.6 9    New balance
```

The interest charge on the unpaid balance for one month is $0.75. The new balance is $50.69.

Find the unpaid balance, the interest to the nearest cent, and the new balance for these monthly statements. Use $1\frac{1}{2}\%$ per month as the interest rate.

1. Purchases: $89.95
   Payment: $10.00

2. Purchases: $220.10
   Payment: $120.10

3. Purchases: $315.50
   Payment: $100.00

4. Purchases: $116.75
   Payment: $40.00

5. Purchases: $88.45
   Payment: $10.00

6. Purchases: $60.50
   Payment: $60.50

7. Rose Hughes used a credit card to charge $134.82. During June and July she paid $20 per month and made no new purchases. How much does she still owe if the interest rate is $1\frac{1}{2}\%$ per month?

8. **Strategy Practice** Alex decided to repay $300 in charges at $75 per month. There will be no new charges. The interest rate is 1.5% on the unpaid balance. How much interest will be paid in all? Hint: Make a table.

Finding a Number when a Percent of It Is Known

The Alvarez Dental Clinic found that 80% of the children it examined did not need dental work. There were 56 children that did not need dental work. How many children did the clinic examine?

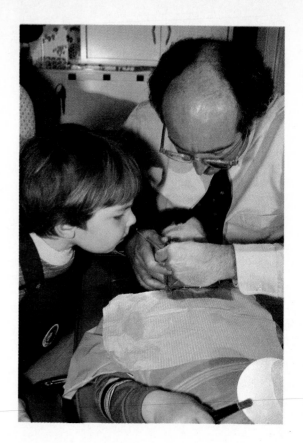

We can write and solve an equation to find the number. Let n = the number of children examined.

Percent equation $\quad 80\% \times n = 56$

$$0.80\, n = 56$$

$$\frac{0.80}{0.80}\, n = \frac{56}{0.80}$$

$$n = 70$$

The clinic examined 70 children.

Other Examples

32% of what number is 20.8?

$32\% \times n = 20.8$
$0.32 \times n = 20.8$
$\dfrac{0.32}{0.32} \times n = \dfrac{20.8}{0.32}$
$n = 65$

125% of what number is 20?

$125\% \times t = 20$
$1.25 \times t = 20$
$\dfrac{1.25}{1.25} \times t = \dfrac{20}{1.25}$
$t = 16$

Warm Up

Solve.

1. $30\% \times n = 15$

2. $50\% \times n = 82$

3. $150\% \times t = 15$

Write and solve an equation for each question.

4. 55% of what number is 22?

5. 10% of what number is 17?

288

Practice Solve.

1. $50\% \times n = 29$
2. $75\% \times n = 24$
3. $4\% \times n = 20$
4. $10\% \times n = 18$
5. $150\% \times n = 24$
6. $75\% \times n = 120$
7. $56\% \times n = 28$
8. $26\% \times n = 26$
9. $6\% \times n = 15$
10. $15\% \times n = 12.15$
11. $28\% \times n = 532$
12. $17\% \times n = 39.95$

Write and solve an equation for each question.

13. 26% of what number is 39?
14. 7% of what number is 84?

15. 55% of what number is 11?
16. 75% of what number is 60?

17. 5% of what number is 12?
18. 125% of what number is 20?

19. 30% of what number is 4.5?
20. 160% of what number is 80?

21. 1% of what number is 2.95?
22. 35% of what number is 14.7?

23. 125% of what number is 110?
24. 300% of what number is 258?

Mixed Applications

25. Helen Chinn's insurance pays for 75% of the cost of her dental surgery. The insurance paid $933.75. What was the overall cost of the surgery?

26. The Delany School has 436 students. This year 24% of the students had dental X-rays. How many students had dental X-rays this year?

SKILLKEEPER

Estimate the percent of each number.

1. 52% of 349
2. 11% of 327
3. 73% of 299
4. 42% of 85
5. 21% of 43

6. $33\frac{1}{3}\%$ of 21
7. 6% of 180
8. 2.3% of 780
9. 8.4% of 25
10. 30% of 7.5

11. 18% of 79
12. 9% of 389
13. 21% of 358
14. 44% of 141

15. 45% of 131
16. 72% of 129
17. 82% of 3,876
18. 65% of 275

19. 29% of 71
20. 6% of 62
21. 17% of 4,998
22. 55% of 355

More Practice, page 451, Set A

Discounts and Sale Prices

Water skiing equipment is on sale. The discount is 20% of the regular price of $230. What is the sale price?

The **discount** is the amount the price is reduced.

Discount = discount percent × regular price

Let d = the discount.

$d = 20\% \times \$230$

$d = 0.20 \times \$230$

$d = \$46$

The discount is $46.

The **sale price** is the price after the discount has been subtracted.

Sale price = regular price − discount

Let p = the sale price.

$p = \$230 - \$46$

$p = \$184$

The sale price is $184.

Practice Find the discount and the sale price.

1. Regular Price: $16
   Discount Percent: 25%

2. Regular Price: $200
   Discount Percent: 40%

3. Regular Price: $84
   Discount Percent: 50%

4. Regular Price: $12
   Discount Percent: 40%

5. Regular Price: $72
   Discount Percent: $12\frac{1}{2}\%$

6. Regular Price: $168
   Discount Percent: 66.6%

7. Regular Price: $500
   Discount Percent: 15%

8. Regular Price: $350
   Discount Percent: 14%

9. Regular Price: $70
   Discount Percent: 8.5%

10. Regular Price: $66.80
    Discount Percent: 5%

11. Regular Price: $7.80
    Discount Percent: 15%

12. Regular Price: $59.95
    Discount Percent: 20%

290

PROBLEM SOLVING: Mixed Practice

QUESTION
DATA
PLAN
ANSWER
CHECK

First estimate the answer.
Then calculate the answer.
Round answers to the nearest cent.

1. Al wants to buy a bicycle. The regular price is $127.40. The sale price offers a 15% discount. What is the sale price?

2. Jean is going to tune up her car. The regular cost of the tune-up is $112.50. She can do the tune-up herself for 45% less. What will the cost be if she does the work herself?

3. The price of a motorcycle is $4,850. The sales tax is 5% of the price. What is the cost of the motorcycle, including sales tax?

4. Dr. Gunther is buying new brake shoes for his car. The mechanic will install the shoes for 15% off the regular price of $90.60. What is the discounted price of the installation?

5. A marine store advertises 10% off on used outboard engines, with a 3-year guarantee. The regular price of an engine is $285. What is the sale price?

6. Sally replaced two defective tires for $88. The replacement cost was 55% of the regular price of the new tires. What is the regular price of two new tires?

7. Ike bought a sun roof for his car. A 20% discount was offered on the regular price of $262. The installation of the sun roof cost an additional $120. What was the total cost of the sun roof, including installation?

8. The original cost of a new camping trailer was $13,800. After one year the trailer sold for $12,558. What was the percent of depreciation (decrease in price) after one year?

9. DATA HUNT Use a newspaper ad to find an item on sale. What is the regular price, the sale price, and the discount percent of the item?

10. Strategy Practice The price of a used sailboat was reduced to 80% of the original price during the first week of a sale. The second and third weeks the price was again reduced to 80% of the previous week's sale price. After the three discounts, the boat sold for $1,536. What was the price of the sailboat before the sale began?

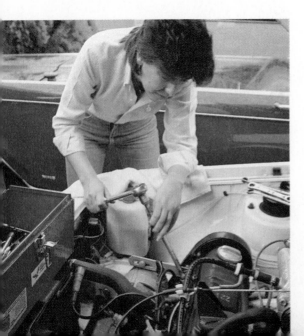

Mixed Practice: Percent

Write each percent as a decimal.

1. 23% **2.** 18% **3.** 64% **4.** 85% **5.** 7%

6. 130% **7.** $13\frac{1}{2}$% **8.** 5% **9.** 140% **10.** 17.8%

Write each decimal as a percent.

11. 0.48 **12.** 0.04 **13.** 0.53 **14.** 0.2 **15.** 0.01

16. 4.16 **17.** 0.15 **18.** 0.032 **19.** 7.00 **20.** 0.003

Find the percent for each fraction. Round the percent to the nearest tenth of a percent if necessary.

21. $\frac{3}{10}$ **22.** $\frac{1}{4}$ **23.** $\frac{3}{20}$ **24.** $\frac{7}{100}$ **25.** $\frac{1}{5}$

26. $\frac{5}{8}$ **27.** $\frac{6}{25}$ **28.** $\frac{1}{6}$ **29.** $\frac{1}{2}$ **30.** $\frac{5}{12}$

31. $\frac{2}{3}$ **32.** $\frac{3}{60}$ **33.** $\frac{4}{15}$ **34.** $\frac{7}{9}$ **35.** $\frac{5}{16}$

Find the lowest-terms fraction for each percent.

36. 15% **37.** 42% **38.** 74% **39.** 145% **40.** 8%

41. 60% **42.** 130% **43.** 24% **44.** 45% **45.** 75%

46. 220% **47.** 26% **48.** 10% **49.** 16% **50.** 1%

Find the percent of each number. Use a fraction for the percent.

51. 25% of 32 **52.** 40% of 165 **53.** $12\frac{1}{2}$% of 48

54. 50% of 380 **55.** $66\frac{2}{3}$% of 51 **56.** 75% of 112

Find the percents.

57. 12 is what percent of 20? **58.** 24 is what percent of 60?

59. 45 is what percent of 135? **60.** 21 is what percent of 300?

Find the numbers.

61. 32% of a number is 16. **62.** 75% of a number is 27.

63. 80% of a number is 52. **64.** 150% of a number is 48.

Proportions and Percents

Percent problems can be solved by writing and solving a proportion.

Find 40% of 50.

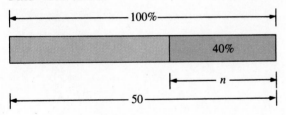

$$\frac{n}{50} = \frac{40}{100}$$
$$100\,n = 2{,}000$$
$$n = 20$$

40% of 50 is 20.

27 is what percent of 90?

75% of what number is 72?

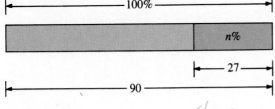
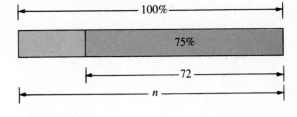

$$\frac{n}{100} = \frac{27}{90}$$
$$90\,n = 2{,}700$$
$$n = 30$$

27 is 30% of 90.

$$\frac{75}{100} = \frac{72}{n}$$
$$75\,n = 7{,}200$$
$$n = 96$$

75% of 96 is 72.

Practice Write and solve a proportion for each question.

1. What is 40% of 65?

2. 26 is what percent of 65?

3. 50% of what number is 46?

4. What is 30% of 450?

5. 25% of what number is 21?

6. 18 is what percent of 200?

7. 6 is what percent of 40?

8. What is 65% of 60?

9. What is 250% of 86?

10. 35% of what number is 21?

11. 117 is what percent of 150?

12. 510 is what percent of 425?

13. Yural weighs 70 kg. His percent of body fat is 11.6%. What is the weight of his body fat? Write and solve a proportion.

14. Out of 95 men weighed, 46 were found to be overweight. What percent is this? Write and solve a proportion.

More Practice, page 451, Set B

293

PROBLEM SOLVING: Using the Strategies

QUESTION
DATA
PLAN
ANSWER
CHECK

Problem-Solving Strategies

✔ Guess and Check

✔ Choose the Operations

✔ Make an Organized List

✔ Work Backward

✔ Draw a Picture

✔ Make a Table

✔ Solve a Simpler Problem

✔ Find a Pattern

✔ Use Logical Reasoning

The strategies listed in the table are the ones you have learned to use in this book. Choose one or more of the strategies to solve each problem below.

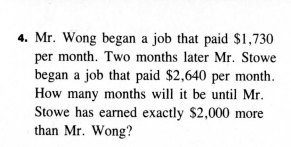

1. Don is a reporter for the school newspaper. He surveyed 52 students who saw the film "Space Trek." He found that the number of students who liked the film was 3 times the number who did not like it. How many of the students surveyed liked the film?

2. Henry bought 175 shares of AMB stock for $87\frac{1}{2}$ dollars per share. One week later he bought 125 more shares but now it cost $93\frac{1}{4}$ dollars per share. What is the average price that Henry paid for all the shares of AMB stock?

3. Doris, Bern, Ann, and Rotishia went to the cafe after the play. One of them ordered a salad, one a bowl of soup, one a sandwich, and one a glass of juice. Bern didn't need a soup spoon or a salad fork. Rotishia ordered something in a glass. Doris doesn't like soup. What did each person order?

4. Mr. Wong began a job that paid $1,730 per month. Two months later Mr. Stowe began a job that paid $2,640 per month. How many months will it be until Mr. Stowe has earned exactly $2,000 more than Mr. Wong?

294

Write each ratio as a fraction, a decimal, and a percent.

1. 8 out of 100 **2.** 24 to 100 **3.** 5 for 100

Write each percent as a decimal.

4. 74% **5.** 4% **6.** 30% **7.** 2%

Write each fraction as a percent.

8. $\frac{4}{10}$ **9.** $\frac{3}{20}$ **10.** $\frac{3}{4}$ **11.** $\frac{5}{8}$

Write each fraction or decimal as a percent.

12. $\frac{125}{100}$ **13.** 0.042 **14.** $\frac{9}{6}$ **15.** 5.0

16. Find 37% of 500.

17. Find 74% of 420.

18. A price rose from $40 to $50. What is the percent of increase?

19. A price fell from $25 to $20. What is the percent of decrease?

20. 9 is what percent of 15?

21. 70 is what percent of 35?

22. Estimate 48% of 286.

23. Estimate what percent 34 is of 71.

24. 15% of what number is 9?

25. 64% of what number is 16?

Write and solve a proportion for each question.

26. 25 is what percent of 80?

27. What is 58% of 250?

28. In an election for mayor, Margaret Katz won 73% of the votes. If 4,358 people voted, about how many people voted for Margaret Katz?

29. Gary borrowed $400 for 6 months. The interest rate was 15% per year. What amount had to be repaid?

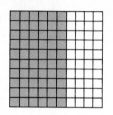

Ratio: **60** out of **100**

Fraction: $\frac{60}{100} = \frac{3}{5}$

Decimal: **0.60**

Percent: **60%**

Write a ratio, a fraction, a decimal, and a percent for the region that is shaded.

1.

2.

Write each ratio as a fraction, a decimal, and a percent.

3. 73 out of 100

4. 54 to 100

0.582   **= 58.2%**

28.4%   **= 0.284**

3%   **= 0.03**

Write each decimal as a percent.

5. 0.76   **6.** 0.06   **7.** 1.45   **8.** 0.001

Write each percent as a decimal.

9. 90%   **10.** 45%   **11.** 3%   **12.** 200%

$\frac{1}{6} \rightarrow$ $6\overline{)1.00}$ $\quad 0.16\frac{2}{3} = 16\frac{2}{3}\%$

Write each fraction as a percent.

13. $\frac{3}{4}$ **14.** $\frac{3}{8}$ **15.** $\frac{1}{20}$ **16.** $\frac{5}{12}$

30% of 66

0.30 × 66 = 19.80

16 is what percent of 40?

$\frac{16}{40} = \frac{2}{5} = 0.4 = 40\%$

30% of what number is 18?

0.30 × n = 18

$n = \frac{18}{0.30} = 60$

17. Find 45% of 800.   **18.** What is 25% of 72?

19. 60 is what percent of 300?   **20.** 36 is what percent of 60?

21. 12% of what number is 84?   **22.** 60% of what number is 15?

Compound Interest

The table below shows interest earned on $1,200. At the end of
each time period the interest earned is added to the principal. This
is called **compound interest**. The interest rate is 8% per year,
compounded **semiannually** (every six months or 0.5 yr).

Time Period	Principal	$PRT = I$	New Principal
First six months	$1,200.00	$1,200 × 0.08 × 0.5 = $48.00	$1,200.00 + $48.00 = $1,248.00
Second six months	$1,248.00	$1,248 × 0.08 × 0.5 = $49.92	$1,248.00 + $49.92 = $1,297.92
Third six months	▨	?	?

1. Copy the table above and complete the third interest period.

2. The table below is for interest paid on $2,000. The interest rate is 12% compounded annually. At the end of each year an additional $2,000 is deposited. Copy and complete the table.

Time	$PRT = I$	Deposit	New Principal
1 year	$2,000 × 0.12 × 1 = $240	$2,000	$2,000 + $240 + $2,000 = $4,240
2 years	$4,240 × 0.12 × 1 = $508.80	$2,000	?
3 years	?	▨	?
4 years	?	▨	?
5 years	?	▨	?

3. What was the total interest earned on the account at the end of 5 yr?

1. Which is correct?

A $^-32 > ^-25$ **B** $^-7 < ^-6$
C $9 < ^-10$ **D** not given

2. Which is not correct?

A $|^-97| = 97$ **B** $|97| = 97$
C $|^-4| = ^-4$ **D** not given

3. What is $25 - 6a$ if $a = 3$?

A $^-7$ **B** 7
C 16 **D** not given

Solve.

4. $\frac{n}{17} = ^-9$

A $n = ^-153$ **B** $n = ^-26$
C $n = ^-8$ **D** not given

5. $^-7x - 9 = 12$

A $x = 3$ **B** $x = 0$
C $x = ^-2$ **D** not given

6. Which is the same as 9^{-3}?

A 9^3 **B** 3^{-9}
C $\frac{1}{9^3}$ **D** not given

7. Choose the pair of equal ratios.

A $\frac{14}{5}, \frac{28}{10}$ **B** $\frac{7}{8}, \frac{12}{15}$
C $\frac{3}{8}, \frac{4}{10}$ **D** not given

8. Simplify the rate. 85 km in 5 h.

A $\frac{17 \text{ km}}{5 \text{ h}}$ **B** 42.5 km/3h
C 17 km/h   **D** not given

9. Solve.

$\frac{3}{8} = \frac{48}{x}$

A $x = 42$ **B** $x = 18$
C $x = 128$ **D** not given

10. $\triangle ABC \sim \triangle XYZ$. Find length x.

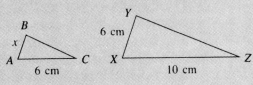

A $x = 10$ cm   **B** $x = 3.6$ cm
C $x = 3$ cm   **D** not given

11. Find the unit price.

36 cans for $13.32

A $0.37/can   **B** $0.52/can
C $0.13/can   **D** not given

12. Which side of a right triangle is always opposite the right angle?

A tangent   **B** adjacent
C opposite   **D** not given

13. Petrea said, "I thought of an integer. I multiplied it by 9 and added $^-6$. My answer was 30." What was her integer?

A 3   **B** $^-4$
C 4   **D** not given

14. How many times would your heart beat in 40 min if it beats 90 times in 1 min? Which proportion would you use?

A $\frac{90}{60} = \frac{x}{40}$ **B** $\frac{40}{90} = \frac{x}{1}$
C $\frac{90}{1} = \frac{x}{40}$ **D** not given

Perimeter, Area, and Volume

In a space of about 300 m² there are 15 large rocks arranged in 5 groups. White gravel has been raked in careful patterns around the rocks. The only sign of plant life is the moss growing around the perimeters of the rocks. This is a famous dry-landscape garden in Kyoto, Japan.

There are many other kinds of Japanese gardens. A small Japanese hill garden with a width of 2 m and a length of 3 m can capture the feeling of a mountainous landscape. Carefully chosen jagged rocks, each about 30 cm in diameter, represent mountains. Gravel pieces that are each 19 mm in diameter make up the bed of a man-made stream that cascades down a miniature waterfall. Small dwarf trees called bonsai with heights less than a meter suggest a forest.

Each Japanese garden is unique, and each one possesses a simple, natural beauty.

Perimeter

James Bondurant is an interior designer. He plans to stencil a pattern around the walls of a room. How many meters is it around the room?

The distance around a plane geometric figure is the **perimeter** (**P**) of the figure.

We add the length of each side of the room to find the perimeter.

$$P = 4.5 + 2.0 + 1.5 + 4.3 + 6.5 + 5.8$$
$$P = 24.6$$

The perimeter of the room is 24.6 m.

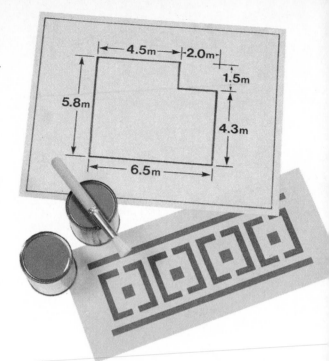

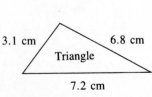

Other Examples

Rectangle
$P = 2(l + w)$

$w = 2$ cm

$l = 8$ cm

$P = 2(8 + 2) = 20$
$P = 20$ cm

Parallelogram
$P = 2(b + s)$

$s = 6$ m

$b = 24$ m

$P = 2(24 + 6) = 60$
$P = 60$ m

Equilateral triangle
$P = 3s$

$s = 8$ cm

$P = 3 \times 8 = 24$
$P = 24$ cm

Warm Up

Find the perimeter of each figure.

1.

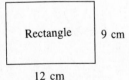

Rectangle 9 cm

12 cm

2.

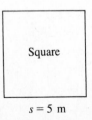

Square

$s = 5$ m

3.

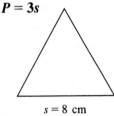

Regular hexagon

$s = 1.5$ cm

4.

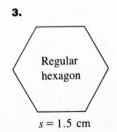

3.1 cm   6.8 cm

Triangle

7.2 cm

Practice Find the perimeter of each figure.

1.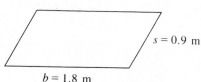
3.2 cm   3.2 cm
3.2 cm   3.2 cm

2.
40 cm
60 cm

3.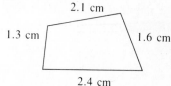
2.5 cm   2.5 cm
3.7 cm

4.
$s = 0.9$ m
$b = 1.8$ m

5.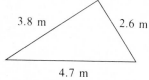
3.8 m   2.6 m
4.7 m

6.
2.1 cm
1.3 cm   1.6 cm
2.4 cm

7. Rectangle:
$l = 18.4$ cm
$w = 12.1$ cm

8. Parallelogram:
$b = 10$ m
$s = 6.5$ m

9. Equilateral triangle:
$s = 2.24$ m

10. Square:
$s = 3.8$ km

11. Regular hexagon:
$s = 19$ mm

12. Regular pentagon:
$s = 16$ cm

Mixed Applications

13. A tacking strip for a carpet is to be placed around the hallway in the drawing below. What is the perimeter of the hallway?

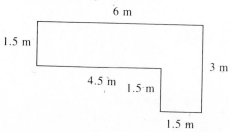

6 m
1.5 m
3 m
4.5 m   1.5 m
1.5 m

14. How much greater is the perimeter around the outside of the frame than around the inside of the frame shown below?

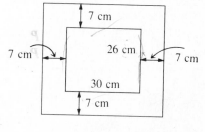

7 cm
7 cm   26 cm   7 cm
30 cm
7 cm

15. A polygon with n (a positive integer) sides is called an ***n*-gon**. A **regular *n*-gon** has all sides of equal length and all angles of the same measure. Write a formula for the perimeter of a regular *n*-gon with sides of length s.

★ **16.** An inlaid table top has a regular hexagon in the center that is 85 cm on each side. The hexagon is encircled with 6 squares and 6 equilateral triangles that are also 85 cm on each side. How many meters of molding are needed for the perimeter of the table top?

More Practice, page 451, Set C

Area of Rectangles and Parallelograms

The **area** of a region is the number of **unit squares** that are needed to cover the region. Any square can be chosen for the unit square.

A Unit Square

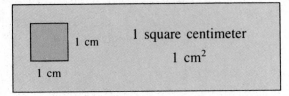

1 cm

1 cm

1 square centimeter
1 cm^2

To find the area of a rectangle, we multiply the length (l) by the width (w).

A square is a rectangle with sides (s) of equal length.

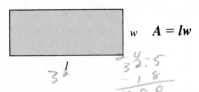

w $A = lw$

$A = s \times s = s^2$

We can use the formula for the area of a rectangle to find a formula for the area of a parallelogram with **base b** and **height h**. $A = bh$

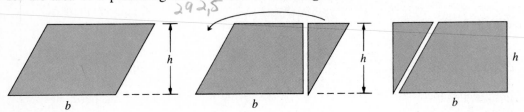

h h h

b b b

Other Examples

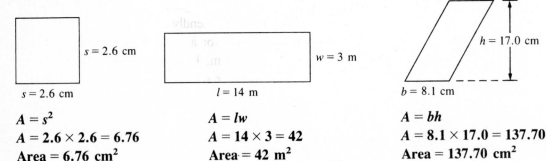

$s = 2.6$ cm

$s = 2.6$ cm

$w = 3$ m

$l = 14$ m

$h = 17.0$ cm

$b = 8.1$ cm

$A = s^2$
$A = 2.6 \times 2.6 = 6.76$
Area = 6.76 cm²

$A = lw$
$A = 14 \times 3 = 42$
Area = 42 m²

$A = bh$
$A = 8.1 \times 17.0 = 137.70$
Area = 137.70 cm²

Warm Up

Find the area of each figure.

1. Square:
$s = 18$ cm

2. Rectangle:
$l = 2.5$ m; $w = 0.8$ m

3. Parallelogram:
$b = 28$ cm; $h = 15$ cm

Practice Find the area of each square.

1.

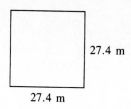

27.4 m

27.4 m

2.

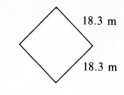

18.3 m

18.3 m

3.

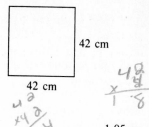

42 cm

42 cm

Find the area of each rectangle.

4.

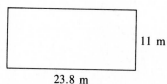

11 m

23.8 m

5.

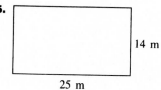

14 m

25 m

6.

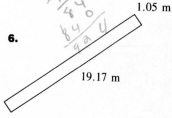

1.05 m

19.17 m

Find the area of each parallelogram.

7.

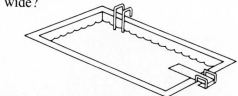

$h = 24$ cm

$b = 57$ cm

8.

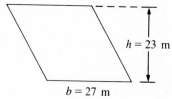

$h = 23$ m

$b = 27$ m

9.

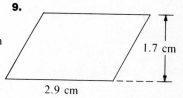

1.7 cm

2.9 cm

Mixed Applications

10. What is the area of a pool cover for a rectangular pool 25 m long and 13 m wide?

★ **11.** Green's Market pays $4,050 a month for a rectangular floor space 25 m by 36 m. Friendly Stores pays $792 a month for a rectangular floor space 8 m by 18 m. How much does each business pay per square meter of floor space?

More Practice, page 451, Set D

Area of Triangles and Trapezoids

The two congruent triangles form a parallelogram.

The area of one triangle is $\frac{1}{2}$ the area of the parallelogram.

Any side of a triangle can be the **base**. The **height** is the perpendicular distance from the opposite vertex to the base.

$A = \frac{1}{2} bh$

$A = \frac{1}{2} \times 13 \times 8$

$A = 52$

The area of the triangle is 52 cm².

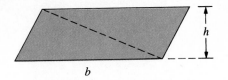

Area of parallelogram = bh

Area of triangle = $\frac{1}{2} bh$

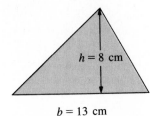

The two congruent trapezoids form a parallelogram.

The area of one of the trapezoids is $\frac{1}{2}$ the area of the parallelogram.

The parallel sides of the trapezoid, b_1 and b_2, are the **bases**. The **height** is the perpendicular distance between the bases.

$A = \frac{1}{2}(b_1 + b_2)h$

$A = \frac{1}{2}(12 + 9)8$

$A = \frac{1}{2} \times 21 \times 8$

$A = 84$

The area of the trapezoid is 84 m².

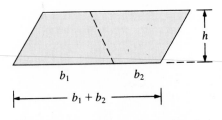

Area of parallelogram = $(b_1 + b_2)h$

Area of trapezoid = $\frac{1}{2}(b_1 + b_2)h$

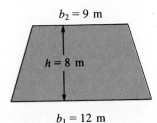

Warm Up

Find the area of each figure.

1. Triangle:
  $b = 6$ cm
  $h = 8$ cm

2. Trapezoid:
  $b_1 = 9$ cm, $b_2 = 7$ cm
  $h = 4$ cm

Practice Find the area of each triangle.

1.

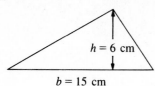

h = 6 cm
b = 15 cm

2.

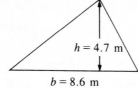

h = 4.7 m
b = 8.6 m

3.

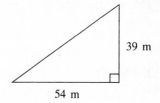

39 m
54 m

4. b = 63.2 m
  h = 24.8 m

5. b = 5.67 cm
  h = 0.75 cm

6. b = 8.74 m
  h = 2.30 m

7. b = 108.3 cm
  h = 2.9 cm

8. b = 8 m
  h = 2 m

9. b = 6.5 m
  h = 3.2 m

10. b = 9.8 m
  h = 3.4 m

11. b = 8.2 m
  h = 2.1 m

Find the area of each trapezoid.

12.

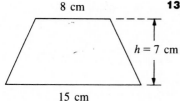

8 cm
h = 7 cm
15 cm

13.

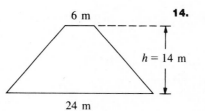

6 m
h = 14 m
24 m

14.

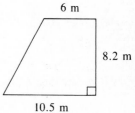

6 m
8.2 m
10.5 m

15. b_1 = 3.86 m
  b_2 = 5.97 m
  h = 8.64 m

16. b_1 = 24 cm
  b_2 = 48 cm
  h = 64 cm

17. b_1 = 9.6 m
  b_2 = 4.2 m
  h = 3.8 m

18. b_1 = 12 m
  b_2 = 16 m
  h = 8 m

Mixed Applications

19. What is the area of a triangle with a base of 24 cm and a height of 19 cm?

★ **20.** Which figure has the greater area, a triangle with b = 8 m and h = 6 m, or a trapezoid with b_1 = 8 m, b_2 = 6 m, and h = 4 m? How much greater?

More Practice, page 452, Set A

305

Circumference

The **circumference** (C) is the distance around the circle.

Object	Circumference (C)	Diameter (d)	$\frac{C}{d}$
Bicycle wheel	207.5 cm	66 cm	$\frac{207.5}{66} \approx 3.14$
Stereo record	95.8 cm	30.5 cm	$\frac{95.8}{30.5} \approx 3.14$

The ratio of the circumference to the diameter is the same for all circles. The Greek letter π (**pi**) is used for this number. π is about 3.14 or $3\frac{1}{7}$. The first 50 places of the number π are given below.

$\pi = 3.14159265358979323846264338327950288419716939937510\ldots$

Since $\frac{C}{d} = \pi$ for all circles, then $C = \pi d$ or $C = 2\pi r$, where r is the radius.

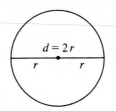

$d = 2r$

What is the circumference of a circle if $d = 16$ cm? Use 3.14 for π.

$C = \pi d$
$C \approx 3.14 \times 16$
$C \approx 50.24$

The circumference is about 50.24 cm.

What is the circumference of a circle if $r = 14$ m? Use $3\frac{1}{7} = \frac{22}{7}$ for π.

$C = 2\pi r$
$C \approx 2 \times \frac{22}{\overset{}{7}} \times \overset{2}{\cancel{14}}$
$\overset{}{\underset{1}{}}$
$C \approx 88$

The circumference is about 88 m.

Warm Up

Find the circumference of each circle. Use 3.14 for π.

1.

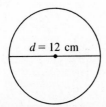

$d = 12$ cm

2.

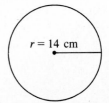

$r = 14$ cm

Practice Find the circumference of each circle. Use 3.14 for π.

1. Automobile tire
$d = 60$ cm

2. 45 rpm record
$d = 17.8$ cm

3. Clockface
$r = 16.9$ cm

4. $d = 9$ cm

5. $d = 4$ cm

6. $r = 3$ m

7. $r = 12$ cm

8. $d = 4.6$ cm

9. $d = 12.3$ m

10. $d = 56$ cm

11. $d = 72$ cm

12. $r = 18$ cm

13. $r = 8.4$ m

14. $r = 24$ cm

15. $r = 6.2$ cm

16. $d = 2.5$ m

17. $r = 16$ mm

18. $d = 2.9$ m

19. $d = 33$ cm

Mixed Applications

20. A small bicycle wheel has a diameter of 61 cm. What is the circumference of the wheel?

21. A tractor tire tread mark that is 405.06 cm long shows each complete revolution. What is the tire's diameter?

★ **22.** A stereo record has a diameter of 17.8 cm and makes 45 revolutions per minute (rpm). How far will a point on the outer edge of the record travel while the record plays one song that lasts for 2 min 30 s?

23. **DATA HUNT** Choose a circular object. Measure the diameter and find the circumference to the nearest tenth of a centimeter. Using your measurements and the ratio $\frac{C}{d}$, find the value of π. What is your value for π?

THINK MATH

Circle Measurement

The dimensions of a running track are shown in the drawing.

How much farther is it around the outside of the track than around the inside of the track?

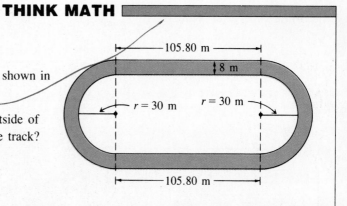

More Practice, page 452, Set B

307

Area of Circles

A central water filtration plant has a large circular pool with a radius of 22 m. What is the area of the surface of the pool?

To find the area of a circle, we can use a formula. The diagram shows why the formula is reasonable.

A circle is divided into parts.

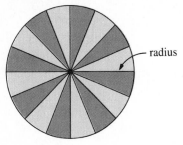

radius

The parts fit together to form a shape like a parallelogram.

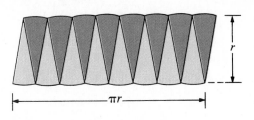

The "parallelogram" has the same area as the circle. The base of the "parallelogram" is $\frac{1}{2}$ the circumference (πr). The height is r.

Area of circle $= \pi r \times r$

$A = \pi r^2$

$A \approx 3.14 \times 22^2$

$A \approx 3.14 \times 484$

$A \approx 1,519.76$

The area of the circular region is about 1,519.76 m².

Other Examples

Find A if $r = 2.1$ km.

$A = \pi r^2$

$A \approx 3.14 \times (2.1)^2$

$A \approx 3.14 \times 4.41$

$A \approx 13.8474$

The area is about 13.8474 km².

Find A if $d = 10$ cm.

$A = \pi r^2$

$A \approx 3.14 \times 5^2$

$A \approx 3.14 \times 25$

$A \approx 78.5$

The area is about 78.5 cm².

Warm Up

Find the area of each circle. Use 3.14 for π.

1. $r = 12$ mm   **2.** $d = 16$ cm   **3.** $r = 0.5$ km   **4.** $d = 100$ m

Practice Find the area of each circle. Use 3.14 for π.

1. $r = 4$ cm

2. $r = 14$ m

3. $r = 3.6$ m

4. $r = 5.9$ cm

5. $d = 10$ cm

6. $d = 32$ m

7. $d = 24$ m

8. $d = 64.8$ cm

9. $r = 15$ cm

10. $r = 100$ m

11. $r = 0.75$ m

12. $d = 56.4$ cm

13. $r = 8$ mm

14. $d = 1,000$ km

15. $r = 0.1$ m

16. $d = 6.8$ dm

Mixed Applications

17. A rotating sprinkler sprays water in a circle with a 3 m radius. What is the area of the circle?

18. A sprinkler head set in the corner of a rectangular region sprinkles $\frac{1}{4}$ of a circular area with a radius of 5 m. What is the area of the region that is sprinkled?

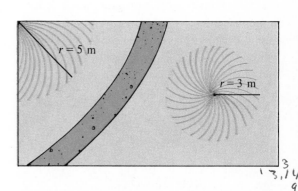

19. A water filtration plant has three pools. The radii of the pools are 15 m, 20 m, and 25 m. What is the total area of the two smallest pools?

20. What is the total area of the three pools in problem 19? Is the combined area of the two smallest pools less than, greater than, or the same as the area of the largest pool?

More Practice, page 452, Set C

PROBLEM SOLVING: Estimating Perimeter and Area

| QUESTION |
| DATA |
| PLAN |
| ANSWER |
| CHECK |

Problems about measurement occur frequently in our daily lives. Quite often, all that is needed is a good estimate of the answer to a problem.

Estimate the answer to each of these problems. Check your estimate for some answers by using a calculator.

1. A triangle has sides with lengths 48.5 cm, 62.4 cm, and 39.6 cm. Estimate the perimeter of the triangle.

2. A pentagon has sides of length 48.4 cm, 60.8 cm, 58.4 cm, 62.4 cm, and 49.3 cm. Which is the best estimate of the perimeter?

   A. 250 cm **B.** 280 cm **C.** 300 cm

3.

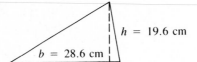

Is the area of this triangle more than 300 cm² or less than 300 cm²? Estimate.

4.

The inner square has a perimeter of 32 cm. Which is the best estimate of the perimeter of the outer square?

   A. 45 cm **B.** 64 cm **C.** 80 cm

5. A circular straw mat has a diameter of 2.8 m. Estimate the area that the mat will cover. Which estimate below is the best?

   A. 4 m² **B.** 6 m² **C.** 10 m²

6. About what percent of the square region does the shaded circular region fill?

   A. 50% **B.** 75% **C.** 90%

7. The perimeter of the square is 100 cm. Which is the best estimate of the perimeter of the regular octagon inside the square?

   A. 50 cm **B.** 120 cm **C.** 80 cm

8. Strategy Practice The sum of the perimeters of two squares is 56 cm. When the two squares are placed side by side as in the figure, the perimeter of the region is 46 cm. What is the length of the sides of each square?

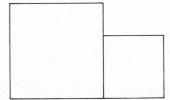

PROBLEM SOLVING: Multiple-Step Problems

QUESTION
DATA
PLAN
ANSWER
CHECK

Each of the problems on this page are multiple-step problems. That means that you will need to use more than one operation to solve the problem. Sometimes you need to solve 2 or more one-step problems to solve the given problem.

1. Joan Jellison's house has a wooden deck that is a rectangle 6.5 m long and 4 m wide. Deck paint comes in 1-liter cans and costs $6.00 a can. Each liter of paint will cover about 8 m². How many cans of paint should Joan buy to paint the deck?

2. Joan needs 4 L of paint. She found paint sold in 1-liter cans for $6.00 per can and in 3-liter cans for $15.96 per can. Which is the less expensive way to buy 4 L of paint? How much less expensive is it?

3. A deck that measures 6.5 m by 4.0 m needs 2 coats of paint. The first coat will use 1 L to cover 8 m², and the second coat will use 1 L to cover 10 m². How many liters of paint will be needed for the 2 coats? Round the answer to the next larger number.

4. To increase the size of a deck, a width of 1 m was added to the three sides shown in the diagram below. What is the new perimeter and the new area of the deck?

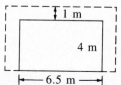

5. Will a circular mat 4 m in diameter cover more or less than $\frac{1}{2}$ of a rectangular floor area that measures 6.5 m by 4.0 m? How much more or less than $\frac{1}{2}$ will it cover?

6. A bedroom has dimensions of 4.6 m by 3.7 m. How much will it cost, to the nearest cent, to carpet the floor if the carpet costs $12.95 per square meter?

7. **Strategy Practice** Joan bought 1 three-liter can of paint for $15.96 and 1 one-liter can of paint for $6.00. What is the cost, to the nearest cent, of the paint per liter?

Surface Area of Space Figures

Prisms and cylinders are **space figures** with two bases that are
congruent regions in parallel planes. Pyramids and cones have one
base.

The **surface area** of a space figure is the sum of the areas of all
its bases, faces, or curved regions.

Triangular prism

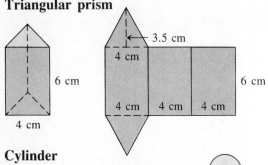

Area of each triangle $= \frac{1}{2} \times 4 \times 3.5 = 7.0$ cm^2
Area of each rectangle $= 4 \times 6 = 24$ cm^2
Surface area $= (2 \times 7) + (3 \times 24)$
$A = 86$ cm^2

Cylinder

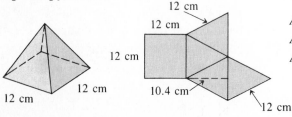

Area of each circle $= \pi \times 1^2 \approx 3.14$ cm^2
Area of the rectangle $= 2\pi \times 1 \times 7 \approx 43.96$ cm
$A \approx (2 \times 3.14) + 43.96 = 50.24$ cm^2

Square pyramid

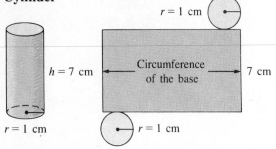

Area of the square $= 12 \times 12 = 144$ cm^2
Area of each triangle $= \frac{1}{2} \times 10.4 \times 12 = 62.4$ cm
$A = (4 \times 62.4) + 144 = 393.6$ cm^2

Warm Up

Find the total surface area of each space figure.

1.

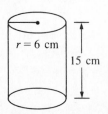

$r = 6$ cm
15 cm

2.

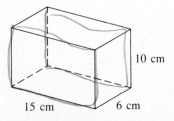

10 cm
15 cm   6 cm

3.

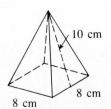

10 cm
8 cm   8 cm

Practice Find the total surface area of each prism.

1.

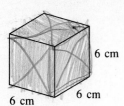

6 cm
6 cm
6 cm

2.

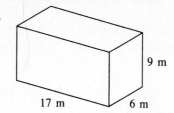

9 m
17 m
6 m

3.

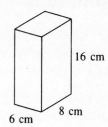

16 cm
6 cm
8 cm

Find the total surface area of each cylinder.

4.

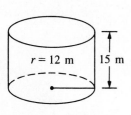

$r = 12$ m   15 m

5.

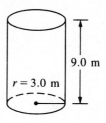

9.0 m
$r = 3.0$ m

6.

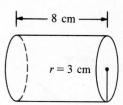

8 cm
$r = 3$ cm

Find the total surface area of each figure.

7.

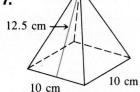

12.5 cm
10 cm
10 cm

Square pyramid

8.

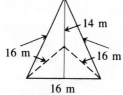

14 m
16 m   16 m
16 m

Triangular pyramid

9.

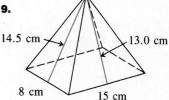

14.5 cm   13.0 cm
8 cm   15 cm

Rectangular pyramid

Mixed Applications

10. What is the total surface area of a rectangular prism with a length of 4 m, a width of 3 m, and a height of 5 m?

11. A cylinder has a radius of 4 cm and a height of 12 cm. How many square centimeters of paper are needed to cover the curved region of the cylinder but not the bases?

12. The total surface area of any cone is: 🖩 $A = \pi rs + \pi r^2$. What is the total surface area of the cone at the right?

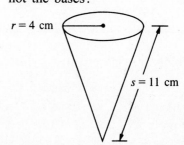

$r = 4$ cm

$s = 11$ cm

13. DATA HUNT The formula for the total surface area of a sphere is $A = 4\pi r^2$. What is the total surface area of Earth?

313

Volume of Prisms and Cylinders

The **volume** of a space figure is the number of **unit cubes** that are needed to fill a region of space.

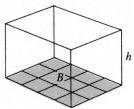

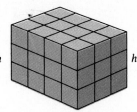

Common units for volume are **cubic centimeters (cm³)**, **cubic meters (cm³)**, and **cubic kilometers (km³)**.

The volume of a prism is the product of the area of the base (*B*) and the height (*h*).

$V = Bh$

The area of the base is *B* square units.

The prism has *h* layers of cubes with *B* cubes in each layer.

The same formula can be used to find the volume of a cylinder.

In a cylinder, the area of the base (*B*) equals πr^2.

$V = \pi r^2 h$

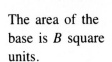

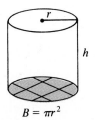

$B = \pi r^2$

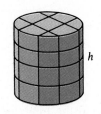

The area of the base is *B* square units.

The cylinder has *h* layers of cubes with *B* cubes in each layer.

Other Examples

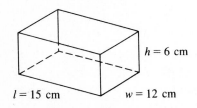

$h = 6$ cm
$l = 15$ cm
$w = 12$ cm

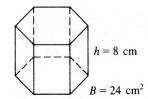

$h = 8$ cm
$r = 3$ cm

$h = 8$ cm
$B = 24$ cm²

Rectangular prism
$B = lw$
$V = lwh$
$V = 15 \times 12 \times 6$
$V = 1{,}080$ cm³

Cylinder
$V = \pi r^2 h$
$V \approx 3.14 \times 3^2 \times 8$
$V \approx 3.14 \times 9 \times 8$
$V \approx 226.08$ cm³

Hexagonal prism
$V = Bh$
$V = 24 \times 8$
$V = 192$ cm³

Warm Up

Find the volume of each prism or cylinder.

1. Prism:
  $B = 33.1$ cm²
  $h = 7.0$ cm

2. Cylinder:
  $r = 4$ m
  $h = 3$ m

3. Rectangular prism:
  $l = 1.2$ m
  $w = 1.2$ m
  $h = 0.5$ m

4. Cylinder:
  $r = 15$ cm
  $h = 20$ cm

Practice Find the volume of each prism.

1.
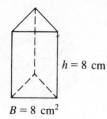
$h = 8$ cm
$B = 8$ cm^2

2.
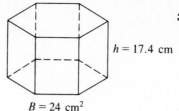
$h = 17.4$ cm
$B = 24$ cm^2

3.
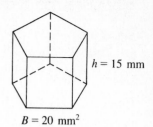
$h = 15$ mm
$B = 20$ mm^2

Find the volume of each rectangular prism.

4. $l = 19$ cm
$w = 8$ cm
$h = 29$ cm

5. $l = 4$ m
$w = 2$ m
$h = 4$ m

6. $l = 8.2$ cm
$w = 4.9$ cm
$h = 10$ cm

Find the volume of each cylinder.

7.
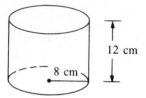
12 cm
8 cm

8.
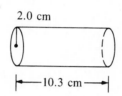
2.0 cm
10.3 cm

9.
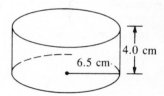
4.0 cm
6.5 cm

10. $r = 5$ cm
$h = 16$ cm

11. $r = 1.5$ m
$h = 2.0$ m

12. $r = 0.4$ mm
$h = 1.5$ mm

Mixed Applications

13. What is the volume of a cylinder that has a radius of 2 cm and a height of 20 cm?

14. One cylinder has a circumference of 36 cm and a height of 22 cm. Another cylinder has a circumference of 22 cm and a height of 36 cm. Are the volumes the same?

SKILLKEEPER

Find the area of each trapezoid. Use $A = \frac{1}{2}(b_1 + b_2)h$.

1. $b_1 = 13$ m
$b_2 = 15$ m
$h = 6$ m

2. $b_1 = 20$ cm
$b_2 = 42$ cm
$h = 60$ cm

3. $b_1 = 8.4$ m
$b_2 = 5.6$ m
$h = 5$ m

4. $b_1 = 30.2$ m
$b_2 = 12.5$ m
$h = 6.4$ m

5. $b_1 = 15$ cm
$b_2 = 9.2$ cm
$h = 8.05$ cm

6. $b_1 = 2.25$ cm
$b_2 = 4.75$ cm
$h = 1.05$ cm

7. $b_1 = 5.1$ m
$b_2 = 4.28$ m
$h = 2.3$ m

8. $b_1 = 8.2$ m
$b_2 = 5.9$ m
$h = 3.7$ m

9. $b_1 = 6.4$ cm
$b_2 = 10.6$ cm
$h = 8.2$ cm

10. $b_1 = 33.8$ m
$b_2 = 46.2$ m
$h = 10$ m

Volume of Pyramids and Cones

The areas of the bases (B) and the heights of the prism, the pyramid, and the cone are equal.

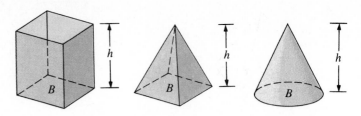

It takes three pyramids of sand to fill the prism. It takes three cones of sand to fill the prism.

Volume of pyramid = Volume of cone

The volume of either the pyramid or the cone is $\frac{1}{3}$ the volume of the prism.

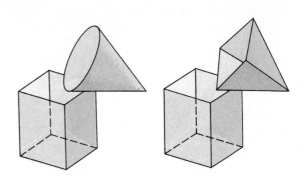

Prism: $V = Bh$

Pyramid: $V = \frac{1}{3}Bh$

Cone: $V = \frac{1}{3}Bh$ or $V = \frac{1}{3}\pi r^2 h$ $\quad \boxed{B = \pi r^2}$

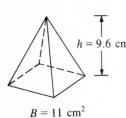

$V = \frac{1}{3}Bh$

$V = \frac{1}{3} \times 11 \times 9.6$

$V = 35.2$ cm^3

$h = 9.6$ cm

$B = 11$ cm^2

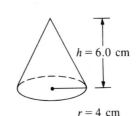

$h = 6.0$ cm

$r = 4$ cm

$V = \frac{1}{3}\pi r^2 h$

$V = \frac{1}{3} \times \pi \times 4^2 \times 6$

$V \approx 32 \times 3.14$

$V \approx 100.48$ cm^3

The volume of the pyramid is 35.2 cm^3.   The volume of the cone is about 100.48 cm^3.

Warm Up

Find the volume of each figure.

1.
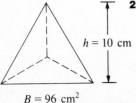
$h = 10$ cm
$B = 96$ cm^2

2.
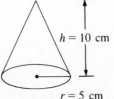
$h = 10$ cm
$r = 5$ cm

3.
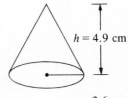
$h = 4.9$ cm
$r = 2.6$ cm

4.
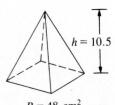
$h = 10.5$ cm
$B = 48$ cm^2

Practice Find the volume of each pyramid.

1.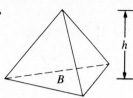

$B = 30$ cm^2
$h = 9$ cm

2.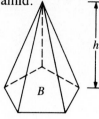

$B = 63$ dm^2
$h = 12$ dm

3.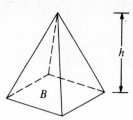

$B = 2.25$ m^2
$h = 1.2$ m

4. $B = 1,200$ m^2
$h = 60$ m

5. $B = 2.4$ m^2
$h = 0.6$ m

6. $B = 4,224$ mm^2
$h = 7.2$ mm

Find the volume of each cone. Round your answer
to the nearest hundredth.

7.

$r = 2$ cm
$h = 3$ cm

8.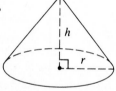

$r = 6.3$ m
$h = 8$ m

9.

$r = 0.4$ cm
$h = 2.7$ cm

10. $r = 10$ cm
$h = 12$ cm

11. $r = 1.8$ m
$h = 2.4$ m

12. $r = 33$ mm
$h = 40$ mm

Mixed Applications

13. The cone and the cylinder have the
same base and the same height. What is
the volume of the cone? What is the
volume of the cylinder?

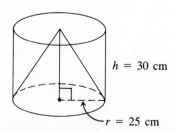

$h = 30$ cm

$r = 25$ cm

14. The prism and the pyramid have the
same base and the same height. The
volume of the pyramid is 338 cm^3.
What is the volume of the prism?

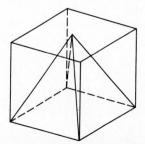

More Practice, page 453, Set A

Volume and Capacity

In the metric system, units of volume have a simple relation to units of capacity.

Volume: **1 cm³**
Capacity: **1 mL**

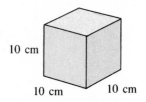

Volume: **1,000 cm³**
Capacity: **1,000 mL = 1 L**

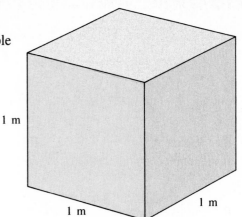

Volume: **1 m³**
Capacity: **1,000 L = 1 kL**

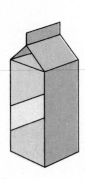

The volume of a milk carton is 1,890 cm³. A milk carton has a capacity of 1.89 L or 1,890 mL.

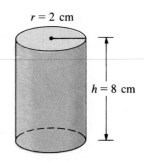

The volume of the cylinder is $\pi r^2 h$ or $3.14 \times 4 \times 8 = 100.48$ cm³. The capacity of the cylinder is about 100.48 mL.

Find the volume and the capacity of each figure.

1.

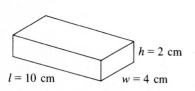

$h = 2$ cm
$l = 10$ cm $w = 4$ cm

2.

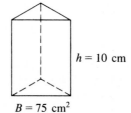

$h = 10$ cm
$B = 75$ cm²

3.

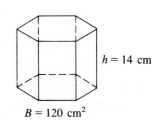

$h = 14$ cm
$B = 120$ cm²

4.

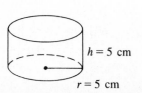

$h = 5$ cm
$r = 5$ cm

5.

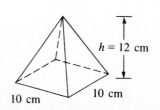

$h = 12$ cm
10 cm   10 cm

6.

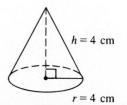

$h = 4$ cm
$r = 4$ cm

318

PROBLEM SOLVING: Mixed Practice

> QUESTION
> DATA
> PLAN
> ANSWER
> CHECK

Solve.

1. A field truck has a cargo space that is 1.3 m high, 1.6 m wide, and 2.5 m long. What is the volume of the cargo space?

2. A conical paper filter has a diameter of 16 cm and a height of 12 cm. What is the maximum amount of liquid, in milliliters, that the filter could hold?

3. A cylindrical can has a radius of 4.5 cm and a height of 12 cm. What is the area of a label that will just cover the curved surface of the can?

4. Jaime wants to pour 1 L (1,000 mL) of oil into a cylindrical can. The radius of the can is 7.6 cm and the height is 17 cm. To what depth would 1 L of oil be poured? Round the answer to the nearest tenth of a centimeter.

5. A pyramid has a square base 8 cm on each side and a height of 10 cm. A cone has a radius of 5 cm and a height of 10 cm. Find the volume, to the nearest tenth, of each figure. Which figure has the greater volume? How much greater is it?

6. A can with a diameter of 10 cm and a height of 10 cm is packed inside a cube that is 10.2 cm on each edge. To the nearest tenth, what is the volume of the part of the cube not filled with the can?

7. **DATA BANK** A case of canned peaches contains 24 cans. How much greater is the total volume of No. $2\frac{1}{2}$ cans in one case than the total volume of No. 2 cans in one case? Round the volumes to the nearest cubic centimeter. (See page 431.)

8. **Strategy Practice** A cabinet maker has a cube of wood 20 cm on each edge. A circular hole is to be drilled through the centers of two opposite cube faces. To the nearest tenth of a centimeter, what is the largest possible radius of a hole which will remove $\frac{1}{2}$ the volume of the cube?

319

APPLIED PROBLEM SOLVING

QUESTION
DATA
PLAN
ANSWER
CHECK

You have been given an animal as a pet. You want to build your pet a pen in your back yard. You need to decide what size and shape pen you are going to build.

Some Things to Consider

· You have 48 feet of wire fence to use for the pen. You plan to use all of it.

· You want to give the pet as much space as possible in the pen.

· You want the pen to have an attractive, geometric shape.

· One side of the pen will be along a wall on the side of the yard, so that side of the pen will not use any wire fence.

wall
_____

| pen |

Some Questions to Answer

1. If you plan a rectangle for the shape of the pen and make the width of the pen 8 feet, how much fence will be left to form the length of the pen?

2. What is the area of the pen in Question 1?

3. If you made the pen in the shape of a rectangle 20 feet long, how wide could the pen be?

4. What is the area of the pen with the length and width of the pen in Question 3?

5. What are some other sizes and shapes of pet pens that you could build with the 48 feet of fence?

What Is Your Decision?

What size and shape will you make the pen? Make a drawing that will show your plan.

Find the perimeter of each figure.

1.
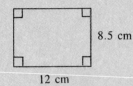
8.5 cm
12 cm

2.
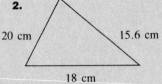
20 cm   15.6 cm
18 cm

3.
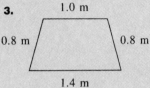
1.0 m
0.8 m   0.8 m
1.4 m

Find the area of each figure.

4.
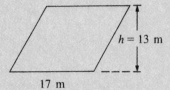
h = 13 m
17 m

5.

h = 12.5 cm
18.6 cm

6.
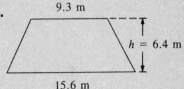
9.3 m
h = 6.4 m
15.6 m

Find the circumference and the area of each circle. Use 3.14 for π.

7.
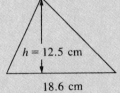
r = 1.8 m

8.
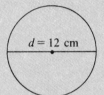
d = 12 cm

9.

r = 4 cm

Find the total surface area of each figure. Use 3.14 for π if necessary.

10.
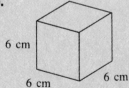
6 cm
6 cm   6 cm

11.

h = 9 m
r = 3 m

12.
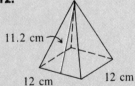
11.2 cm
12 cm   12 cm

Find the volume of each figure.

13. Pyramid:
$B = 44.8$ cm^2
$h = 21.0$ cm

14. Rectangular prism:
$l = 13$ cm
$w = 8$ cm
$h = 4$ cm

15. Cylinder:
$r = 5$ cm
$h = 7$ cm

16. How many square meters of carpeting are needed to cover the floor of a room that is 10 m long and 8.5 m wide?

17. A bicycle wheel has a diameter of 66 cm. What is the circumference of the wheel?

321

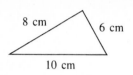

8 cm   6 cm

10 cm

Perimeter = the distance around
a polygon

$P = 6 + 8 + 10$

$P = 24$ cm

Find the perimeter of each figure.

1.

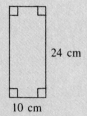

24 cm

10 cm

2.

25 m

19 m   19 m

25 m

Area formulas:

Rectangle: $A = lw$

Triangle: $A = \frac{1}{2}bh$

Parallelogram: $A = bh$

Trapezoid: $A = \frac{1}{2}(b_1 + b_2)h$

Find the area of each figure.

3.

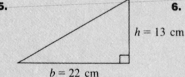

0.9 cm

2.8 cm

4.

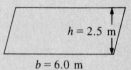

$h = 2.5$ m

$b = 6.0$ m

5.

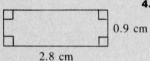

$h = 13$ cm

$b = 22$ cm

6.

$b_1 = 26$ cm

$h = 9$ cm

$b_2 = 17$ cm

Circumference:

$C = \pi d$ or $C = 2\pi r$

Area of a circle:

$A = \pi r^2$

Find the circumference and the area of each circle.
Use 3.14 for π.

7.

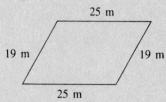

$d = 18$ cm

8.

$r = 5$ m

Volume formulas:

Prism: $V = Bh$

Cylinder: $V = Bh$ or
$V = \pi r^2 h$

Find the volume. Use 3.14 for π if necessary.

9.

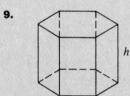

h

$B = 300$ cm^2

$h = 15$ cm

10.

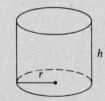

h

r

$r = 6.0$ cm

$h = 10$ cm

Space Perception

By following the instructions, you can fold a square sheet of paper into a cube. Dotted lines are folds. Only one side of the paper is colored.

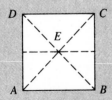

Fold a square sheet of paper three times as shown.

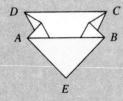

Make a triangular shape.

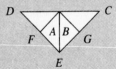

Fold points A and B down to E.

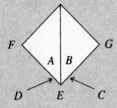

Fold points D and C down to E, behind A and B.

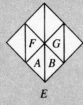

Fold the top corners inward at F and G to the center line.

Fold the other two corners backward to the center line on the back.

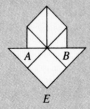

Fold back loose corners A and B. Do the same for the loose corners in the back.

Fold points A and B to the center. Repeat for the points in the back.

Tuck △AXY and △BRS into the pockets under A and B. Repeat for the triangles in the back.

Fold points O and E to the center and back again.

Blow in the hole at point O to inflate the cube.

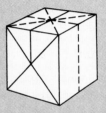

A paperfolded cube!

323

1. What is the measure of an angle that is supplementary to ∠ PQR?

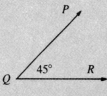

A 45°   **B** 54°

C 135°   **D** not given

2. What kind of triangle is △ABC?

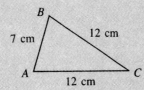

A equilateral   **B** isosceles

C scalene   **D** not given

3. How many sides does a nonagon have?

A 10   **B** 7

C 5   **D** not given

4. What is the name of a line that intersects a circle at one point?

A secant   **B** arc

C tangent   **D** not given

5. What is the symbol for congruence?

A ≅   **B** ⊥

C ≈   **D** not given

6. How many lines of symmetry does an equilateral triangle have?

A 2   **B** 3

C 1   **D** not given

7. What is the percent for 0.092?

A 9.2%   **B** 92%

C 0.92%   **D** not given

8. What is the percent for $\frac{19}{50}$?

A 263%   **B** 3.8%

C 38%   **D** not given

9. What is 37% of 500?

A 185   **B** 13.5

C 18.5   **D** not given

10. What percent of 45 is 18?

A 8.1%   **B** 25%

C 40%   **D** not given

11. 19 is what percent of 95?

A 20%   **B** 500%

C 18%   **D** not given

12. Estimate 29% of 87.

A 18   **B** 27

C 16   **D** not given

13. If a triangle has one right angle, what is the sum of the measures of the other two angles?

A 180°   **B** 60°

C 90°   **D** not given

14. What is the sale price of an item with a regular price of $19.95 and a discount of 20%?

A $16.05   **B** $19.75

C $3.90   **D** not given

Probability

Winds up to 482 kilometers per hour have lifted a 72-ton railroad car, uprooted trees, and splintered buildings in a matter of minutes. Advancing with a roar at 64 kilometers per hour, the swirling funnel of a tornado leaves destruction wherever it touches down.

Scientists at the National Severe Storms Forecast Center are trying to find ways to predict and modify these small, dangerous storms. They use weather balloons, radar, lasers, satellite photographs, and ground reports. They have found that there are about 8 chances in 10 that a tornado will move toward the northeast. About 6 out of 10 tornadoes will occur between noon and sunset. 63% of the tornadoes that have occurred since 1950 have been classified as weak and 2% have been in the most violent category, with winds over 418 kilometers per hour. Experts say that a lot more research is needed to actually control a "twister."

The Basic Counting Principle

How many different kinds of sandwiches are there on the menu?

> ### Rico's Sandwich Shop
>
> Chicken sandwich $1.95   Cheese sandwich $1.75
>
> Tuna sandwich $2.25   Egg sandwich $2.25
>
> Your choice of white, rye, or wheat bread

We can make a **tree diagram** to count the different kinds.

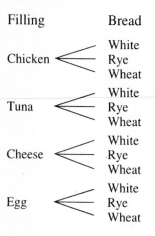

Filling	Bread
Chicken	White, Rye, Wheat
Tuna	White, Rye, Wheat
Cheese	White, Rye, Wheat
Egg	White, Rye, Wheat

The tree diagram shows 12 different sandwiches.

$$4 \times 3 = 12$$

↑ Kinds of filling   ↑ Kinds of bread   ↑ Sandwiches

> **The Basic Counting Principle**
>
> If one thing can be done in n ways and a second thing can be done in m ways, then the two things can be done together in $n \times m$ ways.

Warm Up

Solve.

1. Tortillas: Flour, corn
   Fillings: Bean, cheese, tuna
   How many different kinds of tortilla and filling are possible?

2. Main dishes: Fried chicken, spaghetti
   Side dishes: Peas, carrots, corn, beans
   How many different meals are possible?

326

Practice Solve.

1. If there are 5 kinds of bread and 3 kinds of filling, how many different sandwiches with 1 kind of bread and 1 kind of filling are possible?

2. If there are 3 kinds of soup and 3 kinds of salad, how many different orders of soup and salad are possible?

3. How many different routes are there from *A* to *B* to *C*?

4. How many different routes are there from *R* to *S* to *T*?

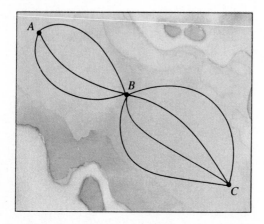

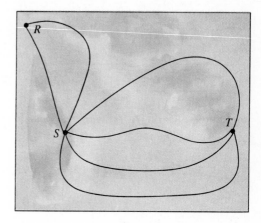

5. How many 2-letter words can be formed using one of the vowels **i** or **a**, followed by one of the consonants **n**, **t**, or **s**? Write all the words.

6. How many 3-letter words can be formed by placing the single letters **b**, **c**, and **f** in front of the letter pairs **at**, **og**, **ar**, **ad**, and **ur**? List the words.

7. A tire company makes 3 grades of tires. Each grade is made in 16 sizes. How many different kinds of tires are made?

8. Walt plays the piano and the violin. Duane plays the trumpet, the flute, and the clarinet. How many ways can they perform a duet with their musical instruments?

9. Tickets for 12 performances of a concert are sold at 5 prices. How many different choices are possible?

★ 10. To fly from New York to Chicago, Karen can take Trans-West (TW) or Air Northwest (AN) airlines. From Chicago to San Francisco she can take Cal-Express (CA) or AirAmerica (AA). She has the same choices for the return trip. How many airline choices are there for a round trip? Make a list.

Counting Arrangements: Permutations

Amy, Bud, and Carmella will be seated side-by-side in a window seat, a center seat, or an aisle seat. How many different seating arrangements are possible?

We can find the arrangements by making a list.

Window	A	A	B	B	C	C
Center	B	C	A	C	B	A
Aisle	C	B	C	A	A	B

There are 6 seating arrangements possible for the 3 people.

We can also find the number of arrangements by multiplying.

$$3 \times 2 \times 1 = 6$$

↑	↑	↑	↑
Choices for the window	Choices for the center	Choices for the aisle	Total arrangements

An arrangement of a group of objects in a certain order is called a **permutation** of the objects.

Other Examples

From a group of 5 books, 3 books are stacked one on top of the other. How many permutations of the 3 books from the 5 books are possible?

$$5 \times 4 \times 3 = 60$$

↑	↑	↑	↑
Choices for the bottom book	Choices for the middle book	Choices for the top book	Number of permutations

Warm Up

1. How many arrangements can be made of 4 books side-by-side on a shelf?

2. Six students are at a table. Three students leave. How many arrangements of the 3 students from the 6 students are possible?

Practice Solve.

1. There are 5 teams in a relay race. How many different orders of finishing the race are possible if there are no ties?

2. Prizes are given to the fastest 3 teams of 5 teams in a relay race. How many different arrangements of 3 teams from 5 teams are possible?

3. There are 10 teams in the egg-catching contest. Prizes are given to the last 2 teams. How many different arrangements of the 2 prizes are possible?

4. There are 4 seats on one side of a picnic table. How many permutations of 4 people for these seats are possible?

5. There are 8 teams in the one-legged race. Prizes are given to the first 3 teams. How many different ways could the prizes be given?

6. In how many different orders can the 8 teams finish the one-legged race if there are no ties?

7. There are 6 students in line at the water fountain. How many different arrangements of students could there be in the line?

8. There were 9 players on a softball team. The first batter is the "leadoff" batter and the second batter is "on deck." How many different orders of leadoff batters and on-deck batters are possible?

★ 9. The coach had 9 players. She wanted Holmes to be the leadoff batter and Carrico, the pitcher, to bat last. How many different batting orders could the coach arrange?

10. There were 12 players who wanted to play softball. Their names were put in a hat and 9 of them were drawn out. How many different orders of the 9 names are possible?

SKILLKEEPER

Find the volume of each prism.

1. $B = 14$ cm^2
   $h = 7$ cm

2. $l = 18$ cm
   $w = 7$ cm
   $h = 30$ cm

3. $B = 23$ mm^2
   $h = 13.3$ mm

4. $l = 2.5$ m
   $w = 1.3$ m
   $h = 4.6$ m

5. $l = 6.4$ m
   $w = 1.05$ m
   $h = 5.5$ m

Find the volume of each cylinder.

6. $r = 6$ cm
   $h = 10$ cm

7. $r = 5$ cm
   $h = 15$ cm

8. $r = 0.6$ m
   $h = 1.4$ m

9. $r = 2.8$ m
   $h = 3$ m

10. $r = 15$ cm
    $h = 10$ cm

Counting Selections: Combinations

How many selections of 2 topics from the 4 topics are possible?

First we find the number of permutations of 2 topics from 4 topics.

Permutations = **4 × 3 = 12**

The **order** of the topics is not important. Choosing A, then B, is the same as choosing B, then A. We need to divide by the number of permutations of 2 topics from 2 topics.

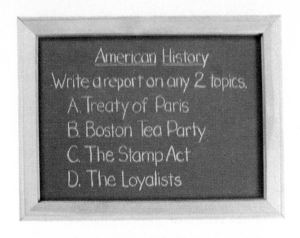

Permutations of
2 topics from 4 topics → $\dfrac{4 \times 3}{2 \times 1} = \dfrac{12}{2} = 6$
Permutations of →
2 topics from 2 topics

There are 6 possible selections.

A selection of a number of objects from a set of objects, *without regard to order*, is called a **combination** of the objects.

List of Permutations

A,B	A,C	A,D	B,C	B,D	C,D
B,A	C,A	D,A	C,B	D,B	D,C

Selections

A and B	A and D	B and D
A and C	B and C	C and D

Other Examples

How many combinations or selections of 3 topics from 5 topics are possible?

Combinations $= \dfrac{5 \times 4 \times 3}{3 \times 2 \times 1} = \dfrac{60}{6} = 10$

Topics	Combinations of 3 topics from 5 topics	
A	ABC	ADE
B	ABD	BCD
C	ABE	BCE
D	ACD	BDE
E	ACE	CDE

Warm Up

Give the number of combinations. Check by making a list.

1. Choose 3 topics from 4 topics.

2. Choose 2 topics from 5 topics.

Practice Find the number of combinations.

1. Choose 2 topics from 3 topics.

2. Choose 2 topics from 7 topics.

3. Choose 3 topics from 6 topics.

4. Choose 4 topics from 6 topics.

5. Choose 5 topics from 6 topics.

6. Choose 6 topics from 6 topics.

Solve.

7. How many combinations of 2 books can be selected from a list of 8 books?

8. How many different selections of 2 students are possible from a group of 28 students?

9. Students must write reports on American Indians in any 2 of the culture regions listed below. How many combinations are possible?

Eastern Woodland	Great Basin
Southeast	Plateau
Great Plains	California
Southwest	Northwest

10. Students must write biographies on the lives of any 3 of these historic people. How many combinations are possible?

Chief Joseph	Winslow Homer
Sojourner Truth	Dorothea Dix
Nat Love	Frederic Remington
Stephen F. Austin	

11. The library received 30 new books. The librarian selected 5 of the books for a display. How many different selections are possible?

12. **DATA HUNT** Find the approximate number of books in your school library. If you check out 3 of the books, how many combinations are possible?

THINK MATH

Factorials

The product of consecutive whole numbers from 1 to a number n is called **factorial n**. The symbol for factorial n is $n!$.

$n! = 1 \cdot 2 \cdot 3 \cdot 4 \cdot 5 \cdot \ldots \cdot (n-1) \cdot n$

$1! = 1 \qquad 2! = 1 \cdot 2 = 2 \qquad 3! = 1 \cdot 2 \cdot 3 = 6$

Find the product for each factorial.

1. 4!   **2.** 5!   **3.** 6!   **4.** 7!   **5.** 8!   **6.** 9!

Solve.

7. $2! \cdot 3!$ **8.** $5! \div 3!$ **9.** $\dfrac{4!}{2!}$ **10.** $5! \cdot 4!$ **11.** $\dfrac{5!}{4!}$ **12.** $6! \div 4!$

Probability

Each spin of the pointer results in an **outcome**, a letter on the spinner.

There is **1 chance in 6** of getting the letter A.

The **probability** of getting the letter A is $\frac{1}{6}$.

We write: $P(\mathbf{A}) = \dfrac{1}{6}$

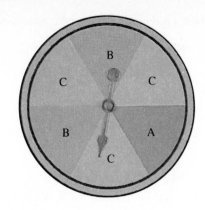

There are **2** chances in **6** of getting **B**. $\qquad P(\mathbf{B}) = \dfrac{2}{6}$ or $\dfrac{1}{3}$

There are **3** chances in **6** of getting **C**. $\qquad P(\mathbf{C}) = \dfrac{3}{6}$ or $\dfrac{1}{2}$

There are **0** chances in **6** of getting **D**. $\qquad P(\mathbf{D}) = \dfrac{0}{6} = \mathbf{0}$

There are **6** chances in **6** of getting **A, B, or C**. $\qquad P(\mathbf{A, B,}$ or $\mathbf{C}) = \dfrac{6}{6} = \mathbf{1}$

Outcomes or combinations of outcomes are called **events**.

$$\text{Probability of an event} = \frac{\text{Possible ways for event to happen}}{\text{Total number of outcomes}}$$

Warm Up

Give the missing outcomes and probabilities.

	Probability experiment	Outcome	Probability
1.	Toss a coin	Heads(H) Tails(T)	$P(H) = $ ▦ $P(T) = $ ▦
2.	Toss a die.	▦, ▦, ▦ ▦, ▦, ▦	$P(3) = $ ▦ $P(4) = $ ▦ $P(7) = $ ▦
3.	Spin the spinner.	▦, ▦, ▦	$P(1) = $ ▦ $P(2) = $ ▦ $P(\text{number} < 4) = $ ▦

Practice List all of the possible outcomes. Then give the probability of each outcome.

1. Spin the spinner.

2. Toss the die.

3. Choose an apple without looking.

Give the probability for the spinner.

4. P(even number) = ▓

5. P(odd number) = ▓

6. $P(5)$ = ▓

7. $P(6)$ = ▓

Give the probability for drawing a marble without looking.

8. P(red marble) = ▓

9. P(blue marble) = ▓

Give the probability of drawing a card without looking.

10. $P(+)$ = ▓

11. $P(\Diamond)$ = ▓

12. $P(\bigcirc)$ = ▓

13. $P(\times)$ = ▓

Give the probability for each spinner.

14. $P(X)$ = ▓

15. $P(Y)$ = ▓

16. $P(Z \text{ or } X)$ = ▓

17. $P(W)$ = ▓

18. P(odd number) = ▓

19. P(even number) = ▓

20. P(number > 7) = ▓

21. P(number < 4) = ▓

22. DATA HUNT What is the probability that your first name will be called if one name is read from the class list?

Probability of Ordered-Pair Events

Rayanne and Kay tossed a penny and a nickel for a probability experiment. Each outcome is an **ordered pair**. What is the probability that both coins will come up heads: $P(H,H)$?

We need to find the total number of outcomes. We can make a list or we can use the Basic Counting Principle.

List of Outcomes

Penny	Nickel	Symbol
Tails	Tails	(T,T)
Tails	Heads	(T,H)
Heads	Tails	(H,T)
Heads	Heads	(H,H)

Number of outcomes $= 2 \times 2 = 4$

↑ Penny outcomes first   ↑ Nickel outcomes   ↑ Pairs of events

Only 1 outcome is (H,H). $P(\textbf{H},\textbf{H}) = \dfrac{1}{4}$

There is 1 chance in 4 to get (Heads,Heads). The probability is $\frac{1}{4}$.

Other Examples

Toss a penny and spin the spinner.

What is the probability of getting tails and B?

There are $2 \times 4 = 8$ outcomes.

     ↑ Penny   ↑ Spinner

One outcome is (T,B).

$P(\textbf{T},\textbf{B}) = \dfrac{1}{8}$

List of Outcomes

(H,A)	(H,C)	(T,A)	(T,C)
(H,B)	(H,D)	(T,B)	(T,D)

Warm Up

Think of tossing the die and spinning the spinner.

1. How many events are possible?

2. What is $P(4,2)$?

3. What is the probability that both numbers in a pair are the same?

4. What is the probability that the number on the die is greater than the number on the spinner?

Practice Use the two spinners for exercises 1–8.

1. How many events are possible when both spinners are spun?

2. List the events as ordered pairs of numbers.

3. What is $P(3,1)$?

4. What is $P(1,3)$?

5. What is the probability that both numbers in a pair will be even?

6. What is the probability that both numbers in a pair will be odd?

7. What is the probability that both numbers in a pair will be equal?

8. What is the probability that the first number will be 1 more than the second number?

Use the red die and the blue die for exercises 9–17. The red die is listed first.

9. How many events are possible when both dice are tossed?

10. What is $P(5,3)$?

11. What is $P(6,6)$?

12. What is P(both numbers are the same)?

13. What is P(both numbers are different)?

14. What is P(sum of the numbers is 10)?

15. What is P(product of the numbers is 12)?

16. What is P(sum of the numbers is 6)?

17. What sum is most likely to occur when two dice are tossed? What is the probability of this sum?

18. **DATA HUNT** Toss a pair of dice at least 75 times. What is P(sum of 6)? Keep a tally of the sums you get. Find the ratio of the number of times the sum is 6 to the total number of tosses.

SKILLKEEPER

Give each probability for spinning a spinner with numbers from 1 to 10.

1. $P(6)$ 2. $P(1)$ 3. $P(13)$ 4. $P(2)$ 5. $P(5)$

6. P(a number less than 3)   7. P(a number greater than 8)

8. P(an odd number)   9. P(an even number)

Predicting with Probability

Based on weather records, a meteorologist said, "The probability of a tornado in a Southwest region of the United States on any day is about $\frac{1}{7}$."

About how many tornadoes would be expected in this region in a year?

Since $P(\text{tornado}) = \frac{1}{7}$, this means we can expect the area to have a tornado on about $\frac{1}{7}$ of the days in a year.

$$\text{Expected tornadoes} = P(\text{tornado}) \times \frac{\text{number}}{\text{of days}}$$

$$\text{Expected tornadoes} = \frac{1}{7} \times 365 = 52\frac{1}{7}$$

About 52 tornadoes would be expected in the Southwest region each year.

Other Examples

Toss a coin 100 times.
Predict the number of heads.

$$P(\text{H}) = \frac{1}{2}$$

$$\text{Expected number of heads} = \frac{1}{2} \times 100 = 50$$

Toss two dice 120 times. Predict the number of times the sum will be 7.

$$P(\text{sum of } 7) = \frac{1}{6}$$

$$\text{Expected sums of } 7 = \frac{1}{6} \times 120 = 20$$

Warm Up

Give the probability of each event. Then predict the number of times the event will occur.

1. Spin the spinner 60 times.

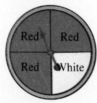

$P(\text{red}) = $ ▦
Expected number red = ▦

2. Toss two pennies 80 times.

$P(\text{H},\text{H}) = $ ▦
Expected number (H,H) = ▦

336

Practice In exercises 1–6, predict the number of times each event will occur.

1. Spin the spinner 50 times.

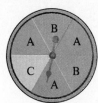

Event: A
$P(A) = \frac{3}{6} = \frac{1}{2}$

2. Draw a marble from the box, then replace it 120 times.

Event: Red marble
$P(\text{red marble}) = \frac{5}{8}$

3. Toss the die 78 times.

Event: 5 on top
$P(5) = \frac{1}{6}$

4. Toss two coins 1,000 times.

Event: (H,H)
$P(H,H) = \frac{1}{4}$

5. Toss the dice 180 times.

Event: Sum of 4
$P(\text{sum of 4}) = \frac{1}{12}$

6. Spin the spinners 600 times.

Event: (B,1)
$P(B,1) = \frac{1}{15}$

In exercises 7–9, give the probability of each event.
Then predict the expected number of times the event will occur.

7. Spin the spinner 72 times.

Event: Y
$P(Y) = $ ▊▊▊▊

8. Toss the dice 300 times.

Event: Sum of 7
$P(\text{sum of 7}) = $ ▊▊▊▊

9. Spin the spinner 1,000 times.

Event: A number > 6
$P(\text{number} > 6) = $ ▊▊▊▊

10. The probability of a rainy day in Columbus, Ohio is about $\frac{3}{8}$. About how many rainy days in 365 days are expected in Columbus?

11. **DATA HUNT** Estimate the probability of a rainy day for your area. Use the probability to estimate the number of rainy days per year. Try to check your estimate with actual weather data.

Odds

Nina is trying to draw a blue marble from the box without looking into the box.

There are **2** ways she can succeed.

There are **3** ways she can fail.

The **odds in favor** of drawing a blue marble are 2 to 3.

$$\frac{2}{3}$$ ← Successes
← Failures

The **odds against** drawing a blue marble are 3 to 2.

$$\frac{3}{2}$$ ← Failures
← Successes

Find the odds for each event.

1. Spin the spinner.

Event: Get a 2
Odds in favor =
Odds against =

2. Draw a marble from the box without looking.

Event: Draw a red marble
Odds in favor =
Odds against =

3. Toss a coin.

Event: Comes up heads
Odds in favor =
Odds against =

4. Spin the spinners.

Event: Sum of 6
Odds in favor =
Odds against =

5. Toss both coins.

Event: The coins match
Odds in favor =
Odds against =

6. Toss the dice.

Event: Sum of 2
Odds in favor =
Odds against =

338

PROBLEM SOLVING: Mixed Practice

QUESTION
DATA
PLAN
ANSWER
CHECK

Solve.

1. Oran, George, and Paula put their names in a hat. One of the names is to be drawn out. What are the odds that Paula's name will be drawn?

2. A multiple-choice test question has 4 choices for the answer. What are the odds against guessing the correct answer?

3. The probability of a rainy day in Portland, Oregon during one year is about $\frac{2}{5}$. How many rainy days per year (365 days) would be expected in Portland?

4. Kent tossed a coin 84 times and kept a tally of the number of heads and tails. How many times would tails be expected?

5. Four students are assigned to sit in 4 seats in a row. How many different seating arrangements are possible for the 4 students?

6. When four coins are tossed, the odds in favor of two coins with heads and two coins with tails is 3 to 5. What are the odds against this event?

7. How many times would you expect to draw a card with a B in 50 trials?

8. The probability that a student will be absent because of illness is $\frac{1}{60}$. In 180 days of school, about how many days would a student be expected to miss because of illness?

9. From a list of 5 topics, a student must give a report on 2 topics. How many different selections of 2 topics are possible?

10. **DATA BANK** What is the ratio of international units (I.U.) of vitamin D to I.U. of vitamin A in one vitamin tablet? (See page 431.)

11. **Strategy Practice** How many different license plates could be formed using any three letters of the alphabet, followed by any three of the digits 0–9?

Multiplying Probabilities:
Independent and Dependent Events

One marble is to be drawn from each of the boxes A and B without looking. What is the probability that both marbles will be red?

$P(R) = \frac{3}{4}$

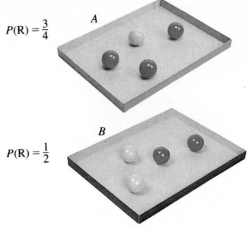

The drawing from box A does not affect the drawing from box B. The drawings are **independent events.**

We can find the probability by multiplying.

$P(R) = \frac{1}{2}$

$$P(\ R\ ,\ R\ ) \ = \ \frac{3}{4} \ \times \ \frac{1}{2} \ = \ \frac{3}{8}$$

↑   ↑   ↑   ↑
Box   Box $P(R)$ $P(R)$
A   B   Box A   Box B

The probability that both marbles will be red is $\frac{3}{8}$.

A box has 2 red marbles and 2 blue marbles. A marble is drawn from the box. Without replacing the first marble, a second marble is drawn.

What is $P(R,R)$?

The outcome for the first draw affects the outcome for the second draw. The drawings are **dependent events.**

$$P(\ R\ ,\ R) \ = \ \frac{1}{2} \ \times \ \frac{1}{3} \ = \ \frac{1}{6}$$

↑   ↑   ↑   ↑
First   Second $P(R)$ $P(R)$
draw   draw   First   Second
            draw   draw

$P(R,R) = \frac{1}{6}$

Warm Up

Toss a coin twice.

1. Are the tosses dependent or independent events?

2. What is $P(H,H)$?

Draw 2 of 6 cards numbered **1** to **6** without replacing them.

3. Are the drawings dependent or independent events?

4. What is the probability that both cards drawn have even numbers?

Practice State if the events are dependent or independent. Then find the missing probability.

1. Toss a die twice.

$P(3) = \frac{1}{6}$, $P(4) = \frac{1}{6}$, $P(3,4) = $ ▦

2. Spin each spinner once.

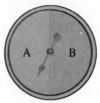

$P(A) = \frac{1}{2}$, $P(C) = \frac{1}{3}$, $P(A,C) = $ ▦

3. Draw 2 cards without replacing them.

$P(\text{odd number, odd number}) = $ ▦
    ↑   ↑
First draw   Second draw

4. Draw 2 marbles without replacing them.

$P(\text{red, blue}) = $ ▦
     ↑ ↑
First draw Second draw

5. Draw 1 marble from box A and 1 marble from box B.

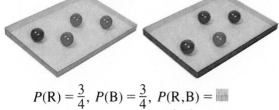

$P(R) = \frac{3}{4}$, $P(B) = \frac{3}{4}$, $P(R,B) = $ ▦
            ↑ ↑
          Box A Box B

6. Draw 2 marbles from the box without replacing them.

$P(R,B) = $ ▦
   ↑ ↑
First draw Second draw

THINK MATH

Estimating Probability

Suppose you tossed 3 dice at a time and found the sum of the number of dots on the tops of the three dice. What sum do you estimate you would get most often? How often do you think you would get this sum? Try the experiment and record your results.

341

Mixed Skills Practice

Computation

Find the answers.

1. $\begin{array}{r} 629 \\ 872 \\ 508 \\ +916 \\ \hline \end{array}$

2. $3\frac{3}{4} + 2\frac{1}{2} + 5\frac{5}{8}$

3. $\begin{array}{r} 2{,}764 \\ \times \quad 7 \\ \hline \end{array}$

4. Solve.

   $\frac{n}{40} = \frac{3}{5}$

5. $\begin{array}{r} 0.98 \\ \times \quad 55 \\ \hline \end{array}$

6. $66\overline{)15{,}444}$

7. $14 \times 3\frac{1}{7}$

8. $\begin{array}{r} \$903.11 \\ - \ 127.45 \\ \hline \end{array}$

9. $3.5\overline{)2.695}$

10. $15 - 8\frac{2}{3}$

11. $\frac{9}{20} = ?\%$

12. 45% of 680

13. Solve.

    $\frac{x}{3} = 5$

14. Solve.

    $x + {}^-5 = {}^-11$

15. Solve.

    $4x + 3 = {}^-9$

16. Solve.

    $\frac{x}{2} + 1 = 7$

Mental Math

Write only the answers.

17. 100×6.3

18. $\frac{2}{3} \times 18$

19. $40 + 37 + 60$

20. $890 - 120$

21. 3×4.2

22. $350 \div 7$

23. 70×60

24. $2.5 + 7 + 3.5$

25. $\frac{1}{2} \times 500$

26. $0.1 \times \$25.00$

27. 50% of 80

28. $625 + 175$

29. $^-12 + 7$

30. $6 - 10$

31. $^-3 \times {}^-7$

32. $8 \times ({}^-7 + {}^-2)$

Estimation

Estimate.

33. $\frac{1}{3} \times \$89.50$

34. $719\overline{)648.3}$

35. 80.43×7.3

36. $903.44 - 654.83$

37. $8.75\overline{)29.664}$

38. 11% of $56.80

39. $\frac{1}{8} \times 243$

40. 0.73×0.614

41. $\begin{array}{r} \$246.50 \\ 138.77 \\ 108.45 \\ + \ 263.50 \\ \hline \end{array}$

42. $\begin{array}{r} 9.83 \\ 7.44 \\ +6.45 \\ \hline \end{array}$

43. $\begin{array}{r} 6\frac{11}{12} \\ +8\frac{1}{10} \\ \hline \end{array}$

44. $\begin{array}{r} 2{,}133 \\ 1{,}946 \\ 2{,}048 \\ +1{,}977 \\ \hline \end{array}$

45. $\frac{3}{8}$ of 31

46. 49% of 61.3

47. 9.74×0.79

48. $6{,}393 \div 80$

APPLIED PROBLEM SOLVING

QUESTION
DATA
PLAN
ANSWER
CHECK

You are a tennis player and several of your games have been videotaped and analyzed. You would like to decide what is the best serving strategy to use.

Some Things to Consider

- In tennis, each point is determined by one or two serves. If the first serve is not good, you get a second serve.

- You have two kinds of serves: A hard serve (H) and a soft serve (S).

- You can make a good soft serve (S) on 90% of your tries, but you only win the point 40% of the time when this serve is good.

- You can make a good hard serve (H) 50% of your tries, but you win the point 60% of the time when this serve is good.

Some Questions to Answer

Strategy	First serves	Good first serves	Points won	Second serves	Good second serves	Points won	Total points won
S,S	100	▦	▦	▦	▦	▦	▦

1. How many points out of 100 would you win by using the service strategy of the soft serve on both the first and second serves (S,S)? Copy and complete the table above.

2. How many points out of 100 would you win by using the strategy of the soft serve first and the hard serve on the second serve (S,H)? Extend the table to show the results of this strategy.

3. How many points out of 100 would you win by using the hard serve first and the soft serve second (H,S)?

4. How many points out of 100 would you win by using the hard serve on both the first and second serves?

What Is Your Decision?

Which strategy should you use to win as many points as you can while serving?

PROBLEM SOLVING: Using the Strategies

| QUESTION |
| DATA |
| PLAN |
| ANSWER |
| CHECK |

Problem-Solving Strategies

✔ Guess and Check   ✔ Make a Table

✔ Choose the Operations   ✔ Solve a Simpler Problem

✔ Make an Organized List   ✔ Find a Pattern

✔ Work Backward   ✔ Use Logical Reasoning

✔ Draw a Picture

You have learned to use different strategies to solve some of the problems in this book. Use one or more of the strategies to solve each problem below.

1. Three boys and 5 girls were at a party. Each boy danced with a different girl each dance and the two extra girls danced with each other. How many different couples danced if no two couples danced together twice?

2. Four towns lie on the same straight road. It is 50 km from Ames to Baker. It is 20 km from Columbus to Ames. It is 60 km from Dalton to Columbus. Ames is between Dalton and Columbus. How many kilometers is it from Baker to Dalton?

3. Scott had two boards. He wanted to cut the first board into 6 pieces of equal length. He wanted to cut the second board into 4 pieces of equal length. What is the total number of cuts? (The boards are not stacked up to make a cut.)

4. Adult tickets to a school play cost $3.00 while student tickets cost $1.00. The total income from the play was $325. There were 166 student tickets sold. How many adult tickets were sold?

5. Laura dropped a rubber ball from a height of 18 m to the ground. Each time the ball hit the ground it rebounded $\frac{1}{3}$ its previous height. How far had the ball traveled when it hit the ground the fourth time?

6. Gary is 12 years old and his father is 35. How old will Gary be when he is half as old as his father?

1. How many different routes are there from A to C?

2. In how many different orders can 4 runners finish a race if there are no ties?

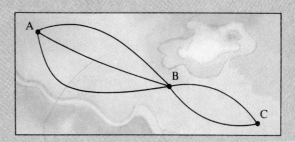

Find the number of combinations.

3. Choose 3 topics from 9 topics.

4. Choose 2 topics from 5 topics.

Give the probability of each outcome for a die numbered **1** through **6**.

5. What is $P(6)$?

6. What is $P(8)$?

7. What is $P(\text{odd number})$?

Use the two spinners for questions 8–10.

8. What is $P(1,1)$?

9. What is the probability that both numbers are greater than 1?

10. How many times would you expect both numbers to be 1 if you spin both spinners 200 times?

Give the odds for the spinner.

11. Odds in favor of getting C

12. Odds against getting B

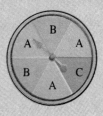

13. If you toss a die twice, are the outcomes dependent or independent?

14. If you toss a die twice, what is the probability of getting 3 on each toss?

15. A box contains 2 red marbles and 2 white marbles. What is the probability of drawing 1 red marble, and, without replacing the first marble, drawing another red marble?

16. From a list of 7 topics, reports must be written on 3 topics. How many different selections of 3 topics are possible?

3 chances in **6** of getting **A**

$P(A) = \frac{3}{6}$ or $\frac{1}{2}$

$P(B) = \frac{2}{6}$ or $\frac{1}{3}$

$P(C) = \frac{1}{6}$

Use the spinner at the right for exercises 1–6. Give the probabilities.

1. $P(1) = $ ▦

2. $P(2) = $ ▦

3. $P(3) = $ ▦

4. $P(\text{even number}) = $ ▦

5. $P(\text{odd number}) = $ ▦

6. $P(\text{number} < 4) = $ ▦

Nine pairs of events

(1,1) (1,2) (1,3)
(2,1) (2,2) (2,3)
(3,1) (3,2) (3,3)

$P(2,2) = \frac{1}{9}$

$P(\text{sum} = 4) = \frac{3}{9} = \frac{1}{3}$

Spin the spinners below for exercises 7–12.

7. How many pairs of events are possible?

8. $P(3,5) = $ ▦

9. $P(\text{sum} = 8) = $ ▦

10. $P(\text{sum} = 6) = $ ▦

11. $P(\text{both numbers are the same}) = $ ▦

12. $P(\text{sum} < 2) = $ ▦

Odds in favor of drawing a yellow marble:

3   to   **2** $= \frac{3}{2}$

↑   ↑

Successes   Failures

Odds against $= \frac{2}{3}$

Use the figure below for exercises 13–16. Give the odds.

13. In favor of drawing a yellow marble

14. Against drawing a yellow marble

15. In favor of drawing a blue marble

16. Against drawing a blue marble

Pascal's Triangle

Can you discover the pattern for the formation of this triangle?

It is called **Pascal's Triangle**. You can add as many rows as you need. You can use the numbers to solve problems about combinations or selections.

From a group of 6 objects, how many combinations of 2 are possible?

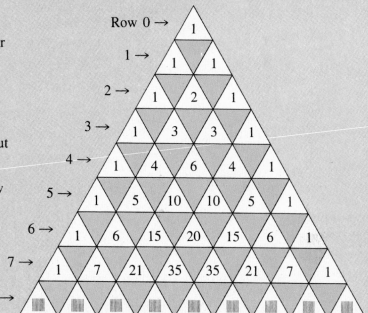

Choose row 6 of the triangle. → **1 6 15 20 15 6 1**

Count over to the number → **0 1 2**
in each combination.

There are 15 combinations possible.

Use Pascal's Triangle to solve these problems.

1. How many combinations of 4 objects from 6 objects are possible?

2. How many combinations of 3 objects from 7 objects are possible?

3. Extend Pascal's Triangle to 12 rows.

4. From a list of 8 subjects, Tom wants to select 4 subjects. How many combinations are possible?

5. A salad may have 3 different ingredients. There are 8 ingredients to choose from. How many different combinations are possible?

6. There were 11 football players on one team on the field. The coach decided to take 4 players out and put in substitutes. How many different combinations of 4 players are possible?

1. Which is correct?

A $\dfrac{17}{34} \neq \dfrac{14}{28}$ B $\dfrac{12}{16} = \dfrac{24}{32}$

C $\dfrac{10}{16} = \dfrac{26}{40}$ D not given

2. Simplify the rate.
$56 in 8 h

A $\dfrac{\$7}{h}$ B $\dfrac{\$8}{h}$

C $448   D not given

3. Solve.

$\dfrac{4}{10} = \dfrac{14}{x}$

A $x = 5.6$
B $x = 35$
C $x = 3.5$
D not given

4. Find the unit price.
24 boxes for $23.28

A $\dfrac{\$0.95}{box}$ B $\dfrac{\$0.28}{box}$

C $\dfrac{\$0.97}{box}$ D not given

5. Which symbol means "is similar to"?

A $\cong$ B $\geq$

C $\sim$ D not given

6. What is the tangent ratio?

A $\dfrac{\text{opposite side}}{\text{adjacent side}}$ B $\dfrac{\text{hypotenuse}}{\text{adjacent side}}$

C $\dfrac{\text{opposite side}}{\text{hypotenuse}}$ D not given

7. What is the perimeter of an equilateral triangle with $s = 6.5$ cm?

A 9.75 cm   B 13 cm
C 42.24 cm   D not given

8. What is the area of a rectangle with $w = 4.3$ m and $l = 12$ m?

A 28.3 m²   B 51.6 m²
C 16.3 m²   D not given

9. Which formula would you use to find the area of a triangle?

A $A = bh$ B $A = 2\,bh$
C $A = \dfrac{1}{2}\,bh$ D not given

For 10, 11, and 13 use 3.14 for π.

10. What is the circumference of a circle with $r = 9.5$ cm?

A 59.66 cm   B 93.6662 cm
C 29.83 cm   D not given

11. Find the area.

$d = 12$ m

A 452.16 m²
B 113.04 m²
C 37.68 m²
D not given

12. What is the volume of a pyramid with $B = 576$ m² and $h = 41$ m?

A 23,616 m³   B 11,808 m³
C 7,872 m³   D not given

13. A wall clock has a diameter of 26 cm. What is the circumference of the clock?

A 40.82 cm   B 81.64 cm
C 530.66 cm   D not given

14. Broccoli sells for $1.36/kg. What is the cost of 0.75 kg of broccoli?

A $1.02   B $1.00
C $1.81   D not given

Statistics and Graphs

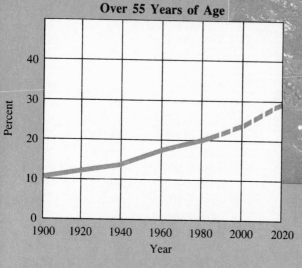

Percent of Population Over 55 Years of Age

Percent

40

30

20

10

0

1900 1920 1940 1960 1980 2000 2020

Year

Any stage in a person's life, such as childhood, youth, or adulthood, can be called *age*. The term is also used to speak of the time when young people become legally responsible for their own actions. Traditionally a person would *come of age*, or reach *legal age* at 21. Since the minimum voting age has been set at 18, many states have also lowered the legal age.

Current figures show that the average life expectancy in the United States is 74.5 years. Today 20% of the population is over 55 years of age. This percentage is expected to continue to rise.

Senior citizens represent 25% of the current American consumer market. Their influence is significant in all areas of life, including the workplace. The traditional retirement age has jumped from 65 years to 70 years. *Old age* can indeed be a stage of life that is full of activity and responsibility.

Tables of Data

George Washington

Thomas Jefferson

Abraham Lincoln

Presidents of the United States 1789–1981

Name and (party)	Term	Age at Inauguration	State of birth
1. Washington (F)	1789–1797	57	VA
2. J. Adams (F)	1797–1801	61	MA
3. Jefferson (DR)	1801–1809	57	VA
4. Madison (DR)	1809–1817	57	VA
5. Monroe (DR)	1817–1825	58	VA
6. J. Q. Adams (DR)	1825–1829	57	MA
7. Jackson (D)	1829–1837	61	SC
8. Van Buren (D)	1837–1841	54	NY
9. W. H. Harrison (W)	1841	68	VA
10. Tyler (W)	1841–1845	51	VA
11. Polk (D)	1845–1849	49	NC
12. Taylor (W)	1849–1850	64	VA
13. Fillmore (W)	1850–1853	50	NY
14. Pierce (D)	1853–1857	48	NH
15. Buchanan (D)	1857–1861	65	PA
16. Lincoln (R)	1861–1865	52	KY
17. A. Johnson (U)	1865–1869	56	NC
18. Grant (R)	1869–1877	46	OH
19. Hayes (R)	1877–1881	54	OH
20. Garfield (R)	1881	49	OH

The branch of mathematics called **statistics** deals with presenting and interpreting **numerical data**.

Data from the table above can be shown by a **frequency distribution**.

Which political party shown in the table has elected the greatest number of Presidents?

The Republican party has elected the greatest number of Presidents.

The **range** of a set of data is the difference between the greatest number and the least number.

The range in the age of the Presidents at time of inauguration is 27 years.

Range = **69 − 42 = 27**

Political Parties

Party	Frequency
Federalist (F)	2
Democrat-Republican (DR)	4
Whig (W)	4
Union (U)	1
Democrat (D)	13
Republican (R)	16

Use the data in the table of Presidents of the United States for exercises 1–10.

1. What was the length of Washington's term of office?

2. Who was the 16th President? What was his term in office?

350

Name and (party)	Term	Age at Inauguration	State of birth
21. Arthur (R)	1881–1885	50	VT
22. Cleveland (D)	1885–1889	47	NJ
23. B. Harrison (R)	1889–1893	55	OH
24. Cleveland (D)	1893–1897	55	NJ
25. McKinley (R)	1897–1901	54	OH
26. T. Roosevelt (R)	1901–1909	42	NY
27. Taft (R)	1909–1913	51	OH
28. Wilson (D)	1913–1921	56	VA
29. Harding (R)	1921–1923	55	OH
30. Coolidge (R)	1923–1929	51	VT
31. Hoover (R)	1929–1933	54	IA
32. F. D. Roosevelt (D)	1933–1945	51	NY
33. Truman (D)	1945–1953	60	MO
34. Eisenhower (R)	1953–1961	62	TX
35. Kennedy (D)	1961–1963	43	MA
36. L. B. Johnson (D)	1963–1969	55	TX
37. Nixon (R)	1969–1974	56	CA
38. Ford (R)	1974–1977	61	NE
39. Carter (D)	1977–1981	52	GA
40. Reagan (R)	1981–	69	IL

Franklin D. Roosevelt

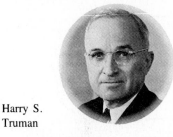
Harry S. Truman

Dwight D. Eisenhower

3. How many Presidents were born in Texas? What are their names?

4. How old was Truman when he was inaugurated?

5. Data is often arranged in **intervals**. Make a frequency distribution table of the ages of the Presidents when inaugurated. Arrange the ages in intervals of 5 yr.

6. How many Presidents were from 40 to 54 years old when inaugurated?

7. How many Presidents were from 55 to 69 years old when inaugurated?

8. Make a frequency distribution table that shows the frequency of the state of birth of the Presidents.

9. Which state has had the second highest frequency of Presidents?

10. How many states have had only one President?

11. **DATA HUNT** Which two Presidents share the same birth month and day?

12. **DATA BANK** In which state has the greatest number of Vice-Presidents been born? How many were born there? (See page 432.)

Mean, Median, and Mode

Cost of 20 Grams of Protein	
Peanut butter	13¢
Eggs	20¢
Hamburger	25¢
Tuna	25¢
Cheese	29¢
Frankfurters	43¢
Bacon	66¢
Beefsteak	69¢

The costs for 20 g of protein from 8 kinds of food are listed in the table in order of expense.

Total: **290¢**

The **arithmetic mean**, or **average**, is the total divided by the number of items.

Mean: $\dfrac{290¢}{8} = \mathbf{36.25¢}$

The **median** is the middle number in a list of numbers given in order. When there is an even number of items in the list, we find the average of the two middle numbers.

Median: $\dfrac{25¢ + 29¢}{2} = \mathbf{27¢}$

The **mode** is the most frequently occurring number or numbers in a list.

Mode: **25¢**

Practice Find the mean, median, and mode of each list of numbers.

1. 21, 24, 24, 27, 29, 30, 34

2. 136, 142, 145, 156, 156

3. $10.00, $8.95, $10.00, $12.50, $13.95, $12.50

4. 824, 1,066, 735, 2,710, 385

5. Which foods in the table above cost 1¢ or less per gram of protein?

6. Which foods in the table cost more than 3¢ per gram of protein?

352

More Practice, page 453, Set B

PROBLEM SOLVING: Using Estimation

QUESTION
DATA
PLAN
ANSWER
CHECK

Make an estimate of the answer first.
Check your estimate by calculating
the answer.

Use the table at the right for problems 1–4.

Average hourly wages	
Michigan	$11.18
Ohio	10.07
Indiana	9.79
Wisconsin	9.37
Illinois	9.31
Minnesota	9.11

1. What is the mean of the hourly wages in the table? Which state is nearest this mean?

2. What is the median hourly wage for the states in the table?

3. What is the range of the hourly wages in the table?

4. An Ohio worker who earned the average hourly wage worked 38.5 hours one week. What were his wages for that week?

Use the table of data at the right for Problems 5–8.

Average Weekly Working Hours	
Massachusetts	38.6 h
New York	38.8
New Jersey	40.2
Delaware	39.2
Virginia	38.4
West Virginia	38.8

5. What is the mean of the average weekly working hours in the table?

6. What is the median of the data in this table?

7. What is the difference between the highest and lowest working hours in the table?

8. About how much would a New Jersey worker earn in that state's average weekly working hours if the rate of pay were $8.60 per hour? Is an estimate of $320 a little too high or a little too low?

9. **Strategy Practice** Glenda earned $369 one week. The next week she worked 6 more hours than the last week. She earned $423 for the week. What was her average hourly wage?

Predicting with Sample Statistics

Jan wanted to find out what the 120 eighth-grade students in her school watched on TV.

Instead of asking every student, she took a **sample** of 30 students.

3 out of 30, or $\frac{1}{10}$, of the students in the sample watched the news special.

The same part of all the students would be expected to have watched the news special.

$$\frac{1}{10} \times 120 = 12$$

Program Watched	Number
News Special	3
Situation comedy	6
Wildlife	4
Other	2
None	15
Total Sample	30

Total eighth-grade students: 120

↑ Sample ratio   ↑ Total number   ↑ Predicted number

Jan can predict that about 12 students watched the news special.

Other Examples

6 out of 30, or $\frac{1}{5}$, of the students in the sample watched a situation comedy.

$\frac{1}{5} \times 120 = 24$

About 24 out of 120 students would be predicted to have watched a situation comedy.

15 out of 30, or $\frac{1}{2}$, of the students in the sample did not watch TV.

$\frac{1}{2} \times 120 = 60$

About 60 out of 120 students would be predicted to have not watched TV.

Warm Up

Use the data in the sample above for exercises 1–4.

1. What fraction of the 30 students watched the wildlife program?

2. Predict the number of students out of 120 students that watched the wildlife program.

3. What fraction of the 30 students watched other programs?

4. Predict the number of students out of 120 students that watched other programs.

Practice Use the data in the sample at the right for exercises 1–4.

1. What fraction of the 40-student sample watched the football game?

2. Predict the number out of 800 students who watched the football game.

3. What fraction of the 40 students watched the ice hockey game?

4. Predict the number out of 800 students who watched the ice hockey game.

TV Sports Watched
Sample total: 40 students

Program watched	Number of students
Football game	16
Baseball game	8
Ice hockey game	6
None of above	10

Use the data in the sample at the right for exercises 5–8.

5. What fraction of the sample families have 2 children per family?

6. Predict the number of families out of 2,000 that have 2 children.

7. Predict the number of families out of 2,000 that have 1 child.

8. Predict the number of families out of 2,000 that have 0 children per family.

Children per Family
Sample total: 50 families

Number of children	Number of families
0	10
1	9
2	15
3	8
4	5
5	2
6 or more	1

9. **DATA HUNT** How many students in your school watch TV for 2 hours or more a day? Take a sample of students and make a prediction.

Bar Graphs and Pictographs

Statistical data is often presented by a **graph**. A graph can help you compare data visually.

It is sometimes difficult to read exact data from some graphs. It may be necessary to *estimate*.

Use the **bar graph** at the right for exercises 1–6.

1. How many different types of aircraft are compared?

2. Which type of aircraft has the least number?

3. How many B-727 aircraft are shown by the graph?

4. How many DC-10 aircraft are shown?

5. Estimate the number of B-747's and the number of DC-8's shown by the graph.

6. Estimate the total number of aircraft shown by the graph.

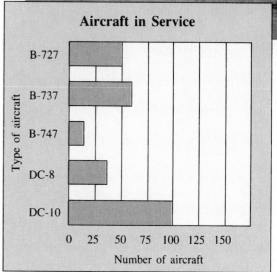

Use the **pictograph** at the right for exercises 7–10.

7. What is the title of the pictograph?

8. How many passengers does each symbol represent?

9. Estimate the number of passengers shown for each year.

10. Estimate how many more passengers are shown for 1980 than for 1965.

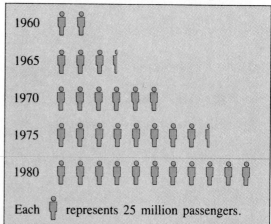

Practice Use the bar graph to estimate the answers for exercises 1–4.

1. What is the flying time from Atlanta in hours and minutes?

2. About how long does it take to fly from Dallas-Ft. Worth to New York?

3. About how many minutes less is the flying time from Chicago than from Miami?

4. Estimate the round-trip flying time from Seattle.

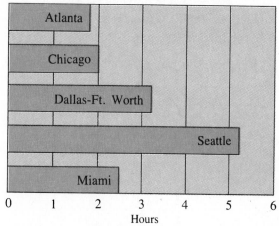

Flying Time to New York

Atlanta

Chicago

Dallas-Ft. Worth

Seattle

Miami

0 1 2 3 4 5 6
Hours

5. A **histogram** is a bar graph of frequencies. Use the data at the right to make a histogram.

Number of Daily Flights from Portland

City	Flights	City	Flights
Denver	14	Seattle	48
Los Angeles	38	Vancouver	5
San Diego	3	San Francisco	32

Use the pictograph to estimate the answers for exercises 6–9.

6. What is the passenger capacity of the DC-9?

7. Can the Super DC-8 carry 200 passengers?

8. What are the passenger capacities of the L-1011 and the B-727?

9. About how many more passengers can the B-747 carry than the DC-9?

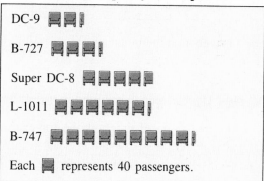

Seating Capacity of Airplanes

DC-9

B-727

Super DC-8

L-1011

B-747

Each represents 40 passengers.

10. Use the data in the table at the right to make a pictograph of the number of public airports.

Number of Public Airports

Alaska	477	Iowa	117
Texas	322	Maine	45
Ohio	133	Hawaii	18

Line Segment Graphs

Joel Maxwell is a demographer. He uses population statistics. He found the data on life expectancy in a data bank.

To see how the different entries are related and to use them to make predictions, he made a **line segment graph**.

Life Expectancy for Men and Women

Present Age	Life Expectancy (Years)	
	Men	Women
At birth	70.6	78.3
20	52.3	59.3
40	34.0	40.3
50	25.2	31.1
65	14.3	18.7

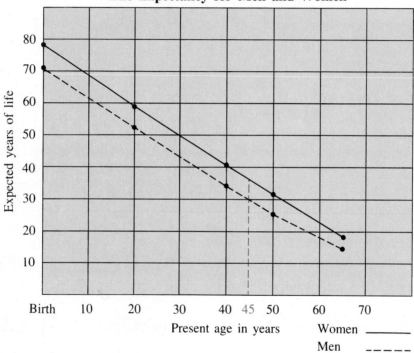

Life Expectancy for Men and Women

Warm Up

Use the line segment graph above for exercises 1–6.

1. What is the title of the graph?

2. What do the numbers on the horizontal axis show?

3. What do the numbers on the vertical axis show?

4. How is the data for women shown?

5. Estimate the life expectancy of a woman whose present age is 45.

6. Estimate the life expectancy of a man whose present age is 45.

358

Practice Use the line segment graph on page 358 to estimate the answers for exercises 1–6.

1. What is the life expectancy of a man whose present age is 30?

2. What is the life expectancy of a woman who is now 30 years old?

3. What is the life expectancy of a girl who is now 10 years old?

4. What is the life expectancy of a boy who is now 10 years old?

5. Estimate the difference at age 55 for the life expectancy of men and women.

6. What is the life expectancy of a man whose present age is 60?

Use the line segment graph at the right for exercises 7–10.

7. In 1920 what was the life expectancy for a woman at birth? How much did the life expectancy of women increase from 1920 to 1980?

8. What was the life expectancy of a man in 1920? In 1980?

9. About how many more years did women live in 1980 than men?

★ 10. The graph shows that life expectancy for both men and women is increasing. What would you predict for the life expectancy of both women and men who are born in the year 2000?

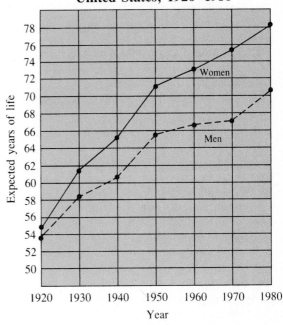

**Life Expectancy at Birth
United States, 1920–1980**

11. Make a line segment graph of the median ages in the table. Use the graph to predict the median age in the year 2000.

**Median Age
United States, 1860–1980**

Year	Age	Year	Age
1860	19.4	1940	29.5
1880	20.9	1960	29.6
1900	22.9	1980	30.0
1920	25.3		

Circle Graphs

A **circle graph** shows how a whole is divided into parts. The parts of the circular region are **sectors** of the circle.

The circle graph at the right shows how the land on a 600-acre farm is used.

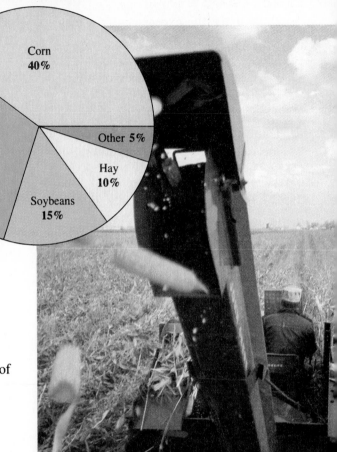

Farm Land Use
Total: 600 acres

Corn 40%

Wheat 30%

Other 5%

Hay 10%

Soybeans 15%

40% of the farm is used for corn. How much land is used for corn?

40% × 600 = 0.40 × 600 = 240

240 acres are used for corn.

What is the measure of the central angle of the sector that shows corn?

We need to find 40% of 360°.

0.40 × 360° = 144°

The central angle of the sector for corn has a measure of 144°.

Warm Up

Use the circle graph above for exercises 1–6.

1. What is the title of the circle graph?

2. What is the sum of all the percents shown on the graph?

3. How many acres are shown for wheat?

4. What is the measure of the central angle of the sector for wheat?

5. Find the number of acres shown by the graph for each of the other sectors.

6. Find the measures of the central angles for the sectors that show soybeans, hay, and other.

Practice Use the circle graph below for exercises 1–10.

Find the number of bushels for each crop.

1. Corn   **2.** Wheat

3. Oats   **4.** Soybeans

Find the measure of the central angle for each sector.

5. Corn   **6.** Wheat

7. Oats   **8.** Soybeans

9. How many more bushels of corn than wheat were produced?

10. How many less bushels of soybeans than oats were produced?

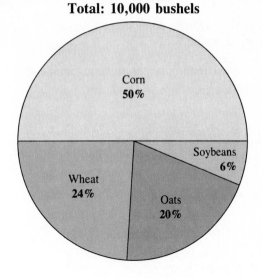

Crop Production
Total: 10,000 bushels

Use the data in the table below for exercises 11–19.

Find the degree measure needed for the central angle for each sector.

11. Corn   **12.** Wheat

13. Soybeans   **14.** Oats

Find the amount of income for each crop.

15. Corn   **16.** Wheat

17. Soybeans   **18.** Oats

19. Construct a circle graph that shows the data in the table.

Income from Crops
Total: $40,000

Crop	Percent of total
Corn	40%
Wheat	30%
Soybeans	25%
Oats	5%

SKILLKEEPER

Find the arithmetic mean, median, and mode of each list of numbers.
Round the answers to the nearest tenth if necessary.

1. 19, 11, 15, 21, 17, 18, 11   **2.** 40, 43, 38, 43, 41

3. 17, 19, 24, 39, 19   **4.** 38, 46, 52, 66, 71, 83, 46

5. 3, 8, 13, 51, 3, 17   **6.** 89, 57, 88, 89

Misleading Statistics

Statistics can be presented in ways that are misleading.

We must read data carefully to decide if the statistics are misleading or not.

Use graph A for exercises 1–5.

1. What was the interest rate in January?

2. What was the interest rate in February?

3. Between which two months did the interest rate rise the most? How much was the rise?

4. What was the interest rate in June?

5. What was the total rise in the interest rate from January to June?

Use graph B for exercises 6–10.

6. What was the interest rate in January?

7. What was the interest rate in February?

8. What was the total rise in the interest rate from January to June?

9. Do both graphs show the same data?

10. Why does graph B suggest that the interest rates grew more slowly than those in graph A?

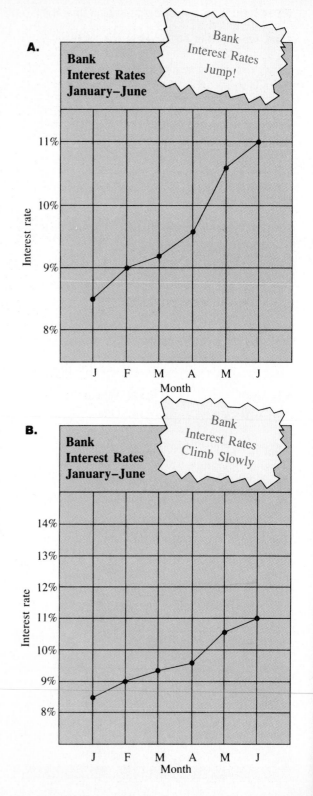

362

Employee Salaries: Adjacs Company

$12,000	J. Watson	14,000	E. Montez
12,000	C. Bell	53,000	B. Miller
12,000	M. Jones	80,000	C. Atwell
13,000	A. Carter		

Wanted: Skilled employees. Good working conditions, paid vacations; average salary $28,000. Call ADJACS   999-9999

Use the table above for exercises 11–17.

11. What is the total amount paid in salaries to the Adjacs employees?

12. What is the mean salary?

13. What is the median salary?

14. What is the mode of the salaries?

15. What percent of the employees (to the nearest percent) earn less than the mean salary?

16. How much below the mean salary is the median salary?

17. How much below the mean salary is the mode of the salaries?

Use the table at the right for exercises 18 and 19.

18. What percent of the sales is the net profit for each year?

19. What is misleading about the "Good News Bulletin?"

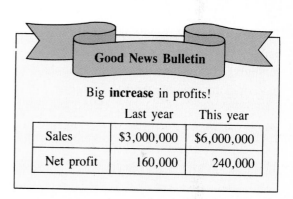

Good News Bulletin

Big **increase** in profits!

	Last year	This year
Sales	$3,000,000	$6,000,000
Net profit	160,000	240,000

THINK MATH

Logical Reasoning

These statistics "prove" that there are only 30 school days in a year.

What is wrong with the proof?

```
  365   ← Days in a year
−  90   ← 3 months' vacation
─────
  275
−  19   ← School vacations
─────
  256
− 122   ← Days sleeping (8 h/day)
─────
  134
− 104   ← 52 weekends
─────
   30   ← School days
```

Scattergrams

A group of students listed their heights and weights. To find out if there is some relation between the heights and the weights, they made a graph.

Height (cm)	Weight (kg)	Height (cm)	Weight (kg)
152	42	142	33
160	45	160	55
183	69	184	78
158	57	173	71
145	34	153	38
183	73	165	55
163	50	148	39

Point A shows a height of 152 kg and a weight of 42 kg.

The graph is called a **scattergram**. The pattern of dots tends to cluster around the red line drawn on the scattergram.

The graph shows a **positive correlation** between the heights and weights of the students. This means that as the heights *increase*, the weights tend to *increase*.

Heights and Weights of Students

The scattergram of temperatures in Chicago and Melbourne shows a **negative correlation**. As the temperatures in Chicago *increase*, the temperatures in Melbourne tend to *decrease*.

Some scattergrams may show **no correlation.**

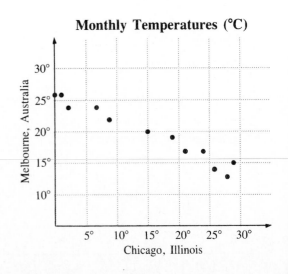

Monthly Temperatures (°C)

Practice State if the scattergram shows a positive correlation, a negative correlation, or no correlation.

1.

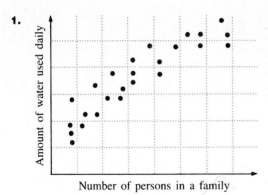

Amount of water used daily

Number of persons in a family

2.

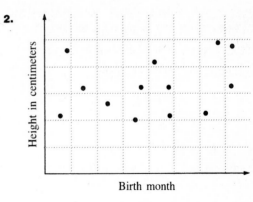

Height in centimeters

Birth month

3.

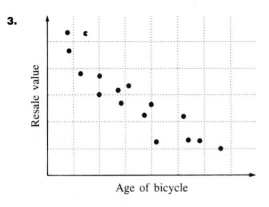

Resale value

Age of bicycle

4.

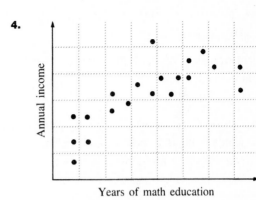

Annual income

Years of math education

State which kind of correlation you would expect for each scattergram described in exercises 5–8.

5. Minutes of exercise and heartbeats per minute

6. Speed of car and its stopping distance

7. Daily temperature and amount of heating fuel used

8. A person's height and the number of brothers and sisters that person has

9. Make a scattergram of the annual temperatures and the latitudes shown in the table at the right.

10. State which kind of correlation is shown in the scattergram for exercise 9.

Latitude (° North)	Annual Temperature (°C)
31	25
47	12
42	15
35	22
40	17
26	28
45	12
43	13

PROBLEM SOLVING: Multiple-Step Problems

QUESTION
DATA
PLAN
ANSWER
CHECK

Your grade in some school subjects may be the result of averages of test scores. One teacher used the method at the right to explain the final grade.

> Final grade = 80% of the mean of the 6 test scores + 20% of the final test score

Beverly had the 6 test scores and the final test score shown in the table. What was Beverly's grade?

Mean = Total ÷ 6   80% of 85 = 0.80 × 85 = 68
   = 510 ÷ 6 = 85

20% of final = 0.20 × 90 = 18

Final grade = 68 + 18 = 86

Test Scores	
	72
	85
	87
	90
	92
	94
Total	510
Final	90

Solve

1. Linda Johnstone had a mean of 93 for the 6 weekly tests. She had 85 on the final test. What was her final grade, using the 80%–20% method?

2. Daniel Chu had a mean of 80 on the 6 weekly tests. His final test score was 90. What was his final grade?

3. Louise had a mean score of 85 on the 6 weekly tests. If she also has a final test score of 85, will her final grade be the same, greater, or less than 85?

4. Dorita had 100 on each of the 6 weekly tests, but had a final test score of 80. What was her final grade?

5. David had a mean score of 80 for the first 6 tests. What is the highest final grade he could get by scoring a maximum of 100 on the final test?

6. There were 34 students in a class. Carl ranked 17th on the final test with a score of 82. Beth ranked 18th with a score of 81. What was the median score?

7. Ashley had a mean of 92 on the first 6 tests. Her final test score was also 92. Will her final grade be different from 92?

8. Rae's test scores were 81, 85, 84, 86, 88, 92 with a final test score of 80. What was Rae's final grade?

9. **Strategy Practice** Frank Funston had an average of 88 for the first 6 tests. He wanted the final test to bring him up to a grade of 90. Using the 80%–20% formula, what is the lowest final test score Frank could have to raise his grade to 90?

366

PROBLEM SOLVING: Mixed Practice

Consumer Price Index 1967–1982

Year	Index %	Year	Index %
1967	100.0	1975	161.2
1968	104.2	1976	170.5
1969	109.8	1977	181.5
1970	116.3	1978	195.4
1971	121.3	1979	217.4
1972	125.3	1980	246.8
1973	133.1	1981	272.4
1974	147.7	1982	287.1

QUESTION
DATA
PLAN
ANSWER
CHECK

The Consumer Price Index (CPI) is a statistic that compares the price of goods and services purchased by an average American family to the price of similar goods and services purchased in a *base year*. The base year in the table is 1967.

$$\frac{\text{Prices in a given year}}{\text{Prices in 1967}} = \text{CPI}$$

Example: The price of a new dress in 1967 was $20.00. What would be the price of a similar dress in 1982?

Solution: 1982 price = 1967 price × 1982 CPI
= $20.00 × 287.1%
= $20.00 × 2.871
= $57.42

Solve. Round the answers to the nearest cent.

1. A sweater cost $8.95 in 1967. What would a similar sweater have cost in 1979?

2. Glynda paid $115 a month for rent in 1967. If her rent increased with the consumer price index, how much was her rent in 1975?

3. In 1967 the Mastron family bought a new home for $18,000. How much more did a similar new home cost 10 yr later?

4. In 1967 Matt Lewis bought a new car for $1,800. In 1978 Matt wanted to buy a similar new car. About how much would he have to pay for the new car?

5. In 1981 a restaurant charged $5.25 for a full luncheon. What would a similar luncheon have cost in 1967?

6. In 1967 the Forkners spent an average of $30.00 a week for food. How much more did the same amount of food cost for a year in 1980?

7. An apartment cost $375 a month in 1981. What was the cost for a similar apartment in 1967?

8. In 1967 a hamburger, fries, and a drink cost $0.55. What did this food cost in 1982?

★ 9. A 2-bedroom apartment rented for $450 a month in 1982. Predict the rent of a similar apartment in 1990.

10. **Strategy Practice** How much more did a car that cost $8,750 in 1979 sell for than a similar car in 1975?

APPLIED PROBLEM SOLVING

QUESTION
DATA
PLAN
ANSWER
CHECK

Suppose you own and operate a truck and do general hauling. Your truck uses regular unleaded gasoline but could also use super unleaded gasoline. You need to decide which kind of gasoline you will buy.

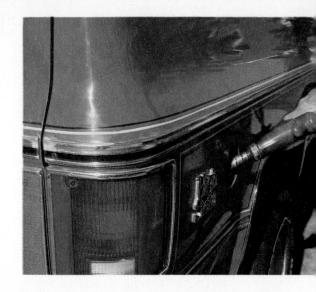

Some Things to Consider

- Regular unleaded gasoline costs $1.199 per gallon.

- Your truck averages about 12 miles per gallon on regular unleaded gasoline.

- You drive your truck about 2,700 miles per month.

- Super unleaded gasoline costs $1.399 per gallon.

- You think that your truck will get 10% to 15% more miles per gallon with super unleaded gasoline.

- Your truck has a little more power using the super unleaded gasoline.

Some Questions to Answer

1. How many gallons of unleaded gasoline will you use in one month? What does it cost?

2. How many miles per gallon will you get using super unleaded gasoline if the mileage is increased by 10%?

3. How many miles per gallon will you get if the mileage increases by 15% using super unleaded gasoline?

4. What will be the costs of the super unleaded gasoline using the 10% and 15% increases in mileage?

What Is Your Decision?

Will you buy the regular unleaded gasoline or the super unleaded gasoline?

1. What is the range of the numbers in this list: 165, 140, 155, 165, 177, 161, 143?

2. What is the median of the numbers in this list: 51, 58, 48, 52, 74, 50, 52?

3. What is the mean of the numbers in this list: 16, 14, 15, 16, 17, 16, 11?

4. What is the mode of the numbers in this list: 51, 58, 48, 52, 74, 50, 52?

Use the graph at the right for 5 and 6.

5. What fraction of the 300-voter sample said they would vote "No"?

6. Predict the number out of 12,000 voters who would vote "No."

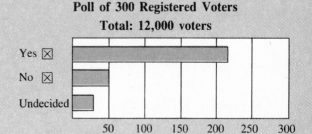

Poll of 300 Registered Voters
Total: 12,000 voters

Use the circle graph at the right for 7–9.

7. What is the percent shown on the circle graph for clothes?

8. What is the dollar amount shown for savings?

9. What is the measure of the angle of the sector for recreation?

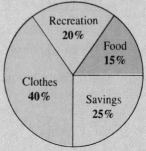

Yearly Living Expenses
Total: $10,000

Use the table at the right for 10–14.

10. What is the average of the allowances?

11. Which allowance statistic is most misleading, the mean, the median, or the mode?

12. Would you expect a positive or a negative correlation for the age of teenagers and their allowances?

Teen allowances too high!

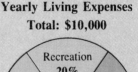

| Potter | $120 | Smith | $12 | Li | $13 |
| Jones | $15 | Diaz | $12 | Allen | $14 |

13. How much greater is Potter's allowance than the median of the list of teen allowances?

14. How many allowances listed are greater than the mode?

369

Range = Greatest−least

Mode = Most frequent

Median = Middle

Mean = Average

Test Scores

85	81	92	90	98
90	84	98	90	82

1. What is the range of the test scores?

2. What is the median test score?

3. What is the mode?

4. What is the mean?

---

8 out of **24** Said "no"

$\frac{8}{24} = \frac{1}{3}$

$\frac{1}{3} \times 90 = 30$ ← **30** out of **90** are predicted to vote "No"

Sample of 24 Voters

yes	16
no	8

5. What fraction of the sample is "Yes"?

6. How many voters out of 90 would be predicted to vote yes?

Amount = Total × percent

Measure of angle = percent × 360°

Favorite Sport: Total: 200 people

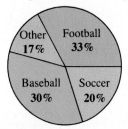

Monthly Budget Total: $1,200

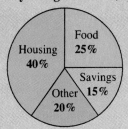

7. What is the title of the circle graph?

8. What is the total amount of money shown?

9. What percent is shown for savings?

10. Which expense uses 25% of the budget?

11. What is the amount shown for food?

12. What is the amount for housing?

13. What is the amount for savings?

14. What is the measure of the angle for the sector for housing?

Finding a Sample Mean

What is the mean number of letters per word used in the article of 100 words at the right?

Instead of counting the letters in each word, you can take a 10-word **random sample** and compute the mean number of letters per word in the sample.

The words in the sample are chosen by finding the number of the word that corresponds to the **random numbers** in the first row of the table.

1 2   3   4   5   6 7   8
The social and economic problems of large cities
are undeniable, and as yet they are largely un-
solved. Some economists feel that the basic problem
of the cities is a problem of scale. A large city
offers considerable economies of scale in the pro-
vision of goods and services for its residents. Bus
rides, kilowatt hours of electricity, and chemically
purified drinking water can all be purchased at
lower cost in big cities because of the large demand
for these goods and services and the accompanying
economies of scale in mass production. But in the
last several decades, prices for such services . . .

Random Numbers

Random number	Word	Number of letters
23	basic	5
77	for	3
30	problem	7
9	are	3
11	and	3
78	these	5
40	scale	5
29	a	1
96	decades	7
85	economies	9
	Total	48

Computer-Generated Random Numbers 1 to 100

23	77	30	9	11	78	40	29	96	85
56	75	75	51	72	45	76	87	61	74
18	57	49	8	76	20	41	32	66	80
4	59	11	17	99	60	26	31	10	81
38	94	22	35	27	62	34	77	18	57
70	21	81	23	93	62	27	4	69	45
43	74	93	29	67	99	21	62	42	15
92	47	30	4	60	97	81	35	5	69
40	38	68	62	33	71	32	50	70	10
66	28	35	2	61	3	74	72	66	81

Mean number of letters per word $= \dfrac{48}{10} = 4.8$

1. Use the second row of numbers in the Random Number table to make a 10-word sample. What is the mean of this sample?

2. What is your estimate of the actual mean number of letters per word in the complete article?

371

1. What is the decimal for 126%?

A 12.6 **B** 0.126
C 1.26 **D** not given

2. What is the fraction for 92%?

A $\frac{43}{50}$ **B** $\frac{23}{25}$
C $\frac{25}{23}$ **D** not given

3. What is 16% of 500?

A 32 **B** 8
C 80 **D** not given

4. 16 is what percent of 40?

A 40% **B** 25%
C 640% **D** not given

5. Estimate 62% of 93.

A 150 **B** 54
C 5.4 **D** not given

6. 56% of a number is 28. What is the number?

A 50 **B** 35
C 52 **D** not given

7. How many arrangements can be made of 3 books side-by-side on a shelf?

A 3 **B** 6
C 12 **D** not given

8. How many combinations of 2 books from a set of 6 books are possible?

A 15 **B** 24
C 12 **D** not given

Use the spinner for 9–12.

9. What is P(odd number)?

A $\frac{1}{2}$ **B** 0
C $\frac{1}{4}$ **D** not given

10. What is P(prime number)?

A $\frac{1}{3}$ **B** $\frac{1}{2}$
C $\frac{1}{4}$ **D** not given

11. What are the odds against getting a 4?

A $\frac{1}{5}$ **B** $\frac{4}{1}$
C $\frac{5}{1}$ **D** not given

12. What are the odds in favor of getting a 3?

A $\frac{3}{1}$ **B** $\frac{1}{5}$
C $\frac{5}{1}$ **D** not given

13. Sadie borrowed $250 for 2 yr. The interest rate is 18% per year. What is the total amount she must repay?

A $90 **B** $45
C $340 **D** not given

14. Robert has 5 library books checked out. 2 of the books are overdue. How many combinations of books could be overdue?

A 10 **B** 3
C 25 **D** not given

15

Square Roots and Right Triangles

Beam bridge

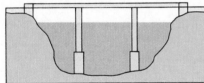

Arch bridge

Suspension bridge

Cable-stayed bridge

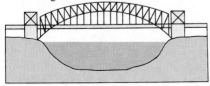

The first bridge was probably a tree that fell across a river. The powerful structures that now span the waters of the world use many modern designs.

One of the most basic designs is the *beam bridge:* a flat bridge supported by piers. A common variation of the beam bridge, made up of triangles linked together, is called a *truss bridge*. The High Bridge, spanning the Pecos River near Langtry, Texas, is a truss bridge that is 423.8 m long.

The *arch bridge* is supported by an arch above or below the bridge's roadway. The New River Gorge Bridge, near Fayetteville, West Virginia, is a steel arch bridge with a main span length of 518 m.

The weight of the road on a *suspension bridge* is carried by cables. They are anchored on land and supported by two towers. A *cable-stayed bridge* may have only one tower because the cables that support the road extend directly from the road to the tower.

Squares and Square Roots

A large square tarpaulin covering a baseball diamond has an area of 900 m². How long is each side of the tarpaulin?

We need to find a number that when multiplied by itself equals 900.

Since $30 \times 30 = 30^2 = 900$, each side is 30 m long.

30 is the **positive square root** of 900 because $30 \times 30 = 900$.

$$\sqrt{900} = 30$$

⁻30 is the **negative square root** of 900 because ⁻30 × ⁻30 = 900.

$$^-\sqrt{900} = {}^-30$$

The symbol $\sqrt{}$ is called a **radical sign**. We read it as "the square root of."

Other Examples

$\sqrt{25} = 5$ because $5 \times 5 = 25$

$\sqrt{100} = 10$ because $10 \times 10 = 100$

$^-\sqrt{16} = {}^-4$ because ⁻4 × ⁻4 = 16

$^-\sqrt{49} = {}^-7$ because ⁻7 × ⁻7 = 49

Warm Up

Give the length of one side of each square.

1.
Area
36 m²

2.
Area
16 cm²

3.
Area
400 mm²

Give each square root.

4. $\sqrt{64}$　　**5.** $^-\sqrt{9}$　　**6.** $\sqrt{121}$　　**7.** $^-\sqrt{4}$　　**8.** $^-\sqrt{81}$

Practice Find the length of one side of each square.

1.

Area
4 cm^2

2.

Area
25 cm^2

3.

Area
1,600 mm^2

4.

Area
225 cm^2

Find each square root.

5. $\sqrt{16}$ **6.** $\sqrt{49}$ **7.** $\sqrt{400}$ **8.** $^-\sqrt{1}$ **9.** $\sqrt{3,600}$

10. $\sqrt{2,500}$ **11.** $\sqrt{144}$ **12.** $^-\sqrt{121}$ **13.** $\sqrt{625}$ **14.** $\sqrt{9}$

15. $\sqrt{1,600}$ **16.** $^-\sqrt{36}$ **17.** $\sqrt{10,000}$ **18.** $^-\sqrt{64}$ **19.** $\sqrt{169}$

20. $\sqrt{8,100}$ **21.** $^-\sqrt{2,500}$ **22.** $\sqrt{6,400}$ **23.** $\sqrt{196}$ **24.** $^-\sqrt{1,600}$

Find the square roots. Then add or subtract.

Example: $\sqrt{25} + \sqrt{9} = 5 + 3 = 8$

25. $\sqrt{100} + \sqrt{16}$ **26.** $\sqrt{49} - \sqrt{9}$ **27.** $\sqrt{16} + \sqrt{16}$

28. $\sqrt{81} - \sqrt{4}$ **29.** $\sqrt{36} + \sqrt{36}$ **30.** $\sqrt{900} - \sqrt{400}$

Mixed Applications

31. A square tarpaulin covering a softball field has an area of 361 m^2. What is the length of one side of the tarpaulin?

32. The Great Pyramid of Cheops has a square base that covers about 52,900 m^2. How long is each side of the base?

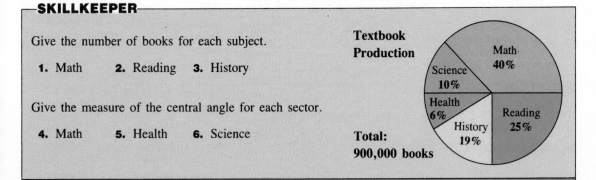

SKILLKEEPER

Give the number of books for each subject.

1. Math **2.** Reading **3.** History

Give the measure of the central angle for each sector.

4. Math **5.** Health **6.** Science

Textbook
Production

Total:
900,000 books

Math
40%

Science
10%

Health
6%

History
19%

Reading
25%

Using a Table of Square Roots

A square panel of an astronaut's space suit has an area of 60 cm². What is the length of each side of the square?

We need to find $\sqrt{60}$.

Since $7 \times 7 = 49$ and $8 \times 8 = 64$, we can *estimate* that $\sqrt{60}$ is between 7 and 8.

To find a better approximation of $\sqrt{60}$, we can use the Table of Squares and Square Roots.

Number	Square	Square root
n	n^2	$\sqrt{n}$
60	3,600	7.746
61	3,721	7.810

© 1983 Harry Benson

$\sqrt{60} \approx 7.746$ (rounded to the nearest thousandth)

Each side of the panel is about 7.7 m, rounded to the nearest tenth.

Other Examples

Use the table on page 377 to check these square roots.

$\sqrt{729} = 27$ $\qquad$ $\sqrt{2,304} = 48$ $\qquad$ $\sqrt{7} \approx 2.646$

$\quad\uparrow\quad\uparrow$ $\qquad\qquad\quad\uparrow\quad\uparrow$ $\qquad\qquad\quad\uparrow\quad\uparrow$

$\quad n^2 \quad n$ $\qquad\qquad\quad n^2 \quad n$ $\qquad\qquad\quad n \quad \sqrt{n}$

Warm Up

Use the table on page 377 to find the square roots.

1. $\sqrt{5}$ $\qquad$ **2.** $\sqrt{83}$ $\qquad$ **3.** $\sqrt{37}$ $\qquad$ **4.** $\sqrt{78}$ $\qquad$ **5.** $\sqrt{66}$

6. $\sqrt{256}$ $\qquad$ **7.** $\sqrt{729}$ $\qquad$ **8.** $\sqrt{5,929}$ $\qquad$ **9.** $\sqrt{1,089}$ $\qquad$ **10.** $\sqrt{9,801}$

Practice Estimate the consecutive integers for each ▦.

1. $\sqrt{93}$ is between ▦ and ▦.

2. $\sqrt{44}$ is between ▦ and ▦.

3. $\sqrt{15}$ is between ▦ and ▦.

4. $\sqrt{32}$ is between ▦ and ▦.

Use the table to find the square roots.

5. $\sqrt{63}$ 6. $\sqrt{77}$

7. $\sqrt{18}$ 8. $\sqrt{45}$

9. $\sqrt{90}$ 10. $\sqrt{11}$

11. $\sqrt{54}$ 12. $\sqrt{82}$

13. $\sqrt{39}$ 14. $\sqrt{68}$

15. $\sqrt{30}$ 16. $\sqrt{60}$

17. $\sqrt{144}$ 18. $\sqrt{10}$

19. $\sqrt{400}$ 20. $\sqrt{784}$

21. $\sqrt{3,025}$ 22. $\sqrt{1,936}$

23. $\sqrt{7,744}$ 24. $\sqrt{2,401}$

Use the table to find the number for n.

25. $\sqrt{n} \approx 7.550$ 26. $\sqrt{n} \approx 6.164$

27. $\sqrt{n} \approx 7.937$ 28. $\sqrt{n} \approx 8.367$

29. $\sqrt{n} \approx 2.646$ 30. $\sqrt{n} \approx 9.220$

31. $\sqrt{n} \approx 5.477$ 32. $\sqrt{n} \approx 1.732$

Table of Squares and Square Roots

Number n	Square n^2	Square root $\sqrt{n}$	Number n	Square n^2	Square root $\sqrt{n}$
1	1	1.000	51	2,601	7.141
2	4	1.414	52	2,704	7.211
3	9	1.732	53	2,809	7.280
4	16	2.000	54	2,916	7.348
5	25	2.236	55	3,025	7.416
6	36	2.449	56	3,136	7.483
7	49	2.646	57	3,249	7.550
8	64	2.828	58	3,364	7.616
9	81	3.000	59	3,481	7.681
10	100	3.162	60	3,600	7.746
11	121	3.317	61	3,721	7.810
12	144	3.464	62	3,844	7.874
13	169	3.606	63	3,969	7.937
14	196	3.742	64	4,096	8.000
15	225	3.873	65	4,225	8.062
16	256	4.000	66	4,356	8.124
17	289	4.123	67	4,489	8.185
18	324	4.243	68	4,624	8.246
19	361	4.359	69	4,761	8.307
20	400	4.472	70	4,900	8.367
21	441	4.583	71	5,041	8.426
22	484	4.690	72	5,184	8.485
23	529	4.796	73	5,329	8.544
24	576	4.899	74	5,476	8.602
25	625	5.000	75	5,625	8.660
26	676	5.099	76	5,776	8.718
27	729	5.196	77	5,929	8.775
28	784	5.292	78	6,084	8.832
29	841	5.385	79	6,241	8.888
30	900	5.477	80	6,400	8.944
31	961	5.568	81	6,561	9.000
32	1,024	5.657	82	6,724	9.055
33	1,089	5.745	83	6,889	9.110
34	1,156	5.831	84	7,056	9.165
35	1,225	5.916	85	7,225	9.220
36	1,296	6.000	86	7,396	9.274
37	1,369	6.083	87	7,569	9.327
38	1,444	6.164	88	7,744	9.381
39	1,521	6.245	89	7,921	9.434
40	1,600	6.325	90	8,100	9.487
41	1,681	6.403	91	8,281	9.539
42	1,764	6.481	92	8,464	9.592
43	1,849	6.557	93	8,649	9.644
44	1,936	6.633	94	8,836	9.695
45	2,025	6.708	95	9,025	9.747
46	2,116	6.782	96	9,216	9.798
47	2,209	6.856	97	9,409	9.849
48	2,304	6.928	98	9,604	9.899
49	2,401	7.000	99	9,801	9.950
50	2,500	7.071	100	10,000	10.000

Mixed Applications

33. A square computer screen on a space shuttle has an area of 576 cm². What is the length of each side of the screen?

34. One square instrument panel has an area of 76 cm². Another square panel has an area of 52 cm². How much longer is the side of the larger square?

Finding Square Roots Without a Table

The directions below show the steps for finding the square root of a number using a method called **divide and average**.

Find $\sqrt{937}$ to the nearest tenth.

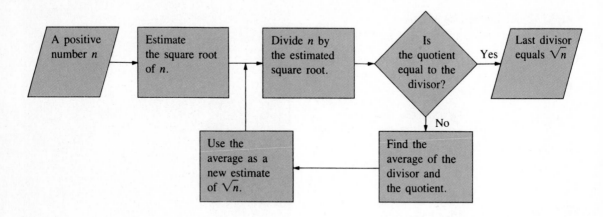

Estimate

$\sqrt{937} \approx 30$

Divide

$$\begin{array}{r} 3\ 1.2 \\ 3\ 0)\overline{9\ 3\ 7.0} \\ 9\ 0 \\ \hline 3\ 7 \\ 3\ 0 \\ \hline 7\ 0 \\ 6\ 0 \\ \hline 1\ 0 \end{array}$$

Average

$$\frac{30 + 31.2}{2} = 30.6$$

Divide

$$\begin{array}{r} 3\ 0.6 \\ 3\ 0.6)\overline{9\ 3\ 7.0\ 0} \\ 9\ 1\ 8 \\ \hline 1\ 9\ 0\ 0 \\ 1\ 8\ 3\ 6 \\ \hline 6\ 4 \end{array}$$

Divisor and quotient are equal, to the nearest tenth.

$\sqrt{937} \approx 30.6$, to the nearest tenth.

Estimate the square roots to the nearest tenth. Use the "divide and average" method.

1. $\sqrt{1,725}$ **2.** $\sqrt{266}$ **3.** $\sqrt{18.5}$ **4.** $\sqrt{92.4}$ **5.** $\sqrt{3,233}$

6. $\sqrt{88.54}$ **7.** $\sqrt{2,700}$ **8.** $\sqrt{43.9}$ **9.** $\sqrt{12,450}$ **10.** $\sqrt{687.4}$

11. $\sqrt{1,000}$ **12.** $\sqrt{123.44}$ **13.** $\sqrt{805.1}$ **14.** $\sqrt{7,000}$ **15.** $\sqrt{2.88}$

More Practice, page 453, Set D

PROBLEM SOLVING: Mixed Practice

QUESTION
DATA
PLAN
ANSWER
CHECK

Solve.

1. A small square field has an area of 40,000 m². What is the length of each side of the field?

2. A square tool shed covers an area of 648 m². What is the length of each side of the tool shed? Round the length to the nearest tenth.

3. A **hectare** (**ha**) is an area of 10,000 m². How many hectares are there in a field that is 500 m long and 160 m wide?

4. How many meters of fence are needed to go around a rectangular field that is 820 m long and 425 m wide?

5. Wire fencing costs $0.58 per meter of length. What would be the cost of fencing to go around the field in problem 4?

6. A square sheet of cloth has an area of 85 m². To the nearest tenth of a meter, what is the length of each side?

7. How much would a farmer get for 6.5 t of alfalfa hay sold in November? Use the graph below.

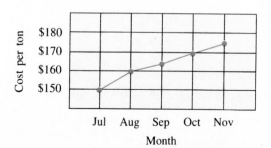

8. A silo is in the shape of a cylinder. The radius of the base of the silo is 4 m. The height of the silo is 20 m. What is the circumference of the base of the silo? What is the volume of the silo?

9. A farmer had a bank loan of $15,000. The rate of interest for the loan was 15% per year. The loan was repaid at the end of 6 months. What was the interest on the loan? What was the total amount repaid?

10. **Strategy Practice** There were 46 animals in a field. There were 3 times as many cows as horses. There were 10 more cows than sheep. How many of each kind of animal were in the field?

The Rule of Pythagoras

The figures at the right show an important relationship between the **legs** and the **hypotenuse** of any right triangle.

Find the area of the squares on legs a and b and hypotenuse c.

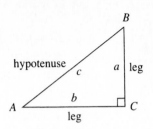

Area of A + Area of B = Area of C

↓	↓	↓
36 +	**64** =	**100**

This relationship was discovered by the Greek mathematician Pythagoras more than 2,000 years ago.

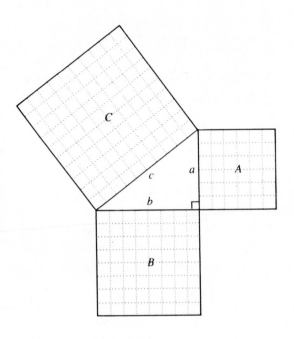

The Rule of Pythagoras

In any right triangle, the sum of the areas of the squares on the legs is equal to the area of the square on the hypotenuse.

This rule can be written as a formula.

$$a^2 \quad + \quad b^2 \quad = \quad c^2$$

↑	↑	↑
leg	leg	hypotenuse

Warm Up

Use the figure to give the missing numbers.

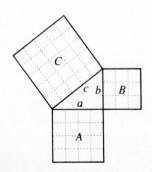

1. $a = $ ▦

2. $b = $ ▦

3. $c = $ ▦

4. $a^2 = $ ▦

5. $b^2 = $ ▦

6. $a^2 + b^2 = $ ▦

7. $c^2 = $ ▦

8. Area of square $A = $ ▦

9. Area of square $B = $ ▦

10. Area of square $C = $ ▦

380

Practice Use the figure at the right for exercises 1–10.
Write the missing numbers.

1. $a = $ ▒

2. $b = $ ▒

3. $c = $ ▒

4. $a^2 = $ ▒

5. $b^2 = $ ▒

6. $c^2 = $ ▒

7. Area of square $A = $ ▒

8. Area of square $B = $ ▒

9. Area of square A + Area of square $B = $ ▒

10. Area of square $C = $ ▒

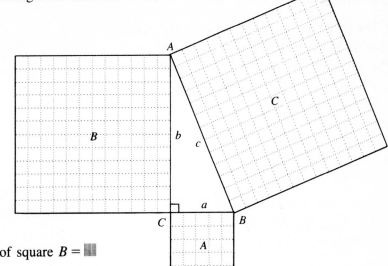

Find the area of square C in each figure.

11.

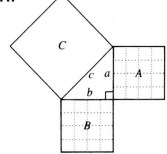

12.

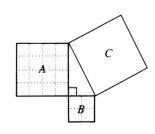

13.

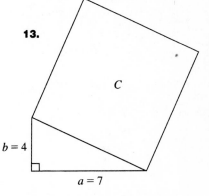

$b = 4$

$a = 7$

THINK MATH

Space Perception

Draw two squares side-by-side. Use the measurements given and cut along the lines and boundaries shown.

Use all five regions to form one square. How long is each side of the square?

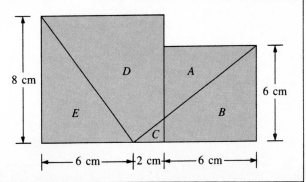

Finding the Length of the Hypotenuse

The size of a rectangular display screen is given as the length of the diagonal of the screen. The length of the screen is 24 cm and the width is 18 cm. What is the length of the diagonal?

The diagonal is the hypotenuse of a right triangle whose legs measure 18 cm and 24 cm.

We can use the Pythagorean formula to find the length.

$$a^2 + b^2 = c^2$$
$$18^2 + 24^2 = c^2$$
$$900 = c^2$$
$$\sqrt{900} = \sqrt{c^2}$$
$$30 = c$$

To solve this equation, find the square root of the numbers on each side.

The diagonal is 30 cm long.

Other Examples

Find the length of the hypotenuse c.

$$a^2 + b^2 = c^2$$
$$6^2 + 8^2 = c^2$$
$$100 = c^2$$
$$10 = c$$
$$c = 10 \text{ cm}$$

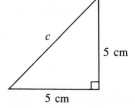

Find the length of the hypotenuse c.

$$a^2 + b^2 = c^2$$
$$5^2 + 5^2 = 50 = c^2$$
$$7.071 \approx c$$
$$c \approx 7.071 \text{ cm}$$

Warm Up

Give the length of the hypotenuse in each right triangle.

1.

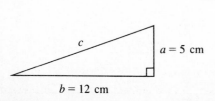

2.

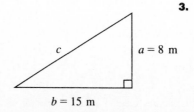

3.

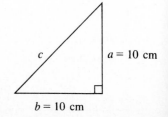

Practice Find the length of the hypotenuse to the nearest thousandth. Use a table of square roots or a calculator.

1.

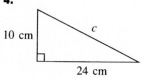

9 cm

12 cm

c

2.

7 m

c

24 m

3.

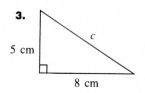

5 cm

c

8 cm

4.

10 cm

c

24 cm

5.

c

3 cm

6 cm

6.

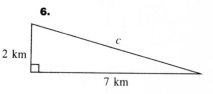

2 km

c

7 km

7. $a = 6$ cm
$b = 5$ cm
$c = $ ▓

8. $a = 15$ m
$b = 20$ m
$c = $ ▓

9. $a = 2$ km
$b = 5$ km
$c = $ ▓

10. $a = 7$ cm
$b = 3$ cm
$c = $ ▓

11. $a = 15$ dm
$b = 15$ dm
$c = $ ▓

12. $a = 9$ cm
$b = 4$ cm
$c = $ ▓

13. $a = 20$ m
$b = 20$ m
$c = $ ▓

14. $a = 1$ km
$b = 9$ km
$c = $ ▓

15. $a = 2$ cm
$b = 2$ cm
$c = $ ▓

Mixed Applications

16. A TV screen is a square that is 36 cm on each side. What is the length of the diagonal of the screen?

★ **17.** Can a right triangle have legs that are 9 cm and 18 cm if the hypotenuse is exactly 20 cm?

SKILLKEEPER

Find each square root.

1. $\sqrt{16}$ **2.** $^-\sqrt{36}$ **3.** $\sqrt{64}$ **4.** $^-\sqrt{81}$ **5.** $\sqrt{121}$

6. $\sqrt{225}$ **7.** $\sqrt{256}$ **8.** $\sqrt{169}$ **9.** $^-\sqrt{441}$ **10.** $^-\sqrt{196}$

11. $^-\sqrt{900}$ **12.** $\sqrt{2,500}$ **13.** $\sqrt{529}$ **14.** $^-\sqrt{289}$ **15.** $^-\sqrt{3,600}$

16. $\sqrt{2,704}$ **17.** $\sqrt{7,744}$ **18.** $\sqrt{2,116}$ **19.** $\sqrt{3,025}$ **20.** $\sqrt{729}$

Finding the Lengths of Legs of Right Triangles

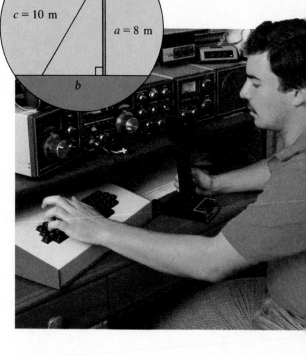

Anthony attached a wire 10 m long to the top of a radio antenna 8 m high. How far from the base of the pole will the wire reach when it is stretched tight?

We can use the Rule of Pythagoras to find the length of leg b.

$$a^2 + b^2 = c^2$$
$$8^2 + b^2 = 10^2$$
$$64 + b^2 = 100$$
$$b^2 = 36$$
$$\sqrt{b^2} = \sqrt{36}$$
$$b = 6$$

The wire will reach 6 m from the pole.

Other Examples

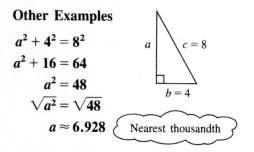

$$a^2 + 4^2 = 8^2$$
$$a^2 + 16 = 64$$
$$a^2 = 48$$
$$\sqrt{a^2} = \sqrt{48}$$
$$a \approx 6.928 \quad \text{(Nearest thousandth)}$$

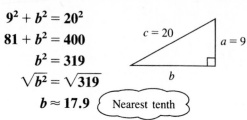

$$9^2 + b^2 = 20^2$$
$$81 + b^2 = 400$$
$$b^2 = 319$$
$$\sqrt{b^2} = \sqrt{319}$$
$$b \approx 17.9 \quad \text{(Nearest tenth)}$$

Find the length of the leg that is not given.

1.

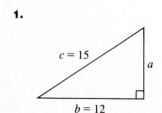
$c = 15$, a, $b = 12$

2.

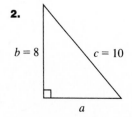
$b = 8$, $c = 10$, a

3.

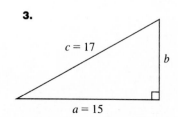
$c = 17$, b, $a = 15$

Find the length of the second leg. Round to the nearest tenth if necessary.

4. $a = 20$
$b = $ ▨
$c = 25$

5. $a = $ ▨
$b = 6$
$c = 12$

6. $a = 16$
$b = $ ▨
$c = 17$

384

More Practice, page 455, Set A

PROBLEM SOLVING: Making Drawings for Problems

QUESTION
DATA
PLAN
ANSWER
CHECK

An A-frame cabin has the shape of an isosceles triangle. The base is 10 m and the two congruent sides are each 9 m. What is the height of the cabin?

To solve some problems, it will help if you make a drawing and label the parts of the drawing with the given data.

The drawing shows that we need to find the length of leg a.

$a^2 + 5^2 = 9^2$

$a^2 + 25 = 81$

$\sqrt{a^2} = \sqrt{56}$

$a \approx 7.48$

The height is about 7.48 m.

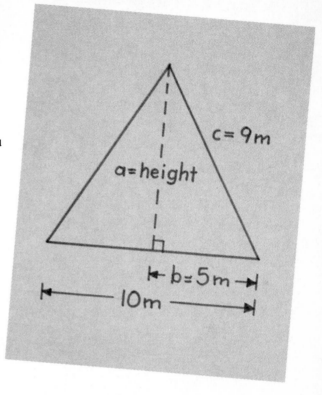

Solve. Make a drawing for each problem. Round to the nearest tenth if necessary.

1. Ruby rode her bicycle 6 km east from her home. Then she rode 8 km north. How far, along a straight line, is she from home?

2. A square quilt piece is 10 cm on each side. If the square is cut along the diagonal to form triangles, how long is the diagonal?

3. A 10-meter ladder is placed against a wall. The base of the ladder is 2 m from the wall. How far up the wall does the ladder reach?

4. A ramp to a bridge is 15 m along the ground and 5 m above the ground at the bridge. How long is the ramp?

5. A rectangular box is 60 cm long and 45 cm wide. Can a skateboard that is 68 cm long fit in the box?

6. An airplane is 2 km above the ground at a point that is 5 km from the landing strip. What is the distance from the plane to the landing strip?

7. A guy wire is stretched 30 m from the top of a pole 28 m high to a point on the ground. How far is the point from the base of the pole?

8. **Strategy Practice** A square TV screen has a diagonal that is 48 cm long. What is the length of each side of the screen?

385

30°–60° Right Triangles

If we fold equilateral $\triangle ABD$ on the line of symmetry, $\overleftrightarrow{BC}$, right $\triangle ABC$ will be formed.

$\triangle ABC$ is a **30°–60° right triangle.**
$\overline{AC}$ is opposite the 30° angle. Since $\overline{AC}$ was formed by folding $\overline{AD}$ in half, $b = \frac{1}{2} c$.
This relation is true in every 30°–60° right triangle.

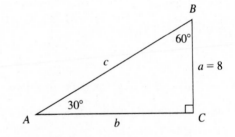

> In any 30°–60° right triangle, the length of the side opposite the 30° angle is $\frac{1}{2}$ the length of the hypotenuse.

Other Examples

What is the length of the hypotenuse c in $\triangle ABC$?

$\overline{BC}$ is opposite the 30° angle, so a is $\frac{1}{2}$ the length of c.

$c = 2 \times a = 2 \times 8 = 16$

What is the length of b? Use the Pythagorean formula.

$$a^2 + b^2 = c^2$$
$$8^2 + b^2 = 16^2$$
$$\sqrt{b^2} = \sqrt{192}$$
$$b \approx 13.86$$

Warm Up

Give the length of the side opposite the 30° angle.

1.

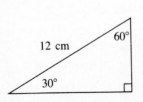

12 cm

30° 60°

2.

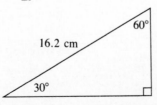

16.2 cm

30° 60°

3.

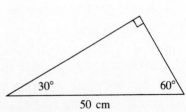

30° 60°

50 cm

Practice Find the length of the side opposite the 30° angle.

1.

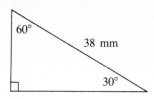
60°
38 mm
30°

2.

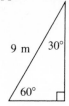
9 m
30°
60°

3.

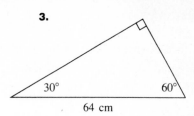
30°
60°
64 cm

Find the length of the hypotenuse.

4.

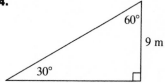
60°
9 m
30°

5.

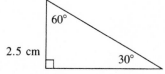
60°
2.5 cm
30°

6.

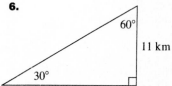
60°
11 km
30°

Find the length of the side opposite the 30° angle. Then use the Pythagorean formula to find the length of the other leg.

7.

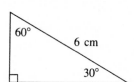
60°
6 cm
30°

8.

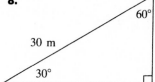
60°
30 m
30°

9.

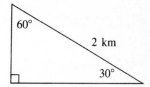
60°
2 km
30°

▌ THINK MATH ▐

Shape Perception

Fold down the middle of a sheet of paper. Fold corner *B* to the center line. △*ABC* is a 30°–60° right triangle.

Make an equilateral triangle by folding paper.

Make a square by folding paper.

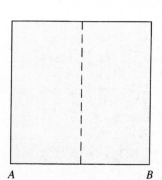

More Practice, page 455, Set B

Rational and Irrational Numbers

Numbers that can be represented by terminating decimals or repeating decimals are called **rational numbers**.

$$\frac{3}{8} = 0.375 \qquad \frac{7}{27} = 0.259259 \ldots = 0.\overline{259}$$

Numbers that can be represented by decimals that are **nonrepeating** and **nonterminating** are called **irrational numbers**.

$$\sqrt{3} = 1.7320508 \ldots$$
$$\pi = 3.1415927 \ldots$$

Together, the rational numbers and irrational numbers form the set of **real numbers**.

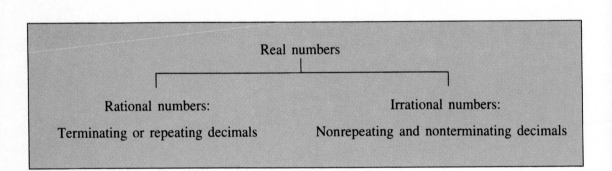

Real numbers

Rational numbers:
Terminating or repeating decimals

Irrational numbers:
Nonrepeating and nonterminating decimals

Other Examples

Rational numbers

2.31 ← Terminating decimal

8.$\overline{109}$ ← Repeating decimal

0.$\overline{6}$ ← Repeating decimal

Irrational numbers

0.32332333233332 . . .   Nonterminating and

$\sqrt{28}$ = 5.2915026 . . .   nonrepeating decimals

Warm Up

State if the decimal represents a rational number or an irrational number.

1. 0.$\overline{72}$

2. 5.84

3. 1.7296044835 . . .

4. 0.$\overline{7}$

5. 0.12012001200012 . . .

6. 101.0

7. 0.$\overline{142857}$

8. 0.02468101214 . . .

9. 0.377476377476 . . .

Practice Each decimal has a pattern in its digits. Find the next three digits in the pattern. State if the number is rational or irrational.

1. 0.686868 . . .

2. 9.9999 . . .

3. 0.040040004 . . .

4. 6.01301301 . . .

5. 5.474647 . . .

6. 0.15263748

7. 0.42857142 . . .

8. 0.01020304 . . .

9. 0.250000 . . .

Find the repeating decimal for each rational number.

10. $\frac{4}{7}$

11. $\frac{5}{6}$

12. $\frac{1}{7}$

13. $\frac{5}{9}$

14. $\frac{3}{11}$

15. $\frac{9}{37}$

16. $\frac{7}{9}$

17. $\frac{7}{99}$

18. $\frac{7}{999}$

19. $\frac{7}{9,999}$

20. $\frac{5}{111}$

21. $\frac{5}{1,111}$

22. $\frac{7}{12}$

23. $\frac{3}{36}$

24. $\frac{3}{74}$

Find the nonrepeating decimal for each irrational number.

25. $\sqrt{5}$

26. $\sqrt{61}$

27. $\sqrt{60}$

28. $\sqrt{83}$

29. $\sqrt{101}$

30. $\sqrt{111}$

31. $\sqrt{137}$

32. $\sqrt{145}$

33. $\sqrt{1,500}$

34. $\sqrt{1,882}$

35. $\sqrt{19}$

36. $\sqrt{285}$

37. $\sqrt{23}$

38. $\sqrt{247}$

39. $\sqrt{2,100}$

★ 40. Is $\sqrt{1497.69}$ a rational number or an irrational number?

41. Write an irrational number which is between 1 and 2.

THINK MATH

Estimation

The number π is an irrational number. Here is an approximation of π to 24 places.

3.141592653589793238462643 . . .

Which rational number is closest to π?

A $\frac{22}{7}$ **B** $\frac{179}{57}$ **C** $\frac{355}{113}$ **D** $\frac{999}{318}$

APPLIED PROBLEM SOLVING

QUESTION
DATA
PLAN
ANSWER
CHECK

You are a shipping clerk filling orders for a gift supply house. You need to decide which carton to use to ship an order of 300 ceramic seals.

Some Things to Consider

• Each ceramic seal is packed in an individual box that measures 12 cm by 10 cm by 8 cm.

• Each shipping carton will contain 100 to 300 boxes.

• There is to be no extra room in the shipping carton.

• Shipping carton sizes
Carton A: 60 cm × 54 cm × 36 cm
Carton B: 80 cm × 80 cm × 60 cm
Carton C: 100 cm × 100 cm × 50 cm
Carton D: 60 cm × 60 cm × 80 cm

Some Questions to Answer

1. Can you stack the boxes so they have a length of 60 cm?

2. Can you stack the boxes so they have a length of 60 cm and a width of 54 cm?

3. Can shipping carton A be used?

4. Can you stack the boxes so they will have a length of 80 cm, a width of 80 cm, and a height of 60 cm?

5. How many boxes could be placed in shipping carton B?

6. Could either carton C or carton D be used?

What Is Your Decision?

Which of the four shipping cartons, A, B, C, or D, would you choose to pack the seals?

Find each square root.

1. $\sqrt{64}$

2. $^-\sqrt{100}$

3. $\sqrt{16}$

4. $\sqrt{400}$

Use the table to find each square root.

5. $\sqrt{13}$

6. $\sqrt{169}$

7. $\sqrt{15}$

8. $\sqrt{256}$

9. $\sqrt{14}$

10. $\sqrt{225}$

n	n^2	$\sqrt{n}$
13	169	3.606
14	196	3.742
15	225	3.873
16	256	4.000
17	289	4.123

Find the length of the hypotenuse of each right triangle.

11.

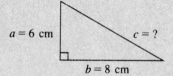

12.

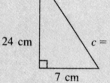

Find the length of the second leg for each right triangle whose hypotenuse is c.

13. $a = 3$ units
$b = $ ▨
$c = 5$ units

14. $a = $ ▨
$b = 6$ units
$c = 10$ units

15. Find the length of leg a.

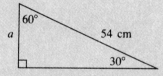

16. Find the length of hypotenuse c.

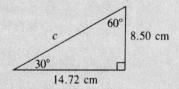

State if the decimal represents a rational number or an irrational number.

17. $7.0\overline{3}$

18. $7.56382 \ldots$

19. 4.9

20. $4.040040004 \ldots$

21. How high above the ground is the kite?

22. How many meters of wire are needed to reach from the top of a 20-meter pole to a point on the ground 15 m from the base of the pole?

$3^2 = 9$ so $\sqrt{9} = 3$

The square root of **9** is **3**.

$^-\sqrt{36} = ^-6$ because $^-6 \times ^-6 = 36$

Find each square root.

1. $\sqrt{16}$ **2.** $^-\sqrt{49}$ **3.** $\sqrt{100}$

4. $\sqrt{1,600}$ **5.** $\sqrt{25}$ **6.** $\sqrt{81}$

7. $\sqrt{2,500}$ **8.** $\sqrt{144}$ **9.** $^-\sqrt{64}$

n	n^2	$\sqrt{n}$
16	256	4.000
17	289	4.123
18	324	4.243

$\sqrt{17} \approx 4.123$

$17^2 = 289$

$\sqrt{289} = 17$

Use the square root table to find each square root.

10. $\sqrt{23}$

11. $\sqrt{529}$

12. $\sqrt{25}$

13. $\sqrt{676}$

14. $\sqrt{24}$

15. $\sqrt{625}$

n	n^2	$\sqrt{n}$
23	529	4.796
24	576	4.899
25	625	5.000
26	676	5.099
27	729	5.196

Area A + Area B = Area C

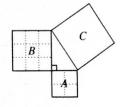

$4 + 9 =$ Area C

Area C = **13** square units

Find the area of C in each figure.

16.

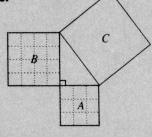

17.

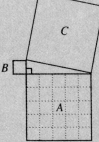

$a^2 + b^2 = c^2$
$6^2 + 8^2 = c^2$
$\quad 100 = c^2$
$\quad\ \ 10 = c$

B

$a = 6$

A $\quad\quad$ C
$\quad b = 8$

Find the length of the hypotenuse of each right triangle.

18.

A $\quad\quad c \quad\quad B$
$\quad b = 12$ cm $\quad C$

19.

A $\quad\quad c \quad\quad B$
$\quad\quad a = 5$ cm
$\quad b = 12$ m $\quad C$
$a = 9$ m

Using a Calculator with a Formula

How fast can you react? Here is an experiment to check your reaction time.

Put your hand on the edge of a desk or table top. Have a classmate hold a meter stick so that the end of the meter stick is even with the top of the desk.

When your classmate drops the meter stick, you must grab it without moving your hand from the desk top.

Find the distance, in centimeters, that the meter stick dropped before you were able to grab it. Then use the formula and a calculator to find your reaction time in seconds.

$$t = \frac{\sqrt{d}}{22.15}$$

t = Reaction time in seconds
d = Distance meter stick falls in centimeters

Example: $d = 38$ cm

$$t = \frac{\sqrt{38}}{22.15} = \frac{6.164414}{22.15} = 0.2783031 \approx 0.28$$

The reaction time is about 0.28 s.

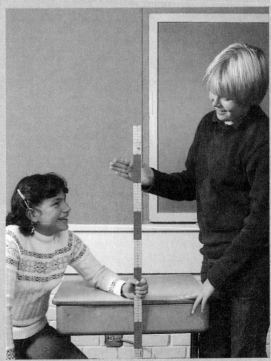

Find the reaction time for these distances.

1. 44 cm   **2.** 60 cm

3. 84 cm   **4.** 15 cm

5. Find your average reaction time for six drops of the meter stick.

1. What is the perimeter of a rectangle if $l = 27$ cm and $w = 15$ cm?

   A 405 cm
   B 84 cm
   C 42 cm
   D not given

2. What is the area of a parallelogram if $b = 22.5$ cm and $h = 8.6$ cm?

   A 193.5 cm^2
   B 31.1 cm^2
   C 62.2 cm^2
   D not given

3. What is the area of a trapezoid if $b_1 = 9.6$ m, $b_2 = 4.2$ m, and $h = 3.8$ m?

   A 17.6 m^2
   B 153.216 m^2
   C 26.22 m^2
   D not given

For 4–6, use 3.14 for π.

4. What is the circumference of a circle if $d = 56$ cm?

   A 87.92 cm
   B 180 cm
   C 28 cm
   D not given

5. What is the area of a circle if $d = 10$ cm?

   A 78.50 cm
   B 15.70 cm
   C 31.40 cm
   D not given

6. What is the volume of a cone if $r = 3$ cm and $h = 4$ cm?

   A 113.04 cm^3
   B 37.68 cm^3
   C 75.36 cm^3
   D not given

7. What is the arithmetic mean of these numbers: 23, 34, 39, 56, and 72?

   A 56
   B 39
   C 44.8
   D not given

8. What is the median of these numbers: 28, 29, 31, 32, 33, 35, and 35?

   A 35
   B 32
   C 31.9
   D not given

9. What is the mode of these numbers: 930, 935, 947, 972, and 972?

   A 947
   B 951.2
   C 972
   D not given

10. What is the name of the branch of mathematics that deals with presenting and interpreting numerical data?

    A geometry
    B statistics
    C metric system
    D not given

11. What is the name of a graph that uses pictures to represent data?

    A bar graph
    B histogram
    C circle graph
    D not given

12. What is the name of a graph that uses sectors to represent data?

    A circle graph
    B bar graph
    C pictograph
    D not given

13. A juice pitcher has a volume of 1,560 cm^3. What is its capacity in milliliters?

    A 15.6 L
    B 156 mL
    C 1.56 L
    D not given

14. Blanche had test scores of 91, 86, 77, 89, and 92. What was the mean of the scores?

    A 77
    B 87
    C 85
    D not given

Measurement: Customary Units

Sandra was not afraid of the steepness of the 5,000-foot ski run before her. It was an open bowl that had a few trees on either side. With the wind chill factor, the temperature was about ⁻3°F. Standing several feet behind, the instructor described the slope in front of the two skiers. Then they both started down, with the instructor constantly calling out instructions and encouragement.

Sandra did not feel that being blind was an extraordinary handicap for a skier. She knew that sighted skiers have handicaps too, such as fear of heights and speed. Sandra believed that the greatest possible handicap for a skier would be a fear of trusting the instructor.

Units of Length

Some commonly-used customary units of length for small measurements are the **inch** (**in.**) and the **foot** (**ft**). Larger measurements are often given in **yards** (**yd**) or **miles** (**mi**).

Customary Units of Length

12 inches (in.) = 1 foot (ft)
3 ft = 1 yard (yd)
36 in. = 1 yd
1,760 yd = 1 mile (mi)
5,280 ft = 1 mi

The shell is about $1\frac{1}{4}$ in. long.

How many yards are there in 60 ft?

60 ÷ 3 = 20
60 ft = **20** yd   *3 ft = 1 yd*

How many inches are there in 4 ft 8 in.?

4 × 12 = 48
48 + 8 = 56   *12 in. = 1 ft*
4 ft **8** in. = **56** in.

Add the lengths.

  4 ft **9** in.
+ 3 ft **7** in.   *16 in. = 1 ft 4 in.*

7 ft **16** in. or **8** ft **4** in.

Find the difference.

       3   15
  ~~4~~ ft ~~5~~ in.
− 1 ft **9** in.

  2 ft **6** in. or **2′6″**

Warm Up

Give the missing numbers.

1. 6 yd = ▓ ft

2. $\frac{1}{4}$ mi = ▓ yd

3. 72 in. = ▓ ft

4. 2 ft = ▓ in.

5. 2 ft 2 in. = ▓ in.

6. 3 mi = ▓ ft

Add or subtract.

7.   3 ft 8 in.
    + 1 ft 6 in.

8.   10 ft
    − 7 ft 4 in.

9.   1 yd 2 ft 3 in.
    + 1 yd 1 ft 10 in.

Practice Write the missing numbers.

1. 2 ft = ▨ in.

2. 7 yd = ▨ ft

3. 3 mi = ▨ ft

4. 3 ft 5 in. = ▨ in.

5. 60 ft = ▨ yd

6. 3 yd 26 in. = ▨ in.

7. 8,800 yd = ▨ mi

8. 216 in. = ▨ yd

9. 6 ft 8 in. = ▨ in.

10. $3\frac{1}{2}$ ft = ▨ in.

11. $3\frac{2}{3}$ yd = ▨ ft

12. 112 in. = ▨ ft ▨ in.

13. $\frac{1}{4}$ ft = ▨ in.

14. 72 in. = ▨ yd

15. 78 in. = ▨ ft ▨ in.

16. 3,960 ft = ▨ mi

Add or subtract.

17.
  4 ft 6 in.
  + 3 ft 9 in.

18.
  9 ft 6 in.
  − 2 ft 4 in.

19.
  5 yd 2 ft
  + 1 yd 2 ft

20.
  6 yd 2 ft
  + 4 yd 1 ft

21.
  2 ft 7 in.
  − 1 ft 4 in.

22.
  6 ft 5 in.
  − 2 ft 10 in.

23.
  7 yd 1 ft
  − 3 yd 2 ft

24.
  8 yd
  − 1 yd 2 ft

25.
  13 ft 8 in.
  − 12 ft 11 in.

26.
  35 yd 1 ft
  + 16 yd 2 ft

27.
  18 ft $6\frac{1}{2}$ in.
  − 7 ft $9\frac{1}{4}$ in.

28.
  15 yd $2\frac{1}{2}$ ft
  + 20 yd $1\frac{1}{2}$ ft

Mixed Applications

29. A platform was built with boards that each measured 5 ft 7 in. long. Each board was cut from a 6-foot long board. How much of each 6-foot board was left over?

30. A costume for a play used 6 ft 2 in. of lace on the collar and 4 ft 10 in. of lace on the cuffs. What was the total length of lace used in the costume?

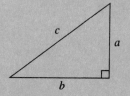

Units of Area

Some commonly-used customary units for measuring area are the **square inch (in.²)**, the **square foot (ft²)**, the **square yard (yd²)**, the **square mile (mi²)**, and the **acre (a.)**.

The table shows how some of these units are related.

Customary Units of Area

$$1 \text{ ft}^2 = 144 \text{ in.}^2$$
$$1 \text{ yd}^2 = 9 \text{ ft}^2$$
$$1 \text{ acre (a.)} = 43{,}560 \text{ ft}^2$$
$$1 \text{ mi}^2 = 640 \text{ a.}$$

Find the area of each region below.

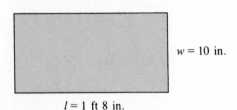

$w = 10$ in.

$l = 1$ ft 8 in.

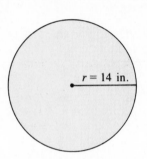

$r = 14$ in.

1 ft 8 in. = 20 in.
$A = lw$
$A = 20 \times 10 = 200$
$A = 200$ in.²

$A = \pi r^2$ Use 3.14 for π.
$A \approx 3.14 \times 14^2$
$A \approx 3.14 \times 196$
$A \approx 615.44$ in.²

Practice Give the missing number.

1. 3 yd² = ▓ ft²

2. 4 ft² = ▓ in.²

3. 36 ft² = ▓ yd²

4. 4 a. = ▓ ft²

5. 5 mi² = ▓ a.

6. 720 in.² = ▓ ft²

7. 1 yd² = ▓ in.²

8. $2\frac{1}{2}$ ft² = ▓ in.²

9. 180 ft² = ▓ yd²

Find the area of each region.

10.

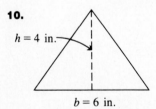

$h = 4$ in.

$b = 6$ in.

11.

$r = 8$ in.

12.

44 ft

18 ft

36 ft

16 ft

13. How many acres are there in a rectangular field that is 540 ft long and 242 ft wide?

14. A football field is 100 yd long and 160 ft wide. How much greater or less than 1 a. is this?

More Practice, page 456, Set C

Units of Volume

The **cubic inch** (**in.³**), the **cubic foot** (**ft³**), and the
cubic yard (**yd³**) are often used as units of volume.

The formula for the volume of a rectangular
prism is $V = lwh$.

1 cubic inch

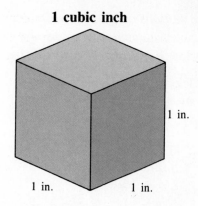

1 in.

1 in.   1 in.

1 cubic foot
$V = 12 \times 12 \times 12 = 1,728$
$V = 1,728$ in.³
1 ft³ $= 1,728$ in.³

1 cubic yard
$V = 3 \times 3 \times 3 = 27$
$V = 27$ ft³
1 yd³ $= 27$ ft³

Practice Give the missing numbers.

1. 3 ft³ $= $ ▓ in.³   **2.** 135 ft³ $= $ ▓ yd³   **3.** 864 in.³ $= $ ▓ ft³   **4.** $\frac{1}{3}$ yd³ $= $ ▓ ft³

5. $1\frac{1}{2}$ ft³ $= $ ▓ in.³   **6.** 5 yd³ $= $ ▓ ft³   **7.** $2,304$ in.³ $= $ ▓ ft³   **8.** 1 yd³ $= $ ▓ in.³

Find the volume of each figure.

9. $V = lwh$ **10.** $V = \pi r^2 h$ Use 3.14 for π.   **11.** $V = \frac{1}{3}Bh$

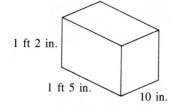

1 ft 2 in.

1 ft 5 in.

10 in.

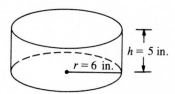

$h = 5$ in.

$r = 6$ in.

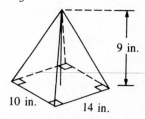

9 in.

10 in.

14 in.

12. What is the volume of a cylinder with
a diameter of 8 in. and a height of
10 in.?

13. How many cubic feet of concrete are
needed for a floor 20 ft long, 14 ft wide,
and $\frac{1}{2}$ ft thick?

THINK MATH

Volume

A box has outside measurements of 6 in. on each side.
The faces and the bottom of the box are each $\frac{1}{4}$ in.
thick. What is the volume of sand needed to fill the
box level with the top?

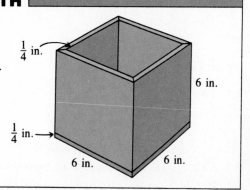

$\frac{1}{4}$ in.

6 in.

$\frac{1}{4}$ in.

6 in.

6 in.

Units of Liquid Measure

The eighth graders used 56 **cups** (c) of pancake batter at their pancake breakfast. How many **quarts** (qt) of batter is this?

The table shows how some of these units are related.

Units of Liquid Measure

8 fluid ounces (fl oz) = 1 cup (c)
2 c = 1 pint (pt)
2 pt = 1 quart (qt)
4 qt = 1 gallon (gal)

To change from a smaller unit to a larger one, we divide.

56 ÷ 4 = 14   (4 c = 1 qt)

14 qt of batter were used.

Practice Give the missing number.

1. 3 c = ▓ fl oz

2. 6 pt = ▓ qt

3. 3 gal = ▓ qt

4. 6 qt = ▓ pt

5. 3 pt = ▓ c

6. 24 fl oz = ▓ c

7. 2 qt = ▓ gal

8. 3 qt = ▓ c

9. $2\frac{1}{2}$ qt = ▓ pt

10. 20 fl oz = ▓ c

11. 1 qt = ▓ fl oz

12. 64 fl oz = ▓ qt

13. 7 pt = ▓ qt

14. 36 pt = ▓ gal

15. $3\frac{1}{2}$ qt = ▓ c

Mixed Applications

16. Pancake syrup was served in bottles that held 1 pt 8 fl oz. How many fluid ounces is this?

17. Each serving of orange juice was 6 fl oz. What part of a cup was each serving?

18. There were $5\frac{1}{2}$ gal of milk. How many quarts of milk was this?

19. **DATA HUNT** How many tablespoons are there in 16 fl oz of vegetable oil?

400

More Practice, page 457, Set B

PROBLEM SOLVING: Using Estimation

QUESTION
DATA
PLAN
ANSWER
CHECK

Choose the best estimate.

1. Gerald estimates he will need 27 qt of paint. The paint is sold in gallons only. How many gallons should he buy?

   A 7 gal   **B** 15 gal
   c 6 gal   **D** 4 gal

2. You can buy a quart of shellac for $6.97, or a gallon of shellac for $24.05. About how much will you save by buying a gallon of shellac in a gallon container rather than in quart containers?

   A about $6   **B** about $10
   c about $4   **D** about $17

3. Dan is sanding a rectangular hardwood floor that measures 28 ft by 19 ft. Estimate the area of the floor.

   A 400 ft^2 to 500 ft^2
   B 500 ft^2 to 600 ft^2
   c 600 ft^2 to 700 ft^2
   D 700 ft^2 to 800 ft^2

4. Consuelo used about 7 gal of floor finish to cover a rectangular area 54 ft by 28 ft. Estimate the number of square feet that 1 gal of the floor finish covers.

   A about 50 ft^2 **B** about 200 ft^2
   c about 400 ft^2 **D** about 600 ft^2

5. Ray bought 16 qt of paint at $18.95 a gallon. About how much was the total cost of the paint?

   A between $150 and $160
   B between $300 and $325
   c between $40 and $50
   D between $70 and $80

6. Rita needs 5 qt of redwood stain. The stain costs $6.95 per quart and $19.79 per gallon. Estimate the less expensive way to buy the stain.

   A about $27   **B** about $35
   c about $47   **D** about $60

7. The outside of the Chang's house has about 2,500 ft^2 of painted area. One gallon of paint covers about 400 ft^2. How many gallons should they buy to give the house 2 coats of paint?

   A 6 gal   **B** 9 gal
   c 11 gal   **D** 13 gal

8. **Strategy Practice** A plastering contractor multiplied the number of square feet plastered by $0.65 to get the labor charge. Then she added $58.72 for materials and $45.00 for debris hauling. The total bill was $279.22. how many square feet did she plaster?

401

Units of Temperature

The **degree Fahrenheit (°F)** is the basic unit of temperature in the customary system. The temperature scale at the right gives some reference points for Fahrenheit temperatures.

Practice Choose the best estimate of temperature.

1. A cold drink
   A 35°F   B 55°F   C 155°F

2. Inside a freezer
   A 25°F   B 35°F   C 65°F

3. Hot tap water
   A 95°F   B 150°F   C 220°F

4. An oven for baking bread
   A 70°F   B 100°F   C 350°F

5. The melting point of gold
   A 192°F   B 212°F   C 1,064°F

6. A cool breeze
   A 97°F   B 53°F   C 32°F

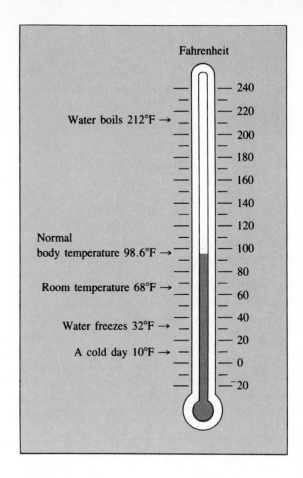

Fahrenheit

Water boils 212°F →

Normal body temperature 98.6°F →

Room temperature 68°F →

Water freezes 32°F →

A cold day 10°F →

Mixed Applications

7. The average temperature in San Juan, Puerto Rico varies from 60°F to 96°F. What is the range of these temperatures?

8. The average temperature at the surface of the earth is 70°F. The average temperature at the earth's core is about 108.6 times hotter. What is the average temperature at the earth's core?

9. The average temperature in Helena, Montana varies from ⁻42°F to 105°F. What is the range of these temperatures?

10. A child has a temperature that is 3.4° above normal. What is the child's temperature?

11. The hottest average annual temperature on earth, 94°F, is in Dallol, Ethiopia. The coldest average annual temperature, ⁻72°F, is in Nedostupnosti, Antarctica. How many degrees higher is the temperature in Dallol than in Nedostupnosti?

12. **DATA BANK** The temperature of the ocean varies at different places on the earth. At which latitude does the ocean have the hottest average temperature? What is the temperature? (See page 432.)

Units of Weight

A skateboard weighs about $1\frac{3}{4}$ **pound (lb)**. About how many **ounces (oz)** does the skateboard weigh?

The table shows how units of weight are related.

Since 1 lb is equal to 16 oz, we can multiply the number of pounds by 16 to get ounces.

$$1\frac{3}{4} \times 16 = \frac{7}{4} \times \frac{16}{1} = 28$$

The skateboard weighs about 28 oz.

Customary Units of Weight

16 ounces (oz) = 1 pound (lb)
2,000 lb = 1 ton (T)

Practice Give the missing numbers.

1. 32 oz = ▓ lb

2. 7 lb = ▓ oz

3. 3 T = ▓ lb

4. 10,000 lb = ▓ T

5. 80 oz = ▓ lb

6. 8,000 lb = ▓ T

7. 8 oz = ▓ lb

8. $\frac{1}{4}$ T = ▓ lb

9. $1\frac{1}{2}$ lb = ▓ oz

10. 56 oz = ▓ lb

11. 5,000 lb = ▓ T

12. 2 oz = ▓ lb

13. $2\frac{3}{4}$ lb = ▓ oz

14. $\frac{1}{2}$ T = ▓ lb

15. 20 oz = ▓ lb

Mixed Applications

16. The wheels for a skateboard weigh about 14 oz. What part of a pound is this amount?

17. A skateboard with wheels weighs 35 oz. How many pounds and ounces is this amount?

PROBLEM SOLVING: Using a Calculator

| QUESTION |
| DATA |
| PLAN |
| ANSWER |
| CHECK |

Use your calculator to compare the prices of these grocery items. Round all answers to the nearest tenth of a cent.

1. Find the cost per ounce of each bar of soap.

2. Which bar of soap gives you the most soap for your money?

3. What is the cost per ounce of each size of dry roasted peanuts?

4. Which peanut can size has the lowest unit price?

5. Which detergent size has the higher unit price?

6. Which detergent size is less expensive?

7. What is the cost, per fluid ounce, of each polish?

8. Which polish has the lowest unit price?

9. **Strategy Practice** A grocer has 4 brands of soap—Brand O, Brand X, Brand Y, and Brand Z. How many ways can the soaps be placed on 4 shelves if Brand X soap is never placed on the bottom shelf?

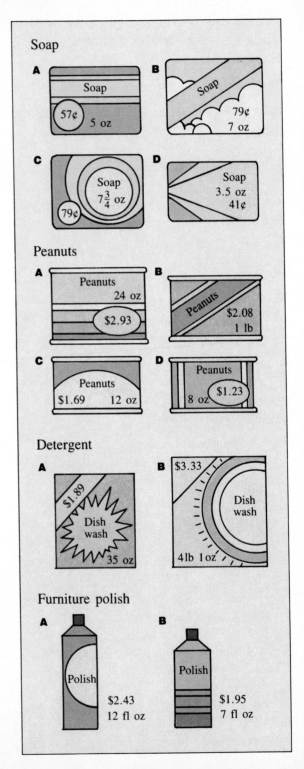

Soap

A Soap 57¢ 5 oz
B Soap 79¢ 7 oz
C Soap 7¾ oz 79¢
D Soap 3.5 oz 41¢

Peanuts

A Peanuts 24 oz $2.93
B Peanuts $2.08 1 lb
C Peanuts $1.69 12 oz
D Peanuts 8 oz $1.23

Detergent

A $1.89 Dish wash 35 oz
B $3.33 Dish wash 4 lb 1 oz

Furniture polish

A Polish $2.43 12 fl oz
B Polish $1.95 7 fl oz

PROBLEM SOLVING: Using Data from a Drawing

QUESTION
DATA
PLAN
ANSWER
CHECK

Use the data in the drawings at the right to solve these problems.

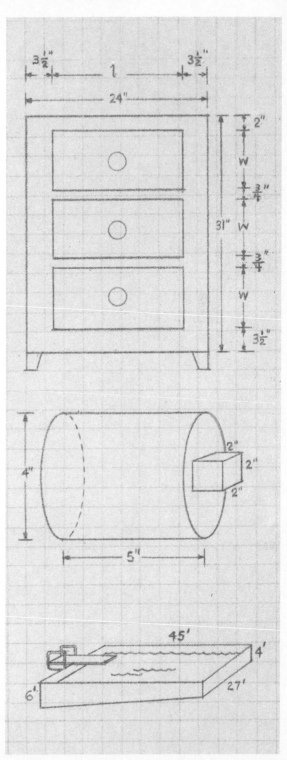

1. The chest has three drawers of equal size. What is the length (*l*) of each drawer face?

2. What is the width (*w*) of each drawer face?

3. What is the volume of the machine part in cubic inches? Use 3.14 for π.

4. Cast iron weighs 0.26 pound per cubic inch. To the nearest pound, what would the machine part weigh if it were made of cast iron?

★ 5. What is the volume of the pool in cubic yards?

★ 6. About how many gallons of water will it take to fill the pool? (1 yd^3 holds about 200 gal of water.)

7. **Strategy Practice** Rick, Nan, Keiko, and Beth live in four apartments. The front door of each apartment is a different color. One door is yellow, but that is not Rick's door. The door next to Nan's apartment is white. Beth is Nan's only neighbor. Keiko's door is tan. The fourth color is brown. What color is each person's front door?

405

Mixed Skills Practice

Computation
Find the answers.

1. $\begin{array}{r} \$600.00 \\ -\ 174.68 \end{array}$

2. $\begin{array}{r} 29.3 \\ \times\ 6.5 \end{array}$

3. $\begin{array}{r} 9,287 \\ 3,844 \\ 2,109 \\ +\,6,188 \end{array}$

4. $\begin{array}{r} \$3.77 \\ 4.29 \\ +\ 8.88 \end{array}$

5. $8.3)\overline{4.731}$

6. 27% of 400

7. $12 \div 2\frac{1}{2}$

8. $27\frac{1}{2} - 15\frac{3}{4}$

9. $\frac{20}{25} = ?\%$

10. $3\frac{2}{3} \times 4\frac{1}{2}$

11. $3\frac{2}{3} + 9\frac{1}{2}$

12. $0.8)\overline{5.04}$

13. Solve.
$3x = {}^-54$

14. Solve.
$x - 17 = {}^-7$

15. Solve.
$2x + \frac{1}{2} = 3\frac{1}{2}$

16. Solve.
$0.6x = 4.2$

Mental Math
Write only the answers.

17. $0.1 \times \$7.00$

18. $\frac{1}{6} \times 54$

19. $90 + 90 + 90 + 90$

20. $2,700 - 2,000$

21. $10 \times 7 \times 6$

22. $200 - 98$

23. 2×7.1

24. $\frac{1}{2} \times 68$

25. $1,500 \div 30$

26. 100×7.83

27. $9,000 \div 3,000$

28. $6\frac{1}{2} + 3\frac{1}{2}$

29. $8 + {}^-5$

30. $4 \times {}^-6$

31. ${}^-20 \div {}^-4$

32. $({}^-2 + 6) \times 5$

Estimation
Estimate.

33. 0.011×788

34. $28)\overline{2,217}$

35. $\frac{1}{4} \times \$19.95$

36. $9\frac{1}{2}\%$ of 505

37. $209 + 189 + 196 + 211$

38. 7.2×9.83

39. $6.9)\overline{15.04}$

40. $12\frac{5}{8} + 7\frac{3}{7}$

41. $\begin{array}{r} 8,127 \\ -\,3,135 \end{array}$

42. $\begin{array}{r} 0.983 \\ 0.714 \\ +\,0.608 \end{array}$

43. $\begin{array}{r} \$16.38 \\ 32.44 \\ +\,29.95 \end{array}$

44. $\frac{2}{3} \times 37$

45. $80)\overline{7,319}$

46. $\begin{array}{r} \$50.00 \\ -\ 19.73 \end{array}$

47. $\frac{9}{10} \times 19.6$

48. 6.088×7.929

406

APPLIED PROBLEM SOLVING

QUESTION
DATA
PLAN
ANSWER
CHECK

Your family has a lawn that needs landscaping. The lawn must be rototilled and soil conditioner and fertilizer must be added before new sod is laid. Your family has offered to hire you if you can do the whole project a little less expensively than the professional gardener. You must decide if you will do the job.

Some Things to Consider

- The rectangular lawn has an area of 1,800 ft^2.

- A bag of soil conditioner costs $5.95 and will cover approximately 100 ft^2.

- Sod comes in rolls that cover 9 ft^2 and costs $0.45 per square foot.

- A bag of fertilizer will cover 2,000 ft^2 and costs $18.29.

- A rototiller rents for $36.00 and a roller rents for $8.00.

- The gardener does not have to rent any equipment.

- The gardener gets a 20% discount on the cost of the sod and a 10% discount on soil conditioner and fertilizer.

- The gardener will charge $300.00 for labor plus the full cost of materials.

Some Questions to Answer

1. What will be your total cost for all the materials and the equipment rental?

2. How much less is the cost of materials for the gardener than for you?

3. What will be the gardener's total charge for materials and labor?

4. How much more is the gardener's total charge than your cost for materials and equipment?

What Is Your Decision?

Will you take the job or not?

PROBLEM SOLVING: Using the Strategies

QUESTION
DATA
PLAN
ANSWER
CHECK

Problem-Solving Strategies

✔ Guess and Check   ✔ Make a Table

✔ Choose the Operations   ✔ Solve a Simpler Problem

✔ Make an Organized List   ✔ Find a Pattern

✔ Work Backward   ✔ Use Logical Reasoning

✔ Draw a Picture

You have learned to use different strategies to solve some of the problems in this book. Use one or more of these strategies to solve each problem below.

1. Jane's grandmother deposited $1.00 in a savings account on Jane's first birthday. On Jane's second birthday her grandmother deposited $3.00, on her third birthday, $5.00 and so on. What will be the total amount of birthday money her grandmother will have given to Jane on Jane's 21st birthday?

2. Hal sawed a board that was 216 cm long into two pieces. One piece was 3 times as long as the other. What was the length of each piece?

3. Frank had $5.00. Frank made a long distance telephone call that cost 70 cents for the first minute and 22 cents for each additional minute. After paying for the call, Frank had $1.88 left. How long was the telephone call?

4. Annie, Diane, John and Mark all teach at the same school. One teaches art, one teaches English, another teaches science, and the other teaches math. Diane's brother teaches science and he is married to the English teacher. The art teacher is an only child. Mark and the math teacher are both single. What subject does each person teach?

5. Abbe and Bobbi started on a bicycle trip from the same point. Abbe rode 8 miles east then 3 miles south. Bobbi rode 7 miles west then 5 miles north. How far apart were the two girls now?

6. A carton of milk cost 15¢ more than a loaf of bread. A box of cereal costs 60¢ more than the milk. The total cost is $3.57. What is the cost of each item?

Write the missing numbers.

1. 9 ft = ▦ yd

2. 2 ft = ▦ in.

3. 2 mi = ▦ ft

4. 2 ft 3 in. = ▦ in.

5. 3 yd = ▦ in.

6. 18 in. = ▦ yd

Add or subtract.

7.   5 ft 6 in.
    + 2 ft 8 in.

8.   3 ft 2 in.
    − 1 ft 7 in.

9.   1 yd 7 ft 9 in.
    +   3 ft 4 in.

Find the area of each region. Use 3.14 for π.

10.

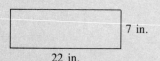

7 in.

22 in.

11.

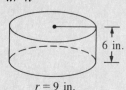

5 ft

7 ft 6 in.

12.

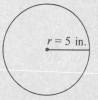

$r = 5$ in.

Find the volume of each figure. Use 3.14 for π.

13. $V = lwh$

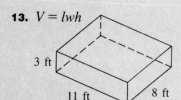

3 ft

11 ft

8 ft

14. $V = \pi r^2 h$

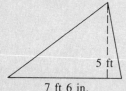

6 in.

$r = 9$ in.

15. $V = \frac{1}{3}Bh$

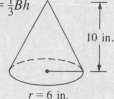

10 in.

$r = 6$ in.

Write the missing numbers.

16. 3 qt = ▦ pt

17. 16 qt = ▦ gal

18. 4 pt = ▦ c

19. 2 T = ▦ lb

20. 48 oz = ▦ lb

21. $2\frac{1}{2}$ lb = ▦ oz

Choose the best estimate of temperature.

22. Hot water in a bathtub
   A 195°F   **B** 110°F   **c** 32°F

23. Water in a mountain pond
   A 165°F   **B** 45°F   **c** ⁻25°F

24. A 1 lb 4 oz loaf of bread sells for $1.68. To the nearest cent, what is the cost per ounce?

25. The inside temperature is 70°F. The outside temperature is 19° hotter. What is the outside temperature?

Length: **1** ft = **12** in.
         1 yd = **3** ft
         1 mi = **5,280** ft
         1 mi = **1,760** yd

Write the missing numbers.

1. 12 ft = ▨ yd   **2.** 5 ft = ▨ in.

3. 3 ft 9 in. = ▨ in.   **4.** $\frac{1}{2}$ mi = ▨ yd

4 in. + 12 in. = 16 in.

6 16
7̶ ft 4̶ in.
− 2 ft 7 in.
─────────
  4 ft 9 in.

Add or subtract.

5.   7 ft 9 in.   **6.**   4 ft 3 in.
       + 3 ft 7 in.   − 2 ft 10 in.

Area formulas:

Rectangle: $A = lw$
Triangle: $A = \frac{1}{2} bh$
Circle: $A = \pi r^2$

Volume formulas:

$V = lwh$ $V = \pi r^2 h$

Find the area of each region. Use 3.14 for π.

7.

5 ft 2 in.

3 ft 5 in.

8.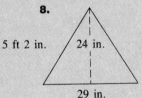

24 in.

29 in.

9.

r = 2 ft

Find the volume of each figure. Use 3.14 for π.

10.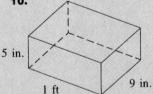

5 in.

1 ft   9 in.

11.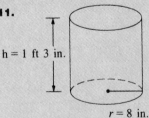

h = 1 ft 3 in.

r = 8 in.

Capacity   Weight

1 c = **8** fl oz   **1** lb = **16** oz
1 pt = **2** c   **1** T = **2,000** lb
1 qt = **2** pt
1 gal = **4** qt

Write the missing numbers.

12. 3 qt = ▨ pt   **13.** 20 qt = ▨ gal

14. 5 c = ▨ pt   **15.** 2 qt = ▨ c

16. 4 lb = ▨ oz   **17.** 8,000 lb = ▨ T

410

Shape Perception

An **ellipse** is an oval-shaped geometric figure. The path of the earth around the sun is an ellipse. Arches of bridges are often parts of ellipses.

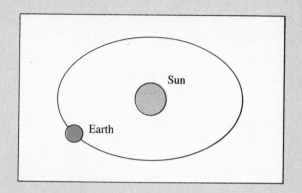

The picture at the right shows one way to draw an ellipse.

Place a loop of string around the two map pins. Place the point of your pencil in the loop and, keeping the loop taut against the pins, draw the ellipse.

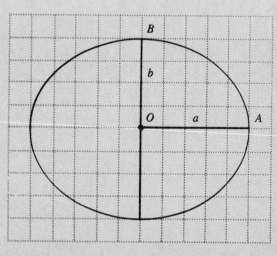

Cardboard or soft wooden board

Try these experiments with ellipses.

1. Keep the loop of string the same size but change the distance between the two map pins. How does this change the shapes of the ellipses?

2. Keep the two pins in the same location but use longer loops of string. How are the shapes of the ellipses affected?

3. Estimate the area of the ellipse at the right using one of the small squares of the grid as the unit square.

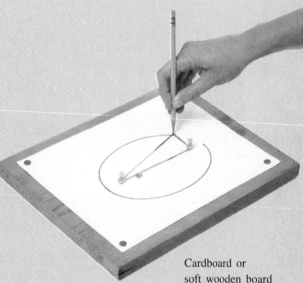

4. The area of the ellipse can be found using this formula:
   Area $= \pi \times$ length $(\overline{OA}) \times$ length $(\overline{OB})$,
   or $A = \pi \cdot ab$
   Find the area of the ellipse and compare it with your estimate.

5. Draw an ellipse on graph paper. Estimate the area. Then use the formula to find the area.

1. What is the mean of these numbers: 168, 160, 157, 155, and 147?

A 157 **B** 161

C 157.4 **D** not given

2. What is the median of these numbers: 37, 43, 26, 50, 38, and 27?

A 26 **B** 37.5

C 50 **D** not given

3. What is the mode of these amounts: $2.98, $3.44, $2.99, $2.98, and $2.75?

A $3.03 **B** $2.99

C $2.98 **D** not given

4. What is the median of these amounts: $21.66, $32.49, $27.95, $25.00, and $27.50?

A $26.92 **B** $32.49

C $27.50 **D** not given

5. What is the mode of these numbers: 35, 38, 27, 42, 38, and 63?

A 34.5 **B** 40.5

C 38 **D** not given

6. What is the name for a bar graph that shows frequencies?

A histogram **B** pictograph

C circle graph **D** not given

Find the square roots.

7. $\sqrt{4,900}$

A 490 **B** 100

C 700 **D** not given

8. $^-\sqrt{81}$

A $^-9$ **B** $^-8$

C 9 **D** not given

9. Find the square roots. Then add.

$\sqrt{36} + \sqrt{144}$

A 180 **B** 48

C 18 **D** not given

10. In a right triangle, what is the length of hypotenuse c if $a = 9$ m and $b = 12$ m?

A 21 m **B** 54 m

C 15 m **D** not given

11. In a right triangle, find the length of the leg a if $b = 14$ cm and $c = 18$ cm.

A $a \approx 11.6$ cm **B** $a \approx 11.3$ cm

C $a = 12$ cm **D** not given

12. Find the length of the leg x.

A 12.1 cm

B 14 cm

C 15.7 cm

D not given

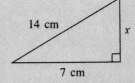

14 cm

x

7 cm

13. On 5 days a car wash washed 18 cars, 15 cars, 26 cars, 35 cars, and 41 cars. What is the mean?

A 26 **B** 28

C 27 **D** not given

14. A ramp runs 10 m along the ground and is 2 m high. How long is the ramp?

A 10.2 m **B** 8 m

C 5 m **D** not given

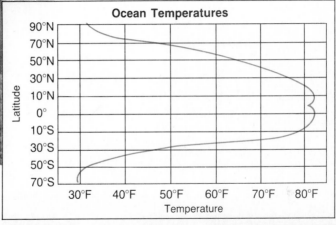

Ocean Temperatures

Computer Programs and Flowcharts

To solve the simplest kind of problem, a computer must be given a detailed list of instructions called a **program**.

To develop a program, a computer programmer may make a **flowchart** of the steps in the program.

The flowchart and the program in BASIC below find the sales tax and the total for any given price.

```
                    05/10/85
SOAP
SPONGE              .84 T
POLISH              .67 T
SCRUB PAD          1.89 T
CLEANSER            .79 T
                   1.45 T
TXBL TOT           5.64
5.0% TX             .28
TOTAL              5.92

# ITEMS          5
```

Flowchart	BASIC Program	Comments
Start	NEW	Clears memory.
	10 PRINT "ENTER THE PRICE."	Prints exactly what is inside the quotation marks.
Input the price.	20 INPUT P	Data you give the computer.
	30 S = 0.05 * P	* means × in BASIC.
Sales tax = 0.05 of price	40 T = P + S	T, P, and S are **variables**. They are the locations of the numbers stored in the computer's memory.
Total = Price + tax	50 PRINT "PRICE = $";P	
	60 PRINT "SALES TAX = $ ";S	
Print the price, the sales tax, and the total.	70 PRINT "TOTAL = $ ";T	
	80 END	Last statement.
Stop		

Type RUN to see the **output** of this program. The INPUT was 184.60.

```
RUN
ENTER THE PRICE.
?184.60
PRICE = $184.60
SALES TAX = $9.23
TOTAL = $193.83
```

414

Use the program on page 414 for questions 1–4.

1. What does the computer do to find the sales tax *S*? Which line of the program shows this?

2. What does the computer do to find the total? Which line shows this?

3. What would a RUN of the program show for the sales tax if the price (INPUT *P*) were $65.00?

4. What would a RUN of the program show for a price of $3.80 and a sales tax of 0.065?

Write a RUN for each computer program. Use the given INPUT numbers.

5.
```
10 INPUT A,B,C
20 S = A + B + C
30 PRINT "THE SUM = ";S
40 END
```
INPUT: A = 554, B = 628, C = 917

6.
```
10 PRINT "TYPE A NUMBER,"
20 INPUT N
30 S = 100 * N
40 PRINT "100 TIMES YOUR"
50 PRINT "NUMBER = ";S
60 END
```
INPUT: 37.5

7.
```
10 INPUT A
20 INPUT B
30 Q = A/B
40 PRINT "THE QUOTIENT = ";Q
50 END
```
INPUT: A = 21, B = 6

8.
```
10 PRINT "HOURS WORKED?"
20 INPUT H
30 PRINT "PAY PER HOUR?"
40 INPUT P
50 E = H * P
60 PRINT "EARNINGS = $ ";E
70 END
```
INPUT: H = 40, P = 7.80

9. Make a flowchart that shows the steps for finding the amount of money you get back when you buy something.

10. Write a computer program for your flowchart in exercise 9. Show a RUN of the program if you buy something for $37.50 and pay for it with $40.00

COMPUTER INSTRUCTION

FOR-NEXT Counting Loops

A computer can keep track of the number of times an instruction is to be performed. A program with a **counting loop** is used to do this. The special words FOR and NEXT are used to repeat an instruction for a given number of times.

Compare the flowchart and the computer program below that count and print the first five multiples of 10.

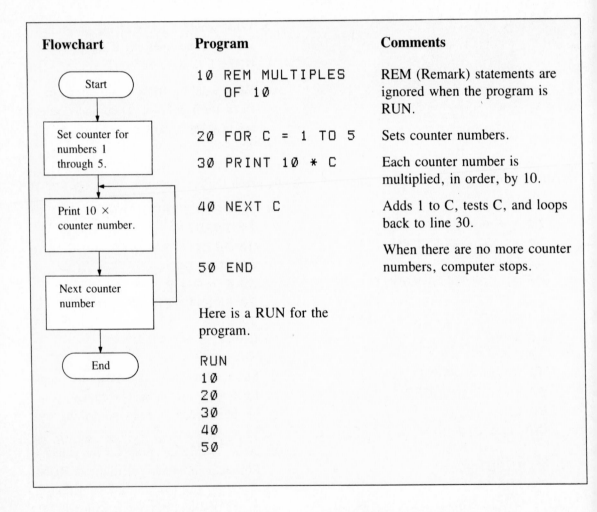

Flowchart	Program	Comments
Start	10 REM MULTIPLES OF 10	REM (Remark) statements are ignored when the program is RUN.
Set counter for numbers 1 through 5.	20 FOR C = 1 TO 5	Sets counter numbers.
	30 PRINT 10 * C	Each counter number is multiplied, in order, by 10.
Print 10 × counter number.	40 NEXT C	Adds 1 to C, tests C, and loops back to line 30.
Next counter number	50 END	When there are no more counter numbers, computer stops.
End		

Here is a RUN for the program.

```
RUN
10
20
30
40
50
```

1. How could the program be changed so that the computer would list the first 12 multiples of 10?

2. If line 20 were FOR C = 0 to 5, what would a RUN of the program be?

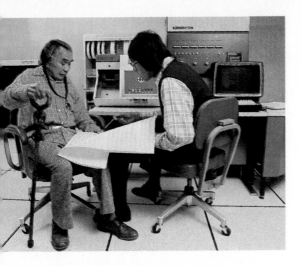

Write the RUN for each program.

1.
```
10 REM FIRST 10 SQUARES
20 FOR N = 1 TO 10
30 PRINT N * N
40 NEXT N
50 END
```

2.
```
10 FOR N = 1 TO 5
20 PRINT 5 * N - 1
30 NEXT N
40 PRINT "WHAT ARE THE
   NEXT"
50 PRINT "3 NUMBERS?"
60 END
```

3.
```
10 PRINT "HELLO! I CAN
   COUNT"
20 PRINT "BY 19'S, EASILY."
30 FOR N = 1 TO 10
40 PRINT 19 * N
50 NEXT N
60 PRINT "DO YOU KNOW
   YOUR 19'S?"
70 END
```

4.
```
10 A = 10↑6
20 FOR N = 1 TO 6
30 PRINT A/10↑N
40 NEXT N
50 PRINT "I RAN OUT OF
   ZEROS."
60 END
```

5.
```
10 REM LIST OF PRIME
   NUMBERS
20 FOR N = 1 TO 10
30 PRINT N * N - N + 17
40 NEXT N
50 PRINT "ALL THESE
   NUMBERS"
60 PRINT "ARE PRIME."
70 END
```

6. The program below has a "bug", or error, in it. "Debug" the program by rewriting it correctly. Then show a RUN of the program.

```
10 REM SQUARES OF ODD
   NUMBERS
20 FOR N = 1 TO 10
30 T = 2 * N - 1
40 PRINT T * T
50 NEXT T
60 END
```

★ **7.** Write the RUN for this program.

```
10 REM CUMULATIVE TOTALS
20 T = 0
30 FOR N = 1 TO 5
40 T = T + N
50 PRINT T
60 NEXT N
70 END
```

417

COMPUTER INSTRUCTION

Using String Variables

To store numbers in the memory of a computer, we use letter variables such as A, N, and S. To store data like names, letters, special symbols, or strings of symbols, we use a **string variable**. A string variable is a letter followed by the $ symbol, for example, N$ = "MARY" is a BASIC statement to store the name "MARY."

Study the programs below to see how string variables are used in computer programs.

Program	Comments
`10 REM  STRING VARIABLES` `20 REM  D$=DATE,N$=NAME,S=TEST SCORE`	REM statements are ignored when the program is RUN.

`30 D$ = "MARCH 21"`
`40 N$ = "MARY WEAVER"`
`50 S = 92`
	Quotation marks are used around names assigned to string variables.

`60 PRINT D$;" ";N$;" ";S` `70 END`	Empty quotation marks allow an extra space between characters.

Here is a RUN of the program.

```
RUN
MARCH 21 MARY WEAVER 92
```

The program below combines string variables with INPUT statements.

```
10 REM  STRING VARIABLE INPUT
20 PRINT "TYPE YOUR NAME,"
30 INPUT N$
40 PRINT "TYPE YOUR AGE, ";N$
50 INPUT A
60 PRINT N$,A
70 PRINT "THANKS, ";N$
80 END
```

Here is a RUN of the program using Melanie and 14.

```
RUN
TYPE YOUR NAME,
?MELANIE
TYPE YOUR AGE, MELANIE
?14
MELANIE         14
THANKS, MELANIE
```

418

4. Change the program for exercise 3 to your own name and address and zip code. Write a RUN for the program.

5. Write a RUN of this program. Use your own name and favorite color as INPUTS.

```
10 PRINT "TYPE YOUR NAME,"
20 INPUT N$
30 PRINT "TYPE YOUR
   FAVORITE COLOR,"
40 INPUT C$
50 PRINT C$;" IS MY
   FAVORITE"
60 PRINT "COLOR TOO, ";N$
70 END
```

1. Write the RUN of this program.

```
10 S$ = "HAWAII"
20 N$ = "50TH"
30 PRINT S$;" IS THE "
40 PRINT N$;" STATE,"
50 END
```

6. Write a RUN of this program. Use your own name and age.

```
10 PRINT "TYPE YOUR NAME,"
20 INPUT N$
30 PRINT "SUBTRACT 6 FROM
   YOUR AGE,"
40 PRINT "MULTIPLY THAT
   ANSWER BY 8,"
50 PRINT "THEN ADD 50,"
60 PRINT "WHAT IS YOUR
   ANSWER?"
70 INPUT T
80 C = (T - 2)/8
90 PRINT "YOU ARE ";C
100 PRINT "YEARS OLD, ";N$
110 END
```

2. Change the program for exercise 1 to show that Utah is the 45th state in the United States. Write a RUN for the program.

3. Write the RUN of this program.

```
10 REM  NAME AND ADDRESS
20 N$ = "JEAN SAGE"
30 A$ = "275 AMES ST,"
40 S$ = "HOPEWELL, NJ"
50 Z = 19999
60 PRINT N$
70 PRINT A$
80 PRINT S$;" ";Z
90 END
```

7. Write a computer program that uses string variables. Write a RUN of your program.

Computer Graphics

Logo is a special computer language that can be used to draw geometric shapes on the computer screen.

A small triangle called a **turtle** ($\triangle$) acts like a pencil. The point of the turtle shows the direction in which lines or circles will be drawn.

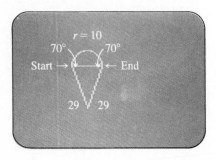

The program for drawing the picture of the ice cream cone is given below.

Command	Meaning
FD 30	Draw a segment forward 30 units.
BK 50	Draw a segment backward 50 units.
RT 20	Turn the turtle 20° to the *right* (clockwise).
LT 45	Turn the turtle 45° to the left (counterclockwise).
CIRCLER 20	Draw a circle with radius of 20 units to the right.
CIRCLEL 30	Draw a circle with radius of 30 units to the left.

Command	Comments
TO ICECREAMCONE	The program is named.
ARCR 10 180	Draw the semicircle.
RT 90 FD 20	Turn right 90°, then draw the diameter.
LT 110 FD 29	Turn left 110° (supplement of 70°), then draw 29 units.
LT 140 FD 29	Turn left 140° and draw the other 29-unit segment.
END	End of program

Now when you type ICECREAMCONE and press RETURN, the turtle will draw the picture.

Would you like more?

Type REPEAT 3 [ICECREAMCONE].

420

Command	Meaning
ARCR 30 90	Draw an arc to the right with radius 30 and through 90°.
ARCL 50 180	Draw an arc to the left with radius 50 and through 180°.
PU FD 20	Pen Up, Forward 20 Move the turtle 20 units without drawing.
PD	Pen Down. Resume drawing.
HT	Hide the turtle.
ST	Show the turtle.
CS	Clearscreen
REPEAT 4	Repeat a command 4 times.

Use the program below for exercises 1–6.

```
TO HAPPYFACE
CIRCLER 40
PU FD 20
RT 90 FD 20
PD FD 8
PU FD 24
PD FD 8
RT 90 PU
FD 20 PD
ARCR 20 180
END
```

1. What is the radius of the large circle?

2. How many units long is the left eye?

3. Which line draws the right eye?

4. How many units apart are the eyes?

5. What is the radius of the "smile?"

6. Where will the turtle be at the end?

Use the figure below for exercises 7–10.

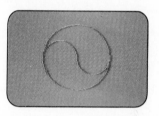

7. Write a Logo command to draw the large circle with radius of 50 units.

8. What is the radius of each of the two arcs if the large circle has a radius of 50 units?

9. Write a command to draw the left hand arc.

10. Write a command to draw the right hand arc.

11. Write a Logo program that will draw a square inside a circle.

12. Write a Logo program of your own. Draw the picture for your program.

COMPUTER-ASSISTED PROBLEM SOLVING

Problem 1 (for use after page 49)
You have $25.00 to spend on 4 gifts for
friends. There will be sales tax of 7 cents per
dollar on the items you buy. Use a catalog or
advertisement for some small gifts and their
prices. How close to the total of $25.00 can
you come?

Program 1

```
10 REM COST AND SALES TAX
30 PRINT "ENTER EACH PRICE WITHOUT A
   $ SIGN"
40 FOR K = 1 TO 4:INPUT "PRICE ";P
50 T = T + P : NEXT K
60 S = INT(T*0.07*100)/100: T1 = T + S
70 PRINT:PRINT "SUBTOTAL", "SALES
   TAX", "TOTAL"
80 PRINT T, S, T1:PRINT
90 IF T1 > 25 THEN PRINT "NOT ENOUGH
   MONEY":GOTO 120
100 IF T1 < 25 THEN PRINT "YOU WILL
    HAVE"
110 PRINT "$"; INT((25 -
    T1)*100)/100;" LEFT"
120 END
```

Problem 2 (for use after page 127)
You know how to find a repeating decimal
for $\frac{5}{11}$ by dividing 5 by 11 to get
0.454545... . How can you find a lowest-
terms fraction for a repeating decimal? The
computer program below will help you do
this.

Program 2

```
10 REM REPEATING DECIMALS
20 PRINT "USE ONLY REPEATING DECI
   MALS BETWEEN 0 AND 1"
30 PRINT "SUCH AS 0.2454545... IN
   THIS PROGRAM."
40 PRINT:INPUT "TYPE IN A REPEATING
   DECIMAL SUCH AS
   0.52141414...";D$
50 PRINT:PRINT "HOW MANY DIGITS
   AFTER THE DECIMAL ARE NOT"
60 PRINT "PART OF THE REPEATING
   PERIOD OF THE DECIMAL?"
70 INPUT "TYPE 0 IF THERE ARE NONE";A
80 PRINT "TYPE THOSE DIGITS WITHOUT A
   DECIMAL"
90 INPUT "OR HIT <RETURN> IF THERE
   ARE NONE";K
100 PRINT:INPUT "HOW MANY DIGITS ARE
    IN ONE PERIOD OF THE REPEATING
    PART?"; P
110 INPUT "TYPE THE DIGITS IN ONE
    PERIOD OF THE REPEATING PART";B
120 N = K*(10↑P-1)+B : D =
    (10↑A)*(10↑P-1)
130 N1 = N : D1 = D
140 Q = INT(D/N) : R = INT(D-Q*N+0.5)
150 IF R = 0 THEN 170
160 D = N : N = R : GOTO 140
170 PRINT:PRINT "THE FRACTION FOR
    "D$" IS "N1/N"/"D1/N
180 END
```

Problem 3 (for use after page 105)
Beth and Brian were playing a game. They
tried to find numbers that were larger than
100 and were prime. Can you find some
prime numbers larger than 100? Use the
computer to check your choices.

Program 3

```
10 REM FINDING PRIME NUMBERS
20 INPUT "WHAT IS YOUR NUMBER?";N
30 PRINT "N = ";
40 M = N : P = INT(SQR(N)+1)
50 FOR I = 2 TO P:IF M = 1 THEN 120
60 IF I = P THEN PRINT M: GOTO 120
70 D = M/I: F = INT(D)
80 IF F<>D THEN 110
90 PRINT I;:IF D<>1 THEN PRINT "*";
100 LET M = F: GOTO 50
110 NEXT I
120 IF N = M THEN PRINT "YOUR NUMBER
    IS PRIME!"
130 END
```

Problem 4   (for use after page 151)
Suppose you had 50 two-step equations like
$4x + 7 = 83$. How long do you think it
would take you to solve them using pencil
and paper? Save a lot of time by using the
program below to solve some equations.

Program 4

```
10 REM EQUATION SOLVER
20 PRINT "THIS PROGRAM WILL SOLVE"
30 PRINT "EQUATIONS LIKE THIS:"
40 PRINT " AX + B = C , WHERE"
50 PRINT "A , B , AND C ARE INTEGERS."
60 PRINT:PRINT "ENTER A , B , AND C"
70 INPUT "A = ";A:INPUT "B = ";B: IN-
    PUT "C = ";C:X = (C - B)/A
80 PRINT:PRINT "X = ";X
85 PRINT "CHECK:"; A;"*";(C-B) /A;"
    + ";B;" = ";C
90 PRINT:INPUT "DO YOU WANT ANOTHER
    EQUATION?";Y$
100 IF LEFT$(Y$,1) = "Y" THEN 60
110 END
```

Problem 5   (for use after page 25)
Can you find 3 consecutive numbers whose
sum is 189? Use Guess and Check to help.

Program 5

```
10 REM GUESS AND CHECK
20 I = INT (99*RND (1) + 1):S = 3*I
30 PRINT "THE SUM OF 3
    CONSECUTIVE NUMBERS IS "S
40 INPUT "GUESS THE SMALLEST
    NUMBER"; N
50 PRINT:PRINT "CHECKING THE
    GUESS: THE 3"
60 PRINT "NUMBERS ARE:" N; N+1; N+2
70 S1 = 3*N+3 :PRINT "SUM = "; S1
80 IF S1 = S THEN PRINT "IT
    CHECKS!": GOTO 110
90 PRINT:PRINT "NOT CORRECT"
100 PRINT "GUESS AGAIN" : GOTO 40
110 END
```

Problem 6   (for use after page 73)
Bowling usually costs 90¢ a game, but if you
pay $10 to join a bowling league, it costs only
50¢ a game. How many games would you
have to bowl before you save money by join-
ing the league? Use program 6.

Program 6

```
10 REM BOWLING COSTS
20 INPUT "HOW MANY GAMES WILL YOU
    BOWL?";G
30 L = 10 + 0.5*G : N = 0.9*G
40 PRINT:PRINT "HERE ARE THE COSTS:"
50 PRINT "LEAGUE" , "NO LEAGUE"
60 PRINT L ,N : PRINT
70 PRINT "DO YOU WANT TO TRY ANOTHER
    NUMBER OF GAMES?"
80 INPUT Y$
90 IF LEFT$(Y$,1) = "Y" THEN 20
100 END
```

COMPUTER-ASSISTED PROBLEM SOLVING

Problem 7 (for use after page 173)
Can you use a unit segment and estimate the length of a given segment within 0.2 of a unit of the actual length? Computer Program 7 will help you improve your measurement estimation skills.

Program 7

```
10 REM ESTIMATING LENGTH
20 PRINT: U = INT(6*RND(1)+3)
30 FOR N = 1 TO U: PRINT "-";:NEXT
   N:PRINT" 1 UNIT"
40 PRINT
50 S = INT(78*RND(1)+1)
60 L = INT(S/U*10)/10
70 FOR N = 1 TO S:PRINT "-";:NEXT N
80 PRINT:INPUT "ESTIMATE THE LENGTH
   ";E
90 PRINT:PRINT "LENGTH",
   "ESTIMATE", "DIFF,"
100 PRINT L,E,ABS (INT ((L-
    E+.05)*10)) /10
110 PRINT:INPUT "WANT TO TRY AGAIN?
    "; Y$
120 IF LEFT$(Y$,1) = "Y" THEN 20
130 END
```

Problem 8 (for use after page 321)
An open box can be made by cutting the same size square from the corners of a rectangular piece of cardboard. Fold the cardboard on the dotted lines.

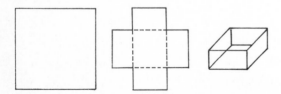

Glenn had a piece of cardboard that was square and 20 cm on each side. What size square should he cut from each corner to form a box with the greatest volume?

Program 8

```
10 REM LARGEST BOX
20 INPUT "WHAT IS THE LENGTH OF THE
   RECTANGLE?";L
30 INPUT "WHAT IS THE WIDTH OF THE
   RECTANGLE?";W
40 PRINT "WHAT IS THE LENGTH OF THE
   SIDE OF THE"
50 INPUT "SQUARE TO BE CUT FROM THE
   CORNERS?";C
55 IF C >= L/2 OR C >= W/2 THEN PRINT
   "TOO LONG!":GOTO 20
60 LET V = (L - 2*C)*(W - 2*C)*C
70 PRINT "VOLUME = ";V; "CUBIC
   CENTIMETERS"
80 PRINT: INPUT "DO YOU WANT TO TRY
   AGAIN?";Y$
90 IF LEFT$(Y$,1) = "Y" THEN 20
100 END
```

Problem 9 (for use after page 265)
Larry measured the angle to the top of a building from a point on the ground 120 feet in front of the building. The angle was 48°. What was the height of the building?

Program 9

```
10 REM BUILDING HEIGHTS
20 INPUT "ENTER DISTANCE FROM
   BUILDING";D
30 INPUT "ENTER MEASURE OF ANGLE TO
   TOP IN DEGREES";A
35 PRINT
40 R = A/57.2958 : H = D*TAN(R)
50 PRINT:PRINT
60 PRINT "HEIGHT = ";H
70 PRINT:PRINT
80 INPUT "DO YOU WANT ANOTHER
   PROBLEM?";Y$
90 IF LEFT$(Y$,1) = "Y" THEN 20
100 END
```

Problem 10 (for use after page 345)
How accurately can you predict the number of times a given number on a die will come up when the die is tossed several times? Use the computer program below to check your predictions. You can choose how many faces you want on the "die." It can be more or less than 6. Play a game with a friend to see who is better at making predictions.

Program 10
```
10 DIM D(20): REM ROLLING A DIE
20 PRINT:INPUT "HOW MANY FACES DO YOU
   WANT ON THE DIE?";X
30 FOR N = 1 TO X:D(N)=0: NEXT N
40 INPUT "HOW MANY DIE TOSSES";Y
50 INPUT "WHAT NUMBER DO YOU WANT?";Z
60 IF Z > X THEN 50
70 INPUT "PREDICT THE NUMBER OF TIMES
   YOUR NUMBER WILL COME UP?";G
80 FOR N = 1 TO Y: R = INT(X*RND(1))+1
90 LET D(R)=D(R) + 1 : NEXT N
100 PRINT:PRINT "NUMBER","FREQUENCY"
110 FOR N = 1 TO X :PRINT N, D(N):NEXT
    N
120 PRINT "YOU MISSED YOUR GUESS BY
    "; ABS(G - D(Z))
130 END
```

Problem 11 (for use after page 295)
Carol saw the same camera on sale in two different stores.

Store	Regular price	Discount rate
A	$242.00	30%
B	$195.00	12%

Which store would sell the camera for the least amount? Find the discount and sale price.

Program 11
```
10 REM DISCOUNTS AND SALE PRICE
20 INPUT "WHAT IS THE REGULAR PRICE?";P
30 INPUT "ENTER THE DISCOUNT RATE
   (USE 12.5 FOR 12 1/2 %)";R
40 PRINT:PRINT "REG. PRICE",
   "DISCOUNT", "SALE PRICE"
50 R = R/100: D = INT(P*R*100)/100: S
   = P - D
60 PRINT P, D, S
70 PRINT:INPUT "DO YOU WANT ANOTHER
   PROBLEM?"; Y$
80 IF LEFT$(Y$,1) = "Y" THEN 20
90 END
```

Problem 12 (for use after page 211)
Play a game with equations of lines. If you give the coordinates of a point on a line correctly, you win a point. If not, you lose a point.

Program 12
```
10 REM POINTS ON A LINE
20 INPUT "TYPE YOUR NAME, "; N$
30 A = INT (20 * RND (1) - 9):
   B = INT (20 * RND (1) - 9)
40 X = INT (18 * RND (1) - 9)
50 PRINT : PRINT "Y = "; A; "X + "
   ; B
60 PRINT "FIND X AND Y FOR THIS LINE
70 PRINT
80 PRINT "IF X = "; X; " THEN WHAT
   IS Y?"
90 INPUT "Y = "; Y
100 IF Y = A * X + B THEN PRINT
    "CORRECT!":T = T + 1: GOTO 120
110 PRINT "NO, Y = "; A * X + B:
    T = T-1
120 PRINT N$; "'S SCORE: "; T
130 PRINT : INPUT "TRY AGAIN? "; Y$
140 IF LEFT$ (Y$,1) = "Y" THEN 30
150 PRINT "SO LONG ": END
```

COMPUTER-ASSISTED PROBLEM SOLVING

Problem 13 (for use after page 237)
Play the game of 21 Nim with a classmate or friend. Start with 21 counters. Each player, in turn, takes 1, 2, or 3 counters. The player who is forced to take the last counter loses the game. Can you find some strategies that will help you win this game?

Program 13

```
10 REM 21 NIM GAME
20 S = 21
30 FOR N = 1 TO S: PRINT "* ";: NEXT N:
   PRINT S
40 PRINT : FOR K = 1 TO 2: GOSUB 70:
   NEXT K
50 IF S > 0 THEN 40
60 END
70 PRINT "PLAYER ";K: INPUT "CHOOSE
   1, 2, OR 3 STARS, ";C
80 IF C < 1 OR C > 3 THEN 70
90 S = S - C
100 IF S < 1 THEN PRINT "PLAYER "K"
    LOSES,": GOTO 60
110 PRINT : FOR N = 1 TO S: PRINT "* ";
120 NEXT N: PRINT S" STARS LEFT"
130 RETURN
```

Problem 14 (for use after page 409)
Jan made a model of a cylinder that had a diameter of 5 in. and a height of 8 in. She wants to make another cylinder with the same height but wants the second cylinder to have twice the volume of the first. How long should she make the diameter of the second cylinder? Use computer program 14 to help you solve this problem.

Program 14

```
10 REM VOLUME OF CYLINDERS
20 PRINT "ENTER THE DIAMETER AND
   HEIGHT OF THE CYLINDER"
30 INPUT "DIAMETER = ";D : INPUT
   "HEIGHT = ";H
40 PRINT:PRINT "DIAMETER",
   "HEIGHT", "VOLUME"
50 PRINT D,H,(D/2)↑2*3.14*H:
   PRINT
60 INPUT "DO YOU WANT TO TRY ANOTHER
   DIAMETER AND HEIGHT?";Y$
70 IF LEFT$(Y$,1) = "Y" THEN 20
80 END
```

Problem 15 (for use after page 369)
Lisa is a sales manager and often needs to estimate an average or mean of the number of units sold by her salespersons. How well can you estimate the mean of several numbers? Check your skill by using computer program 15.

Program 15

```
10 REM COMPUTING THE MEAN
20 INPUT "HOW MANY NUMBERS DO YOU
   WANT IN THE LIST?";N
30 PRINT "WHAT IS THE RANGE OF THE
   NUMBERS?"
40 INPUT "SMALLEST NUMBER = "; A
50 INPUT "LARGEST NUMBER = "; B
60 PRINT:FOR I = 1 TO N
70 K = INT((B-A)*RND(1) + A + 1)
80 PRINT,K: T = T + K:NEXT I
90 PRINT:INPUT "ESTIMATE THE MEAN";E
100 PRINT "MEAN", "EST. MEAN",
    "DIFF,"
110 PRINT T/N, E, ABS(T/N-E)
120 END
```

426

Problem 16 (for use after page 391)
A carpenter must find the length to make a brace that will be the hypotenuse of a right triangle whose legs are 4.8 ft and 6.2 ft. What is the length of the hypotenuse? Use program 16 to solve this problem and other right triangle problems.

Program 16

```
10 REM PYTHAGOREAN THEOREM
20 PRINT "DO YOU WANT TO FIND A "
30 INPUT "1, HYPOTENUSE 2, LEG ";N
40 IF N = 2 THEN GOTO 80
50 INPUT "LEG A = ";A:INPUT "LEG B =
   ";B
60 C = SQR(A*A + B*B)
70 PRINT "HYPOTENUSE = ";C: GOTO 120
80 INPUT "HYPOTENUSE = ";C
90 INPUT "LEG = ";A
100 B = SQR(C*C - A*A)
110 PRINT "OTHER LEG = ";B
120 END
```

Calculator-Assisted Problem Solving

Problem 17 (for use with page 59)
The 1983 population of Mexico was about 67.4 million. The population was increasing at a rate of 1.027 per year. Thus the 1984 population would be 1.027×67.4 million and the 1985 population would be 1.027 times the 1984 population. At this rate, what year will the population of Mexico reach 100 million?

Problem 18 (for use with page 101)
Jason was using his calculator to solve a problem. He multiplied a number by 2.4 when he should have divided the number by 2.4. The incorrect result on the calculator display was 6.048. What was the correct result?

Problem 19 (for use with page 13)
The map shows the price of an airline flight between any two of the four cities. Mr. Carlis lives in El Paso and must travel on business to Chicago, Denver, Houston and return to El Paso. If he can go to any of the 3 cities from El Paso in any order, what route should he plan so that the cost will be the least? What will be the cost of the trip?

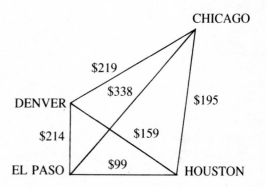

Problem 20 (for use with page 45)
Chris and Patrick played 18 holes of miniature golf. They decided to score the game in this manner. The first hole was worth 1 point, the second 2 points, the third 4 points, and so on, doubling the number of points for each successive hole. Chris won the first 17 holes but Patrick won the 18th hole. How many points did each player score? Who was the winner and by how many points did he win?

Problem 21 (for use with page 149)
Reggie threw a baseball from right field to home plate. The formula for the height (h) of the ball in feet for the time (t) in seconds since he threw it is given below.
$$h = 6 + 30t - 16t^2$$
Find the height of the ball for each of the number of seconds in the table.

t (sec)	0.2	0.5	1.0	1.5	2.0
h (ft)					

At what time was the ball at its greatest height?

CALCULATOR-ASSISTED PROBLEM SOLVING

Problem 22 (for use with page 163)
Salt may be obtained by evaporating sea water. How many kiloliters of water from the Pacific Ocean must be evaporated to get 100 kg of salt? How many kiloliters of water from the Great Salt Lake would it take to get 100 kg of salt? Use the Data Bank, page 432, for the needed data.

Problem 23 (for use with page 207)
Linda needed to make a table of values for the equation $y = 7.4x - 3.8$. She chose the values for x in the table below. What are the corresponding values for y?

x	-3	-1	0	2	5
y					

Problem 24 (for use with page 227)
Suppose you wanted to make a scale model of the sun, moon, and Earth. You have decided to make the model of the Earth a ball with a diameter of 2 cm. Since the diameter of the Earth is 12,756 km this means that 1 cm on the model represents 12,756/2 or 6,738 km. Using the same scale, what would be the diameters of the sun and moon and at what distances would the models of the Earth and moon be placed from the model of the sun? Use the data below.

Diameter (km)		Distance from Earth
Earth	12,756	
Moon	3,540	386,230
Sun	1,390,000	149,665,000

Problem 25 (for use with page 251)
Heavy rainfall and an unusually large runoff from melting snow has caused the area of Great Salt Lake to increase to approximately 1,500 square miles. What is the new area in square kilometers? Write and solve a proportion for this problem. Use the Data Bank, page 429, to find the data.

Problem 26 (for use with page 291)
The percents and type of blood of the American population is given in the table.

Blood Type	Percent of Population
O	44%
A	37%
B	13%
AB	6%

What is the approximate number of people with each type of blood in a city of 75,000 people?

Problem 27 (for use with page 319)
A number 2 size can of peaches costs 69 cents. What would be the cost of a number 10 size can of peaches if the cost per unit of volume were the same as for a number 2 can? Use the Data Bank, page 431, for the data needed for this problem.

Problem 28 (for use with page 353)
What is the mean or average height of the 5 major dams in Switzerland that are given in the Data Bank, page 431? What is the average height of the 4 U.S.S.R. dams given in the Data Bank? Which average height is greater and how much greater is it?

Problem 29 (for use with page 385)
Mindy is packing her suitcase for a trip. The inside length of her suitcase is 50 cm and the inside width is 36 cm. Can she pack a long slender object like an umbrella flat in her suitcase if the object is 60 cm long? Could she pack an umbrella flat in the suitcase if it were 63 cm long? Hint: Use the Pythagorean Theorem.

Problem 30 (for use with page 402)
During the cold winter months it cost the Wilson Family $12.00 a day to heat their house with gas. They kept the temperature of the house at 72°F all the time. In the gas company newsletter the company informed its customers that they could save 3% of their heating bill for every 1° they reduced the temperature in their houses. The Wilsons reduced their house temperature to 70°F from 6:00 A.M. to 9:00 P.M. From 9:00 P.M. to 6:00 A.M. they reduced their house temperature to 60°F. About how much should they save per day in heating costs?

DATA BANK

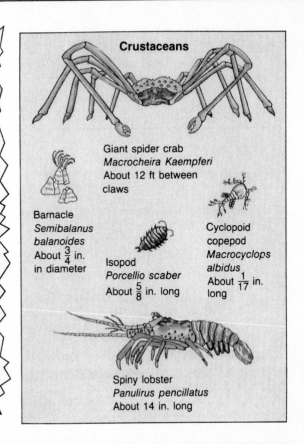

Crustaceans

Giant spider crab
Macrocheira Kaempferi
About 12 ft between claws

Barnacle
Semibalanus balanoides
About $\frac{3}{4}$ in. in diameter

Isopod
Porcellio scaber
About $\frac{5}{8}$ in. long

Cyclopoid copepod
Macrocyclops albidus
About $\frac{1}{17}$ in. long

Spiny lobster
Panulirus pencillatus
About 14 in. long

No. 359. AREAS OF SELECTED NATURAL LAKES

Lake and Location	Square miles	Square kilometers	Lake and Location	Square miles	Square kilometers
Becharof (Alaska).............	458	1,186	Mille Lacs (Minn.)	207	536
Champlain (N.Y., Vt., and Canada)	490	1,269	Naknok (Alaska)	242	627
			Okeechobee (Fla.).............	700	1,813
Flathead (Montana)	197	510	Pontchartrain* (La.)	625	1,619
Great Salt* (Utah)	1,361	3,525	Pyramid (Nev.)	168	435
Iliamma (Alaska).............	1,000	2,590	Rainy (Minn. and Canada)	345	894
Erie (Mich, N.Y., Ohio, Pa., and Canada)..........	9,940	25,745	Red Lake, Upper and Lower (Minn.)..............	451	1,168
Huron (Mich. and Canada)	23,010	59,596	St. Clair (Mich. and Canada)	460	1,191
Michigan (Ill., Ind., Mich., and Wis.)....................	22,400	58,016	Salton Sea* (Calif.)..........	375	971
Ontario (N.Y. and Canada)	7,540	19,529	Tahoe (Calif. and Nev.)	193	500
Superior (Mich., Minn., Wis., and Canada).........	31,820	82,414	Teshekpuk (Alaska)..........	315	816
Leech (Minn.)	176	456	Winnebago (Wis.).............	215	557

*Salty

429

Common Brick Sizes

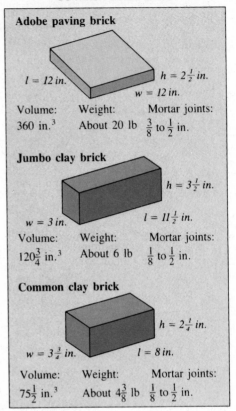

Adobe paving brick

$l = 12$ in. $h = 2\frac{1}{2}$ in. $w = 12$ in.

Volume:	Weight:	Mortar joints:
360 in.^{3}	About 20 lb	$\frac{3}{8}$ to $\frac{1}{2}$ in.

Jumbo clay brick

$h = 3\frac{1}{2}$ in. $w = 3$ in. $l = 11\frac{1}{2}$ in.

Volume:	Weight:	Mortar joints:
$120\frac{3}{4}$ in.^{3}	About 6 lb	$\frac{1}{8}$ to $\frac{1}{2}$ in.

Common clay brick

$h = 2\frac{1}{4}$ in. $w = 3\frac{3}{4}$ in. $l = 8$ in.

Volume:	Weight:	Mortar joints:
$75\frac{1}{2}$ in.^{3}	About $4\frac{3}{8}$ lb	$\frac{1}{8}$ to $\frac{1}{2}$ in.

SOUTHPORT ZOO

ANIMAL PROFILE

Zoo ID __0091247__
Band ☐ Tag ☐ Tattoo ☒ Location _South fork_
Date of birth _6-15-84_ Age: _1 year_
Sex: male ☒ female ☐ Unk. ☐

Sc Name _Felis sylvestris_
Com Name _wildcat_
House Name _"Mr. Buds"_
☐ Transfer ☒ Birth

HISTORY: Present weight : 7.9 kg
Temperature : 38.6°C
Vaccinations : Panleukopenia 7-1-83
Rhinotracheitis 7-5-83
Calici virus 8-1-83
Dietary problem at 7 weeks: average daily intake
down. — Improved at weaning

FEEDING: Birth: Embilac formula 4x day
Weaned at 8 weeks
Present diet: 0.54 kg horsemeat/chicken mash
1 x day

BEHAVIOR: Playful, stubborn
Destroys cardboard boxes, likes PVC pipe,
branches, sticks
Has tendency to bite handlers

Major Land Biomes: Winter Temperatures

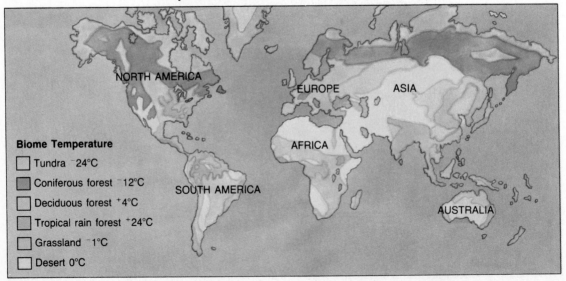

NORTH AMERICA

EUROPE ASIA

AFRICA

SOUTH AMERICA

AUSTRALIA

Biome Temperature

☐ Tundra ⁻24°C
☐ Coniferous forest ⁻12°C
☐ Deciduous forest ⁺4°C
☐ Tropical rain forest ⁺24°C
☐ Grassland ⁻1°C
☐ Desert 0°C

No. 912. World Facts — Major World Dams

Name of Dam	Year	Country	Height (Feet)
Akosombo-Main	1965	Ghana	463
Almendra	1970	Spain	662
Alpe Gera	1965	Italy	584
Beas	1975	India	435
W.A.C. Bennett	1967	Canada	600
Bhakra	1963	India	742
Bratsk	1964	U.S.S.R.	410
Castaic	1973	United States	340
Charvak	1970	U.S.S.R.	551
Chirkey	1975	U.S.S.R.	764
Chivor	1975	Colombia	778
Cougar	1964	United States	519
Dartmouth	1978	Australia	591
Don Pedro	1971	United States	585
Dworshak	1974	United States	717
Emosson	1974	Switzerland	590
Gepatsch	1965	Austria	500
Glen Canyon	1964	United States	710
Goscheneralp	1960	Switzerland	508
Grand Coulee	1942	United States	550
Grande Dixence	1962	Switzerland	935
High Aswan	1970	Egypt	364
Hoover	1936	United States	726
Hungry Horse	1953	United States	564
Daniel Johnson	1968	Canada	703
Kariba	1959	Zambia	420
Keban	1974	Turkey	679
King Paul	1965	Greece	541
Kurobegawa No. 4	1964	Japan	610
Luzzone	1963	Switzerland	682
Mangla	1967	Pakistan	380
Mauvoisin	1957	Switzerland	777
Mica	1974	Canada	794
Navajo	1963	United States	407
New Bullards Bar	1970	United States	637
New Melones	1975	United States	625
Okutadami	1961	Japan	515
Oroville	1968	United States	770
Place Moulin	1965	Italy	502
Reza Shah Kabir	1975	Iran	656
Sakuma	1956	Japan	510
Shasta	1945	United States	602
Swift	1958	United States	610
Talbingo	1971	Australia	530
Tarbela	1975	Pakistan	486
Trinity	1962	United States	537
Yellowtail	1966	United States	525
Zeya	1975	U.S.S.R.	369

Vitamin Supplements

One tablet daily provides:

VITAMIN	Amount	U.S. RDA* % RDA
Vitamin A (Acetate)	5,000 I.U.	100%
Vitamin D (Ergosterol)	400 I.U.	100%
Vitamin C (Ascorbic Acid)	60 mg.	100%
Vitamin B-1 (Thiamine Mono.)	2.5 mg.	166%
Vitamin B-2 (Riboflavin)	2.5 mg.	147%
Niacinamide	15 mg.	75%
Vitamin B-6 (Pyrodoxine HCL.)	1 mg.	50%
Vitamin B-12 (Cyanocobalamin)	1 mcg.	16%
d-Calcium Pantothenate	5 mg.	50%
Vitamin E (d-Alpha Tocopheryl)	15 I.U.	50%

*Recommended Daily Allowance

I-Beams

Weight per meter length

h Height (cm)	68.6	50.8	38.1	25.4
w Width (cm)	22.9	18.1	15.4	13.9
t Thickness (cm) of web	1.3	1.8	1.7	0.6
Weight per meter length, kg/m	60.35	60.35	43.58	15.02

Common Can Sizes

Number	Inside Diameter	Height
303	7.7 cm	11.1 cm
2	8.3 cm	11.6 cm
$2\frac{1}{2}$	9.9 cm	11.9 cm
3	10.5 cm	17.8 cm
10	15.3 cm	17.8 cm

Vice Presidents of the United States

Name and party	Term	State of birth	Name and party	Term	State of birth
1. John Adams (F)	1789-1797	Massachusetts	23. Adlai E. Stevenson (D)	1893-1897	Kentucky
2. Thomas Jefferson (DR)	1797-1801	Virginia	24. Garret A. Hobart (R)	1897-1899	New Jersey
3. Aaron Burr (DR)	1801-1805	New Jersey	25. Theodore Roosevelt (R)	1901	New York
4. George Clinton (DR)	1805-1812	New York	26. Charles W. Fairbanks (R)	1905-1909	Ohio
5. Elbridge Gerry (DR)	1813-1814	Massachusetts	27. James S. Sherman (R)	1909-1912	New York
6. Daniel D. Tompkins (DR)	1817-1825	New York	28. Thomas R. Marshall (D)	1913-1921	Indiana
7. John C. Calhoun	1825-1832	South Carolina	29. Calvin Coolidge (R)	1921-1923	Vermont
8. Martin Van Buren (D)	1833-1837	New York	30. Charles G. Dawes (R)	1925-1929	Ohio
9. Richard M. Johnson (D)	1837-1841	Kentucky	31. Charles Curtis (R)	1929-1933	Kansas
10. John Tyler (D)	1841	Virginia	32. John N. Garner (D)	1933-1941	Texas
11. George M. Dallas (D)	1845-1849	Pennsylvania	33. Henry A. Wallace (D)	1941-1945	Iowa
12. Millard Fillmore (W)	1849-1850	New York	34. Harry S. Truman (D)	1945	Missouri
13. William R. King (D)	1853	North Carolina	35. Alben W. Barkley (D)	1949-1953	Kentucky
14. John C. Breckinridge (D)	1857-1861	Kentucky	36. Richard M. Nixon (R)	1953-1961	California
15. Hannibal Hamlin (R)	1861-1865	Maine	37. Lyndon B. Johnson (D)	1961-1963	Texas
16. Andrew Johnson (U)	1865	North Carolina	38. Hubert H. Humphrey (D)	1965-1969	South Dakota
17. Schuyler Colfax (R)	1869-1873	New York	39. Spiro T. Agnew (R)	1969-1973	Maryland
18. Henry Wilson (R)	1873-1875	New Hampshire	40. Gerald R. Ford (R)	1973-1974	Nebraska
19. William A. Wheeler (R)	1877-1881	New York	41. Nelson A. Rockefeller (R)	1974-1977	Maine
20. Chester A. Arthur (R)	1881	Vermont	42. Walter F. Mondale (D)	1977-1981	Minnesota
21. Thomas A. Hendricks (D)	1885	Ohio	43. George A. Bush (R)	1981	Massachusetts
22. Levi P. Morton (R)	1889-1893	Vermont			

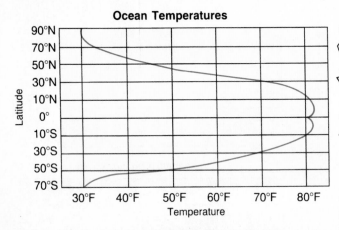

Ocean Temperatures

Salinity of Water
(grams per liter)

Dead Sea	226 g/L	Mediterranean Sea	38 g/L
Great Salt Lake	150 g/L	Red Sea	40 g/L
Pacific Ocean	35 g/L		

Insect Name	Adult Length (in.)
Flea	$\frac{1}{16}$
Dragonfly	2
Firefly	$\frac{7}{16}$
Giant water bug	$1\frac{7}{8}$
Goliath beetle	$4\frac{1}{4}$
Golden-eye lacewing	$\frac{2}{3}$
Harlequin bug	$\frac{7}{16}$
Horsefly	$\frac{7}{8}$
Seventeen-year locust	$1\frac{5}{16}$

MORE PRACTICE

Set A   For use after page 5

Write $<$ or $>$ for each ▓ .

1. 3,421 ▓ 3,862   **2.** 9,828 ▓ 9,954   **3.** 12,663 ▓ 1,661

4. 100,387 ▓ 10,387   **5.** 1,512,300 ▓ 1,512,200   **6.** 525,691 ▓ 535,691

Round to the nearest million.

7. 325,590,000   **8.** 94,092,581   **9.** 9,302,300,000   **10.** 13,051,800,100

Set B   For use after page 9

Estimate each sum or difference. Use rounding or front-end estimation.

1. 414 + 609   **2.** 78 + 58 + 43   **3.** 916 − 620   **4.** 2,875 + 3,244

5. 3,842 − 1,761   **6.** 277 + 330 + 196   **7.** 2,719 + 3,344   **8.** 671 + 889 + 213

9. 50,400 − 29,800   **10.** 8,822 + 4,297   **11.** 97 + 64 + 98   **12.** 808 + 315 + 511

Set C   For use after page 11

Add or subtract.

1.	2.	3.	4.	5.
$312 488 + 524	23,040 − 5,903	$13,400 8,926 + 32,311	$ 6,842 10,300 31,888 + 46,619	158,509 169,138 301,645 +275,833

6.	7.	8.	9.	10.
$1,209,865 3,811,413 + 5,020,991	87,310 −69,811	$3,500 − 2,909	$830,000 − 290,825	230,000 −169,743

Set D   For use after page 15

Estimate the products or quotients.

1. 88 × 97   **2.** 5 × 881   **3.** 6 × 2,473   **4.** 71 × 903   **5.** 387 × 463

6. 71,820 ÷ 862   **7.** 47,580 ÷ 62   **8.** 13,782 ÷ 24   **9.** 4,451 ÷ 49   **10.** 28,312 ÷ 742

11. 8 × 704   **12.** 6,411 ÷ 7   **13.** 28 × 53   **14.** 2,894 ÷ 33   **15.** 511 × 68

Set A   For use after page 17

Multiply.

| 1. | 806
× 61 | 2. | 323
× 66 | 3. | 857
× 58 | 4. | 307
× 21 | 5. | 5,196
× 53 |

6. 405 × 282   7. 686 × 204   8. 420 × 904   9. 838 × 677   10. 374 × 218

11. 526 × 265   12. 320 × 96   13. 88 × 358   14. 901 × 634   15. 1,283 × 94

Set B   For use after page 19

Find the quotients and remainders.

1. 62)$75.02   2. 28)3,209   3. 123)8,667   4. 71)10,882   5. 82)357

6. 53)$128.79   7. 45)19,821   8. 612)90,036   9. 242)61,232   10. 48)9,000

11. 87,615 ÷ 38   12. 41,020 ÷ 361   13. 9,924 ÷ 259   14. 14,888 ÷ 799   15. 5,937 ÷ 484

Set C   For use after page 35

Write >, < or = for each ▓.

1. 23.06 ▓ 23.0601   2. 0.383 ▓ 0.038   3. 0.300 ▓ 0.3   4. 0.7 ▓ 0.07

5. 0.90260 ▓ 0.90206   6. 200.1 ▓ 200.100   7. 7.8513 ▓ 78.513   8. 2.830 ▓ 2.816

9. 12.03 ▓ 12.3   10. 0.00003 ▓ 0.00030   11. 0.5060 ▓ 0.5160   12. 1.10 ▓ 1.01

Set D   For use after page 37

Round to underlined place.

1. 1.037_61   2. 82.3_532   3. 10.00_11   4. 0.900_49   5. 16._884

6. 12.0_740   7. 3.00_07   8. 0.0_105   9. 2_0.9850   10. 0._0975

11. 0.000_29   12. 0.9_0903   13. 49.9_098   14. 89.3_412   15. 4._582

434

Set A   For use after page 39

Add.

1. 8.0324 0.1670 + 20.9366	**2.** 0.09005 0.00301 + 0.00009	**3.** 1.825 7.634 + 9.055	**4.** 3.9007 11.3205 + 0.0136	**5.** 208.006 871.350 + 95.976

1. 8.0324   **2.** 0.09005   **3.** 1.825   **4.** 3.9007   **5.** 208.006
    0.1670   0.00301   7.634   11.3205   871.350
  + 20.9366   + 0.00009   + 9.055   + 0.0136   + 95.976

6. $23.07   **7.** $100.83   **8.** $50.00   **9.** $ 20.33   **10.** $ 81.21
     1.54   72.04   3.29   281.27   20.05
    18.90   258.00   41.83   666.92   0.03
  + 0.37   + 63.50   + 15.77   + 39.73   + 129.92

Set B   For use after page 41

Subtract.

1. 85.09   **2.** 1.3342   **3.** 121.90   **4.** 200.00   **5.** 0.58040
  − 27.85   − 0.0883   − 3.54   − 154.62   − 0.03555

6. $13.23   **7.** $54.07   **8.** $125.00   **9.** $183.66   **10.** $3,540.81
  − 6.76   − 29.99   − 88.60   − 57.91   − 876.93

Set C   For use after page 42

Estimate each sum or difference by rounding or by front-end estimation.

1. 3.82 + 7.04 + 18.23   **2.** $13.96 + $20.05 + $0.53   **3.** 1.409 − 0.699

4. 0.932 + 1.05 + 0.215   **5.** $25.35 − $11.17   **6.** 20.08 − 13.053

7. $8.47 + $3.17 + $5.53   **8.** 267.4 − 159.6   **9.** 16.75 + 21.38 + 34.09

Set D   For use after page 55

Multiply. Round amounts of money to the nearest cent.

1. 54   **2.** $3.43   **3.** 12.3   **4.** $125.40   **5.** 750
  × 3.5   × 0.12   × 480   × 0.21   × 28.6

6. 0.813 × 0.55   **7.** 61.7 × 0.112   **8.** 0.98 × 0.105
9. 0.07 × 215   **10.** 8.09 × 3.77

Set A   For use after page 57

Estimate each product.

1. 6.081×7.8 **2.** 581×0.39 **3.** 0.055×3.32 **4.** 0.71×0.005

5. 7.63×38.1 **6.** 0.028×35 **7.** 6.96×0.309 **8.** 2.57×3.412

9. 18×91.73 **10.** 0.716×0.005 **11.** 43.05×433 **12.** 0.899×99.3

Set B   For use after page 61

Find the quotients to the nearest hundredth.

1. $19\overline{)71.3}$ **2.** $22\overline{)51.6}$ **3.** $8\overline{)420.3}$ **4.** $53\overline{)312.1}$ **5.** $67\overline{)493.6}$

6. $26\overline{)1,759}$ **7.** $361\overline{)83.5}$ **8.** $73\overline{)4,052}$ **9.** $13\overline{)108.4}$ **10.** $94\overline{)1,246}$

11. $9\overline{)37.64}$ **12.** $69\overline{)54.88}$ **13.** $38\overline{)99.154}$ **14.** $50\overline{)318.66}$ **15.** $73\overline{)158.45}$

Set C   For use after page 63

Find the quotients to the nearest hundredth.

1. $89 \div 5.3$ **2.** $142.5 \div 0.88$ **3.** $3.44 \div 0.44$ **4.** $567 \div 23$ **5.** $2.75 \div 0$

6. $3.8\overline{)0.297}$ **7.** $5.2\overline{)8.001}$ **8.** $0.7\overline{)8.304}$ **9.** $0.001\overline{)0.385}$ **10.** $9.15 \div 3$

11. $16 \div 0.89$ **12.** $400 \div 31$ **13.** $5 \div 0.051$ **14.** $7 \div 0.017$ **15.** $0.88 \div 0$

Set D   For use after page 65

Estimate the quotients. Use compatible numbers or rounding.

1. $44\overline{)89.35}$ **2.** $8.4\overline{)35.32}$ **3.** $0.9\overline{)0.374}$ **4.** $0.093\overline{)0.827}$ **5.** $61\overline{)493.6}$

6. $0.336\overline{)2.706}$ **7.** $0.513\overline{)41.21}$ **8.** $6.9\overline{)41.09}$ **9.** $29.3\overline{)62.77}$ **10.** $0.71\overline{)14.3}$

11. $4.93\overline{)355.01}$ **12.** $0.33\overline{)28.08}$ **13.** $1.8\overline{)15.95}$ **14.** $2.1\overline{)505.1}$ **15.** $60.7\overline{)253.1}$

Set A   For use after page 69

Write the standard numeral.

1. 12^2
2. 6^6
3. 127^0
4. 1^{22}
5. 17^2

6. 5^4
7. $(1.4)^3$
8. 10^5
9. $(53.1)^1$
10. $1,000^2$

Set B   For use after page 71

Write the standard numeral.

1. 1.8×10^3
2. 5.3×10^4
3. 2.9×10^4
4. 6.6×10^7
5. 6.1×10^5

6. 9.9×10^{12}
7. 8.1×10^2
8. 3.02×10^4
9. 1.8×10^6
10. 3.2×10^9

Write in scientific notation.

11. 3,600,000,000 **12.** 250,000 **13.** 28,600,000 **14.** 6,000 **15.** 50,000,000,000

16. 8,600 **17.** 1,500,000 **18.** 85,100,000,000 **19.** 300 **20.** 16,000,000,000,000

Set C   For use after page 79

Write the prime factorization of each number.

1. 20 **2.** 36 **3.** 32 **4.** 40 **5.** 25 **6.** 100 **7.** 54

8. 125 **9.** 210 **10.** 39 **11.** 90 **12.** 770 **13.** 64 **14.** 66

Set D   For use after page 81

Find the GCF of each pair of numbers.

1. 21, 15 **2.** 40, 48 **3.** 52, 39 **4.** 9, 10 **5.** 80, 32

6. 22, 24 **7.** 36, 64 **8.** 12, 28 **9.** 100, 150 **10.** 125, 75

Set A   For use after page 83

Write the missing numerator or denominator.

1. $\frac{1}{3} = \frac{4}{\text{▥}}$ 2. $\frac{3}{2} = \frac{\text{▥}}{16}$ 3. $\frac{5}{3} = \frac{35}{\text{▥}}$ 4. $\frac{4}{9} = \frac{\text{▥}}{45}$ 5. $\frac{5}{8} = \frac{\text{▥}}{48}$

6. $\frac{12}{17} = \frac{36}{\text{▥}}$ 7. $\frac{1}{9} = \frac{10}{\text{▥}}$ 8. $\frac{3}{7} = \frac{\text{▥}}{28}$ 9. $\frac{9}{16} = \frac{63}{\text{▥}}$ 10. $\frac{10}{3} = \frac{\text{▥}}{45}$

Set B   For use after page 85

Write each fraction in lowest terms.

1. $\frac{20}{35}$ 2. $\frac{16}{20}$ 3. $\frac{32}{30}$ 4. $\frac{8}{18}$ 5. $\frac{10}{25}$ 6. $\frac{14}{20}$ 7. $\frac{30}{45}$

8. $\frac{48}{50}$ 9. $\frac{60}{72}$ 10. $\frac{80}{45}$ 11. $\frac{28}{42}$ 12. $\frac{52}{26}$ 13. $\frac{30}{100}$ 14. $\frac{40}{60}$

Set C   For use after page 87

Write each mixed number as an improper fraction.

1. $3\frac{1}{3}$ 2. $5\frac{7}{9}$ 3. $1\frac{10}{11}$ 4. $6\frac{3}{8}$ 5. $9\frac{6}{7}$ 6. $2\frac{7}{8}$ 7. $9\frac{1}{4}$

8. $2\frac{7}{12}$ 9. $3\frac{4}{7}$ 10. $5\frac{4}{5}$ 11. $3\frac{7}{9}$ 12. $21\frac{8}{9}$ 13. $1\frac{9}{10}$ 14. $3\frac{1}{7}$

Write each improper fraction as mixed number or a whole number.

15. $\frac{13}{2}$ 16. $\frac{11}{3}$ 17. $\frac{22}{9}$ 18. $\frac{31}{14}$ 19. $\frac{10}{3}$ 20. $\frac{12}{5}$ 21. $\frac{100}{3}$

22. $\frac{80}{16}$ 23. $\frac{28}{5}$ 24. $\frac{53}{13}$ 25. $\frac{92}{13}$ 26. $\frac{241}{18}$ 27. $\frac{500}{8}$ 28. $\frac{132}{11}$

Set D   For use after page 89

Find the LCM of each group of numbers.

1. 3, 13   2. 10, 14   3. 7, 8   4. 3, 9   5. 15, 20

6. 6, 11   7. 2, 21   8. 5, 13   9. 8, 10   10. 5, 6

Set A   For use after page 91

Compare the fractions or mixed numbers. Write $>$ or $<$ for each ⬤.

1. $\frac{3}{4}$ ⬤ $\frac{4}{5}$

2. $\frac{4}{7}$ ⬤ $\frac{5}{8}$

3. $\frac{2}{3}$ ⬤ $\frac{5}{7}$

4. $11\frac{2}{13}$ ⬤ $10\frac{12}{13}$

5. $\frac{5}{12}$ ⬤ $\frac{6}{15}$

6. $6\frac{1}{7}$ ⬤ $5\frac{6}{7}$

7. $\frac{10}{7}$ ⬤ $\frac{12}{10}$

8. $4\frac{4}{9}$ ⬤ $4\frac{7}{10}$

Set B   For use after page 93

Find the sums.

1. $\frac{3}{8} + \frac{7}{10}$

2. $\frac{3}{5} + \frac{14}{15}$

3. $\frac{1}{4} + \frac{4}{5}$

4. $\frac{8}{9} + \frac{5}{6}$

5. $\frac{7}{12} + \frac{6}{15}$

6. $\begin{array}{r} 5\frac{3}{8} \\ + 11\frac{5}{6} \\ \hline \end{array}$

7. $\begin{array}{r} 16\frac{2}{3} \\ + 23\frac{3}{4} \\ \hline \end{array}$

8. $\begin{array}{r} 41\frac{11}{12} \\ + 19\frac{7}{8} \\ \hline \end{array}$

9. $\begin{array}{r} 20\frac{9}{10} \\ + 59\frac{3}{7} \\ \hline \end{array}$

10. $\begin{array}{r} 101\frac{5}{16} \\ + 47\frac{5}{6} \\ \hline \end{array}$

Set C   For use after page 95

Find the differences.

1. $\frac{5}{6} - \frac{2}{3}$

2. $\frac{11}{12} - \frac{2}{3}$

3. $\frac{13}{16} - \frac{1}{6}$

4. $\frac{5}{7} - \frac{13}{21}$

5. $\frac{7}{10} - \frac{2}{3}$

6. $\begin{array}{r} 10\frac{3}{4} \\ - 9\frac{1}{2} \\ \hline \end{array}$

7. $\begin{array}{r} 31\frac{5}{6} \\ - 16\frac{1}{18} \\ \hline \end{array}$

8. $\begin{array}{r} 25\frac{1}{3} \\ - 17\frac{1}{4} \\ \hline \end{array}$

9. $\begin{array}{r} 5\frac{9}{10} \\ - \frac{5}{6} \\ \hline \end{array}$

10. $\begin{array}{r} 24\frac{4}{5} \\ - 24\frac{5}{8} \\ \hline \end{array}$

Set D   For use after page 97

Subtract.

1. $\begin{array}{r} 10\frac{1}{3} \\ - 5\frac{5}{6} \\ \hline \end{array}$

2. $\begin{array}{r} 14\frac{2}{5} \\ - 11\frac{7}{10} \\ \hline \end{array}$

3. $\begin{array}{r} 7\frac{5}{12} \\ - \frac{3}{4} \\ \hline \end{array}$

4. $\begin{array}{r} 20\frac{2}{9} \\ - 13\frac{5}{6} \\ \hline \end{array}$

5. $\begin{array}{r} 11 \\ - 5\frac{7}{8} \\ \hline \end{array}$

6. $12 - 7\frac{2}{3}$

7. $6\frac{1}{2} - 3\frac{3}{4}$

8. $9\frac{1}{3} - 4\frac{2}{3}$

9. $1\frac{1}{5} - \frac{1}{2}$

10. $8\frac{2}{3} - 4\frac{5}{6}$

Set A   For use after page 111

Multiply. Use the shortcut when possible.

1. $\frac{3}{10} \times \frac{5}{7}$ **2.** $\frac{2}{3} \times \frac{3}{16}$ **3.** $\frac{7}{8} \times \frac{3}{5}$ **4.** $\frac{3}{16} \times \frac{16}{19}$ **5.** $\frac{1}{2} \times \frac{2}{5}$

6. $\frac{8}{9} \times \frac{5}{12}$ **7.** $\frac{1}{2} \times \frac{3}{5}$ **8.** $\frac{13}{20} \times \frac{5}{7}$ **9.** $\frac{4}{9} \times \frac{1}{12}$ **10.** $\frac{6}{10} \times \frac{5}{3}$

11. $\frac{3}{11} \times \frac{1}{7}$ **12.** $\frac{7}{16} \times \frac{5}{8}$ **13.** $\frac{14}{15} \times \frac{25}{28}$ **14.** $\frac{2}{25} \times \frac{3}{16}$ **15.** $\frac{7}{16} \times \frac{4}{7}$

Set B   For use after page 113

1. $1\frac{1}{3} \times 1\frac{1}{4}$ **2.** $1\frac{4}{5} \times 10$ **3.** $2\frac{7}{10} \times 2\frac{2}{9}$ **4.** $\frac{5}{7} \times 4\frac{2}{3}$ **5.** $\frac{1}{2} \times 4\frac{1}{2}$

6. $3\frac{1}{5} \times 1\frac{2}{3}$ **7.** $2\frac{5}{8} \times \frac{4}{5}$ **8.** $6 \times 7\frac{5}{6}$ **9.** $1\frac{1}{2} \times 5\frac{2}{3}$ **10.** $2\frac{2}{3} \times 6$

11. $4\frac{8}{9} \times \frac{9}{11}$ **12.** $1\frac{8}{9} \times \frac{6}{11}$ **13.** $3\frac{5}{7} \times 1\frac{1}{4}$ **14.** $6\frac{6}{7} \times 2\frac{1}{24}$ **15.** $100 \times 1\frac{3}{4}$

Set C   For use after page 114

Estimate each product.

1. $\frac{1}{4} \times \$37.11$ **2.** $\frac{1}{5} \times 38.21$ **3.** $\frac{3}{5}$ of $\$32$ **4.** $\frac{1}{3} \times 18.4$ **5.** $\frac{1}{6} \times \$13.11$

6. $\frac{5}{7} \times \$54.70$ **7.** $\frac{3}{8} \times 43$ **8.** $\frac{2}{3} \times 35.3$ **9.** $\frac{2}{3} \times 5.85$ **10.** $\frac{1}{8} \times \$33.25$

11. $\frac{1}{2} \times 97.2$ **12.** $\frac{3}{10} \times 127.5$ **13.** $\frac{3}{4}$ of $\$62.28$ **14.** $\frac{1}{2} \times \$11.79$ **15.** $\frac{9}{10} \times 896$

Set D   For use after page 115

Write the reciprocal of each number.

1. $\frac{1}{16}$ **2.** $3\frac{4}{5}$ **3.** $5\frac{1}{6}$ **4.** $1\frac{5}{12}$ **5.** $\frac{7}{9}$ **6.** $\frac{5}{3}$ **7.** $1\frac{3}{4}$

8. 20 **9.** $2\frac{7}{8}$ **10.** $1\frac{1}{3}$ **11.** $\frac{9}{13}$ **12.** $5\frac{1}{7}$ **13.** $\frac{3}{10}$ **14.** $1\frac{1}{10}$

Set A   For use after page 117

Find the quotients.

1. $\frac{3}{7} \div \frac{6}{7}$ **2.** $\frac{4}{5} \div \frac{1}{5}$ **3.** $\frac{7}{8} \div \frac{13}{12}$ **4.** $\frac{3}{14} \div \frac{5}{14}$ **5.** $\frac{4}{9} \div \frac{2}{3}$

6. $\frac{3}{18} \div \frac{9}{8}$ **7.** $\frac{9}{11} \div \frac{9}{11}$ **8.** $\frac{5}{16} \div \frac{5}{6}$ **9.** $\frac{1}{3} \div \frac{2}{5}$ **10.** $\frac{3}{5} \div \frac{1}{10}$

Set B   For use after page 119

Divide.

1. $1\frac{1}{4} \div 1\frac{1}{8}$ **2.** $2\frac{3}{5} \div 2\frac{3}{5}$ **3.** $8\frac{2}{3} \div 1\frac{5}{6}$ **4.** $2 \div 1\frac{5}{9}$ **5.** $1 \div 2\frac{1}{2}$

6. $3\frac{7}{10} \div 1\frac{2}{3}$ **7.** $2\frac{1}{2} \div 8\frac{1}{4}$ **8.** $3\frac{1}{3} \div 4$ **9.** $6\frac{3}{4} \div 1\frac{1}{6}$ **10.** $12 \div 1\frac{1}{4}$

11. $2\frac{1}{3} \div 1\frac{1}{9}$ **12.** $5\frac{2}{5} \div 1\frac{3}{10}$ **13.** $2\frac{1}{8} \div 1\frac{7}{10}$ **14.** $3\frac{3}{7} \div 3\frac{2}{7}$ **15.** $8\frac{2}{3} \div 26$

Set C   For use after page 123

Write a decimal for each fraction. Use a bar to show repeating decimals.

1. $\frac{3}{4}$ **2.** $\frac{3}{8}$ **3.** $\frac{1}{5}$ **4.** $\frac{2}{3}$ **5.** $\frac{5}{6}$ **6.** $\frac{11}{20}$ **7.** $\frac{7}{25}$

8. $\frac{9}{10}$ **9.** $\frac{4}{15}$ **10.** $\frac{2}{11}$ **11.** $\frac{12}{60}$ **12.** $\frac{15}{16}$ **13.** $\frac{4}{9}$ **14.** $\frac{1}{7}$

Set D   For use after page 133

Copy and complete each table by evaluating the expressions.

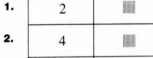

	x	$\frac{5x}{4}$
1.	2	
2.	4	
3.	20	

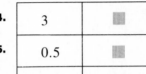

	y	$(y \times 2) + 11$
4.	3	
5.	0.5	
6.	16	

	a	$\frac{8}{a-3}$
7.	11	
8.	8	
9.	7	

Set A   For use after page 137

Solve the equations.

1. $30 + y = 55$ **2.** $b - 16 = 100$ **3.** $5 + s = 71$ **4.** $f + 27 = 49$

5. $103 + j = 150$ **6.** $c - 42 = 120$ **7.** $p + \frac{5}{8} = \frac{15}{16}$ **8.** $w - 2.8 = 5.3$

9. $d + 19 = 83$ **10.** $\frac{3}{4} + m = 2\frac{1}{2}$ **11.** $t - \frac{3}{5} = \frac{17}{20}$ **12.** $9.4 + r = 10.5$

Set B   For use after page 143

Solve the equations.

1. $\frac{d}{12} = 9$ **2.** $5p = 75$ **3.** $\frac{x}{5} = 16$ **4.** $16f = 64$

5. $17z = 51$ **6.** $10h = 10$ **7.** $12j = 96$ **8.** $\frac{m}{8} = 13$

9. $13w = 39$ **10.** $\frac{y}{3.1} = 2$ **11.** $4.2n = 0.84$ **12.** $\frac{b}{20} = 31$

Set C   For use after page 145

Solve the equations.

1. $\frac{m}{5} + 3 = 9$ **2.** $4b - 16 = 4$ **3.** $\frac{y}{7} - 11 = 2$

4. $12w + 20 = 80$ **5.** $15r - 21 = 54$ **6.** $6n - 23 = 37$

7. $\frac{c}{14} + 5 = 25$ **8.** $\frac{f}{10} - 13 = 24$ **9.** $26e + 5.5 = 83.5$

10. $80i - 12 = 148$ **11.** $\frac{s}{3} + 3.5 = 5.3$ **12.** $4p - \frac{3}{4} = \frac{1}{4}$

Set D   For use after page 157

Write the missing numbers.

1. $0.1 \text{ cm} = \blacksquare \text{ mm}$ **2.** $100 \text{ dam} = \blacksquare \text{ km}$ **3.** $1 \text{ m} = \blacksquare \text{ hm}$ **4.** $100 \text{ mm} = \blacksquare \text{ m}$

5. $10 \text{ dm} = \blacksquare \text{ mm}$ **6.** $10 \text{ dam} = \blacksquare \text{ m}$ **7.** $100 \text{ mm} = \blacksquare \text{ cm}$ **8.** $0.1 \text{ m} = \blacksquare \text{ cm}$

9. $0.01 \text{ km} = \blacksquare \text{ m}$ **10.** $100 \text{ dm} = \blacksquare \text{ cm}$ **11.** $0.01 \text{ m} = \blacksquare \text{ mm}$ **12.** $10 \text{ km} = \blacksquare \text{ m}$

Set A   For use after page 159

Write the missing numbers.

1. 2.5 dm = ▨ cm   **2.** 1.250 km = ▨ m   **3.** 52 cm = ▨ m

4. 0.83 km = ▨ m   **5.** 13.2 dm = ▨ m   **6.** 3,425 m = ▨ km

7. 0.31 m = ▨ dm   **8.** 0.502 dm = ▨ mm   **9.** 0.005 m = ▨ mm

10. 0.25 km = ▨ m   **11.** 350 m = ▨ dm   **12.** 15.8 m = ▨ cm

Set B   For use after page 160

Write the missing numbers.

1. 2 kL = ▨ L   **2.** 300 mL = ▨ L   **3.** 0.33 L = ▨ mL

4. 1,250 L = ▨ kL   **5.** 1.5 L = ▨ mL   **6.** 53 hL = ▨ kL

7. 800 L = ▨ kL   **8.** 25 L = ▨ dL   **9.** 10.3 L = ▨ mL

10. 8.5 kL = ▨ L   **11.** 25 mL = ▨ L   **12.** 90.6 L = ▨ kL

Set C   For use after page 162

Write the missing numbers.

1. 2 g = ▨ mg   **2.** 100 mg = ▨ g   **3.** 8 t = ▨ kg

4. 4,300 g = ▨ kg   **5.** 7.5 kg = ▨ g   **6.** 5,020 kg = ▨ t

7. 0.34 g = ▨ mg   **8.** 450 kg = ▨ t   **9.** 0.9 kg = ▨ g

10. 25 g = ▨ kg   **11.** 0.18 t = ▨ kg   **12.** 910 mg = ▨ g

Set D   For use after page 164

Write the Kelvin temperature.

1. 25°C   **2.** 0°C   **3.** 64°C   **4.** 81°C

5. ⁻14°C   **6.** 13°C   **7.** 240°C   **8.** 10°C

Set A   For use after page 165

Write the missing numbers.

1. 3 h = ▓ min

2. 15 min = ▓ s

3. 5 wk = ▓ d

4. 210 min = ▓ h

5. 72 h = ▓ d

6. 3 s = ▓ ms

7. 165 d = ▓ wk ▓ d

8. 3 min 25 s = ▓ s

9. 6.5 d = ▓ h

10. 750 s = ▓ min ▓ s

11. 580 ms = ▓ s

12. 5.8 h = ▓ min

Set B   For use after page 169

Write the GPE of each measurement.

1. 2 cm

2. 25 m

3. 23 mm

4. 3.2 dm

5. 4.8 cm

6. 57.1 m

7. 0.3 mm

8. 5.2 km

9. 1.235 mm

10. 16.51 cm

11. 21 m

12. 0.25 cm

Set C   For use after page 179

Write the opposite of each number.

1. 13

2. $^-18$

3. 99

4. $^-500$

5. $\frac{1}{3}$

6. $^-2$

7. 12

8. $^-1.1$

9. $^-\frac{3}{5}$

10. $^-34$

11. 103.2

12. $^-\frac{9}{8}$

13. $^-1,005$

14. 3.8

15. 1

Find the missing numbers. Use the opposites property.

16. $8 + {}^-8 = $ ▓

17. $^-3 + $ ▓ $ = 0$

18. $\frac{^-3}{10} + $ ▓ $ = 0$

19. $15 + $ ▓ $ = 0$

20. ▓ $ + {}^-\frac{1}{2} = 0$

21. $^-6 + 6 = $ ▓

22. $^-0.8 + 0.8 = $ ▓

23. $\frac{8}{15} + $ ▓ $ = 0$

24. ▓ $ + 99 = 0$

Set A For use after page 181

Find the sums.

1. $^-2 + ^-2$ 2. $^-2 + 3$ 3. $^-10 + 8$ 4. $^-1 + 7$

5. $^-11 + ^-1$ 6. $^-5 + 1$ 7. $^-5 + ^-8$ 8. $2 + 11$

9. $^-3 + 10$ 10. $6 + ^-4$ 11. $^-9 + 3$ 12. $^-13 + ^-6$

13. $^-12 + 7$ 14. $^-9 + ^-9$ 15. $16 + ^-7$ 16. $^-20 + ^-10$

Set B For use after page 183

Subtract.

1. $5 - ^-4$ 2. $^-8 - 3$ 3. $11 - ^-5$ 4. $^-5 - 6$

5. $^-9 - ^-9$ 6. $6 - ^-5$ 7. $8 - 11$ 8. $^-9 - ^-13$

9. $^-33 - 12$ 10. $10 - ^-8$ 11. $^-20 - 10$ 12. $^-18 - ^-20$

13. $10 - 15$ 14. $^-4 - 9$ 15. $17 - ^-3$ 16. $^-12 - ^-9$

Set C For use after page 187

Multiply.

1. $5 \cdot ^-3$ 2. $^-4 \cdot ^-9$ 3. $7 \cdot 3$ 4. $^-10 \cdot 8$

5. $9 \cdot ^-1$ 6. $0 \cdot ^-5$ 7. $^-6 \cdot ^-13$ 8. $5 \cdot 4$

9. $^-7 \cdot 8$ 10. $^-4 \cdot ^-15$ 11. $^-8 \cdot 6$ 12. $^-12 \cdot ^-20$

13. $^-9 \cdot ^-7$ 14. $12 \cdot ^-5$ 15. $^-1 \cdot ^-13$ 16. $7 \cdot ^-30$

Set D For use after page 189

Find the quotients.

1. $\dfrac{12}{^-3}$ 2. $\dfrac{^-15}{^-3}$ 3. $\dfrac{45}{9}$ 4. $\dfrac{^-24}{8}$

5. $\dfrac{^-20}{2}$ 6. $\dfrac{50}{^-5}$ 7. $\dfrac{^-52}{^-4}$ 8. $\dfrac{64}{8}$

9. $\dfrac{56}{^-7}$ 10. $\dfrac{12}{^-1}$ 11. $\dfrac{^-60}{12}$ 12. $\dfrac{^-80}{^-16}$

13. $\dfrac{^-27}{^-9}$ 14. $\dfrac{28}{^-4}$ 15. $\dfrac{^-25}{5}$ 16. $\dfrac{^-18}{^-6}$

Set A   For use after page 191

Evaluate each expression.
Let $d = 3$, $e = {}^-5$, and $f = {}^-6$.

1. $e - 6$

2. $\dfrac{{}^-12}{f}$

3. $4d$

4. $2e + 8$

5. $\dfrac{18}{2d}$

6. $10 - f$

7. $\dfrac{3e}{d}$

8. $7(e + 3)$

9. $\dfrac{f}{d}$

10. $\dfrac{{}^-6f}{d}$

11. $\dfrac{44}{f + e}$

12. $\dfrac{f}{e + d}$

Set B   For use after page 193

Solve each equation.

1. $c + 11 = 3$

2. $r - {}^-5 = {}^-12$

3. $x + {}^-3 = 10$

4. $w - 18 = {}^-17$

5. $b + 1 = 22$

6. $m + 15 = 10$

7. $\dfrac{e}{3} = {}^-5$

8. ${}^-8b = 24$

9. $10w = {}^-50$

10. $\dfrac{f}{15} = 3$

11. $\dfrac{s}{5} = {}^-12$

12. $6c = 48$

Set C   For use after page 197

Find the sums.

1. $\dfrac{5}{9} + \dfrac{{}^-1}{9}$

2. $\dfrac{{}^-3}{4} + \dfrac{1}{4}$

3. $\dfrac{{}^-1}{10} + \dfrac{{}^-3}{10}$

4. $\dfrac{1}{6} + \dfrac{{}^-5}{6}$

5. $\dfrac{1}{2} + \dfrac{{}^-1}{6}$

6. $\dfrac{{}^-2}{3} + \dfrac{{}^-1}{2}$

7. $0.9 + {}^-0.3$

8. ${}^-2.8 + 1.5$

Find the differences.

9. $\dfrac{3}{8} - \dfrac{7}{8}$

10. $\dfrac{{}^-3}{10} - \dfrac{4}{10}$

11. $\dfrac{2}{3} - \dfrac{{}^-1}{3}$

12. $\dfrac{{}^-1}{4} - \dfrac{1}{4}$

13. $\dfrac{1}{16} - \dfrac{1}{4}$

14. $\dfrac{5}{6} - \dfrac{{}^-1}{3}$

15. $\dfrac{1}{2} - \dfrac{5}{8}$

16. $1.5 - 2.7$

Set D   For use after page 199

Find the products.

1. $\dfrac{2}{5} \cdot \dfrac{{}^-5}{6}$

2. $\dfrac{{}^-1}{2} \cdot \dfrac{4}{5}$

3. $\dfrac{{}^-3}{10} \cdot \dfrac{{}^-5}{3}$

4. $\dfrac{1}{4} \cdot {}^-12 \; {}^-3$

5. $\dfrac{{}^-6}{7} \cdot \dfrac{14}{15}$

6. $\dfrac{{}^-2}{3} \cdot \dfrac{{}^-9}{10}$

7. ${}^-0.1 \cdot {}^-8$

8. $3.2 \cdot {}^-0.5$

Find the quotients.

9. $\dfrac{1}{2} \div \dfrac{{}^-4}{5}$

10. $\dfrac{{}^-7}{8} \div \dfrac{{}^-1}{4}$

11. $\dfrac{9}{10} \div {}^-3$

12. $\dfrac{{}^-5}{8} \div \dfrac{{}^-5}{4}$

13. $3 \div \dfrac{{}^-1}{4}$

14. $\dfrac{{}^-9}{10} \div \dfrac{{}^-6}{5}$

15. ${}^-6.8 \div 4$

16. ${}^-0.8 \div {}^-0.2$

Set A   For use after page 201

Write < or > for each ⬤.

1. $2 \; ⬤ \; {}^-5$ **2.** ${}^-11 \; ⬤ \; {}^-12$ **3.** $20 \; ⬤ \; \dot{2}$ **4.** ${}^-16 \; ⬤ \; 16$

5. ${}^-45 \; ⬤ \; 0$ **6.** ${}^-5 \; ⬤ \; {}^-10$ **7.** ${}^-11 \; ⬤ \; 8$ **8.** $3 \; ⬤ \; {}^-5$

9. $\dfrac{{}^-3}{8} \; ⬤ \; \dfrac{{}^-7}{8}$ **10.** $\dfrac{3}{4} \; ⬤ \; \dfrac{{}^-1}{3}$ **11.** $\dfrac{{}^-9}{10} \; ⬤ \; \dfrac{{}^-1}{2}$ **12.** $\dfrac{{}^-3}{4} \; ⬤ \; \dfrac{{}^-1}{2}$

Find the absolute values.

1. $|9|$ **2.** $|{}^-11|$ **3.** $|{}^-123|$ **4.** $|50|$ **5.** $\left|\dfrac{{}^-3}{8}\right|$

6. $|{}^-2.7|$ **7.** $|6 - 7|$ **8.** $|{}^-8 + 10|$ **9.** $|9 + {}^-6|$ **10.** $|4 + 2|$

11. $|10 - 13|$ **12.** $|{}^-3 + {}^-16|$ **13.** $|11 + {}^-12|$ **14.** $\left|\dfrac{3}{8} - \dfrac{5}{8}\right|$ **15.** $\left|\dfrac{{}^-3}{10} + \dfrac{7}{10}\right|$

Set B   For use after page 203

Solve.

1. $8a - 5 = 27$ **2.** $\dfrac{h}{5} + {}^-10 = {}^-12$ **3.** $18i - 3 = {}^-39 \quad i =$

4. $-\dfrac{y}{5} - {}^-11 = {}^-8$ **5.** $12p + {}^-3 = {}^-39$ **6.** $-\dfrac{j}{7} - 15 = 2 \quad j =$

7. ${}^-12d + 4 = 28$ **8.** $\dfrac{n}{2} - 1 = {}^-2$ **9.** ${}^-16w + 2 = 82$

10. $\dfrac{M}{2} + \dfrac{{}^-9}{10} = 0$ **11.** $2h + {}^-1\dfrac{1}{2} = 2\dfrac{1}{2}$ **12.** $\dfrac{F}{4} + 0.8 = 1.6$

Set C   For use after page 205

Copy and complete each table. Then graph each equation.

1. $y = x + 6$

x	${}^-3$	${}^-2$	${}^-1$	0	1	2	3	4
y								

2. $y = 3x + 2$

x	${}^-4$	${}^-3$	${}^-2$	${}^-1$	0	1	2	3
y								

Set A   For use after page 209

Write in scientific notation.

1. 0.0038   **2.** 0.00015   **3.** 0.000205   **4.** 0.0000137

Write the decimals.

5. 8.5×10^{-4} **6.** 6.22×10^{-3} **7.** 4×10^{-4} **8.** 1.11×10^{-7}

Set B   For use after page 219

Give the measure of a complement to each given angle.

1.
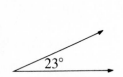
23°

2.
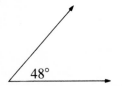
48°

3.
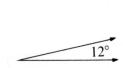
12°

4. $m\angle O = 35°$ **5.** $m\angle F = 7°$ **6.** $m\angle C = 87°$

Give the measure of a supplement to each given angle.

7.
75°

8.
104°

9.
160°

10. $m\angle P = 45°$ **11.** $m\angle H = 90°$ **12.** $m\angle C = 143°$

Set C   For use after page 243

Write = or ≠ for each 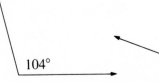. Use cross products to decide.

1. $\frac{5}{6}$ ⬤ $\frac{15}{18}$ **2.** $\frac{10}{3}$ ⬤ $\frac{5}{2}$ **3.** $\frac{18}{22}$ ⬤ $\frac{26}{33}$ **4.** $\frac{36}{32}$ ⬤ $\frac{9}{8}$

5. $\frac{4}{5}$ ⬤ $\frac{12}{15}$ **6.** $\frac{8}{6}$ ⬤ $\frac{10}{4}$ **7.** $\frac{15}{21}$ ⬤ $\frac{5}{7}$ **8.** $\frac{10}{16}$ ⬤ $\frac{15}{24}$

9. $\frac{12}{28}$ ⬤ $\frac{8}{20}$ **10.** $\frac{16}{28}$ ⬤ $\frac{12}{21}$ **11.** $\frac{12}{32}$ ⬤ $\frac{16}{36}$ **12.** $\frac{6}{14}$ ⬤ $\frac{15}{35}$

Set A   For use after page 244

Simplify each rate.

1. $\dfrac{25 \text{ m}}{5 \text{ s}}$
2. $\dfrac{\$7.50}{5 \text{ h}}$
3. $\dfrac{72 \text{ km}}{6 \text{ min}}$
4. $\dfrac{72 \text{ h}}{3 \text{ revolutions}}$
5. $\dfrac{100 \text{ ft}}{20 \text{ s}}$

Set B   For use after page 249

Solve each proportion.

1. $\dfrac{4}{5} = \dfrac{8}{w}$
2. $\dfrac{1}{7} = \dfrac{h}{21}$
3. $\dfrac{3}{10} = \dfrac{F}{50}$
4. $\dfrac{7}{5} = \dfrac{28}{M}$
5. $\dfrac{6}{15} = \dfrac{30}{n}$

6. $\dfrac{2}{5} = \dfrac{14}{s}$
7. $\dfrac{3}{8} = \dfrac{b}{40}$
8. $\dfrac{7}{2} = \dfrac{35}{p}$
9. $\dfrac{27}{21} = \dfrac{18}{n}$
10. $\dfrac{5}{9} = \dfrac{x}{36}$

Set C   For use after page 273

Write each percent as a decimal.

1. 20%   **2.** 2%   **3.** 32%   **4.** 1.8%   **5.** 13%   **6.** 85%   **7.** 2.5%

8. 6.7%   **9.** 30%   **10.** 128%   **11.** 45%   **12.** 26.5%   **13.** 90%   **14.** 200%

Write each decimal as a percent.

15. 0.11   **16.** 0.50   **17.** 0.41   **18.** 0.01   **19.** 0.012   **20.** 1.50   **21.** 0.06

22. 1.00   **23.** 0.66   **24.** 1.85   **25.** 0.321   **26.** 0.75   **27.** 0.05   **28.** 0.065

Set D   For use after page 275

Write the percent for each fraction.

1. $\dfrac{1}{10}$
2. $\dfrac{7}{20}$
3. $\dfrac{21}{100}$
4. $\dfrac{7}{50}$
5. $\dfrac{4}{5}$
6. $\dfrac{11}{25}$
7. $\dfrac{1}{20}$

8. $\dfrac{1}{7}$
9. $\dfrac{3}{40}$
10. $\dfrac{5}{8}$
11. $\dfrac{1}{3}$
12. $\dfrac{3}{8}$
13. $\dfrac{19}{20}$
14. $\dfrac{13}{40}$

Write the lowest-terms fraction for each percent.

15. 40%   **16.** 95%   **17.** 12%   **18.** 83%   **19.** 54%   **20.** 60%   **21.** 15%

22. 28%   **23.** 99%   **24.** 24%   **25.** $62\frac{1}{2}\%$ **26.** $5\frac{1}{2}\%$ **27.** 150%   **28.** 72%

Set A　For use after page 277

Write each percent as a decimal.

1. 9%　　**2.** 550%　　**3.** 23%　　**4.** $5\frac{3}{4}\%$　　**5.** 0.8%　　**6.** 87.5%

7. 126%　　**8.** $2\frac{1}{4}\%$　　**9.** 0.01%　　**10.** 0.57%　　**11.** 90.2%　　**12.** 1.5%

Write each decimal as a percent.

13. 0.75　　**14.** 0.08　　**15.** 2.50　　**16.** 0.12　　**17.** 0.075　　**18.** 0.01

19. 6.25　　**20.** 0.61　　**21.** 0.09　　**22.** 0.95　　**23.** 0.0036　　**24.** 0.054

Set B　For use after page 279

Find the percent of each number.

1. 75% of 100　　**2.** 3% of 20　　**3.** 40% of 300　　**4.** 17% of 650　　**5.** 10% of 600

6. 8% of 93　　**7.** 5.5% of 120　　**8.** 120% of 12　　**9.** 16.5% of 35　　**10.** 2% of 5,100

Set C　For use after page 280

Find the interest and the amount.

1. $P = \$1,000$
$R = 16\%$ per year
$T = 2$ yr

2. $P = \$400$
$R = 13\%$ per year
$T = 6$ mo

3. $P = \$1,800$
$R = 8.5\%$ per year
$T = 3$ year

4. $P = \$800$
$R = 10\%$ per year
$T = 8$ yr

Set D　For use after page 283

Find the percents.

1. What percent of 60 is 12?

2. 45 is what percent of 150?

3. What percent of 200 is 6?

4. What percent of 450 is 405?

5. What percent is 9 out of 20?

6. What percent is 18 out of 45?

7. 15 is what percent of 90?

8. What percent of 22 is 12?

450

Set A   For use after page 289

Solve.

1. $30\% \times n = 24$ **2.** $45\% \times n = 54$ **3.** $20\% \times n = 70$ **4.** $16\% \times n = 80$

5. $120\% \times n = 48$ **6.** $15\% \times n = 27$ **7.** $65\% \times n = 195$ **8.** $19\% \times n = 7.6$

Set B   For use after page 293

Write and solve a proportion for each equation.

1. 20% of what number is 18?

2. 6 is what percent of 50?

3. 8 is what percent of 400?

4. What is 8% of 125?

5. 45% of what number is 27

6. What is 3% of 240?

7. 72 is what percent of 60?

8. What is 35% of 150?

9. 30 is what percent of 75?

Set C   For use after page 301

Find the perimeter of each figure.

1. Rectangle:
$l = 12$ km
$w = 5.3$ km

2. Square:
$s = 23$ m

3. Regular pentagon:
$s = 19.1$ cm

4. Regular decagon:
$l = 3.5$ cm

5. Equilateral triangle:
$h = 10.8$ cm

6. Parallelogram:
$b = 20.2$ m
$s = 12$ m

7. Regular octagon:
$s = 3.8$ cm

8. Rectangle:
$l = 70$ m
$w = 33.5$ m

Set D   For use after page 303

Find the area of each figure.

1. Square:
$s = 14$ cm

2. Parallelogram:
$b = 5$ m
$h = 3.1$ m

3. Rectangle:
$l = 12.2$ km
$w = 5$ km

4. Square:
$s = 2.5$ m

5. Parallelogram:
$b = 31$ cm
$h = 15$ cm

6. Square:
$s = 35$ km

7. Rectangle:
$l = 38$ cm
$w = 5.2$ cm

8. Parallelogram:
$b = 10$ cm
$h = 6.5$ cm

451

Set A   For use after page 305

Find the area of each triangle.

1. $b = 8$ cm
   $h = 5$ cm

2. $b = 3.1$ m
   $h = 4$ m

3. $b = 12.2$ cm
   $h = 3$ cm

4. $b = 1.25$ cm
   $h = 4.6$ cm

5. $b = 52$ m
   $h = 6$ m

6. $b = 5.2$ cm
   $h = 6.41$ cm

7. $b = 7.3$ km
   $h = 8$ km

8. $b = 120$ m
   $h = 40$ m

9. $b = 15.4$ km
   $h = 13$ km

10. $b = 12$ cm
   $h = 18$ cm

11. $b = 1.21$ m
   $h = 5.1$ m

12. $b = 3.6$ cm
   $h = 4.2$ cm

Set B   For use after page 307

Find the circumference of each circle. Use 3.14 for π.

1. $d = 14$ m

2. $r = 6$ cm

3. $d = 5$ cm

4. $d = 11.2$ m

5. $r = 9.4$ m

6. $r = 13$ cm

7. $d = 22$ m

8. $r = 28$ m

Set C   For use after page 309

Find the area of each circle. Use 3.14 for π.

1. $r = 5$ cm

2. $r = 3.8$ m

3. $d = 16$ cm

4. $d = 40.6$ m

5. $r = 19$ cm

6. $d = 72$ m

7. $r = 1.5$ m

8. $r = 14$ km

Set D   For use after page 315

Find the volume of each rectangular prism.

1. $l = 14$ cm
   $w = 5$ cm
   $h = 8.3$ cm

2. $l = 20$ cm
   $w = 4$ cm
   $h = 6$ cm

3. $l = 13.3$ m
   $w = 5.2$ m
   $h = 4$ m

4. $l = 10$ cm
   $w = 6.1$ cm
   $h = 11$ cm

Find the volume of each cylinder.

5. $r = 5$ cm
   $h = 10$ cm

6. $r = 13.3$ mm
   $h = 5$ mm

7. $r = 8$ m
   $h = 12$ m

8. $r = 1.1$ cm
   $h = 5$ cm

Set A   For use after page 317

Find the volume of each pyramid.

1. $B = 550$ m^2
$h = 9$ m

2. $B = 452$ cm^2
$h = 1.2$ cm

3. $B = 1,250$ cm^2
$h = 48$ cm

4. $B = 300$ m^2
$h = 2.4$ m

Find the volume of each cone. Round your answer to the nearest hundredth if necessary.

5. $r = 5$ cm
$h = 6$ cm

6. $r = 3.8$ m
$h = 9.3$ m

7. $r = 0.8$ cm
$h = 1.2$ cm

8. $r = 15$ m
$h = 10.3$ m

Set B   For use after page 352

Find the mean, the median, and the mode of the numbers in each list in exercises 1–4.

1.	**2.**	**3.**	**4.**
85	$2.08	75%	0.05
72	1.97	79%	0.08
97	1.96	85%	0.11
89	2.08	87%	0.07
72	1.89	79%	0.08
	2.02		0.09

Set C   For use after page 375

Find each square root.

1. $\sqrt{81}$

2. $\sqrt{196}$

3. $^-\sqrt{4,900}$

4. $^-\sqrt{1,600}$

5. $^-\sqrt{1}$

6. $\sqrt{225}$

7. $^-\sqrt{900}$

8. $\sqrt{0.49}$

9. $\sqrt{324}$

10. $^-\sqrt{0.25}$

Set D   For use after page 378

Estimate each square root to the nearest tenth.

1. $\sqrt{842}$

2. $\sqrt{114}$

3. $\sqrt{88}$

4. $\sqrt{75.6}$

5. $\sqrt{2,480}$

6. $\sqrt{1,631}$

7. $\sqrt{8,000}$

8. $\sqrt{1.583}$

Set A   For use after page 381

Find the area of square *C* in each figure.

1.

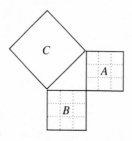

2.

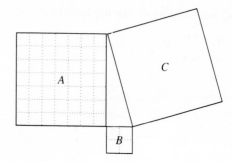

Set B   For use after page 383

Give the length of the hypotenuse in each right triangle.
Round to the nearest thousandth. Use a calculator or a table of square roots.

1.

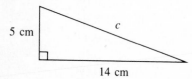

5 cm   *c*   14 cm

2.

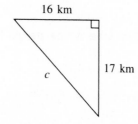

7 cm   *c*   15 cm

3.

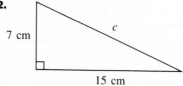

c   12 cm   20 cm

4.

16 km   *c*   17 km

5.

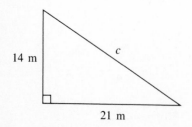

14 m   *c*   21 m

6.

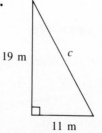

19 m   *c*   11 m

454

Set A   For use after page 384

Find the length of the leg that is not given.

1.

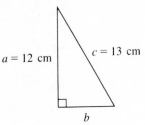

a = 12 cm   c = 13 cm

b

2.

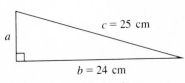

a   c = 25 cm

b = 24 cm

3.

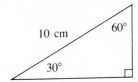

b

c = 5 m   a = 3 m

4.

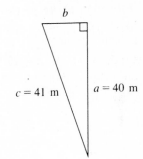

b

c = 41 m   a = 40 m

Set B   For use after page 387

Give the length of the side opposite the 30° angle.

1.

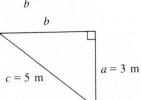

10 cm   60°

30°

2.

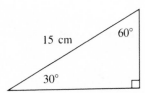

15 cm   60°

30°

3.

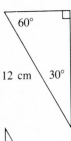

60°

12 cm   30°

4.

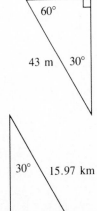

60°

43 m   30°

5.

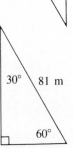

30°   81 m

60°

6.

30°   15.97 km

60°

Set A   For use after page 389

Find the decimal for each rational number. Use a calculator.

1. $\dfrac{5}{9}$ 2. $\dfrac{1}{11}$ 3. $\dfrac{3}{75}$ 4. $\dfrac{7}{20}$ 5. $\dfrac{8}{66}$

6. $\dfrac{7}{55}$ 7. $\dfrac{6}{44}$ 8. $\dfrac{6}{33}$ 9. $\dfrac{6}{22}$ 10. $\dfrac{6}{54}$

11. $\dfrac{6}{50}$ 12. $\dfrac{18}{55}$ 13. $\dfrac{555}{888}$ 14. $\dfrac{300}{88}$ 15. $\dfrac{12}{555}$

Set B   For use after page 397

Write the missing numbers.

1. 15 ft = ▦ yd   2. 180 in. = ▦ yd   3. 4 mi. = ▦ yd

4. 78 in. = ▦ ft   5. 90 in. = ▦ yd   6. 6 in. = ▦ ft

7. $4\dfrac{3}{4}$ ft = ▦ in.   8. 6,160 yd = ▦ mi   9. 137 in. = ▦ ft ▦ in.

10. 23,760 ft = ▦ mi   11. 5.5 yd = ▦ ft ▦ in.   12. $\dfrac{1}{3}$ mi = ▦ ft

Set C   For use after page 398

Write the missing numbers.

1. 5 ft^2 = ▦ in.^{2} 2. 4 yd^2 = ▦ ft^2 3. 10 yd^2 = ▦ ft^2

4. 18 ft^2 = ▦ yd^2 5. 144 in.^{2} = ▦ ft^2 6. 1,296 in.^{2} = ▦ ft^2

Add or subtract

7.   3 ft 5 in.
  − 1 ft 4 in.

8.   5 yd 2 ft
  + 6 yd 2 ft

9.   12 ft 2 in.
  − 9 ft 10 in.

10.   10 yd 1 ft
  − 8 yd 2 ft

11.   2 ft 6 in.
  + 6 ft 8 in.

12.   16 ft 3 in.
  − 15 ft 9 in.

13.   22 yd
  − 19 yd 2 ft

14.   5 yd 2 ft
  + 11 yd 2 ft

Set A   For use after page 399

Write the missing numbers.

1. $3 \text{ yd}^3 = \text{▦} \text{ ft}^3$

2. $9{,}504 \text{ in.}^3 = \text{▦} \text{ ft}^3$

3. $117 \text{ ft}^3 = \text{▦} \text{ yd}^3$

4. $2{,}160 \text{ in.}^3 = \text{▦} \text{ ft}^3$

5. $6\frac{2}{3} \text{ yd}^3 = \text{▦} \text{ ft}^3$

6. $4\frac{1}{2} \text{ ft}^3 = \text{▦} \text{ in.}^3$

7. $18 \text{ ft}^3 = \text{▦} \text{ yd}^3$

8. $2.5 \text{ ft}^3 = \text{▦} \text{ in.}^3$

9. $225 \text{ ft}^3 = \text{▦} \text{ yd}^3$

Find the volume.

10.

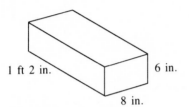

1 ft 2 in.   6 in.   8 in.

11.

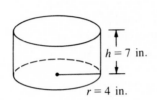

$h = 7 \text{ in.}$ $r = 4 \text{ in.}$

12.

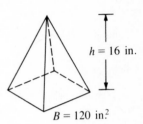

$h = 16 \text{ in.}$ $B = 120 \text{ in.}^2$

Set B   For use after page 400

Write the missing numbers.

1. $12 \text{ fl oz} = \text{▦} \text{ c}$

2. $6 \text{ gal} = \text{▦} \text{ qt}$

3. $6 \text{ pt} = \text{▦} \text{ c}$

4. $2\frac{1}{2} \text{ qt} = \text{▦} \text{ c}$

5. $18 \text{ qt} = \text{▦} \text{ gal}$

6. $12 \text{ c} = \text{▦} \text{ qt}$

7. $48 \text{ fl oz} = \text{▦} \text{ qt}$

8. $4 \text{ pt} = \text{▦} \text{ gal}$

9. $4\frac{1}{4} \text{ c} = \text{▦} \text{ fl oz}$

10. $5\frac{1}{2} \text{ qt} = \text{▦} \text{ pt}$

11. $4 \text{ qt} = \text{▦} \text{ fl oz}$

12. $1\frac{1}{2} \text{ gal} = \text{▦} \text{ pt}$

Set C   For use after page 403

Write the missing numbers.

1. $64 \text{ oz} = \text{▦} \text{ lb}$

2. $4{,}000 \text{ lb} = \text{▦} \text{ T}$

3. $11 \text{ lb} = \text{▦} \text{ oz}$

4. $5\frac{1}{2} \text{ T} = \text{▦} \text{ lb}$

5. $1\frac{1}{4} \text{ T} = \text{▦} \text{ lb}$

6. $8 \text{ oz} = \text{▦} \text{ lb}$

7. $5.75 \text{ lb} = \text{▦} \text{ oz}$

8. $1.2 \text{ T} = \text{▦} \text{ lb}$

9. $68 \text{ oz} = \text{▦} \text{ lb}$

10. $3.6 \text{ T} = \text{▦} \text{ lb}$

11. $0.75 \text{ T} = \text{▦} \text{ lb}$

12. $3.25 \text{ lb} = \text{▦} \text{ oz}$

TABLE OF MEASURES

Metric System

Customary Units

Length

1 meter (m)	{ 1,000 millimeters (mm) 100 centimeters (cm) 10 decimeters (dm)
1 kilometer (km)	1,000 meters (m)
1 hectometer (hm)	100 meters (m)
1 dekameter (dam)	10 meters (m)
1 decimeter (dm)	0.1 meter (m)
1 centimeter (cm)	0.01 meter (m)
1 millimeter (mm)	0.001 meter (m)

1 foot (ft)	12 inches (in.)
1 yard (yd)	{ 36 inches (in.) 3 feet (ft)
1 mile (mi)	{ 5,280 feet (ft) 1,760 yards (yd)
1 nautical mile	6,076 feet (ft)

Area

1 square meter (m²)	{ 100 square decimeters (dm²) 10,000 square centimeters (cm²)
1 hectare (ha)	{ 0.01 square kilometer (km²) 10,000 square meters (m²)
1 square kilometer (km²)	{ 1,000,000 square meters (m²) 100 hectares (ha)

1 square foot (ft²)	144 square inches (in.²)
1 square yard (yd²)	{ 9 square feet (ft²) 1,296 square inches (in.²)
1 acre (a.)	{ 43,560 square feet (ft²) 4,840 square yards (yd²)
1 square mile (mi²)	640 acres (a.)

Volume

| 1 cubic decimeter (dm³) | { 0.001 cubic meter (m³)
1,000 cubic centimeters (cm³)
1 liter (L) |
| 1 cubic meter (m³) | { 1,000,000 cubic centimeters (cm³)
1,000 cubic decimeters (dm³) |

| 1 cubic foot (ft³) | 1,728 cubic inches (in.³) |
| 1 cubic yard (yd³) | { 27 cubic feet (ft³)
46,656 cubic inches (in.³) |

Capacity

1 teaspoon	5 milliliters (mL)
1 tablespoon	12.5 milliliters (mL)
1 liter (L)	{ 1,000 milliliters (mL) 1,000 cubic centimeters (cm³) 1 cubic decimeter (dm³) 4 metric cups
1 kiloliter (kL)	1,000 liters (L)

1 cup (c)	8 fluid ounces (fl oz)
1 pint (pt)	{ 16 fluid ounces (fl oz) 2 cups (c)
1 quart (qt)	{ 32 fluid ounces (fl oz) 4 cups (c) 2 pints (pt)
1 gallon (gal)	{ 128 fluid ounces (fl oz) 16 cups (c) 8 pints (pt) 4 quarts (qt)

Weight

1 gram (g)	1,000 milligrams (mg)
1 kilogram (kg)	1,000 grams (g)
1 metric ton (t)	1,000 kilograms (kg)

| 1 pound (lb) | 16 ounces (oz) |
| 1 ton (T) | 2,000 pounds (lb) |

MATHEMATICAL SYMBOLS

=	Is equal to	$\overleftrightarrow{AB}$	Line through points A and B
≠	Is not equal to	$\overrightarrow{AB}$	Ray AB
>	Is greater than	$\overline{AB}$	Segment with endpoints A and B
<	Is less than	$\angle ABC$	Angle ABC
≥	Is greater than or equal to	$m(\angle ABC)$	Measure of angle ABC
≤	Is less than or equal to	$\triangle ABC$	Triangle ABC
≈	Is approximately equal to	$\overset{\frown}{RS}$	Arc with endpoints R and S
≅	Is congruent to	$\overleftrightarrow{AB} \perp \overleftrightarrow{CD}$	Line AB perpendicular to line CD
~	Is similar to	$\overleftrightarrow{AB} \parallel \overleftrightarrow{CD}$	Line AB is parallel to line CD
%	Percent	$35°$	Thirty-five *degrees*
π	Pi		
$0.\overline{6}$	Repeating decimal		
$\sqrt{}$	Square root		

METRIC SYSTEM PREFIXES

tera	T	one trillion	deci	d	one tenth
giga	G	one billion	centi	c	one hundredth
mega	M	one million	milli	m	one thousandth
kilo	k	one thousand	micro	μ	one millionth
hecto	h	one hundred	nano	n	one billionth
deka	da	ten	pico	p	one trillionth

FORMULAS

$P = a + b + c$	Perimeter of triangle	$a^2 + b^2 = c^2$	Pythagorean Theorem
$P = 2(l + w)$	Perimeter of rectangle	$C = \pi d$	Circumference of circle
$A = lw$	Area of rectangle	$A = \pi r^2$	Area of circle
$A = bh$	Area of parallelogram	$A = 2\pi rh$	Lateral area of cylinder
$A = \frac{1}{2}(b_1 + b_2)h$	Area of trapezoid	$A = 2\pi r^2 + 2\pi rh$	Surface area of cylinder
$A = \frac{1}{2}bh$	Area of triangle	$A = 2(lh + lw + wh)$	Surface area of rectangular prism
$V = lwh$	Volume of rectangular solid		
$V = Bh$	Volume of prism	$A = 4\pi r^2$	Surface area of sphere
$V = \pi r^2 h$	Volume of cylinder		
$V = \frac{1}{3}Bh$	Volume of pyramid		
$V = \frac{1}{3}\pi r^2 h$	Volume of cone		

GLOSSARY

absolute value   The number of units from a point on the number line to the origin. The absolute value of a number is never negative. Absolute value is shown by vertical lines.
$|^-3| = 3;\ |6| = 6;\ |0| = 0$

absolute zero   The temperature at which a substance would have no molecular motion or heat. This temperature is 0 K, $^-273.15°C$, or $^-459.67°F$.

acute angle   An angle that has a measure less than 90°.

acute triangle   A triangle in which each angle has a measure less than 90°.

addend   A number that is added.

angle   Two rays with a single endpoint, called the vertex of the angle.

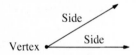

arc   A part of a circle.

area   The measure of a plane region in terms of square units.

arithmetic mean   The quotient obtained when the sum of two or more numbers is divided by the number of addends.

associative property   The sum (or product) of three or more numbers is the same regardless of grouping:
$(a + b) + c = a + (b + c)$ or $(a \cdot b) \cdot c = a \cdot (b \cdot c)$

average   See *arithmetic mean*.

axis   See *coordinate axes*.

base (in numeration)   The type of grouping involved in a system of numeration. In base eight, 346 means 3 sixty-fours, 4 eights, and 6.

base (of a polygon)   Any side of a polygon may be referred to as a base.

BASIC   A simple programming language.

basic counting principle   If one thing can be done in n ways and a second thing can be done in m ways, then the two things can be done together in $n \times m$ ways.

binary   A base-two system of numeration.

bisect   To divide into two congruent parts.

bit   Binary digit, 0 or 1.

byte   String of bits whose length is the smallest accessible unit in computer memory.

capacity   The volume of a space figure given in terms of liquid measurement.

central angle   An angle that has its vertex at the center of a circle.

chord   A segment with both endpoints on a circle.

circle   All the points in a plane that are the same distance from one point called the center.

circumference   The distance around a circle.

combination   A selection of a group of objects from a set without regard to order. The number of combinations of 2 objects from a set of 3 objects is 3.

commutative property   The sum (or product) of any two numbers is the same regardless of the order in which they are added (or multiplied):
$a + b = b + a$ or $a \cdot b = b \cdot a$

complementary angles   Two angles whose measures have a sum of 90°.

composite number   A number greater than 0 with more than two different factors.

concentric circles   Two or more circles that have the same center.

cone   A space figure with a base that is a circular region and one vertex that is not in the same plane as the base.

congruent   Two geometric figures are congruent if they have the same size and shape.

coordinate axes   Two intersecting perpendicular number lines used for graphing ordered number pairs.

coordinates An ordered pair of numbers matched with a point in the coordinate plane. See figure for *coordinate axes*.

cross products In the equation $\frac{a}{b} = \frac{c}{d}$, the products *ad* and *bc* are called cross products. Two ratios $\frac{a}{b}$ and $\frac{c}{d}$ are equal if and only if *ad = bc*.

cube (numeration) A number raised to the third power. 8 is the cube of 2 because $2^3 = 8$. Also, to raise a number to the third power.

cube (space figure) A prism whose faces are all congruent squares.

cylinder A space figure with two congruent bases that are circular regions in parallel planes, and a curved face.

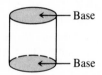

data A collection of unorganized facts that have not been processed into information.

decagon A polygon that has ten sides.

degree (°) A unit of measure for angles, $\frac{1}{90}$ of a right angle.

degree Celsius (°C) A unit for measuring temperature. On the Celsius scale, water freezes at 0°C and boils at 100°C.

degree Fahrenheit (°F) A unit for measuring temperature. On the Fahrenheit scale, water freezes at 32°F and boils at 212°F.

denominator For each fraction $\frac{a}{b}$, *b* is the denominator.

diagonal A segment connecting two nonconsecutive vertices of a polygon.

diameter A chord that contains the center of a circle.

difference The number resulting from subtraction.

digits The basic symbols used in a place-value system of numeration. In base ten, the symbols are *0, 1, 2, 3, 4, 5, 6, 7, 8,* and *9*.

distributive property Connects addition and multiplication when both operations are involved.
$$a(b + c) = a \cdot b + a \cdot c$$

dividend The number to be divided in a division problem.

$$\text{Divisor} \rightarrow \ 5\overline{)17} \begin{array}{l} 3 \leftarrow \text{Quotient} \\ \ \ \ \leftarrow \text{Dividend} \\ 15 \\ \hline 2 \leftarrow \text{Remainder} \end{array}$$

divisible A given number is divisible by a second number if the remainder is zero.

divisor See *dividend*.

dodecahedron A polyhedron with twelve faces.

edge One of the segments making up any of the faces of a space figure.

ellipse A closed plane curve generated by a point (*P*) moving in such a way that the sum of the distances from two fixed focal points (F_1 and F_2) is constant.

equally likely outcomes Outcomes that have the same chance of occurring.

equal ratios Ratios that give the same comparison. $\frac{9}{27}$ and $\frac{1}{3}$ are equal ratios.

equation A mathematical sentence using the equality symbol (=). $x - 27 = 102$ is an equation.

equilateral triangle A triangle with all three sides the same length.

equivalent fractions Fractions that represent the same number, such as $\frac{1}{3}$, $\frac{2}{6}$, and $\frac{3}{9}$.

estimate An approximation for a given number. Often used in the sense of a rough calculation.

expanded numeral   Representations of numbers as a sum of multiples of 10, such as:
$4,325 = 4,000 + 300 + 20 + 5$ or
$4 \times 10^3 + 3 \times 10^2 + 2 \times 10 + 5$

exponent   A number that tells how many times another number is to be used as a factor.

$$5 \cdot 5 \cdot 5 = 5^3 \leftarrow \text{Exponent}$$
$$\leftarrow \text{Base}$$

exponential notation   A system of representing a number using an exponent.

expression (algebraic)   Symbols or the combination of symbols, such as numerals, letters, operation symbols, and parentheses, used to name a number.

face   Any one of the bounding polygonal regions of a space figure.

factorial   If n is a positive whole number, factorial n denoted by $n!$, is defined to be $n! = 1 \cdot 2 \cdot 3 \cdot 4 \ldots (n-2) \cdot (n-1) \cdot n$. $0!$ is defined to be 1.

factors   Numbers that are to be multiplied.

flowchart   A diagram that gives instructions in a logical order.

formula   A general fact or rule expressed by symbols. For example, the area (A) of any parallelogram with base b and height h is given by the formula $A = bh$.

fraction   A number in the form $\frac{a}{b}$ when $b \neq 0$.

frequency   The number of times a given item occurs in a set of data.

frequency distribution   A set of data in tabular or graphical form which is classified so that the frequency of each class is given.

greatest common factor (GCF)   The greatest number that is a factor of each of two or more numbers.

greatest possible error (GPE)   Half of the basic unit in which a measurement is given. For example, if a length is given as 18 cm, the greatest possible error is 0.5 cm.

heptagon   A seven-sided polygon.

hexagon   A six-sided polygon.

histogram   A bar graph showing frequencies.

hypotenuse   The side of a right triangle opposite the right angle.

improper fraction   A fraction whose numerator is greater than or equal to its denominator.

INPUT   Data that is put in a computer for processing.

integer   Any whole number or its opposite, and zero.

intersecting lines   Lines with one common point.

inverse (operation)   Two operations that are opposite in effect. Adding 5 is the inverse of subtracting 5.

irrational number   A real number that cannot be expressed as the quotient of two integers. Irrational numbers have nonrepeating decimal representations.

isosceles triangle   A triangle with at least two congruent sides.

Kelvin (K)   A temperature scale in which 0 K represents absolute zero. Water freezes at 273.15 K. Celsius temperature = Kelvin temperature $^-273.15°$

least common denominator (LCD)   The least common multiple of the denominators of two or more fractions. For example, the least common denominator of $\frac{5}{6}$ and $\frac{3}{4}$ is 12.

least common multiple (LCM)   The smallest nonzero number that is a multiple of each of two or more given numbers. The LCM of 4 and 6 is 12.

line   A straight path of points that goes on endlessly.
Line AB or $\overleftrightarrow{AB}$

line of symmetry   A line on which a figure can be folded so that the two parts fit exactly.

loop   A command that causes a computer to go back to an earlier step in the program and repeat it.

lowest-terms fraction   A fraction for which the greatest common factor (GCF) of the numerator and denominator is 1.

median The middle number of a set of numbers that are arranged in order.

midpoint A point that divides a segment into two congruent segments.

mixed number A number, such as $4\frac{2}{3}$, that has a whole number part and a fractional part.

mode In a list of data the mode is the number or item that occurs most often. There may be more than one mode.

multiple A number that is the product of that number and a whole number.
$3 \cdot 8 = 24$ 24 is a multiple of 3.

negative integer The numbers less than zero that are opposites of natural numbers.
$\{^-1, {}^-2, {}^-3, \ldots\}$

nonagon A nine-sided polygon.

numeral A symbol for a number.

numerator For each fraction $\frac{a}{b}$, a is the numerator.

obtuse angle An angle with a measure greater than 90° and less than 180°.

obtuse triangle A triangle with one angle measuring more than 90°.

octagon An eight-sided polygon.

opposites property The sum of any number and its opposite is zero. $n + {}^-n = 0$

ordered pair A number pair arranged in order so that there is a first number and a second number. The coordinates of a point in a plane, such as (2,7), are an ordered pair of numbers.

origin The intersection of the coordinate axes; the point associated with the number pair (0,0).

outcome A possible result in a probability experiment.

OUTPUT The processed data or information that a computer displays or prints.

parallel lines Lines in the same plane that do not intersect.

parallelogram A quadrilateral whose opposite sides are parallel.

pentagon A five-sided polygon.

percent (%) Literally, "per hundred." 6% means 6 per hundred, $\frac{6}{100}$, or 0.06.

perimeter The sum of the length of the sides of a polygon.

period Each group of three digits starting with the ones' digit is a period.

permutation An ordered selection of a group of objects from a given set. For example, there are 6 permutations of 2 letters from the 3 letters A, B, and C. The permutations are AB, BA, AC, CA, BC, and CB.

perpendicular bisector A line that bisects a segment and is perpendicular to it.

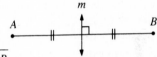

$m \perp \text{bis } \overline{AB}$

perpendicular lines Two intersecting lines that form right angles.

pi (π) The ratio of the circumference of a circle to its diameter. The decimal for π is unending and does not repeat.
$\pi = 3.141592 \ldots$

place value The value given to the place a digit may occupy in a numeral. In the decimal numeration system, each place of a numeral has ten times the value of the place to its right.

polygon A closed plane figure formed by segments.

polyhedron A closed space figure whose faces are polygonal regions.

positive integer An integer greater than zero $\{1, 2, 3, \ldots\}$.

precision One measurement is more precise than another if its greatest possible error is less than the other. 12 mm (GPE = 0.5 mm) is more precise than 12 cm (GPE = 0.5 cm).

463

prime factorization   The expression of a composite number as the product of prime factors. $36 = 2^2 \cdot 3^2$

prime number   A whole number, greater than 1, whose only factors are itself and 1.

prism   A space figure whose bases are congruent polygonal regions in parallel planes and whose faces are parallelograms.

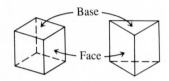

probability   The ratio of the number of times a certain outcome can occur to the number of total possible outcomes.

product   The number that results when two numbers are multiplied.

program   Step-by-step instruction that directs the computer to perform operations.

property of one   Any number multiplied by 1 will equal the number:
$a \times 1 = a$ or $a \div 1 = a$

property of zero   For every integer a, $a + 0 = a$.

proportion   An equation stating that two ratios are equal: $\frac{3}{18} = \frac{1}{6}$

protractor   An instrument for measuring the number of degrees (°) in an angle.

pyramid   A space figure with a polygonal base and triangular faces with a common vertex.

Pythagorean Theorem (Rule of Pythagoras)
In any right triangle, the sum of the areas of the squares on the legs is equal to the area of the square on the hypotenuse. The Pythagorean formula is $a^2 + b^2 = c^2$.

quadrilateral   A four-sided polygon.

quotient   See *dividend*.

radius   A segment or length of a segment from the center of a circle to a point on the circle.

range   The difference between the greatest number and the least number in a set of data.

rate   A ratio that compares different kinds of units.

ratio   The ratio of two numbers a and b is their quotient, $\frac{a}{b}$.

rational numbers   Positive and negative fractional numbers and zero.

ray   A part of a line that has one endpoint and extends endlessly in one direction. Ray AB or $\overrightarrow{AB}$

real numbers   The rational numbers and irrational numbers form the set of real numbers.

reciprocals   Two numbers are reciprocals if their product is 1. 7 and $\frac{1}{7}$ are reciprocals.

rectangle   A parallelogram with four right angles.

regular polygon   A polygon with all sides the same length and all angles the same measure.

relatively prime   Two numbers with a greatest common factor (GCF) of 1 are relatively prime. 8 and 27 are relatively prime.

repeating decimal   A decimal whose digits from some point on repeat endlessly. 6.2835835 . . . and 0.3333333 . . . are repeating decimals. They may also be written as $6.2\overline{835}$ and $0.\overline{3}$ respectively.

rhombus   A parallelogram whose sides all have the same length.

right angle   An angle that measures 90°.

right triangle   A triangle with a right angle.

scale drawing   A drawing made so that distances in the drawing are proportional to actual distances. A scale of 1:10 indicates that distances in the drawing are $\frac{1}{10}$ of the actual distances.

scalene triangle   A triangle with all three sides having different measures.

scattergram   A graph of ordered pairs of points representing two sets of data used to determine whether or not the two sets of data are related by a formula or a function.

scientific notation   A system of writing a number as the product of a power of 10 and a number between 1 and 10.
$2,300,000 = 2.3 \times 10^6$

secant A line that intersects a circle at two points.

segment Two points and all the points between them.

sequence A set of numbers given in a specific order, usually by a rule or pattern.

similar figures Two or more figures with the same shape but not necessarily the same size.

skew lines Lines in space that are not parallel and do not intersect.

space figure A three-dimensional geometric figure whose points do not all lie in the same plane.

sphere The set of all points in space at a fixed distance from a given point.

square (geometry) A quadrilateral with four right angles and all sides the same length.

square (numeration) A number raised to the second power. 9 is the square of 3. Also, to raise a number to the second power. $3^2 = 9$.

square root If $x^2 = y$, then x is a square root of y. Each positive number has two square roots that are opposites of each other. 3 and $^-3$ are square roots of 9. The symbol $\sqrt{9}$ denotes only the positive square root, 3. $^-\sqrt{9} = {^-3}$.

statistics Facts or data of a numerical kind.

straight angle An angle that has a measure of 180°.

string variables Locations in a computer that store data of any kind. A letter and the $ symbol form string variables. A$, B$, etc.

sum The result of the addition operation.

supplementary angles Two angles whose measures have a sum of 180°.

surface area The sum of the areas of all the faces of a space figure.

symmetric figure A plane figure that can be divided into two congruent parts by a line of symmetry.

tangent A line that intersects a circle at just one point.

tangent ratio In a right triangle ABC, the ratio $\frac{a}{b}$ is called the tangent of $\angle A$.

$\tan A = \frac{a}{b}$

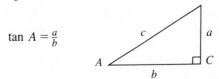

terminating decimal A decimal that represents the quotient of a whole number and a power of 10.

$0.5 = \frac{5}{10}$ $1.28 = \frac{128}{10^2}$ $0.0307 = \frac{307}{10^4}$

tetrahedron A polyhedron with four triangular faces.

transversal A line which intersects two or more lines.

trapezoid A quadrilateral with one pair of parallel sides.

triangle A three-sided polygon.

unit An amount or quantity used as a standard of measurement.

variable A symbol, usually a letter, used to represent a number in an expression or an equation.

vertex (vertices) A point that two rays of an angle have in common. Also, the common point of any two sides of a polygon or the common point of intersection of three or more faces of a polyhedron.

Vertex

volume The measure of a space figure in terms of a chosen unit, usually a unit cube.

whole number Any number in the set {0, 1, 2, 3, . . .}.

zero property See *property of zero*.

Acknowledgments cont.:

© 1979 **Jeff Lowenthal/Woodfin Camp & Associates:** 166

© 1981 **David Madison/Bruce Coleman Inc.:** 177 bottom right

© 1982 **David Madison/Bruce Coleman Inc.:** 24

Magdalene College, Cambridge, by permission of the Masters and Fellows: 241 top right

© **Gregg Mancuso/After-Image:** 40

© 1977 **Michael Philip Manheim/After-Image:** 120

© **Kim Massie/Rainbow:** 77 bottom right

Sheryl S. McNee/Tom Stack & Associates: 185 right, 328

Charles McNulty/Atoz Images: 267

© **Ken McVey/After-Image:** 356

Peter Menzel/Stock, Boston: 309

© 1982 **Peter Menzel/Stock, Boston:** 161, 349 center

© **J. Messerschmidt/Bruce Coleman Inc.:** 131 top left

© 1982 **Dan Miller/Woodfin Camp & Associates:** 1 top right

© 1981 **Momatiuk/Eastcott/Woodfin Camp & Associates:** 77 top left

© **Hank Morgan/Rainbow:** 177 top left

© **B.G. Murray, Jr./Animals Animals:** 162

Museum of Fine Arts, Boston; Boston Athenaeum Fund—Portrait of George Washington by Gilbert Stuart (detail): 350 top

National Maritime Museum, London: 226

New York State Historical Association, Cooperstown—"The Peaceable Kingdom" by Edward Hicks (detail): 284

© 1982 **Naoki Okamoto/Black Star:** 46–47

© **M. Timothy O'Keefe/Bruce Coleman Inc.:** 96, 131 top center

© **Chuck O'Rear/West Light:** 2, 131 center, 136, 216

R.R. Pawlowski/Bruce Coleman Inc.: 31 bottom

© 1982 **Stacy Pick/Stock, Boston:** 419

Richard Pilling/Focus on Sports: 134, 374

Bil Plummer*: 319

Public Archives Canada, Ottawa, Picture Division: 185 left

Quincy-Lynn Enterprises, Inc.: 65

© **Bill Ross/West Light:** 167

© **Nancy Safford/Woodfin Camp & Associates:** 155 top right

Scala/Art Resource, Inc.: 215

© **Rene Sheret/After-Image:** 349 top

James Simon/Atoz Images: 131 top right

© 1979 **Chad Slattery/After-Image:** 1 top left

Bradley Smith/Animals Animals: 163

Peter Southwick/Stock, Boston: 54, 288

© **Ted Spiegel/Black Star:** 264

© 1983 **Ted Spiegel/Black Star:** 38

Tom Stack/Tom Stack & Associates: 53 center bottom

© **Dennis Stock/Magnum Photos:** 379

© 1970 **Dennis Stock/Magnum Photos:** 53 center top

© 1983 **James Sugar/Black Star:** 186

© **Harald Sund:** 109 top right, 158, 172

© **Dale R. Thompson/After-Image:** 202

© 1982 **Dale R. Thompson/After-Image:** 305

Norman Owen Tomalin/Bruce Coleman Inc.: 1 center right, 118 bottom

© **Tom Tracy:** 23, 84, 112, 269 top

Mark Tuschman*: 16, 34, 64, 109 center left, 109 bottom left, 146, 210 (both), 244, 274, 282, 291, 311, 326, 338 top, 384, 393 (both), 400, 407

Don & Pat Valenti/Tom Stack & Associates: 77 center right

Peter Vandermark/Stock, Boston: 401

Richard Walker/Bruce Coleman Inc.: 290

© **Peter Ward/Bruce Coleman Inc.:** 31 center

© **White House Historical Association, photograph by National Geographic Society:** 350 center

© **Marv Wolf/After-Image:** 234

Reinhart Wolf: 373

© **Baron Wolman/Woodfin Camp & Associates:** 256 top left

*Photographs provided expressly for the publisher.

SELECTED ANSWERS

1 Whole Number Operations

Page 3
1. 6 thousand, 5 hundred   **7.** 537,000
15. 87,295,000,000

Page 5
1. <   **5.** >   **11.** 13,992,249; 13,992,248;
13,920,929   **17.** 126,000   **23.** 510,000
31. 83,000,000   **37.** 34,110,000

Page 6
1. 28; Zero   **7.** 70; Distributive   **11.** 103;
Commutative   **15.** Zero

Page 7
1. 9   **7.** 20   **13.** 6   **17.** 4
23. $(12 - 9) \times 7$; 21

Page 8
1. 10,000   **5.** 1,400

Page 9
3. 4,800   **7.** $9,000   **11.** 4,000
17. 4,000   **23.** 1,800   **31.** 3,000 m

Page 10
1. 31,693   **5.** $6,667

Page 11
1. 18,575   **7.** 88,155   **15.** $2,484
21. 2,321   **27.** $4,033

Page 12
1. 38,968 T

Page 13
1. 13,150 a.   **5.** $24,870,000   **9.** 6,078 a.

Page 14
3. 5,000   **15.** 540,000   **23.** 5   **31.** 30
41. 120   **45.** 72

Page 15
2. 1,600   **8.** 4,800   **14.** 320,000
22. 6   **31.** 30   **37.** 30 trips

Page 16
1. 1,631   **7.** $21,000

Page 17
1. 472   **5.** 6,882   **11.** 66,290
17. $56,070   **25.** 1,642,249   **32.** 4,749,461

Page 18
1. 350 R54   **7.** 57 R113

Page 19
1. 13 R50   **7.** 206 R6   **15.** 121 R175
21. 30 R37   **29.** 615   **35.** 81 min

Page 20
1. B; 235   **5.** C; $1

Page 21
3. yes   **7.** $98

Page 22
1. 57,251   **7.** 24,822   **11.** 173,636
17. 3,693   **27.** 470,187   **31.** $12,320,100

Page 23
1. 82,414 km^2, Lake Superior   **5.** 100
7. 94,710 mi^2 or 245,300 km^2

Page 24
2. Adrian 8; Stefan 25

Page 26
1. >   **9.** 1,520,000   **13.** 2   **17.** $400;
$422   **23.** 20,425   **29.** 208 R49

Page 27
1. 396   **7.** 3,596

474

2 Addition and Subtraction of Decimals

Page 32
1. 0.8   **7.** 0.0005   **13.** 0.006

Page 33
3. 0.00054   **9.** 0.4406   **13.** 0.4
21. 0.000006   **25.** 0.000509
33. one and eight thousand, six hundred sixty-five millionths

Page 34
1. >   **5.** >

Page 35
1. >   **7.** <   **15.** =   **21.** 4.6991; 4.7; 4.967; 4.98

Page 36
1. 1.728   **5.** 0.8

Page 37
2. 607   **8.** 1   **14.** 0.1   **20.** 0.93
26. 1.782   **32.** 0.337   **38.** 100

Page 38
1. 18.463   **5.** $4,424.92

Page 39
3. 179.5   **9.** 18.067   **15.** $59.44
21. $2,601.42   **25.** 17 s

Page 40
1. 22.86   **5.** $203.22   **9.** 0.15

Page 41
2. 50.45   **6.** 732.2   **12.** $28.15
20. 68.2   **26.** 2.846   **32.** 2.67 s

Page 42
1. 0.600   **5.** $2.20   **13.** 15

Page 43
1. $401.99 **5.** $26.85 **9.** $6,628.05

Page 44
2. 17.98   **8.** 0.1357   **14.** 22.2363
20. 0.0947   **24.** 1.433   **30.** 1,734.49
34. $0.71   **40.** $3.40   **46.** 4.246

Page 45
1. $215.85   **5.** $45.00

Pages 46–47
1. 5.33   **5.** $12.02   **9.** $22.50
13. $31.63

Page 48
1. $5,997

Page 50
1. 0.15   **5.** 0.05   **9.** 18.70
15. 209.121   **21.** 0.0155   **27.** 2.4

3 Multiplication and Division of Decimals

Page 54
1. 2.66   **5.** 300.0   **9.** 537.00

Page 55
1. 5.36   **3.** 2.313   **9.** $2,280.00
15. 1.064   **21.** 21.443   **27.** 5.040
33. 1   **37.** 0.729   **41.** Full service (credit card) $27.25; Self service (cash) $24.14

Page 56
2. 1.667   **6.** 19,094   **12.** 36,700
18. 0.0049   **22.** $13.90   **26.** $80.00

Page 57
1. 18   **7.** $36   **13.** $32.40
19. $96   **23.** $1,248

Page 58
1. Missing: number of homes in U.S.
7. 21,000 lines per minute

Page 59

1. 731 km **5.** $711.54 **7.** $1,356.80

Page 60

1. 6.4 **5.** 1.438 (1.44)

Page 61

4. 6.28 **10.** 5.868 (5.87)
16. 3.082 (3.08) **22.** 8.8125 (8.813)
28. 2.677 **34.** 4.4 m

Page 62

1. 8.31 (8.3) **3.** 5.666 (5.67)

Page 63

1. 5.31 (5.3) **7.** 0.5
13. 2.770 (2.77) **19.** 37.000
25. 194.682 **33.** 95.04 kg/m

Page 64

1. 2.67 **5.** 0.5600 **11.** 0.075
17. 0.0005 **23.** $0.84 **27.** $1.27

Page 65

1. 4 **7.** 50 **15.** $3

Page 66

2. 136.8 **6.** 3.492 **12.** 1.42
18. 0.74 **26.** 0.0038 **32.** 52
36. 2.80 (2.8) **40.** 3.844 (3.84)

Page 67

3. 941 kg **9.** 36 million/day

Page 68

1. 3 base, 5 exponent **7.** 32 **13.** 49
19. 6^4

Page 69

1. 8^4 **5.** 2^8 **13.** 243 **19.** 4,096
25. 7 **33.** 2

Page 70

1. 3 **5.** 2.8

Page 71

1. 45,000 **5.** 2,000,000 **11.** 60,100,000
17. 5.9×10^{11} **23.** 1×10^9
31. 2,000,000

Page 72

1. 12

Page 74

1. 1.52 **7.** 160 **13.** 0.145
17. 1.561 (1.56) **23.** 0.5

4 Addition and Subtraction of Fractions

Page 79

1. 2 **9.** 132,793 **11.** $71 \cdot 73 \cdot 79$

Page 80

1. 1, 2; 2 **5.** 4

Page 81

1. 3 **7.** 10 **15.** 7 **21.** 10
27. 3 **33.** 6 **37.** 21

Page 82

1. $\frac{4}{8}$, $\frac{5}{10}$, $\frac{6}{12}$ **5.** $\neq$

Page 83

1. $\frac{12}{32}$ **5.** $\frac{36}{64}$ **11.** 12 **17.** =
23. = **27.** $\frac{16}{32}$ **33.** $\frac{36}{60}$

Page 84

1. $\frac{4}{5}$ **5.** $\frac{1}{2}$ **9.** $\frac{1}{3}$

Page 85

1. $\frac{2}{3}$ **5.** $\frac{2}{3}$ **11.** $\frac{7}{8}$ **17.** $\frac{1}{4}$ **23.** $\frac{19}{25}$
29. = **33.** $\frac{15}{33} = \frac{5}{11}$ **37.** $\frac{13}{22}$

Page 86

1. $\frac{11}{4}$ **5.** $\frac{100}{3}$ **9.** $37\frac{1}{2}$

Page 87

1. $\frac{8}{3}$ 5. $\frac{22}{7}$ 9. $\frac{11}{6}$ 15. $\frac{27}{10}$

21. $2\frac{2}{3}$ 27. $2\frac{1}{2}$ 35. $3\frac{11}{12}$ 39. 9

43. $52\frac{1}{7}$

Page 88

1. 24   7. 120

Page 89

2. 24   6. 30   10. 90   16. 300

20. $\frac{3}{30}, \frac{25}{30}$ 26. $\frac{16}{60}, \frac{27}{60}$ 32. $\frac{3}{6}, \frac{2}{6}, \frac{1}{6}$

36. 75 cm; 15 rectangles

Page 90

1. >   5. <

Page 91

1. >   5. >   11. >   17. <

23. >   27. $\frac{3}{4}, \frac{5}{6}, \frac{7}{8}$

Page 92

1. $\frac{7}{8}$ 3. $\frac{11}{12}$

Page 93

1. $1\frac{1}{24}$ 5. $1\frac{3}{16}$ 9. $1\frac{17}{20}$ 15. $40\frac{15}{28}$

19. $191\frac{83}{120}$ 25. 100   27. $7\frac{63}{64}''$

Page 94

1. $\frac{4}{9}$ 3. $\frac{1}{4}$

Page 95

1. $\frac{1}{6}$ 5. $\frac{7}{20}$ 13. $\frac{19}{48}$ 21. $3\frac{7}{12}$

29. $13\frac{5}{12}$

Page 96

1. $6\frac{3}{4}$ 5. $\frac{13}{16}$ 9. $17\frac{63}{100}$

Page 97

1. $2\frac{3}{8}$ 5. $7\frac{1}{16}$ 11. $9\frac{5}{12}$ 17. $43\frac{19}{20}$

25. $9\frac{3}{8}$ 31. $2\frac{1}{6}$ h

Page 98

1. $\frac{1}{2}$ 5. $\frac{2}{3}$ 9. $\frac{2}{3}$ 11. $\frac{1}{2}$

Page 99

3. 21 in.   5. $d = 8$ in.

Page 100

1. $\frac{3}{4}$ 5. $\frac{2}{5}$ 9. $23\frac{1}{8}$ 15. $70\frac{25}{36}$

23. $7\frac{1}{4}$ 29. $383\frac{2}{3}$ 35. $9\frac{3}{8}$ 39. $\frac{8}{45}$

43. $46\frac{1}{5}$

Page 101

2. $6\frac{1}{4}$ yd   6. $2\frac{1}{2}$ in.

Page 102

13. $111.10   18. 360   42. 12

Page 106

1. 1, 2, 5, 10   5. 8, 16, 24, 32

11. 28   19. $\frac{1}{4}$ 27. $41\frac{5}{8}$ 33. $18\frac{13}{15}$

Page 107

2. $\frac{297}{527}$ 4. $\frac{37}{126}$

5 Multiplication and Division of Fractions

Page 110

1. $\frac{3}{10}$ 5. $\frac{5}{12}$ 11. $\frac{1}{6}$

Page 111

1. $\frac{5}{12}$ 5. $1\frac{2}{3}$ 11. $\frac{5}{8}$ 17. $\frac{2}{3}$

23. 20   31. 1   33. $\frac{3}{8}$

Page 112

1. 18   5. 24   11. $2\frac{1}{4}$

Page 113

1. 14   5. $1\frac{1}{3}$ 11. $4\frac{7}{8}$ 17. 1

23. $8\frac{1}{3}$ 31. 3   35. $26\frac{1}{2}$ in.

Page 114

1. $4   5. $35   11. $36

1. $\frac{5}{1}$ **5.** $\frac{3}{5}$ **11.** $\frac{2}{25}$ **17.** $n = \frac{2}{1}$

23. $n = 6$

Page 116

1. 2   **5.** $\frac{1}{2}$

Page 117

2. $\frac{3}{8}$ **6.** $\frac{4}{5}$ **12.** $\frac{1}{2}$ **22.** $1\frac{1}{6}$

28. $4\frac{1}{2}$ **31.** 4

Page 118

1. $2\frac{4}{9}$ **5.** 3

Page 119

1. $1\frac{7}{11}$ **5.** $1\frac{19}{32}$ **15.** $2\frac{3}{5}$ **23.** 9

31. 6

Page 120

1. $0.71   **5.** $1.38   **9.** $2\frac{1}{4}$ lb

Page 121

3. 19 lb   **6.** $1.80   **10.** 29 lb, 21 lb

Page 122

1. $0.\overline{72}$ **5.** $0.\overline{6}$

Page 123

2. 0.4   **6.** $0.\overline{24}$ **12.** 0.125

20. 1.25   **28.** >   **36.** $0.\overline{5}$

45. $0.\overline{89}$ **50.** 9

Page 124

4. 30   **10.** $\frac{7}{40}$ **18.** $3\frac{1}{2}$ **26.** 0

34. $\frac{1}{14}$ **40.** $17\frac{3}{8}$ **46.** $34\frac{1}{5}$

Page 125

1. 3; 45 mi   **5.** 1 in.

Page 126

1. freight 24 cm, caboose 12 cm

Page 128

3. $\frac{2}{5}$ **9.** $2\frac{3}{16}$ **15.** 6   **23.** 2   **31.** $1.8\overline{3}$

6 Equations

Page 132

1. 138   **5.** 2   **9.** 8

Page 133

1. 17   **7.** 4   **13.** 14   **23.** 4

29. 149   **35.** 10   **44.** 6

Page 134

1. B; $j + 8$ **5.** $v + 25$

Page 135

1. $f + 40$ **7.** $x + 44$ **15.** $f + 4$

Page 136

3. $n = 29$

Page 137

1. $b = 23$ **5.** $r = 37$ **13.** $a = 33$

21. $y = 45$ **29.** $x = 26{,}692$

33. $h = 233$; 233 m

Page 138

2. $b - 60 = 120$; $b = 180$

Page 139

1. $p + 8 = 112$; $p = 104$; 104 calories

5. $r + 70 = 214$; $r = 144$; 144 calories

Page 140

2. C; $9w$ **6.** $3n$

Page 141

2. $6z$ **6.** $\frac{50}{x}$ **11.** $16e$ **18.** $\frac{z}{5} - 2$

Page 142

1. $t = 10$ **5.** $s = 75$

Page 143

1. $y = 8$ **7.** $w = 92$ **15.** $g = 7$

23. $s = 9$ **31.** $\frac{d}{72} = 3$; $d = 216$; 216 mi

Page 144

3. $y = 4$

Page 145
4. $r = 8$ **10.** $b = 33$ **20.** $z = 310.5$
28. $k = 1,860$

Page 146
3. $7n + 36 = 106$; $n = 10$

Page 147
1. $7n + 11 = 67$; $n = 8$
7. $12p + 180 = 2,160$; $p = 165$, $165

Page 148–149
1. 16; 12; 10; 8
5. 163¢; 422¢; 385¢; 755¢; 1,125¢

Page 150
1. 7 min

Page 152
1. 13   **13.** $\frac{z}{6}$ **23.** $y = 35$

Page 153
1. 13, 16, 19, 22   **7.** 1, 3, 5, 7, 9, 11
14. $n^2 + 3$

7 Measurement: Metric Units

Page 156
3. mm   **7.** 100   **11.** =

Page 157
2. km   **10.** 1,000   **18.** l   **26.** <
34. =

Page 158
3. 0.532

Page 159
3. 0.53   **11.** 4.5   **19.** km
27. 6 mm, 0.06 dm, 0.006 m

Page 160
1. L   **7.** 0.1   **13.** 4,500

Page 161
2. 4.5 kL   **6.** 409.5 L

Page 162
2. mg   **8.** 2   **18.** 5 kg

Page 163
1. lost; 1.6 kg   **7.** 2 g

Page 164
2. 100°C   **8.** 16.3°C   **14.** 258.15 K

Page 165
3. 4,000   **9.** 2, 25   **13.** 7 days 1 h

Page 166
2. 7 h   **6.** 3:45 p.m.

Page 167
2. $18   **7.** 18 h 20 min

Page 168
5. 23 cm; 0.5 cm, 0.5 dm

Page 169
7. 0.05 m   **16.** 62.35 mm to 62.45 mm

Page 170
1. $\frac{1}{4}$ **17.** 8.2   **33.** 36

Page 174
1. 26.7   **7.** 0.38   **15.** 7.28

Page 175
2. Flight 860, 3 h 15 min   **5.** 1 h 45 min

8 Integers and Rational Numbers

Page 179
1. $^-9$ **9.** 0   **19.** $^-5.4$ **25.** $^-8$
31. 5.1   **37.** commutative

Page 180
4. $^-7$ **10.** $^-2$

Page 181
2. 1   **8.** $^-6$ **18.** $^-2$ **24.** $^-8$
34. $^-10 + 6 = ^-4$

Page 182
1. $^-2$ **7.** 2

Page 183
4. $^-1$ **14.** 12   **32.** 6   **46.** $^-7$
57. 24m

Page 184
2. $^-10$ **26.** 0   **45.** 8   **49.** 7

Page 185
1. $^-5°C$ **7.** 30,240

Page 186
1. $^-24$ **5.** 12

Page 187
1. 42   **11.** 0   **19.** $^-120$ **31.** 48
37. $^-30$ **43.** 9

Page 188
2. 6   **8.** 9

Page 189
1. $^-2$ **9.** $^-3$ **17.** $^-4$ **29.** 9
41. $^-12$

Page 190
2. $^-14$ **24.** $^-3$ **55.** $^-5$ **75.** $^-1$

Page 191
2. $^-5$ **8.** $^-14$ **21.** $^-2$

Page 192
2. $x = 4$ **6.** $n = ^-90$

Page 193
2. $f = 15$ **10.** $t = ^-7$ **16.** $u = ^-32$
22. $x = ^-38$ **28.** $c = ^-12$ **36.** $w = ^-25$

Page 194
1. $^-6$ **4.** $^-8$ **7.** $1.35

Page 195
4. $m - 2,305 = ^-336$; $m = 1,969$; A.D. 1969

Page 196
1. $\frac{1}{2}$ **8.** $^-4$ **15.** $^-0.92$

Page 197
2. $\frac{^-2}{5}$ **6.** $^-1\frac{2}{5}$ **16.** $\frac{^-1}{3}$ **18.** $^-1$
21. $\frac{9}{10}$ **24.** $\frac{^-11}{40}$ **26.** $^-0.8$ **35.** $6\frac{1}{2}$

Page 198
2. 0.12

Page 199
3. $\frac{1}{4}$ **8.** $\frac{^-5}{8}$ **12.** $2\frac{2}{5}$ **17.** $1\frac{1}{5}$
21. $^-2\frac{2}{3}$ **26.** $\frac{^-23}{32}$ **31.** 3.55
40. Gain of $\frac{5}{12}$ lb

Page 200
1. $<$ **8.** $>$ **16.** $>, <$ **17.** $>, <$
22. Grassland; $^-24°C < 12°C$

Page 201
1. 6   **9.** $\frac{5}{8}$ **20.** 3.2

Page 202
1. $c = 2$ **5.** $d = ^-24$

Page 203
16. $h = ^-32$ **26.** $c = ^-4$ **38.** $x = ^-840$

Page 205
1. $(^-6,3)$ **13.** Y   **18.** E
25. $^-6; ^-5; ^-4; ^-3; ^-2; ^-1; 0; 1$

Page 206
3. yes; (3,1)

Page 207
2. $^-3, 1, 5, 9, 11; 6, 4, 2, 1, 0; (2, 3)$ **9.** $(^-2,2)$

Page 208
3. $\frac{1}{10^5}$ **11.** 7^{-2} **23.** 10^2

480

Page 209

2. 8.5×10^{-4} **14.** 0.0000000004

Page 210

1. 66 pieces

Page 212

3. $^-8$ **11.** $^-5$ **17.** 4   **23.** $^-72$
27. $t = ^-4$

9 Geometry

Page 217

7. $\overleftrightarrow{ED}$, $\overleftrightarrow{DF}$, $\overleftrightarrow{EF}$ **15.** line

Page 218

1. acute   **5.** $\angle A$ and $\angle D$

Page 219

1. $\angle ABE$, $\angle CBE$ **7.** 30°   **15.** 45°
21. 42°

Page 221

1. $\angle 4$, $\angle 3$, $\angle 2$ **7.** 70°

Page 222

1. obtuse, scalene

Page 223

1. isosceles   **5.** obtuse   **11.** 125°

Page 224

1. 110°

Page 225

1. pentagon; 540°   **5.** heptagon; 900°
11. 25°   **15.** 135°

Page 226

1. $\overline{AB}$ **5.** tangent

Page 227

1. $\overline{SR}$ **7.** $\overleftrightarrow{TU}$ **11.** isosceles

Page 231

3. $\triangle XYZ \cong \triangle DEF$

Page 233

1. ASA   **5.** SSS

Page 234

1. yes   **5.** no

Page 235

1. 3   **5.** 1

Page 236

1. Sally rode a moped, Laura rode a bicycle, and Tom used a skateboard.

Page 238

2. right   **12.** tangent   **16.** SAS

10 Ratio and Proportion

Page 242

5. =   **7.** ≠

Page 243

2. 3 to 5, $\frac{3}{5}$ **10.** 6 to 7, $\frac{6}{7}$ **18.** =
28. $\frac{16}{4}$, $\frac{8}{2}$, $\frac{4}{1}$

Page 244

1. $7/h   **13.** 6.25 m/s

Page 245

1. 48 words/min   **5.** 300 km   **11.** 7.10 m/s

Page 246

1. $2.20/L

Page 247

2. $7/kg   **10.** B; 3 for $1.00   **16.** $2.97

Page 248

3. $n = 6.\overline{6}$

Page 249

1. $n = 36$ **11.** $n = 54$ **21.** $x = 36$

Page 250

1. $\frac{16}{10} = \frac{b}{60}$, $b = 96$

Page 251

7. $\frac{5}{8} = \frac{p}{10,000}$, $p = 6,250$; 6,250 for;

3,750 against

Page 252

1. $f = 6$ cm

Page 253

3. $x = 24$ **7.** $v = 10$; $x = 30°$, $y = 60°$

Pages 254–255

1. $h = 16.8$ m **5.** $h = 150$ m

Page 256

1. $33.\overline{3}$ km

Page 257

2. 3.8 cm: 108 km **6.** 7.0 cm: 198 km

Page 258

1. $\tan 28° \approx 0.533$

Page 259

3. $\tan A \approx 0.609$ **9.** $\tan A \approx 2.909$

Page 260

1. 0.231 **7.** 0.176 **13.** 22° **20.** 87°

Page 261

1. 57.08 m ≈ 57 m **5.** $a = 3.728$ m

Page 262

1. 423 **27.** 0.4 **41.** 300

Page 263

1. 10,000 fish **2.** 8,000 fish

Page 266

2. $\frac{8}{15}$ **8.** $\neq$ **14.** \$6/kg **20.** $n = 108$

11 Percent

Page 271

1. $\frac{23}{100}$; 0.23; 23% **11.** $\frac{61}{100}$; 0.61; 61%

17. 17%

Page 272

1. 0.74 **7.** 30%

Page 273

1. 0.83 **9.** 0.16 **17.** 38% **31.** 0.30

Page 274

3. $16\frac{2}{3}\%$ **7.** $\frac{1}{4}$

Page 275

2. 45% **14.** $19\frac{4}{9}\%$ **18.** $33\frac{1}{3}$
26. 62.5 **35.** $\frac{7}{8}$ **43.** 65%

Page 276

2. 0.0075 **8.** 350%

Page 277

1. 2.25 **13.** 0.0025 **21.** 4.5%
29. 18.5% **35.** 110% **47.** 0.01%

Page 278

3. 1,350 **7.** 38

Page 279

2. 5.04 **8.** 4.65 **16.** 27
26. 15.75 **34.** 112

Page 280

1. $I = \$450$; $A = \$1,450$
7. $I = \$472.50$; $A = \$1,222.50$

Page 281

1. $1,320   **7.** $75

Page 282

4. 80%

Page 283

2. 20%   **12.** 250%   **20.** 68.9%
26. 225%

Page 284

1. 80%   **5.** 30

Page 285

4. 50%   **12.** 80%   **18.** 40   **26.** 6
32. about 80%

Page 286

3. 8; 12.5%   **10.** 12; 37.5%

Page 287

5. $78.45; $1.18; $79.63

Page 288

3. $t = 10$ **5.** $10\% \times n = 17$; $n = 170$

Page 289

2. $n = 32$ **8.** $n = 100$ **16.** $75\% \times n = 60$;
$n = 80$ **26.** 105

Page 290

1. $4; $12   **7.** $75; $425
11. $1.17; $6.63

Page 291

3. $5,092.50   **8.** 9%

Page 292

4. 0.85   **16.** 416%   **28.** 16.7%
44. $\frac{9}{20}$ **56.** 84   **62.** 36

Page 293

1. $\frac{40}{100} = \frac{n}{65}$; $n = 26$ **11.** $\frac{n}{100} = \frac{117}{150}$; $n = 78$

Page 294

1. 39

Page 296

2. 9:100; 0.09; 9%   **8.** 0.1%   **14.** $37\frac{1}{2}\%$
20. 60%

12 Perimeter, Area, and Volume

Page 300

1. 42 cm

Page 301

1. 12.8 cm   **7.** 61 cm   **13.** 18 m

Page 302

1. 324 cm^2

Page 303

3. 1,764 cm^2 **7.** 1,368 cm^2

Page 304

2. 32 cm^2

Page 305

2. 20.21 m^2 **10.** 16.66 m^2 **18.** 112 m^2

Page 306

1. 37.68 cm

Page 307

3. 106.132 cm   **15.** 38.936 cm

Page 308

2. 200.96 cm^2

Page 309

6. 803.84 m^2 **12.** 2,497.0536 cm^2
20. 3,925.00 m^2; the same

Page 310

2. B   **5.** B   **8.** 9 cm and 5 cm

Page 311
1. 4   **6.** $220.41

Page 312
2. 600 cm^2

Page 313
1. 216 cm^2 **5.** 226.08 m^2 **9.** 431 cm^2

Page 314
3. 0.72 m^3

Page 315
2. 417.6 cm^3 **8.** 129.368 cm^3

Page 316
4. 168 cm^3

Page 317
4. 24,000 m^3 **10.** 1,256 cm^3

Page 318
5. 400 cm^3; 400 mL

Page 319
1. 5.2 m^3 **6.** 276.2 cm^3

Page 320
1. 32 ft   **4.** 280 sq ft

Page 322
2. 88 m   **6.** 193.5 cm^2 **10.** 1,130.4 cm^3

13 Probability

Page 326
1. 6

Page 327
2. 9   **8.** 6

Page 328
1. 24

Page 329
4. 24   **10.** 79,833,600

Page 330
2. 10

Page 331
3. 20   **7.** 28   **11.** 142,506

Page 332
1. $\frac{1}{2}$; $\frac{1}{2}$

Page 333
1. 1, 2, 3, 4; $\frac{1}{4}$ **7.** 0   **13.** $\frac{1}{6}$ **17.** 0

Page 334
2. $\frac{1}{24}$

Page 335
3. $\frac{1}{12}$ **9.** 36   **13.** $\frac{5}{6}$ **17.** 7; $\frac{1}{6}$

Page 336
2. $\frac{1}{4}$; 20

Page 337
1. 25   **5.** 15   **9.** $\frac{3}{10}$; 300

Page 338
2. $\frac{3}{5}$; $\frac{5}{3}$ **6.** $\frac{1}{35}$; $\frac{35}{1}$

Page 339
1. $\frac{1}{3}$ **5.** 24   **9.** 10

Page 340
3. dependent events

Page 341
2. independent events, $\frac{1}{6}$
6. dependent events; $\frac{2}{9}$

Page 342
8. $775.66   **30.** $^-$4   **45.** 12

484

2. 39 points

Page 346
1. $\frac{2}{4}$ or $\frac{1}{2}$ **9.** $\frac{1}{10}$ **13.** $\frac{4}{6}$ or $\frac{2}{3}$

14 Statistics and Graphs

Pages 350–351
2. Lincoln; 1861–1865   **9.** Ohio

Page 352
3. $11.32; $11.25; $10.00 and $12.50

Page 353
3. Estimate $2; Exact $2.07

Page 354
1. $\frac{2}{15}$

Page 355
1. $\frac{2}{5}$ **5.** $\frac{3}{10}$ **8.** 400

Page 356
2. B-747   **8.** 25 million

Page 357
4. about 10 h 30 min
8. L-1011; 250, B-727; 130

Page 358
1. Life Expectancy for Men and Women
5. about 36 yr

Page 359
1. about 43 yr   **7.** about 54.5 yr; 22.5 yr

Page 360
2. 100%   **6.** 54°, 36°, 18°

Page 361
1. 5,000   **7.** 72°   **13.** 90°

Page 362
2. 9%   **8.** 2.5%

Page 363
12. $28,000   **18.** 5.3%, 4%

Page 365
1. positive   **7.** negative

Page 366
2. 82   **6.** 81.5   **9.** 98

Page 367
3. $32,670   **7.** $137.67

Page 368
4. $286.16; $273.72

Page 370
1. 17   **5.** $\frac{2}{3}$ **11.** $300

Page 371
1. 5.5

15 Square Roots and Right Triangles

Page 374
2. 4 cm   **6.** 11

Page 375
1. 2 cm   **9.** 60   **18.** $^{-}8$ **23.** 14
31. 19 m

Page 376
2. 9.110   **8.** 77

Page 377
2. 6, 7   **8.** 6.708   **20.** 28   **28.** 70
34. 1.507 cm

Page 378
1. 41.5   **7.** 52.0   **13.** 28.4

Page 379

3. 8 ha   **9.** $I = \$1,225$; $A = \$16,125$

Page 380

2. 3   **8.** 16

Page 381

2. 12   **8.** 144   **12.** $c = 20$

Page 382

1. $c = 13$ cm

Page 383

1. $c = 15$ cm   **7.** 7.810 cm   **15.** 2.828 cm

Page 384

3. $b = 8$

Page 385

1. 10 km   **5.** yes

Page 386

2. 8.1 cm

Page 387

3. 32 cm   **7.** 3 cm; 5.20 cm

Page 388

2. rational   **8.** irrational

Page 389

4. 301; rational   **11.** $0.8\overline{3}$
19. $0.\overline{0007}$ **27.** 7.745966   **35.** 4.3588989

Page 390

1. yes   **5.** 400

Page 392

1. 4   **9.** $^{-}8$ **15.** 25   **19.** $c = 15$ m

Page 393

3. 0.415

16 Measurement: Customary Units

Page 396

3. 6   **9.** 3 yd 1 ft 1 in.

Page 397

4. 41   **14.** 2   **22.** 3 ft 7 in.   **30.** 11 ft

Page 398

1. 27   **7.** 1,296   **13.** 3 a.

Page 399

1. 5,184   **5.** 2,592   **10.** 565.2 in^3

Page 400

3. 12   **7.** $\frac{1}{2}$ **13.** $3\frac{1}{2}$

Page 401

1. A; 7 gal   **7.** D; 13 gal

Page 402

1. A; 35°F   **5.** C; 1,064°F   **10.** 102°F

Page 403

1. 2   **5.** 5   **15.** $1\frac{1}{4}$

Page 404

2. C   **6.** B 5.1¢/oz.

Page 405

1. 17″   **5.** 225 yd^3

Page 406

8. $11\frac{3}{4}$ **18.** 9   **34.** 70

Page 410

1. 4   **7.** 2,542 in.^{2} **13.** 5

More Practice

Page 433

Set A: 1. $<$ **3.** $>$ **5.** $>$
Set B: 1. 1,000   **3.** 300   **5.** 2,000
Set C: 1. \$1,324   **3.** \$54,637   **7.** 17,499
Set D: 1. 9,000   **2.** 4,500   **9.** 90

Page 434

Set A: 1. 49,166   **3.** 49,706   **7.** 139,944
Set B: 1. \$1.21   **5.** 4r29   **7.** 440r21
9. 253r6   **12.** 113r227
Set C: 1. $<$ **3.** $=$ **5.** $>$ **7.** $<$
Set D: 1. 1.038   **5.** 16.9   **7.** 3.001
13. 49.91

Page 435

Set A: 1. 29.1360   **5.** 1,175.332
7. \$494.37
Set B: 1. 57.24   **3.** 118.36   **5.** 0.54485
Set C: 1. 29   **3.** 1   **5.** \$14.00
Set D: 1. 189   **4.** \$26.33   **6.** 0.44715

Page 436

Set A: 1. 48   **5.** 320   **7.** 2.1
9. 1,800   **11.** 16,000
Set B: 1. 3.752 (3.75)   **4.** 5.888 (5.89)
6. 67.653 (67.65)
Set C: 2. 161.931 (161.93)   **5.** 3.666 (3.67)
Set D: 1. 2   **3.** 0.4   **5.** 8

Page 437

Set A: 1. 144   **3.** 1   **7.** 2.744
9. 53.1
Set B: 1. 1,800   **5.** 610,000   **11.** 3.6×10^9
Set C: 1. $2^2 \cdot 5$ **3.** 2^5 **7.** $2 \cdot 3^2$
Set D: 2. 8   **4.** 1   **6.** 2

Page 438

Set A: 1. 12   **4.** 20   **7.** 90
Set B: 1. $\frac{4}{7}$ **3.** $\frac{16}{15}$ **6.** $\frac{7}{10}$ **9.** $\frac{5}{6}$
Set C: 2. $\frac{52}{9}$ **4.** $\frac{51}{8}$ **6.** $\frac{23}{8}$ **15.** $6\frac{1}{2}$
18. $2\frac{3}{14}$ **23.** $5\frac{3}{5}$
Set D: 1. 39   **5.** 60   **8.** 65

Page 439

Set A: 1. $<$ **3.** $<$ **5.** $>$
Set B: 2. $1\frac{8}{15}$ **5.** $\frac{59}{60}$ **8.** $61\frac{19}{24}$
Set C: 1. $\frac{1}{6}$ **5.** $\frac{1}{30}$ **7.** $15\frac{7}{9}$ **10.** $\frac{7}{40}$
Set D: 2. $2\frac{7}{10}$ **4.** $6\frac{7}{18}$

Page 440

Set A: 1. $\frac{3}{14}$ **3.** $\frac{21}{40}$ **6.** $\frac{10}{27}$
Set B: 2. 18   **4.** $3\frac{1}{3}$ **8.** 47
10. 16   **12.** $1\frac{1}{33}$
Set C: 1. \$9   **5.** \$2   **9.** 4
Set D: 2. $\frac{5}{19}$ **4.** $\frac{12}{17}$ **7.** $\frac{4}{7}$

Page 441

Set A: 1. $\frac{1}{2}$ **3.** $\frac{21}{26}$ **7.** 1
Set B: 1. $1\frac{1}{9}$ **5.** $\frac{2}{5}$ **7.** $\frac{10}{33}$
Set C: 1. 0.75   **3.** 0.2   **7.** 0.28
Set D: 2. 5   **4.** 17   **9.** 2

Page 442

Set A: 2. $b = 116$ **4.** $f = 22$
7. $p = \frac{5}{16}$ **11.** $t = 1\frac{9}{20}$
Set B: 1. $d = 108$ **4.** $f = 4$ **6.** $h = 1$
10. $y = 6.2$
Set C: 1. $m = 30$ **4.** $w = 5$ **9.** $e = 3$
Set D: 2. 1   **4.** 0.1   **6.** 100   **8.** 10

Page 443

Set A: 1. 25   **3.** 0.52   **5.** 1.32
Set B: 2. 0.3   **4.** 1.25   **7.** 0.8
Set C: 1. 2,000   **5.** 7,500   **8.** 0.45
Set D: 1. 298.15 K   **3.** 337.15 K
5. 259.15 K

Page 444

Set A: 1. 180   **3.** 35   **7.** 23 wk 4 d
11. 0.58
Set B: 2. 0.5 m   **4.** 0.05 dm
10. 0.005 cm
Set C: 1. $^-13$ **4.** 500   **8.** 1.1

487

Page 445
Set A: 1. $^-4$ **3.** $^-2$ **5.** $^-12$ **8.** 13
Set B: 2. $^-11$ **4.** $^-11$ **7.** $^-3$ **10.** 18
Set C: 1. $^-15$ **3.** 21   **7.** 78   **11.** $^-48$
Set D: 3. 5   **5.** $^-10$ **9.** $^-8$ **12.** 5

Page 446
Set A: 1. $^-11$ **5.** 3   **7.** $^-5$ **11.** $^-4$
Set B: 2. $r = ^-17$ **5.** $b = 21$ **8.** $b = ^-3$
10. $f = 45$
Set C: 3. $\frac{^-2}{5}$ **7.** 0.6   **11.** 1
Set D: 1. $\frac{^-1}{3}$ **3.** $\frac{1}{2}$ **11.** $\frac{^-3}{10}$

Page 447
Set A: 1. $>$ **5.** $<$ **8.** $>$
Set B: 2. $h = ^-10$ **4.** $y = 95$ **8.** $n = ^-2$
Set C: 1. 3, 4, 5, 6, 7, 8, 9, 10

Page 448
Set A: 1. 3.8×10^{-3} **3.** 2.05×10^{-4}
6. 0.00622   **8.** 0.000000111
Set B: 2. $42°$ **5.** $83°$ **8.** $76°$
Set C: 1. $=$ **3.** $\neq$ **7.** $=$ **12.** $=$

Page 449
Set A: 1. 5 m/s   **3.** 12 km/min
Set B: 2. $h = 3$ **7.** $b = 15$
Set C: 1. 0.2   **3.** 0.32   **9.** 0.30
15. 11%   **18.** 1%
Set D: 2. 35%   **4.** 14%   **7.** 5%
15. $\frac{2}{5}$ **19.** $\frac{27}{50}$

Page 450
Set A: 1. 0.09   **5.** 0.008   **13.** 75%
18. 1%
Set B: 2. 0.6   **4.** 110.5   **6.** 7.44
Set C: 2. $I = 26$; $A = \$426$
Set D: 1. 20%   **5.** 45%   **8.** 54.5%

Page 451
Set A: 1. $n = 80$ **5.** $n = 40$
Set B: 2. $\frac{n}{100} = \frac{6}{50}$; $n = 12$
Set C: 1. 34.6 km   **5.** 32.4 cm
Set D: 2. 15.5 m^2 **6.** 1,225 km^2

Page 452
Set A: 1. 20 cm^2 **3.** 18.3 cm^2
7. 29.2 km^2 **11.** 3.0855 m^2
Set B: 2. 37.68 cm   **7.** 69.08 m
Set C: 1. 78.5 cm^2 **5.** 1,133.54 cm^2
Set D: 1. 581 cm^3 **7.** 2,411.52 m^3

Page 453
Set A: 1. 1,650 m^3 **5.** 157 cm^3
Set B: 3. 81%; 79%; 79%
Set C: 1. 9   **4.** $^-40$ **8.** 0.7
Set D: 2. 10.7   **7.** 89.4

Page 454
Set A: 2. $C = 53$
Set B: 5. $c = 25.239$ m

Page 455
Set A: 3. $b = 4$ m
Set B: 4. 21.5 m

Page 456
Set A: 1. $0.\overline{5}$ **3.** 0.04   **7.** $0.1\overline{36}$
Set B: 3. 7,040   **5.** $2\frac{1}{2}$ **9.** 11, 5
Set C: 1. 720   **5.** 1   **9.** 2 ft 4 in.
12. 6 in.

Page 457
Set A: 3. $4\frac{1}{3}$ **8.** 4,320   **11.** 351.68 in.^{3}
Set B: 1. $1\frac{1}{2}$ **3.** 12   **8.** $\frac{1}{2}$
Set C: 1. 4   **5.** 2,500   **9.** $4\frac{1}{4}$